WITHDRAWN

Computer Control Systems Technology

UNIVERSITY OF CALIFORNIA
ENGINEERING EXTENSION SERIES

Beckenbach · Modern Mathematics for the Engineer, First Series

Beckenbach · Modern Mathematics for the Engineer, Second Series

Brown and Weiser · Ground Support Systems for Missiles and Space Vehicles

Dorn · Mechanical Behavior of Materials at Elevated Temperatures

Huberty and Flock · Natural Resources

Langmuir and Hershberger · Foundations of Future Electronics

Leondes · Computer Control Systems Technology

Puckett and Ramo · Guided Missile Engineering

Ramo · Peacetime Uses of Outerspace

Ridenour · Modern Physics for the Engineer, First Series

Ridenour and Nierenberg · Modern Physics for the Engineer, Second Series

Robertson · Modern Chemistry for the Engineer and Scientist

Sines and Waisman · Metal Fatigue

·

COMPUTER CONTROL SYSTEMS TECHNOLOGY

LLEWELLYN M. K. BOELTER

CORNELIUS T. LEONDES

HARRY D. HUSKEY

ROBERT MINNICK

GERALD ESTRIN

IRWIN PFEFFER

WALTER J. KARPLUS

CHARLES B. TOMPKINS

JOHN G. TRUXAL

JOHN A. ASELTINE

RICHARD E. KUBA

JOHN M. SALZER

HAROLD DAVIS

LOTFI A. ZADEH

ROBERT O. FERNER

ALFRED F. SCHMITT

HANS GIESECKE

YAO TZU LI

E. RICHARD COHEN

JACK ROSENBERG

GARY K. L. CHIEN

Edited by
CORNELIUS T. LEONDES
Associate Professor of Engineering
University of California, Los Angeles

1961

McGraw-Hill Book Company, Inc.

NEW YORK   TORONTO   LONDON

COMPUTER CONTROL SYSTEMS TECHNOLOGY

37195

THE MAPLE PRESS COMPANY, YORK, PA.

The Authors

Llewellyn M. K. Boelter, Dean, College of Engineering, University of California, Los Angeles

Cornelius T. Leondes, Associate Professor of Engineering, University of California, Los Angeles

Harry D. Huskey, Professor of Electrical Engineering and Mathematics, University of California, Berkeley

Robert Minnick, Senior Research Engineer, Stanford Research Institute, Menlo Park, California

Gerald Estrin, Professor of Engineering, University of California, Los Angeles

Irwin Pfeffer, Senior Member of the Technical Staff, Space Technology Laboratories, Los Angeles, California

Walter J. Karplus, Associate Professor of Engineering, University of California, Los Angeles

Charles B. Tompkins, Professor of Mathematics and Director, Numerical Analysis Research, University of California, Los Angeles

John G. Truxal, Head, Department of Electrical Engineering, Polytechnic Institute of Brooklyn, New York

John A. Aseltine, Director of Sensing and Information Sciences, The Aerospace Corporation, Los Angeles, and Lecturer, University of California, Los Angeles

Richard E. Kuba, Assistant Director of Research, Power Equipment Company, Columbus, Ohio

John M. Salzer, Director, Intellectronics Laboratories, Ramo-Wooldridge Division, Thompson Ramo Wooldridge, Inc., Canoga Park, California

Harold Davis, Assistant Professor of Engineering, University of California, Los Angeles

Lotfi A. Zadeh, Professor of Electrical Engineering, University of California, Berkeley

Robert O. Ferner, Design Specialist, Convair-Astronautics Division, General Dynamics Corporation, San Diego, California

Alfred F. Schmitt, Design Specialist, Convair-Astronautics Division, General Dynamics Corporation, San Diego, California

Hans Giesecke, Bureau of Research and Development, Federal Aviation Agency, Atlantic City, New Jersey

Yao Tzu Li, Professor, Department of Aeronautical and Astronautical Engineering, Massachusetts Institute of Technology, Cambridge, Mass.

E. Richard Cohen, Research Adviser, Atomics International, Canoga Park, California

Jack Rosenberg, Consultant, Los Angeles, California

Gary K. L. Chien, Manager, Process Control Systems Engineering, International Business Machines Corporation, San Jose, California

Preface

The developments of mechanical and electromechanical control, the advancement of electronics, and the evolution of computers are now converging to establish a unified computer control systems technology of unprecedented potential. The requisite utility of the fruits of this technology in the optimal evolution of modern complex control systems is readily apparent in many systems. Some examples of these are air-traffic control systems, the guidance and control of flight for earth as well as space vehicles, automatic machine-tool control, nuclear reactor control, process control systems, self-optimalizing systems, etc.

The objective of this book is to develop insight into the various aspects of this broad field for the interested engineer and scientist. In addition, much information of great value should be provided to individuals already specializing in the various parts of this field.

The book consists of three major parts: The first part deals with the theory of digital and analog computers, the second part deals with control theory, and the third part blends these two major fields by considering the development of some systems with various degrees of complexity.

The computer control systems technology lecture series, on which this book is based, was delivered at five centers of technological and scientific activity in the state of California during the spring semester of 1959. These centers were Los Angeles, San Diego, Riverside, Berkeley, and Palo Alto. The series was sponsored by the University of California Engineering and Physical Sciences Extension Divisions. An essential feature of the lecture series required that each of the lecturers and chapter authors be a recognized leader in his field.

The book and lecture series was made possible only through the cooperative efforts of many people. First of all, gratitude must be expressed to Dean L. M. K. Boelter of the College of Engineering, Los Angeles, who has provided an atmosphere which stimulates and encourages such educational ventures as this. It is quite plain from the reception and results of this series as well as those that preceded it, such as Modern Mathematics for the Engineer, Modern Physics for the Engineer, Modern Chemistry for the Engineer, Space Technology, and

Natural Resources, that such educational ventures do indeed play a fairly significant role in the shaping of technological progress.

Thanks are expressed to the Advisory Committee for this course for their help and suggestions in shaping the content of the lecture series as well as in the selection of the lecturers. Thanks must also be expressed to Clifford Bell, J. C. Dillon, Bernice Park, Tod Singleton, and their associates for their many services in the management of the lecture series. In addition the various coordinators including A. Bergen, Gene Franklin, W. Schart, and S. Schock are to be thanked for their roles in this series. Gratitude is also expressed to Connie L. McClure for his direct and indirect contributions. A great deal of thanks for their efficient assistance must also go to the editor's wife, Nancy, and to his secretary, Mrs. Derfla Guthrie.

Last but not least, our thanks go to the lecturers and authors themselves for their willingness to participate in this venture in spite of the fact that it represented a very great additional burden on top of an already busy professional life.

Cornelius T. Leondes

Contents

PART III.   APPLICATIONS TO COMPLEX SYSTEMS

1

Introduction

LLEWELLYN M. K. BOELTER
DEAN OF THE COLLEGE OF ENGINEERING
UNIVERSITY OF CALIFORNIA, LOS ANGELES

CORNELIUS T. LEONDES
ASSOCIATE PROFESSOR OF ENGINEERING
UNIVERSITY OF CALIFORNIA, LOS ANGELES

In this introductory chapter, a review of recent trends toward increasingly complex systems will be illustrated, in brief, by several examples. Then it will be noted that optimum solutions for the development of these systems are made possible only through the use of computer control systems technology. The chapter will conclude with a general discussion of the introductory aspects of computer control technology. Thus the stage will be set for the chapters to follow.

1.1 Review of Recent Trends toward Increasingly Complex Systems

It is perhaps appropriate to initiate the main body of this chapter by reviewing the trend toward increasingly complex systems. This can probably best be done by briefly considering several examples.

Air-traffic Control. Thus in this regard let us first consider air-traffic control systems. Back in the 1930s when airplanes traveling several hundred miles an hour were considered fast and when there were not many airplanes in the air, the problem of traffic control as such did not exist. This is further underscored by the fact that radar, which is an absolute necessity to modern air-traffic control systems, did not exist in the 1930s and, except possibly for landing during adverse weather conditions, was not particularly missed during that time period for air-traffic control purposes.

However, as time went on, planes flew faster, farther, and in increasing numbers. Indeed, today we now have jet-propelled commercial airplanes in service which can and do fly at speeds approaching the speed

1

of sound.   This situation is further complicated by the fact that there are increasing numbers of military aircraft in the air, many of which travel at supersonic speeds.   The number of planes in the air today is so great that radar observers have commented that the airlane from New York to Chicago, for instance, appears on a radar scope as an almost solid white trace, a rather ominous situation.   It is no wonder, therefore, that every day there are numerous reports of near air collisions between aircraft.

This then provides a very good example of the increasing complexity of computer control systems.   As just pointed out, in the 1930s almost no air-traffic control was required, whereas today it is an extremely grave and complex problem.   In designing a computer control system to cope with the air-traffic control problem, one cannot assume the smug attitude that he is designing for the problem as it exists today.   Indeed, one very keen eye must be focused on the problem as it will be in the future, so that a most effective long-term and not a pitiful stopgap solution will be obtained.   One has only to review the tremendous increase in the complexity of this problem from the 1930s to today to begin to appreciate the probable increase in complexity between today and the 1980s.   The resulting portentous implications on the requirements for the necessary air-traffic control system are all too plain.

Future Aspects of Sea Freighting Methods.   As another example let us consider sea freighting methods.   Up to the present time, sea freighting operations were based almost solely on the use of slow-moving ships requiring little in the way of sophisticated control systems and relying on "dead-reckoning" navigation combined perhaps with radio aids to navigation.   However, there is presently a considerable degree of interest in the development and utilization of high-speed sea freighters traveling at speeds in the neighborhood of 100 miles per hour and better. It is the opinion of some people that the problem of stability and control of such vehicles is almost as difficult and complex as the control of intercontinental ballistic missiles.   Navigation is perhaps best done on a fully automatic basis.

The recent successes of the atomic submarines, the *Nautilus* and the *Skate*, in sailing under the polar cap have again raised the immediate possibility of freighting in this manner; and indeed numerous quarters have suggested this mode of goods transport as a definite likelihood in the future.   The control of such sea freighters will undoubtedly involve rather sophisticated applications of computer control systems technology. Thus consider the navigation problem for such vehicles.   It is likely that navigation will be carried out in a manner similar to that employed by the *Nautilus* and the *Skate*, and thus will be fully automatic.   In order to navigate under the sea accurately over extended lengths of time, a coordinate reference compatible with the earth's geographic coordinate system must be established on the vehicle, and a record of the vehicle's position and velocity in this coordinate system must be continually maintained so that the necessary steering control signals may be generated. The *Nautilus* and the *Skate* relied on inertial navigation equipment. In such a system, a set of three orthogonal axes which are fixed with respect to inertial space are established either explicitly or implicitly through the use of three gyromechanisms whose input-sensing axes also form an orthogonal set. If the initial conditions at the time the vehicle starts on its mission are known, the orientation of the earth's geographic axes with respect to the inertial axes is then also known, and thus a set of axes related to the earth's axes is established on board the vehicle.

The motion of the vehicle is then detected by accelerometers mounted in the inertial equipment. Integrating the output of the accelerometers once yields the velocity with respect to the earth, provided that certain auxiliary computations are made and combined in proper signal form with the signals of the accelerometer. This correction is necessary because the accelerometers obey Newton's law, which holds with respect to inertial space; however, it is the velocity with respect to the earth which is desired. A second integration then yields the vehicle's position on the earth. The knowledge of present velocity and position combined with the coordinates of the destination then makes possible the determination of the necessary heading of the ship, and the ship's heading error signal from which the necessary steering signal is generated.

No further problem would exist if the inertial guidance equipment were perfect. However, the gyromechanisms are affected by an inherent drift signal which causes the loss of completely accurate inertial and earth coordinate reference axes. In addition the accelerometers are not perfect. It may someday be possible to build inertial equipment which will be sufficiently accurate so that self-contained guidance of these vehicles will be possible over the required time of the mission; but for the time being such is not the case.

It is thus necessary to use monitoring equipment in conjunction with the inertial guidance equipment. A logical means of monitoring inertial equipment accurately would be to utilize automatic astrotracking equipment. Thus the submarine by extending its periscope through openings in the polar cap could take rapid, automatic, and accurate star fixes which would correctly reorient the drifting inertial reference of the submarine.

To take rapid, automatic, and accurate star fixes, it is necessary to store for high-speed access complete star-table data and then to interpret these data as astrotracker pointing information. Because of errors which have accumulated in the system, the astrotracker will not point directly at the chosen star. However, it will point close to the star because the inertial guidance equipment is sufficiently accurate. The astrotracker will offset the pointing error by the use of automatic error-correction methods, and in so doing will generate an error-correction signal which will keep the inertial guidance equipment accurately up to date. It may be said that the inertial equipment provides short-term stability and a base from which the automatic astrotracking equipment can perform. The astrotracker provides long-term stability and error-correction or monitoring means for the inertial equipment. The two interact to ensure a high-accuracy system over long periods of operation.

This over-all system for the guidance and control of the sea vehicles under discussion provides another illustration of the increasingly complex nature of applied computer control systems technology. Thus the computer is used to process the data from the inertial equipment and from the results to generate steering information. The computer stores the star-table data and generates the pointing signals for the astrotracker. The error signals from the astrotracker are then processed by the computer to provide the error-correction signals. The whole system is then used in the control of the vehicle. This system is in use today. It is a system which is used on the submarines which will be used to launch the *Polaris* missiles.[1]

Interceptor Fire-control Systems. The preceding are examples of the trend toward increasing complexity of commercial and industrial systems. Other commercial systems could be listed which demonstrate this trend rather forcibly, but the above are at least indicative of the problem. Let us now turn our attention to some military systems which will further highlight this trend.

The first example to be cited involves defense against attack from enemy bombers bearing nuclear bombs. Such systems will be described as aircraft interceptor systems, and it is common terminology to describe the system which guides and controls the weapon intended for use against the enemy bomber and which is carried by the aircraft interceptor as a "fire-control system." This terminology was originally based on the fact that the system was and is used to control the firing of weapons. Although the scope and power of such systems have increased rather extensively, the terminology is still used to describe the over-all system.

During World War II interceptor fire-control systems were relatively simple; and because nuclear bombs did not then exist, the problem was infinitely less critical. At that time, planes flying at 400 miles/hr were considered extremely fast. Radar was not properly developed for use in such systems, and the weapons used were chiefly guns and bullets. By present-day standards such systems can at best be described as elementary.

At present the target, the enemy bomber, is designed to be capable of flying at speeds of 2,000 miles/hr. The interceptor must, of course, be

[1] *Aviation Week*, p. 23, Jan. 11, 1960.

designed to fly at least as fast, in spite of the utilization of the concept of the frontal air attack. Thus if the interceptor and the bomber approach each other head on, the closing speeds will be of the order of 4,000 miles/hr or about 6,000 ft/sec. This speed is better than 1 mile/sec. The only way in which the interceptor can destroy the bomber is to be first directed into the vicinity of the bomber. This problem in itself is extremely complicated when viewed as a whole and in the context of the defense of a continent. Thus an extremely elaborate ground-based detection and tracking network must be used to generate the steering information to place the interceptors in the vicinity of the target bombers. The problem of designing a ground detection and tracking network to furnish steering or vectoring information is enormously complicated and will serve as a good example of the application of computer control systems technology to increasingly complex systems. However, no further consideration of this example will be given here.

Assuming for the time being that the interceptor has been placed in the vicinity of the target bomber, it is then necessary (in the interests of accuracy and weapon direction requirements) for the interceptor to detect and track the target bomber on its own air-borne radar. It must be assumed that the target bomber will take steps to make the radar ineffective by using radar countermeasures. But counter–countermeasures may conceivably be used which will guarantee a break through the enemy radar countermeasures and which will provide the necessary radar detection and tracking information at some minimum distance. For purposes of this discussion the minimum distance is chosen as 25 miles.

Closing rates between the interceptor and the target bomber of 1 mile/sec may be expected. For illustrative purposes it is presupposed that the target must be tracked by the defense radar for at least 10 sec to ensure information sufficiently accurate to fire the weapon which will be used to destroy the enemy bomber. A frontal attack is postulated, and because the detecting and tracking radar will be in the nose of the interceptor it is essential that all the necessary radar tracking data be gathered a little before the bomber and interceptor pass each other going in opposite directions. A geometrical limitation, namely that the radar antenna can only swing up and down in the nose of the interceptor through a limited angle of perhaps a total of 90°, is imposed here.

A total time between target detection and weapon detonation of the order of 25 sec is available for the reason that the countermeasures can penetrate the enemy radar for a distance of 25 miles. Of this time the portion permitted for missile travel for optimum kill probabilities will be of the order of 10 to 20 sec. These times indicate the required speeds of operation of the associated computer control system. The complexity of the system is made evident upon reflecting on the radar detection and tracking filtering computations for the various channels of azimuth, elevation, and range and their interaction. Further complications are introduced by the requirements for the ballistic computations necessary to direct the weapon used to destroy the bomber. Other demands on the system such as possible automatic navigation will add other variables and requirements.

Actually numerous concepts for aircraft interceptor fire-control systems exist and also of ways of approaching the target, but irrespective of the method, the preceding discussion is clearly indicative of the increasing complexity of the problem and the resultant heavy demands placed on computer control technology to continually make available the extended techniques for its optimum solution. There is also the further aspect that in another decade this concept of aircraft interceptors will be replaced by other more advanced defense concepts with even greater demands.

Astronautic Systems. There are numerous other military weapons which could be discussed to further illustrate and amplify the trend toward increasingly complex systems. Some examples of these are bombing navigation systems, intercontinental ballistic missiles, anti-intercontinental ballistic missiles, surface-to-air missiles, air-to-surface missiles, skip glide earth-orbiting bombers, earth reconnaissance satellites, etc. The preceding discussion is, however, at least strongly indicative of the skeletal outlines of some of the general problems and thus no further examples of military systems will be presented here. Instead some of the problems of astronautic systems will be discussed briefly.

At the present time it is expected that in the not too distant future successful landings on the moon will be accomplished. Photographic reconnaissance voyages to Mars and Venus will then transpire, followed subsequently by successful landings for exploratory purposes. It will be assumed that initially, at least, all of these missions will be carried out through the use of unmanned vehicles. Thus, the control of the required astronautic vehicles must be fully automatic and completely reliable.

This last problem, that of reliability, is particularly acute for astronautic missions. For the systems described earlier, reliability is also an extremely significant factor in the over-all system design. Thus for the air-traffic control problem the operational failure of any link in the system could result in a disastrous air crash unless proper design steps are taken in the initial formulation of the over-all system design. In the aircraft interceptor system the failure of a system component can result in disaster in that subsequently a bomber carrying a nuclear-war-head air-to-surface missile could break through to deliver its weapon. So once again the system design must stress reliability.

In each of these cases the longer the system "mean-time-to-failure" the better the system will perform—provided a reasonable economic balance is maintained in the process. In any event a mean-time-to-failure on the order of weeks may be adequate. For astronautic vehicles, on the other hand—in particular those for use on the Mars or Venus mission—the required computer control system must perform reliably for a time period on the order of a year or two in view of the required travel time. The mean-time-to-failure for these systems must then be considerably longer than that for the earlier described systems. The design of computer control systems for a given performance in time, that is, for a given reliability, is the most critical problem facing engineers.

Some of the problems other than system reliability which must be solved in accomplishing an astronautic mission will here receive reference. A trip to Mars to photograph its surface and gather other valuable information, followed by a return trip to earth is postulated. One possible way of accomplishing this mission would be through the use of a ballistic trajectory to Mars followed by the use of a ballistic trajectory for the return trip to earth. At the present time, however, the accuracy capabilities of guidance equipment is immeasurably below that required for this method of operation. It will be many years at best before this method can be regarded as feasible. Actually, there is another basic difficulty involved in the use of ballistic trajectories, and this rests on our knowledge of the astronomic unit. The AU is the distance from the earth to the sun; its magnitude is not known to much better than 0.1 per cent. The travel distance is approximately known, but the accuracy thereof is not adequate to utilize a ballistic trajectory.

A probable mode of operation for an accurate photographic mission then involves an initial ballistic type of trajectory followed by a mid-course guidance mode of operation. That is, the astronautic vehicle for the Mars mission would carry means for continually or periodically correcting its heading while en route to Mars. The vehicle design and construction must then include an accurate guidance and control system so that the vehicle's thrust may be properly directed. It is possible here to use an inertial guidance system monitored by automatic astrotrackers operating in a manner somewhat similar to that described earlier. In the vicinity of Mars a complicated terminal guidance and control system would assume the task of guiding the vehicle in its reconnaissance and data-gathering phase. The return trip to earth could follow in like manner, that is, following an initial ballistic trajectory, mid-course guidance would be initiated at a suitable time, followed by a terminal guidance phase.

It is fairly evident from the preceding discussion that for future systems such as astronautic vehicles the computer control system will have to be fairly elaborate and at the same time extremely reliable. These two conflicting requirements will confront the system designer with perhaps the most challenging problem in computer control systems technology. This concludes our rather brief review of the trend toward increasingly complex systems.

1.2 Optimum Solutions through an Effective Combination of Computer Control Systems Technology

A more detailed examination of a system, namely, the air-traffic control system, will be presented in order to more carefully point out that optimum solutions to the design of modern complex systems are possible only through an effective combination of computer control systems technology.

Any one of a number of examples could be employed to demonstrate the essential utility of computer control systems technology in the optimal evolution of complex systems. The air-traffic control problem will be chosen as the example.

To provide inputs to an air-traffic control system, devices for gathering data on the aircraft in the air must be provided. Such devices are radar sets of various types and capabilities for different purposes. These radar sets will provide information on the position and velocity of the various aircraft which must be kept under surveillance. These data will usually be converted from radar coordinates to coordinates compatible with the over-all air-traffic control system. The process of conversion involves computations which could be carried out by analog-computer-type devices. Many of the aircraft in the system will utilize inertial guidance or dead-reckoning navigation equipment. These equipments may also use or require analog-computer equipment for their actuation. Thus analog-computer theory comprises Chap. 6 in this text, which chapter is written by Mr. Irving Pfeffer.

The results of the analog computation may then be converted to digital numbers for processing by digital computers. Also it will often be desirable to utilize devices in the system which accept data in continuous or analog form at one input, data in digital form at another input, and perform a required mathematical operation on these inputs to produce an output in either analog form or digital form as required. Special topics in analog-computer theory such as these, as well as others, are presented in Chap. 7 by Mr. Walter J. Karplus.

The ground-based computers of the air-traffic control system must process the input data in such a manner as to maintain complete control of the system. This tabulation and computation is accomplished by generating such information as steering and altitude information for the various aircraft in the system. The results of the computation must be sent to the proper aircraft for control use. Techniques for the over-all systems design of digital data-processing equipment which are essential to the realization of an air-traffic control system are presented in Chap. 3 by Mr. Harry D. Huskey.

Suitable circuits must be designed for use in the digital computers in the system. The circuitry must provide required operational speeds, be of low initial cost, and possess low power-consumption requirements. It must be designed for a given and high reliability. The memory devices in the computer must be capable of providing large-capacity high-speed random access to the vast quantities of data which must be stored in the system. These questions and others dealing with the general field of digital-computer circuit design techniques are presented in Chap. 4 by Mr. Robert C. Minnick.

Because reliability is such an important aspect of an air-traffic control system, all possible reasonable means for achieving a high degree of reliability must be considered and exploited. As one approach to high-reliability insurance, it is possible to use redundant circuits in such a manner that when one element fails, another steps into its place to provide continuous fail-free operation. Another approach involves coding the information processed in the system in such a manner that when an error occurs it will reveal itself by presenting the system with data known to be in error because of its form. Furthermore, it is possible to carry out this coding in a manner such that the part of the system which is defective and which is causing the error is revealed, and in this manner the error source may be automatically eliminated. These significant aspects of special topics in digital-computer theory and others are included in Chap. 5 by Mr. Gerald Estrin.

As mentioned earlier, some of the aircraft in the system will utilize inertial guidance or dead-reckoning navigation equipment. For flights over the ocean it is desirable that the aircraft have an accurate knowledge of its position. The combined operation of the inertial guidance equipment and the associated computer must then be analyzed to determine the error-performance capabilities of the system. In this manner specifications on the accuracy required of the various system components to meet an over-all accuracy requirement may be stated. Techniques for conducting such analyses as well as other related topics are presented in Chap. 8, on system error-analysis techniques for analog and digital computers, by Mr. Charles B. Tompkins.

During flight the various commercial aircraft must be controlled to produce comfortable flights in spite of the presence of buffeting winds. Thus it is necessary to write specifications for the autopilot system design for the aircraft which will ensure satisfactory performance, and to select suitable components for the system. During landing operations, especially during adverse weather conditions the aircraft must work in conjunction with ground-controlled landing devices to bring the aircraft safely and smoothly down to earth. Here again a fairly complex control system must be carefully examined in order to determine a satisfactory set of specifications and components. Fundamental considerations such as these are presented in Chap. 9 on basic aspects of control systems theory by Mr. John G. Truxal.

Control system synthesis techniques are presented in Chap. 10 by Mr. John A. Aseltine.

Numerous nonlinearities in the various control systems exist in the over-all air-traffic control system. Examples of sources of these non-linearities are backlash in radar antenna gears, autopilot hydraulic actuator equipment, the operation of quantizing the data for use in the system's digital computers, the coordinate transformations required in changing from radar coordinates to system coordinates, etc. The con-trol system design techniques should be capable of handling such phe-nomena and relationships. In addition it may be desirable to inten-tionally introduce nonlinearities to produce rapid or optimum system response capabilities. This technique is a consideration in the design of ground-controlled landing systems for aircraft. Questions of nonlinear control system design techniques are examined in Chap. 11 by Mr. Richard E. Kuba.

The ground data-gathering and processing network which then directs the aircraft in the system may be viewed as a rather large and complex closed-loop sampled-data control system which must of necessity have suitable dynamic capabilities. Design and synthesis techniques for sampled-data systems are formulated and will be presented in Chap. 12 by Mr. John M. Salzer.

The data as gathered by the radar antennas will be corrupted with various types of background and aircraft-produced noise voltages such as radar target scintillation or glint. At times, resistor-, vacuum-tube- or transistor-produced noise will present a significant corruptive effect. System design must be capable of optimally processing such noisy data. Techniques for accomplishing this design requirement will be presented by Mr. Harold Davis in Chap. 13.

Aircraft in the system, particularly the more advanced aircraft, will operate over widely varying speed regimes and environmental conditions. It will be desirable to incorporate into the aircraft's control system an adaptive capability so that it will be continually capable of performing to specifications in spite of the resultant widely varying parameters of the system being controlled. Adaptive control systems synthesis techniques fall within the realm of advanced control systems theory. Advanced aspects of control systems theory with particular emphasis placed on optimal control problems in discrete time systems will be dealt with by Mr. Lotfi A. Zadeh in Chap. 14. The techniques discussed here provide an approach which can be used to solve a variety of control problems including adaptive system synthesis.

Following this chapter, the remainder of the series will be devoted to the detailed studies of the design of some modern complex systems. The application of the techniques presented in the preceding chapters and their power will be demonstrated as a result.

PART I

Computer Technology

2

Introduction to Digital- and Analog-computer Theory

CORNELIUS T. LEONDES

ASSOCIATE PROFESSOR OF ENGINEERING
UNIVERSITY OF CALIFORNIA, LOS ANGELES

2.1 Introduction

In computer control systems the sources of input information to the system generate signals which must be operated upon to produce a desired result. For example, in what is called a dead-reckoning navigation system, the basic data sources are often the present measured velocity of the vehicle and its heading with respect to north. As a result the north and east components of velocity of the vehicle may be determined and then integrated to determine its displacement or distance traveled in the northern and eastern directions. We may also indicate the distance traveled by indicating the vehicle's present latitude and longitude.

If we know the latitude and longitude of the destination point, it is readily possible by the use of basic relations in spherical trigonometry to compute the heading of the vehicle which will take us to the destination over a path of least distance of travel. Since we know by actual measurements the velocity vector of the vehicle with respect to true north, we therefore, of course, know the actual heading of the vehicle. Knowing the actual heading and having just computed the desired heading, it is possible to compare the two headings to determine if they are identical. Any difference is a heading error and may be used to generate a steering signal for the vehicle.

Such a system of navigation is used on the great majority of the B-52 SAC bombers. Because of the speed of travel and size of these vehicles, it is, of course, necessary that the navigation of these aircraft be carried out in an automatic manner with human participation only in a monitoring sense. Thus between the reception of the input velocity and heading information to the generation of the output heading error or steering

13

signal, there must be a device which can automatically generate the desired heading error (Fig. 2.1).

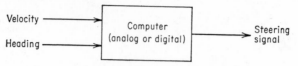

Fig. 2.1 Navigation computer.

Because a number of computations must be performed on the velocity and heading, which together constitute the input data, to generate the heading error or output data, we refer to the intervening device as a computer or sometimes as a data processer. The computer can satisfactorily be either one of two broad classes or types of computer, namely, an analog computer or a digital computer. During the first part of this chapter analog computers will be discussed in an introductory manner. The latter part of this chapter will be devoted to an introduction to digital computers.

2.2 Introductory Analog-computer Theory

To determine the basis for the title of analog computers let us examine the nature of the various operations performed on the input velocity and heading signal to generate the output heading error signal in an analog computer. First of all the input velocity signal, which might be an electrical voltage whose value is directly and continuously proportional to the vehicle's velocity, is passed through a device, which has as another input the vehicle's heading. The outputs of the device are the vehicle's north and east components of velocity again as electrical voltages whose values are directly and continuously proportional to the respective components of velocity. The device is referred to as a resolver because it performs the function of resolving the velocity into north and east components of velocity. Because of the continuous and proportional relation between the computer's electrical voltages or signals and the actual velocities, we may refer to the voltages or signals as the analog of the velocity signal.

This special example demonstrates the basic reason behind the title "analog computer." Actually, as one might suspect, the basic principle can be applied to a very broad class of relations between signals and controlled system physical variables. Thus the analogous relations can exist between computer variables—such as voltages, currents, shaft rotations, etc.—and controlled system physical variables—such as velocities, accelerations, pressures, temperatures, angles, etc.; and the analogies can be established by proceeding as we have done thus far in our navigational system.

Continuing now the study of the flow of signals through our navigation system using an analog computer, the components of velocity north and east are each integrated to obtain distance traveled. In other words the electrical voltages corresponding to velocities are introduced to devices which perform integrations to produce associated electrical signals which are continuously proportional to the displacement of the vehicle in the north and east directions, respectively.

Thus by continuing the study of the flow of the electrical signals through the analog computer in this manner as these signals pass through various devices such as analog adders, subtractors, multipliers, dividers, integrators, resolvers, and function generators, we will eventually come out with the steering or heading error signal. The process is straightforward. With the understanding that we have established some of the necessary basic principles we need not continue the problem the rest of the way. Let us instead turn our attention to some other examples of computer control systems which can advantageously utilize analog computers for their mechanization.

As another example let us consider the radar tracking aspects of an aircraft interceptor fire-control system. As pointed out in the introductory chapter, the aircraft interceptor with its detection and tracking radar antenna located in its nose will typically carry out a frontal attack on the target bomber. After detecting the target bomber with its radar system, the radar will then "lock on" the target. That is, the radar system will automatically track the target with the radar antenna continually pointing at the target. The manner in which this automatic tracking is carried out is again through the use of a computer, and many interceptor systems in use have employed analog computers for this purpose. The analog computer receives as inputs error signals in range and azimuth and elevation angles. From this there are generated automatic angular rate of change signals for the azimuth and elevation angles as well as for the range such that the radar antenna continually and automatically follows or tracks the target. Because this automatic tracking computation involves cross-coupling among the azimuth angle, elevation angle, and range signals, plus additional complications, the required analog computer is fairly complex. However, once again the analog computer consists of the straightforward interconnection of adders, subtractors, multipliers, integrators, etc.

There are, of course, many other examples of systems in operation today which use analog computers for actuation. Some of these are intercontinental ballistic missiles, training simulation devices of various types such as flight trainers, steel mill tandem cold-rolling-mill controls, economic dispatch computers for the automatic control of electrical power systems, and of course many many others. Rather than examine more systems, however, we will now turn our attention to the description of some typical mechanizations for analog-computer elements such as adders, multipliers, integrators, function generators, etc. Following this we will demonstrate the use of analog-computer elements in the solution of differential equations by considering an example. This will then illustrate the general use of analog computers in the actual mechanization of computer control systems.

2.3 Some Analog-computer Elements

Let us first consider some typical integrator mechanizations. In this regard it is probably appropriate to first of all point out that there are various classes of analog computers; namely mechanical,[1] electromechanical or a-c,[2] electronic,[3] thermal,[4] etc. Before pointing out the principal reasons for choosing one over another in a given application we will first consider some computer operation mechanizations. Thus considering a mechanical integrator, let us examine Fig. 2.2. The geometry of the situation shown there indicates that the output z is equal to the integral of y with respect to x. Considering next an electromechanical or a-c (alternating-current) integrator, let us examine Fig. 2.3. Here again we see that the output shaft rotation y is proportional

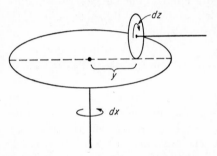

Fig. 2.2 Mechanical integrator. $dz = y\,dx$ or $\int dz = z = \int y\,dx$.

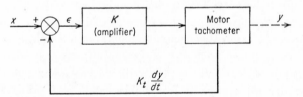

Fig. 2.3 Electromechanical or a-c integrator. $\epsilon = x - K_t(dy/dt)$, or $0 \approx x - K_t(dy/dt)$. Thus $dy = (1/K_t)x\,dt$, or $\int dy = y = (1/K_t)\int x\,dt$.

to the integral with respect to time of the input x where now x is an alternating voltage or a-c signal rather than a shaft rotation as in the first case. Because this integrator utilizes a motor and tachometer with an a-c input, it is referred to as either an electromechanical or a-c integrator.

Now turning our attention to an electronic or d-c integrator, let us examine Fig. 2.4. If we assume that the amplifier draws no current at

---

[1] Number superscripts refer to reference items in the reference listing at the end of the chapter.

its input, then a straightforward application of Kirchhoff's laws relating currents and voltages in electric circuits shows that the output voltage of the device is related to the input voltage through the equation shown in the figure.   For the conditions shown, the device acts as an integrator, and since the input signal E_1 is a d-c (direct-current) signal, the device is referred to as a d-c or electronic integrator.

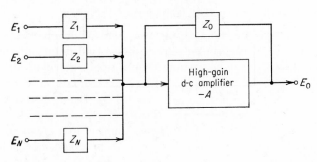

Fig. 2.4   Electronic or d-c integrator.

$$E_0 = -\frac{AZ_0}{Z_0 + Z_1 + AZ_1} E_1$$

$$= -\frac{Z_0}{Z_1} \frac{1}{1 + (1/A)[1(Z_0/Z_1)]} E_1$$

$$\approx -\frac{Z_0}{Z_1} E_1$$

If $Z_0 = 1/CP$ and $Z_1 = R$, then $E_0 = (1/RC)(1/p)E_1$.   In like manner

$$E_0 = -\frac{Z_0}{Z_1} E_1, -\frac{Z_0}{Z_1} E_2, \ldots, -\frac{Z_0}{Z_1} E_n$$

Considering now the mechanization of adders, we continue to examine Fig. 2.4.   It may be noted in this figure that by proceeding in a manner similar to that followed earlier the relation between the input voltage and output voltage shown listed in this figure results.   Thus we have essentially an adder, or for that matter, an adding integrator, depending on what type of electrical components—that is, resistors, capacitors—Z_0 and $Z_1, Z_2, \ldots, Z_N$ are.

A mechanical adder for use in a mechanical analog computer would simply be a differential gear.   An electromechanical or a-c analog-computer adder can, of course, be of the form shown for the d-c or electronic adder.   Other types of a-c or electromechanical adders are possible, but we will not go into these here.

Considering analog-computer multipliers, we may examine Fig. 2.5. In this regard this type of multiplier is referred to as a servomultiplier and may be used as a multiplier in both d-c and a-c analog computers. Actually there are several dozen different types of multipliers,[5] with respective advantages and disadvantages depending on the type of computer control system under consideration. Multiplication in mechanical analog computers is carried out by adding the outputs of two integrators through the relation from elementary calculus on integration by parts shown at the bottom of Fig. 2.5.

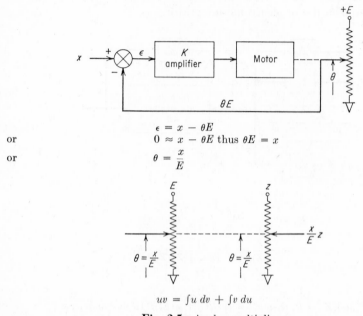

$$\epsilon = x - \theta E$$

or $\quad\quad 0 \approx x - \theta E$ thus $\theta E = x$

or $\quad\quad \theta = \dfrac{x}{E}$

$$uv = \int u \, dv + \int v \, du$$

Fig. 2.5 Analog multipliers.

Chapter 6 will go into the development of other analog-computer elements to perform additional arithmetic operations such as division, square-root computation, the computation of roots of any type, etc. However, we have at least established a base from which to operate through the computer devices we have developed thus far. Let us then consider the analog-computer solution of an illustrative problem to attempt to tie some of our ideas together.

Thus consider the simple differential equation shown in Fig. 2.6 and the solution shown there. While this is a particularly simple equation, it nevertheless demonstrates the technique of using analog computers for the actuation of systems.

Before closing this introductory discussion on analog computers, it is perhaps worthwhile to compare mechanical, electromechanical or a-c, and electronic or d-c computers as to their relative merits for different applications. Chapter 6 will provide further comments in this regard. First of all, d-c electronic analog computers are generally more flexible, elaborate, and expensive than others. In addition they can be designed and built to provide a high degree of accuracy over short-term computer runs, that is, in the order of minutes. The reason computer runs of the order of hours are not feasible is that d-c elements are afflicted with drift

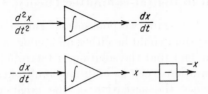

Hence the solution of the desired differential equation is given from

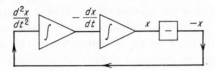

Fig. 2.6 The analog computer solution of a simple differential equation.

$$d^2x/dt^2 + x = 0 \qquad \text{or} \qquad d^2x/dt^2 = -x$$

which is passed right through the high gain d-c amplifiers because drift is a d-c voltage. A-c analog computers do not have the same problem because the a-c amplifiers in the system will not pass the d-c drift voltages. However, a-c computer elements have corresponding problems. Thus the d-c analog computers are used for short-term, high-accuracy runs such as ICBM and missile-impact-prediction problems; the a-c analog computer, on the other hand, is more likely to be used in computer control systems which have long operating periods, such as the B-52 airplane bombing navigation systems, pilot flight trainers, etc. There is in addition, of course, the point that the precision d-c analog computer is up till now more elaborate than the a-c analog computer and not as rugged. It is difficult to quote figures comparing the accuracies of d-c and a-c analog computers, but to impart some "feel" some rough figures will be mentioned. Additional figures are provided in Chap. 6.

Thus for the basic operation of integration the d-c unit (omitting drift) can provide accuracies on a root-mean-square basis which are of the order of magnitude of 0.05 per cent, whereas the a-c unit can provide accuracies on the order of 0.5 per cent. However, as mentioned earlier, the a-c computer is not as complicated as a precision d-c analog computer. The elements of the mechanical analog computer are more accurate than the a-c or electromechanical analog computer, but the a-c analog computer has more flexibility as to the location of computer units and requires less skilled maintenance. Therefore, when the accuracy capabilities of the a-c analog computer are adequate, it is often preferable to the mechanical analog computer.

This concludes our introductory discussion of analog computers.   We now turn attention to an introductory discussion of digital computers.

2.4   Introduction to Digital-computer Theory

Referring to Fig. 2.1 again, we pointed out earlier that the computer for the navigation system could be either an analog or digital computer. This stems from the fact that the solution of the problem is obtained by carrying out computations such as addition, multiplication, integration, etc.   In general, since the actuation of the great variety of control systems mentioned earlier by a computer requires only that the computer be capable of performing such mathematical operations as these, then in principle at least either the analog or the digital computer can be used, since either one is capable of performing these operations.   Thus, theoretically all we have to do is demonstrate the digital computer's ability to carry out the required variety of computations, and we will have taken a necessary step in showing digital-computer control system actuation.

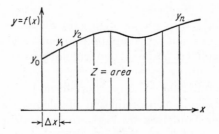

Fig. 2.7   Integration and function generation.

$$Z = \text{area under curve } y = f(x)$$

or

$$Z = \int y \, dx$$

This area or integral can be approximated as

$$Z = \tfrac{1}{2}(y_0 + y_1)\Delta x + \tfrac{1}{2}(y_1 + y_2)\Delta x + \cdots + \tfrac{1}{2}(y_n + y_{n-1})\Delta x$$
$$= (\tfrac{1}{2}y_0 + y_1 + y_2 + \cdots + y_{n-1} + \tfrac{1}{2}y_n)\Delta x$$

$$\sin x = x - \frac{x^3}{3!} + \frac{x^5}{5!} - \cdots + \frac{(-1)^{n-1}x^{2n-1}}{(2n-1)!} + \cdots$$

Actually all a digital computer can do is add, subtract, multiply, and divide, along with sundry other operations such as simple decisions, etc. However, from these operations all other operations such as integration, function generation, etc., required for the actuation of a control system can be carried out.   Thus, referring to Fig. 2.7, we see how simplified approximate integration can be carried out with the basic operations of addition and multiplication.   Actually, this approximation to integration can be improved upon by the use of more elaborate integration techniques, again based on basic arithmetic operations.   Thus we may conclude that in principle at least integration can be carried out on a digital computer to required accuracies for computer control system actuation.

Figure 2.7 also demonstrates how function generation can be carried out again with just the basic arithmetic operations. This same general process can be continued to show that all the various required mathematical operations can be carried out on a digital computer which has the basic capability of just performing addition, subtraction, multiplication, and division—provided, of course, that the digital computer is capable of properly ordering these basic operations. Before demonstrating how this is done, it is now appropriate to reiterate that since the digital computer is now shown to be capable of carrying out such operations as integration, resolving the components of aircraft velocity, etc., it is quite capable of fitting into the navigation system for the B-52 bomber described earlier, and in fact is quite capable of fitting into a great variety of computer control systems.

2.5 Some of the Principles of Digital-computer Mechanization

Let us now demonstrate the manner in which a digital computer orders or properly carries out its operations by actually setting up a simple

$$\sum_{n=1}^{100} (x_n + y_n)^2$$

x_n	y_n	$(x_n + y_n)$	$(x_n + y_n)^2$	$\Sigma(x_n{}^2 + y_n{}^2)$
x_1	y_1	$(x_1 + y_1)$	$(x_1 + y_1)^2$	$(x_1 + y_1)^2$
x_2	y_2	$(x_2 + y_2)$	$(x_2 + y_2)^2$	$(x_1 + y_1)^2 + (x_2 + y_2)^2$
x_3	y_3	$(x_3 + y_3)$	$(x_3 + y_3)^2$	$(x_1 + y_1)^2 + (x_2 + y_2)^2 + (x_3 + y_3)^2$
.	.	.	.	.
.	.	.	.	.
.	.	.	.	.
x_{100}	y_{100}	$(x_{100} + y_{100})$	$(x_{100} + y_{100})^2$	$(x_1 + y_1)^2 + (x_2 + y_2)^2 + \cdots + (x_{100} + y_{100})^2$

Fig. 2.8 An illustrative computer problem.

problem and seeing how it is solved on a digital computer. Thus, in this regard, let us examine the problem shown in Fig. 2.8. This problem is ordered in a manner which a person might use if he carried out the calculations with a desk adding machine and set down his steps on tabulating

and summary sheets. The digital computer would then proceed in a somewhat similar manner to achieve the desired result. Hence let us examine Fig. 2.9 which shows a block diagram of a typical digital computer. This diagram may assume a variety of configurations depending on who is drawing it, but they all are meant to convey essentially the same *modus operandi*.

The input to the digital computer receives the data which must be processed, which in this case is $X_1, X_2, \ldots, X_n, Y_1, Y_2, \ldots, Y_n$. The computer has to be told what to do in a completely orderly manner. Thus, in addition to the data, the input also inserts what is called a

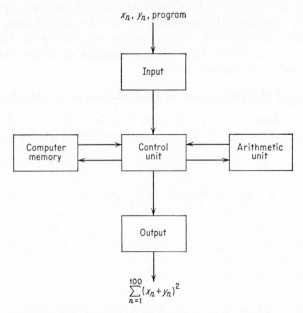

Fig. 2.9   Block diagram of digital computer.

program, which essentially directs the computer's operation during the solution of a given problem. A different program along with different data has to be inserted for each different problem. The input data will pass directly to the computer memory or the arithmetic unit under the direction of the control unit. In the case of this problem all data can be placed directly in the computer memory. The computer program is placed directly in the computer memory under the direction of the control unit.

The computer memory must, of course, provide the capability for storing each of the x and y numbers in some ordered and easily identifiable sequence. It must also provide the capability for storing the program, which consists of a number of sequentially arranged orders. Thus the computer memory must provide enough places to store both the numbers and the orders.   Let us for the time being assume that the orders have the same form as the numbers.   (We will clarify this shortly.) We can see that for the problem under consideration the computer memory must be able to store 200 numbers plus associated orders for directing the processing of these numbers, or altogether one might guess less than 500 information words or numbers.   Just how much less than 500 depends on the form of the orders and how sophisticated we are in preparing the program.   This point will also be clarified shortly.   In other words, to be able to handle this problem, a computer memory which can provide 500 distinct places for storing information will be adequate.

Actually, the memory capacity requirements for a computer control system depends on the control system requirements themselves.   Thus a computer control system for a bombing navigation system might typically require 4,000 places in its memory to store information.   On the other hand, a computer for an air-traffic control system might require 10,000 or more places, depending on just how the system is designed.   In any event, the computer memory requirements for any computer control system are fixed by examining how many data numbers must be stored in the computer memory in the solving of the particular problem, plus how many orders must be stored to properly control the processing of the given data numbers.

After all the data and orders are entered into the computer memory from the input, the control unit then examines the first orders in the memory as a necessary step in the solving of the problem.   For the problem under consideration (see Fig. 2.8) this might consist of taking the numbers x_1 and y_1 and adding them together, using the computer's arithmetic unit to accomplish this addition.   Following this, the next order might state that the sum $(x_1 + y_1)$ should be squared to produce $(x_1 + y_1)^2$. The next order might state that $(x_1 + y_1)^2$ should be taken out of the arithmetic unit and placed back in the memory in a properly designated place.   The next order might consist of taking the numbers x_2 and y_2 and adding them together to get $(x_2 + y_2)$.   The next order will state that the sum $(x_2 + y_2)$ be squared to produce $(x_2 + y_2)^2$.   Following this the next order would be to add $(x_1 + y_1)^2$ to $(x_2 + y_2)^2$ to produce their sum.   The next order might place this sum in an appropriate place in the computer memory.   Following this the term $(x_3 + y_3)^2$ would be produced, and so the problem would proceed.   After the entire program or sequence of orders had been processed, the desired result, which is $\Sigma(x_n + y_n)^2$ will have been produced.

In going through the details of this problem we see that our orders do nothing more than call for the straightforward addition, multiplication, and transferal of numbers from and to specific places in the computer memory.   Thus, with not too many basic orders and a properly arranged program or method of controlling the problem solution, the desired answers may be achieved. Typically the number of basic orders required to solve a problem for a particular computer control system might be of the order of 20 or 30. In addition to the basic arithmetic operations, the orders might also call for such operations as transferring numbers from the arithmetic unit to a specified place in the computer's memory, examining an input channel and bringing its contents to either the computer memory or the arithmetic unit, delivering a number to an output channel, etc. The decision as to the number of basic orders which a computer control system might use is based on the careful examination of the specific problem which the system is intended to handle, and reflects the different possible order structures in terms of computer complexity, problem solution time, flexibility (that is, the provision of capability to handle unforeseen problems), etc.

Having sketched the manner in which the computer provides the solution to the problem of Fig. 2.8, let us now go back and examine this problem in a little more detail, and in the process examine the structure of the orders. We have mentioned that to handle the problem under consideration a computer memory which can store 500 pieces of data is adequate. Let us assume that the numbers are to be stored in memory spaces 300 to 499 in the computer memory, and that the orders are to be stored sequentially in the computer memory beginning with space 000 in the computer memory and running on through 001, 002, 003, etc. In inserting the orders and numbers into the computer, the computer design can be such that it will examine the input and automatically place the first piece of incoming information, which may be the first order, in space 000 in the computer memory. The second piece of information which will be fed in will then be the second order, and it will be automatically placed in space 001 in the computer memory. Subsequently all following orders will be automatically placed sequentially in the computer memory. Then, after all the orders have been inserted, the computer receives the numbers x and y at its input and must place these in their proper places in the computer memory. As just mentioned, spaces 300 to 499 in the computer memory are set aside to store these numbers, and the computer will have provisions for automatically placing x_1 to x_{100} in the spaces 300 to 399, and y_1 to y_{100} in the spaces 400 to 499. This is done by putting the numbers x and y in this order on the input media. Then through the use of a counter, which is set to 300 and which is a part of the computer, these numbers are placed into the computer memory beginning with space 300.

A word is now called for on the structure of the orders. As pointed out, the first order is placed in space 000 of the computer memory. The first order might be to add the contents of computer memory space 300, which is x_1, to the arithmetic unit, whose content at the beginning of the problem is established as zero. Actually, x_1 is added to a register element of the arithmetic unit capable of holding a number of the size of the x's or the y's. This register is sometimes referred to as the accumulator because it can accumulate the results of sequential arithmetic operations.

The next order then calls for the addition of computer memory space 400, which is y_1, to the accumulator. The accumulator then contains the quantity $(x_1 + y_1)$. The next order would then call for the squaring of the contents of the accumulator to produce $(x_1 + y_1)^2$. The next order would then call for transferring the contents of the accumulator to a space in the computer memory which, of course, is not being used to store another number, that is, a free space. Space 299 in the computer memory might be such a space. The problem would then proceed in similar manner to form $(x_2 + y_2)^2$, then $(x_1 + y_1)^2 + (x_2 + y_2)^2$, and so forth.

We now are in a better position to see what the order structure might be. Thus the orders must be capable of calling for a particular memory space such as that containing x_1 or memory space 300. We can see that at least three decimal digits of the order must be set aside for memory space selection. The order must also tell what operation is to be performed on the number in the specified memory space or cell. In our example, x_1 was added to the accumulator and the order must then call for this operation to be performed. The number of operations in a typical computer might, for example, be 20 or 30. Hence we would typically need two decimal digits for the designation of the orders. The order structure is then shown in Fig. 2.10.

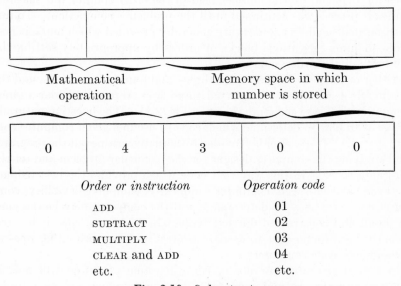

Order or instruction	Operation code
ADD	01
SUBTRACT	02
MULTIPLY	03
CLEAR and ADD	04
etc.	etc.

Fig. 2.10 Order structure.

Referring to Fig. 2.9 again, the computer control unit on referring to the order in space 000 in the memory unit has circuitry which provides means for examining the first two decimal digits of the order word and determining the operation which must be performed. The control unit then "conditions" the arithmetic unit to get ready to carry out the required operation. The control unit examines the next three digits which identify the space in the computer memory where the number on which the arithmetic operation is to be performed is located. The computer control then has circuitry for automatically selecting the specified number in the given memory space, and sending this number to the arithmetic unit where the desired arithmetic operation is performed. The problem proceeds in this manner until completion, at which time a stop order may be programmed to stop the computer and the desired result of the computation may be read out at that time.

Actually, the order structure outlined above is only one type of several which are used in computers. The type described above is referred to as a one-address code, and the computer in which it is used is referred to as a one-address computer. The reason for referring to this as a one-address code is fairly evident, namely, the order word tells what operation is to be performed on a single number and gives the address or memory space location of that single number. In other words the order word just lists one address. The order which is to be performed in a one-address computer is kept track of by a program or instruction counter. Thus in the problem above, this counter started out at 000, then stepped to 001, then to 002, etc., and each time the order in that memory space location depicted by the number held in the order counter was selected, and this process was continued until the problem's completion. To furnish needed flexibility, orders are generally provided which make it possible to jump to various blocks of orders by appropriately setting the contents of the order counter.

Other order codes include two-, three-, and four-address codes, and the computers using these are referred to as two-, three-, and four-address computers. These codes are shown in Fig. 2.11. The question naturally arises as to how to determine which code to use in a given computer control system. The answer is provided by actually writing out the programs and studying the computer designs for the particular problem and for the alternate codes. In this way that code which provides the best balance between solution speed, computer complexity, computer flexibility, computer cost, etc., may be determined, and the computer may be designed in detail and constructed on that basis. In past experience it has frequently been found best to actuate control systems with either one- or two-address code computers.

A digital computer for use in control-system actuation will not, in general, use the decimal number system in carrying out its internal arithmetic operations. It will instead use the binary system. Before

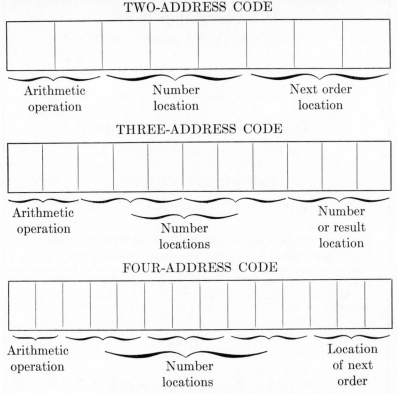

TWO-ADDRESS CODE

Arithmetic operation   Number location   Next order location

THREE-ADDRESS CODE

Arithmetic operation   Number locations   Number or result location

FOUR-ADDRESS CODE

Arithmetic operation   Number locations   Location of next order

Fig. 2.11   The various order codes.

describing the binary system it is appropriate to state why the binary system is used in computer design in preference to the decimal system.

First of all it is desirable in the interests of computer economy and reliability to be able to represent the maximum possible number of numbers with a minimum number of computer circuitry elements. It is known that the number of numbers expressible with n digits radix r is r^n. The largest number which a computer must be capable of expressing in any given control system is fixed or determined by accuracy requirements for any given problem. With this constraint it can be shown[6] that the optimum radix r is the number $e = 2.71828$, or the base of the Napierian number system. The radix 2, or the binary number system, is close to this optimum radix and since it can be physically realized simply with the ON-OFF elements used in computer circuitry, it is used. The decimal number system requires almost twice as many computer elements to realize the representation of the same maximum number capacity.[6]

There is another extremely significant reason for utilizing the binary system in digital computers in preference to the decimal number system. In the actuation of high-speed digital computers, electronic elements must be used to achieve the necessary speeds. By carrying out the

THE DECIMAL SYSTEM

$$6(10)^2 + 3(10)^1 + 7(10)^0 = 637$$

THE RADIX-9 SYSTEM

$$6(9)^2 + 3(9)^1 + 7(9)^0 = 520$$

THE GENERAL RADIX NUMBER

$$a_n R^n + \cdots + a_1 R^1 + a_0 R^0 = N$$

THE BINARY NUMBER

$$a_n(2)^n + \cdots + a_1(2)^1 + a_0(2)^0 = N$$

The digit symbols a_n for the radix R go from 0 to $(R - 1)$ since 0 must always be one of the digit symbols used.

Fig. 2.12 Number representation.

Augend / Addend	0	1	2	3	4	5	6	7	8	9
0	0	1	2	3	4	5	6	7	8	9
1	1	2	3	4	5	6	7	8	9	10
2	2	3	4	5	6	7	8	9	10	11
3	3	4	5	6	7	8	9	10	11	12
4	4	5	6	7	8	9	10	11	12	13
5	5	6	7	8	9	10	11	12	13	14
6	6	7	8	9	10	11	12	13	14	15
7	7	8	9	10	11	12	13	14	15	16
8	8	9	10	11	12	13	14	15	16	17
9	9	10	11	12	13	14	15	16	17	18

Fig. 2.13 Decimal addition tables.

BINARY ADDITION
TABLE

BINARY MULTIPLI-
CATION TABLE

Augend / Addend	0	1
	Sum	
0	0	1
1	1	10

Multiplicand / Multiplier	0	1
	Product	
0	0	0
1	0	1

The number 3		
$1(2)^1 + 1(2)^0$	11	3
Expanded	Binary	Decimal
$1(2)^3 + 0(2)^2 + 0(2)^1 + 1(2)^0$	1001	9
The number 9		

```
    3 =    0011
   +9 =  +1001
   12 =    1100
```

```
    3 =    0011
   ×9 =    1001
            0011
           0000
          0000
         0011
   27 = 0011011
```

Fig. 2.14 Binary addition and multiplication.

design of the computer circuits in terms of binary arithmetic operations rather than decimal arithmetic operations, the resultant computer circuits will, in general, be much more reliable in their operation for the same component tolerances.[6]

Let us now consider some of the details of the binary number system. In Fig. 2.12 the decimal number 637 is shown in conventional form and in addition it is shown in a form which expresses it in a more specific form. That is, unless we state the radix, which in the case of the decimal system is 10, the number 637 can mean any one of several things. To show this, the value of the number 637 in the radix-9 system is also shown in Fig. 2.12 as being equal to 520. The representation of a number in the binary number system is also shown in Fig. 2.12.

It is, of course, possible to carry out all arithmetic operations in the binary system in a manner similar to that employed in the decimal system.   Thus the addition and multiplication tables for the decimal system are shown in Fig. 2.13.   Similarly, the addition and multiplication tables for the binary system are shown in Fig. 2.14.   Also shown in this figure are the binary representations for the decimal numbers 9 and 3 and their sum and product.*

2.6   Considerations in Choosing between Analog or Digital Computers

It is quite natural at this point to inquire as to whether an analog computer or a digital computer should be used in the construction of a computer control system.   More will be said regarding this matter later in this text.   However, we can make a few comments here.   Whenever a computer control system is such that it must process great quantities of data during its operation, a digital computer is the natural choice, provided it can be made dynamically capable of handling the problem solution rates (see Chap. 12).   When digital computers were first built this was much more of a problem than it is today.

As examples of some computer control systems which must handle large amounts of data one might consider a process control system which might involve the control of many variables in many processes (see Chap. 20).   Another example might be the design of a computer control system for an aircraft interceptor.   Such a system might have to actuate an inertial navigation system for the vehicle, in addition to processing terminal-guidance and fire-control data including the ballistic equations of the weapon to be delivered to the target, etc.   Another example might be ground control computers for air-traffic control systems which would have to process data on many aircraft.   There are numerous other examples which might be cited, but the preceding systems illustrate the nature of the problem.

Whenever a computer control system need only process a small amount of data or when high dynamic rates are called for in the computer control system, an analog computer is frequently the most economical computer to use.   For instance, before digital computer technology had so progressed that the computers had sufficient dynamic capability, large-scale complex flight trainers for jet aircraft had to be built with analog computers because they carried out all mathematical operations simultaneously in a parallel manner.

Analog computers as used in a laboratory simulation facility frequently are more convenient to use in the initial synthesis of control systems

---

* The mathematical operations of addition, multiplication, etc., can be carried out in serial or in parallel fashion in a digital computer.   This whole question and its implications are examined in detail in Chap. 3.

because of the ease with which system parameters may be changed and their effects studied by the engineer designing the system. In addition they can frequently be of help in accelerating the rates at which theories for the analysis and synthesis of nonlinear and/or random input control systems can be evolved.

However, in an actual control system the use of a properly designed digital computer can frequently provide greater flexibility than is possible through the use of an analog computer. For instance, considering the flight trainer example again, if the flight trainer for a particular aircraft were to be actuated by a digital computer, then a change of aircraft need only involve a change of the digital-computer program and the simulated cockpit of the aircraft. However, if the trainer were designed such that it utilized an a-c or electromechanical analog computer the required changes might be more extensive and more expensive.

As another example, the guidance system for the nuclear submarines, the *Nautilus* and *Skate*, during their polar operations was the Autonetics type N6A inertial automatic navigator. The N6A navigator was developed and proved out in many airplane and missile flight tests for the U.S. Air Force on the NAVAHO missile program. Flexibility in the design of this system made it possible to accommodate the immediate requirements of the *Nautilus* and the *Skate*. This flexibility stemmed largely from the use of a digital computer in the system. The change in mission from supersonic missile flight for a few hours to submarine operations for weeks was accommodated principally by developing a new mathematical program for the digital computer. This new program was then entered into the computer for the system to give it the necessary mathematical instructions, initial values, and constants.

In any event it is not our attempt here to resolve the question as to which of the two computers should be used in the design of a given computer control system. We only wish to point out certain factors which should be considered. In the remainder of this text additional considerations will be presented. The important thing to be pointed out is that in the initial design of any given computer control system full consideration must be given to both analog or digital computers or combinations of these in the realization of the system in terms of flexibility, system complexity or cost, reliability, accuracy, dynamic capabilities, weight (sometimes), etc.

REFERENCES

1. Greenwood, I. A., Jr., J. V. Holdam, Jr., and Duncan MacRae, Jr. (eds.): "Electronic Instruments," McGraw-Hill Book Company, Inc., New York, 1948.
2. Davidson, G. M.: Basic Math with A-C Analogs, in Byron K. Ledgerwood, "Control Engineering Manual," McGraw-Hill Book Company, Inc., New York, 1957.

3. Korn, G. A., and T. M. Korn: "Electronic Analog Computers," 2d ed., McGraw-Hill Book Company, Inc., New York, 1956.
4. Gohar, N. K.: Experimental Determination of the Electric Field and Equipotential Surfaces Using the Heat Conduction Analogy, *J. Appl. Phys.*, vol. 25, pp. 805–807, 1954.
5. Edwards, C. M.: A Survey of Analog Multiplication Schemes, *J. Assoc. Computing Machinery*, vol. 1, no. 27, 1954.
6. Engineering Research Associates (W. W. Stifler, Jr., ed.): "High-speed Computing Devices," McGraw-Hill Book Company, Inc., New York, 1950.

3

Digital-computer System Design

HARRY D. HUSKEY

PROFESSOR OF ELECTRICAL ENGINEERING AND MATHEMATICS
UNIVERSITY OF CALIFORNIA, BERKELEY

3.1 Introduction

The general organization of a digital data processer is shown in Fig. 3.1. The term *data processer* is used instead of digital computer, because the processes that are carried out may not be computation in the usual sense. On the other hand, the term *data processing* includes computation. In

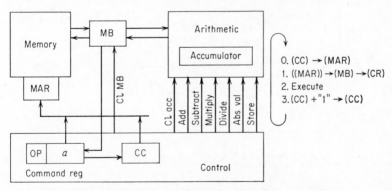

Fig. 3.1 A data-processing unit.

this simplified diagram three boxes are shown. One represents the store or memory, wherein the data to be processed is stored together with the instructions concerned with processing it. Therefore, this presentation can be described as being concerned with a stored-program data-processing system. A second box is called the arithmetic unit or, in the words of Babbage,[1] a "mill" wherein the processing actually takes place. The third box is the control which determines what takes place in the

---

[1] In about 1830 Charles Babbage conceived and partially fabricated a punched card sequenced general-purpose computer.

memory and arithmetic unit. The specification of what takes place, of course, is obtained from the memory.

One thing that is missing in this diagram is the input and output units. In this discussion the concern is with the logical design of the computer or data-processing system; so little attention will be paid to input-output. This is not to infer that input-output is a less important part of the system. In fact, in almost all data-processing systems input-output is a more complex problem than the heart of the data-processing system itself. However, because of the variety of input-output devices which are available to be used with such systems, the uniformity of design such as is found in the portion shown in Fig. 3.1 is not present in the logic of the circuits controlling the input-output processes.

3.2   The Memory

For the moment, the memory will be characterized in a general way, and the discussion will proceed with the logical organization of the processing unit and the control portion of the data processer. Somewhat later in this discussion details in the memory system will be considered.

In Fig. 3.2 is shown a picture of a memory system with a memory buffer and memory access register added.

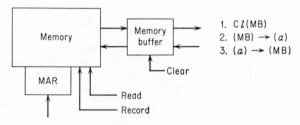

Fig. 3.2   The memory.

The method of operation is the following: The memory buffer stores a quantity of information called "one word." This is usually a fixed number of digits, but need not necessarily be so. The memory is made up of a number of locations, each particular location being able to store the contents of the memory buffer, i.e., one word. The particular memory location to be involved in a transfer of information will be specified by the memory access register. Consequently, the memory access register must store numbers which range from 0, or 1, up to the maximum number of positions in the memory. Basically, two operations take place in the memory, one of these is called READ and the other is called RECORD. The effect of the READ operation is that the contents of the location in memory, specified by the number in the memory access register, is transferred to the memory buffer. The memory buffer may or may not be cleared before this transfer takes place. If it is cleared, the contents of the memory location is established in the memory buffer. If clearing does not take place, then the number left in the memory buffer has bits in it in the positions in which there were bits in the number in memory, and in positions where there were previously bits in the memory buffer register. This process of superposition of bits is sometimes called an OR operation. The other operation that may take place in the memory unit is called RECORD. Again, the contents of the memory access register determines which location in memory is involved and the number stored in the memory buffer is established in that location in the memory.

In order to describe these operations it is convenient to introduce the following notation: Let MB represent the memory buffer, then the number contained in the memory buffer will be referred to by (MB). The contents of the memory access register is called an address. Let this address be represented by a small a. Then (MAR) = a. The number stored in the memory in location a will be referred to as (a). Consequently, ((MAR)) = (a) equals the number stored in location a in the memory. It is also convenient to let the symbol $\rightarrow$ have the meaning "replaces."

In terms of this notation, the READ operation can be written as $(a) \rightarrow$ (MB). This may or may not be preceded by a clear (MB) or $0 \rightarrow$ (MB). Similarly the "RECORD" operation can be written (MB) $\rightarrow (a)$.

Reference to Fig. 3.2, again, shows the control lines labeled CLEAR, READ, and RECORD. The effect of signals on these three lines is indicated by the statements labeled 1, 2, and 3 of that figure.

3.3   The Arithmetic Unit

A simple example of an arithmetic unit is illustrated in Fig. 3.3. As indicated in Fig. 3.3 there is a one-word store or register inside the

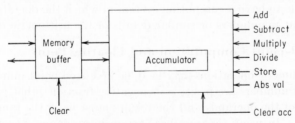

Fig. 3.3   An arithmetic unit

arithmetic unit which is called the accumulator. The results of arithmetic operations, such as additions, will be left in this register. In the left-hand side of Fig. 3.3 there appears the same memory buffer which was shown in Fig. 3.2, and this represents a register for communication with the memory.

Various lines are shown for the application of commands to the arithmetic system. For example, into the memory buffer is the CLEAR line which was mentioned above in the discussion of the memory. Going into the arithmetic unit itself are lines which produce addition, subtraction, multiplication, division, absolute value, a store operation, and clear accumulator.

If a signal is applied to an addition line, the contents of the accumulator is added to the contents of the memory buffer, and the result is left in the accumulator. During the addition operation the contents of the memory buffer is unchanged.

If a new formula is to be evaluated, usually the previous contents of the accumulator must be cleared before proceeding to compute the new numbers.

The subtract line causes the contents of the memory buffer to be subtracted from the contents of the accumulator and the result left in the accumulator. Again, the contents of the memory buffer survives this operation. In MULTIPLY the number left in the accumulator is the product of the previous contents and the contents of the memory buffer. In division the result in the accumulator is the quotient of the previous number in the accumulator divided by the contents of the memory buffer. The absolute-value operation makes the sign of the number in the accumulator positive.

A signal applied to the line labeled STORE causes the contents of the accumulator to be transferred to the memory buffer.

In the above description all questions of location of decimal point and the handling of less significant portions of the product or the remainder in the division process are ignored. One way to look at this process is to assume that all operations are done in a floating-point representation, wherein part of the number records the location of the decimal point and the rest of the number stores the significant figures. In this case it is possible to have a computing system in which the operator does not worry about remainders or similar details of the arithmetic operation.

3.4 Fixed-point Computation and Floating Point

The arithmetic operations may be done in a fixed-point number system wherein all numbers are positive or negative fractions, that is, the absolute value of the operands and the results must lie in the range between 0 and +1. In using this number system in a computational problem, it is necessary for the programmer to arrange the computation so that none of the intermediate results exceed 1 in absolute value. This means that each variable has to be properly scaled. Frequently the values arising in the computation are not known, or are only approximately known, so that with what was thought to be adequate scaling the problem still overflows at some point in the computation, and the results are not

valid. The problem of scaling the variables properly so that the overflow does not occur is a nontrivial problem in large-scale computation.
Note that in the case of division this requires that the numerator does
not exceed the denominator; otherwise, the quotient will be greater
than 1, and overflow will occur.

If the computation is done in floating point then each number must
be stored as two parts, one part being the significant figures, or mantissa,
of the number and the other part being the exponent, or power of 10
which goes with the number. Examples of floating-point numbers are
shown in Table 3.1.

Table 3.1 Floating-point Addition

+ 345	+ 03	$\rightarrow 0.345 \times 10^3 \rightarrow 0.345 \times 10^3$
+ 286	+ 02	$\rightarrow 0.286 \times 10^2 \rightarrow 0.0286 \times 10^3$
+ 374	+ 03	$\longleftarrow \qquad\qquad 0.3736 \times 10^3$

The numbers in the upper left-hand corner which consist of $+345$ and
$+03$ are both the significant figures and the exponent of 10 for this
particular number. All of this is stored in one word location in the
memory, or it can be stored in the memory buffer. In normal scientific
notation it appears as shown in the middle column of Table 3.1.

If one were to add two numbers such as those shown in Table 3.1 it
would be necessary to shift one of the other numbers so that both expo-
nents were the same. This is illustrated in the right-hand column of
Table 3.1. After the addition there may be more than three significant
digits in the answer, in which case it must be rounded off so that it will
fit into a memory buffer, or into a memory location in the data-processing
device. All of this process is illustrated in Table 3.1 where the two
numbers are added and the result is rounded to produce an answer of
0.374×10^3.

In floating-point operations a number system, such as illustrated in
Table 3.1, ranges from a maximum number of $0.999 \times 10^{+99}$, to a minimum number of -0.999×10^{99}. This gives a sufficient range in magnitude so that in most engineering and scientific calculations there is no
danger of overflow, or of exceeding this range in the computed values.
If this range is exceeded, there is very likely no further interest in the
calculation in any case.

The smallest nonzero number in absolute value that can be represented
in the floating-point system, as illustrated in Table 3.1, is 0.001×10^{-99}.
In designing a floating-point system there are a number of decisions a
designer must make; for example, is there any difference in the number
which consists of 000 and an exponent of 27, and in another number
which consists of 000 and an exponent of -13. Actually, one set of

zeros is far more significant than the other; however, many floating-point systems replace any one of these zeros by the smallest possible number in absolute value which can be written using the notation of the system.

In order to obtain the ultimate in terms of accuracy of answers it is customary in some floating-point systems to normalize answers. This means that all answers are shifted left so that there is a nonzero digit in the most significant position. That is, if two numbers in which the first digits are the same are subtracted, then the effect is to shift the answer left and introduce unknown digits in the right-hand end of the number. Thus, after a sequence of such operations one can no longer be certain about the number of significant digits in the answer. In fact, it is possible to carry out inversion of matrices or similar problems using floating-point representation and to obtain answers which are entirely wrong. The alternate scheme of not shifting left, on the other hand, may not produce any answers to the system either, since the answers may turn out to be all zeros because of the loss of significance. This is related to the fact that in many large-scale problems the worst possible error is of the same order of magnitude as the answers themselves. However, the worst situation occurs on such an infrequent basis that if the computation is done, usually reasonable results will be obtained.

3.5   The Control Unit

A typical control system is illustrated in Fig. 3.4. The bottom part of the drawing shows some of the details of the control unit. The memory

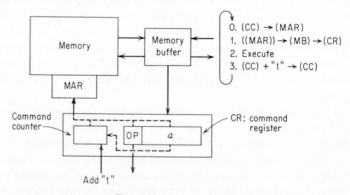

Fig. 3.4   A control unit.

and the memory buffer which have been discussed earlier also appear in this diagram. Inside the control unit there are two storage registers, one which stores a record of where commands have been obtained from the memory, and the other which stores the command about to be executed.

The general sequence of events is that the command counter steps through a sequence of numbers, and corresponding to each numerical value the contents of the corresponding location in the memory is transferred to the command register CR via the memory buffer. This general sequence of operations is illustrated on the right-hand side of Fig. 3.4. Opposite step 0, the contents of the command counter is transferred to the memory access register. In step 1, the number located in the corresponding address in memory is transferred to the memory buffer, and from there to the command register. In step 2, the command now located in the command register is executed; and in step 3, the contents of the command counter is increased by unity. Then the cycle begins again.

The command register is divided into two parts. One part stores an address a, and the other part stores an operation code OP. The address a specifies the location of the number in memory which is involved in the next arithmetic operation. This may be an operand, or it may be a location in which a result is to be stored. The other part of the command, called the operation code OP, specifies which particular operation is to be carried out. For example, if the operation code is ADD, this will cause a signal to be applied to the ADD line (see Fig. 3.3).

Generally, several events must occur in the proper sequence in the process of executing a particular command. For example, the addition operation would involve transferring a to the memory access register, transferring the operand a from the memory to the memory buffer, then applying a signal to the ADD line (Fig. 3.3). A different OP code would stand for CLEAR and ADD, in which case all the above operations would be repeated after a signal had been applied to the line labeled "clear accumulator" (Fig. 3.3).

The STORE operation would involve the following sequence of events: First, there would be a "clear memory buffer signal." Second, a store signal would cause the contents of the accumulator to be transferred to the memory buffer. Third, a would be transferred from the command register to the memory access register and then a "record" signal would be applied to the memory. After that the number contained in the accumulator would be in location a in the memory. It would also be stored in the memory buffer after this operation.

3.6 Transfers of Control

In order to specify a computation it is not sufficient, generally speaking, to put down a list of successive addition, subtraction, multiplication, and division operations. It is also necessary to specify how certain sequences of operations must be repeated. For example, suppose a Newton iteration is to be performed in the course of solving some algebraic equation. It is important that the operator does not need to rewrite the addition, subtraction, multiplication, and division, and store commands each time they are performed. They should be written once to represent the main sequence of events in a particular iteration. Then information should be supplied about how many times this iteration is to be performed. This is characteristic of all computing problems. In order to specify such sequences of events, certain transfers of control have been incorporated in the design of computing systems, and these will now be illustrated in terms of the control unit in Fig. 3.4.

If a sequence of commands is to be done over and over again as long as the computer is allowed to run, it might be convenient to do an operation called transfer of control. Suppose that the five commands to be executed are located in memory locations 01, 02, 03, 04, and 05. In location 06 a command called "transfer of control to 01" is located. When the command counter steps from 05 to 06, this particular command is transferred from memory, via the memory buffer, to the command register. The operation that takes place during execution is the transferring of the number a from the command register to the command counter. The effect of this, in this illustration, is to replace the number 6 which was in the command counter by the number 1. After the transfer of the quantity a to the command counter, it is important that step 3 in the cycle of events (see Fig. 3.4) be skipped, or the effect will be to transfer control not to the location specified by a, but to the location subsequent to that.

In computational processes it is necessary to specify carrying out an iteration a particular number of times, or carrying it out until some variable reaches a particular size. In the early computers this termination of repetitive process was done by means of conditional transfer of control commands. For example, a transfer if the accumulator is negative (TN) would operate as follows: This command would appear in the command register and during the execution phase (phase 2, Fig. 3.4) the contents of the accumulator would be inspected for sign. If the sign of the contents of the accumulator were negative, then this command would operate like the transfer of control described above—whereas, if the contents of the accumulator were zero or positive, then nothing would take place during the execution phase, and the cycle would move on to step 3. In this step the command counter would be incremented by 1, and the next following command would be read for execution.

In addition to transfers on negative, one might have transfers on positive, transfers on zero, transfers on nonzero, and transfers which depend on other characteristics of the computing system. For example, a transfer might depend upon whether a particular switch had been opened or closed by the operator.

3.7   A Computing System

In this section the memory unit, arithmetic unit, and the control unit will be brought together to produce a computing system. All that will be missing will be the details of the input-output processes. The system can be visualized in terms of Figs. 3.2, 3.3, and 3.4.   The process of operation will be described in terms of the flow diagram shown in Table 3.2.

Table 3.2   A Computing-system Flow Diagram

---

0. (CC) → (MAR).
1. ((MAR)) → (MB) → (CR).
2. What is OP?
    (a) AD (add): a → (MAR), Cl (MB), (a) → (MB), add, to (3).
    (b) SU (subtract): a → (MAR), Cl (MB), (a) → (MB), subtract, to (3).
    (c) CA (clear and add): Cl Acc., to (2a).
    (d) CS (clear and subtract): Cl Acc., to (2b).
    (e) MU (multiply): a → (MAR), Cl (MB), (a) → (MB), multiply, to (3).
    (f) DI (divide): a → (MAR), Cl (MB), (a) → (MB), divide, to (3).
    (g) AV (absolute value): $|(Acc.)|$ → (Acc.), to (3).
    (h) ST (store): Clear (MB), (Acc.) → (MB), record, to (3).
    (i) TC (transfer control): a → (CC), to (0).
    (j) TN (transfer negative): $\begin{cases} (Acc.) < 0: \text{to } (2i). \\ (Acc.) \geqslant 0: \text{to } (3). \end{cases}$
3. (CC) + "1" → (CC), to (0).

The diagram appearing on the right-hand side of Fig. 3.4 has been extended to produce a computing system flow diagram as shown in Table 3.2.   The main difference is the expansion of step 2 to show the details with respect to a list of possible operation codes or commands.

3.8   A Simple Example

A favorite request of reporters at the dedication of large-scale automatic computers is to be shown how the device adds the numbers 2 and 3. This request, although it sounds simple to the reporters, is not nearly as simple as they think.   For example, it is necessary that the numbers 2 and 3 be established in a pair of locations in the memory.   (Actually the form of these numbers in terms of the computing system described would be 0.2×10^1 and 0.3×10^1.)   The operation of establishing these numbers in locations in the memory is nontrivial, and very likely the operator would need a simple program to assist him in this operation, or otherwise he must type in quite a number of instructions at the keyboard of the device.   After the numbers are established in the memory, then in other locations in the memory it is necessary to establish a CLEAR and ADD command, an ADD command, and a STORE command.   Very likely, in order to really prove to the reporters that the system did add 2 and 3, it would be necessary to follow this with some kind of an output command that would display the answer 5 to the reporters.

Figure 3.5 shows how the two operands might appear in locations 502 and 503 in the memory of the computing device, and how in locations 1, 2, and 3 there is a sequence of three commands which will produce the addition, and store the result in location 504.

The sequence of events which transpire in the course of adding 2 and 3 can be traced by referring to Table 3.2. The first event is that the contents of the command counter which is unity is transferred to the memory access register, and the contents of location 1, which is CA 502, is transferred via the memory buffer to the command register. In this case the operation code is CLEAR and ADD, so under step 2c (Table 3.2) the accu-

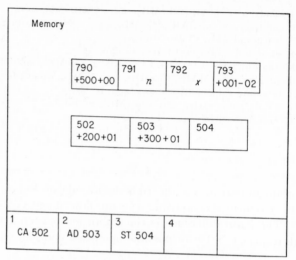

Fig. 3.5 Example of a simple program.

mulator is cleared and the addition is performed which has the effect of transferring the number 0.2×10^1 from memory location 502 to the memory buffer and then to the accumulator. After this the command counter steps up to 2, and the next following addition command is executed. Finally, after 3, the result is stored back in 504, and the command counter steps up to 4. It then continues to do whatever it has been instructed to do after performing this particular addition.

If it is desired to halt the computation, one would place in location 4 a command that reads TC 4. The effect would be that the computer would continue to run, but each time the 4 would be transferred into the command counter, and the device would go to location 4 in the memory for its next command. Thus, it would continue to execute the command TC 4 over and over again. In fact, there is no way to terminate this process, except *perhaps* by pulling out the power plug.

3.9 An Example Involving Iteration

Suppose that the programmer desires to compute the square root of the number n which is stored in location 791 of the memory (see Fig. 3.5). In the list of commands described in Table 3.2 there is no square-root operation, so the first job of the programmer is to decide on a numerical procedure which will produce the square root of the number n.

There are various approaches to this problem.   One possible way is to realize that if one has an approximation x to the square root of a number, then a better approximation will be the average of x and the quotient of the number divided by x.   Thus, the iterative formula which will tend to improve an estimate for the square root of x is shown as Eq. (3.1).

$$0.5 \left(x + \frac{n}{x} \right) \to x \qquad (3.1)$$

The number of times that the iteration will have to be performed depends on how good an approximation x is to the square root of n.   For example, if n is equal to 5, and x is equal to 2, many more iterations will have to be performed than if x is equal to 2.234.   Therefore, it will be necessary to write a program which performs the iteration, and then tests to see if x is sufficiently close to the proper square root.   This test might be represented by Eq. (3.2), which asks if the absolute value of the difference of n and x^2 is less than some constant, such as 0.0001.   If this condition is not satisfied, then the iteration is to be performed again.

$$|n - x^2| < 0.0001 \qquad (3.2)$$

The program which would accomplish this operation is given in Table 3.3.

Table 3.3   Square Root Example

Location	Command	(Acc.) After execution
10	CA 791	n
11	DI 792	n/x
12	AD 792	$x + n/x$
13	MU 790	$(0.5)(x + n/x)$
14	ST 792	$(0.5)(x + n/x)$
15	CS 792	$-x$
16	MU 792	$-x^2$
17	AD 791	$n - x^2$
18	AV 000	$n - x^2$
19	SU 793	$n - x^2 - 0.00001$
20	TN 22	$n - x^2 - 0.00001$
21	TC 10	$n - x^2 - 0.00001$
22		

The various operands are stored in locations 790 to 793 (see Fig. 3.5). The commands are located in memory locations 10 through 21, and these commands, along with the contents of the accumulator after the execution of each command, are shown in Table 3.3.   The commands in locations 10 through 14 perform the iteration operation.   The commands in locations 15 through 19 compute Eq. (3.2) in preparation for the execution of the conditional transfer of control in location 20.

If the result at the time of the execution of transfer on negative command is negative, this would mean that the absolute value $n - x^2$ is sufficiently small, so control would be transferred to location 22 which would represent a continuation of the computation after the square root was available.   If the result is positive, then the absolute value of $n - x^2$ would be too large, and the transfer of control in location 21 would be executed, causing another iteration to be performed.

3.10   Index Registers

Let attention again be given to the control unit.   Some developments will be indicated which have been built into numerous recent machines, but which first appeared in the computer put into operation at Manchester University a decade ago.   The command has been made larger and now has the form of an operation code OP, an address a, and a second address b.   The second address may not have as many digits in it as a, that is, it may have a restricted range.   The b is represented by seven one-word registers in the computer built at Manchester University, while in some other machines it is represented by only one register.   (In other possible designs, of course, b might range over the whole memory. This would make it possible to call every memory location an index register.)   The control circuitry shown in Fig. 3.4 is no longer adequate to interpret this new command. Consider now the control circuit shown in Fig. 3.6.

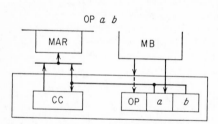

Fig. 3.6   Index register.

The sequence of operations described in Table 3.2 are now modified as follows: After step 1, step 1a will be added, which consists of the following: The contents of location b in the memory is transferred to the memory buffer, and the contents of the memory buffer is then added to the number a, and the result left in a before the command is executed (step 2).   The details of this operation are

(1a) $b \rightarrow$ (MAR)   ((MAR)) = $(b) \rightarrow$ (MB) $a +$ (MB) $\rightarrow a$

The value of this operation is that this makes it possible to deal with numbers in the memory on a subscript basis; that, in effect, the operand is the quantity a_b, and it is possible to modify the b independently of the rest of the program and, therefore, make the program apply to a sequence of numbers, for example, A_1, A_2, A_3, and so forth.

When an index operation such as that illustrated in Fig. 3.6 is present in the design of the data-processing system, then appropriate commands will be added to the list (see 2 in Table 3.2) which makes it easy to set, to increment index registers, and to test them against limits so as to change the process when the last element in a vector has been processed by a program.

3.11   An Example Involving Vectors

Suppose there were two vectors, labeled **A** and **B**, stored in the memory of the computing device; with A_1 stored in location 601, A_2 stored in location 602, and so forth, until A_{20} is stored in location 620. Suppose the vector **B** has its components stored in a similar fashion in locations 701 to 720, as in Fig. 3.7.

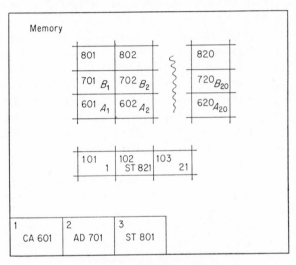

Fig. 3.7   Vector example.

Suppose the required problem is illustrated by Eq. (3.3), which says that it is desired to add the respective components of the two vectors and store the resulting vector in location starting at 801.

$$\{A_i + B_i \rightarrow C_i\} \qquad i = 1, 2, 3, \ldots , 20 \qquad (3.3)$$

In locations 1, 2, and 3 (see Fig. 3.7) there are commands which do this operation for the first components of the vector. In other words, A_1 is added to B_1, and the result C_1 is stored in location 801. In order to add the other components of the two vectors, it is necessary to either repeat these commands an appropriate number of times with an appropriate number of addresses, or to write a subsequent program which modifies the addresses of these three commands and causes them to be executed the proper number of times. The program which accomplishes this without index registers is illustrated in the left-hand portion of Fig. 3.8; the program which accomplishes this, making use of the index register described in the preceding section, is shown in the right-hand portion of Fig. 3.8.

The first three commands on the left-hand side add the first components of the vector. The next group of nine commands, from location 4 through location 12, effectively modifies the address portions of the commands in locations 1, 2, and 3. In order to avoid the question of

Location	Command Operation code OP	a	Location	Command Operation code OP	a	b
1	CA	601	11	CA	101	0
2	AD	701	12	ST	5	0
3	ST	801	13	CA	600	5
4	CA	1	14	AD	700	5
5	AD	101	15	ST	800	5
6	ST	1	16	CA	5	0
7	CA	2	17	AD	101	0
8	AD	101	18	ST	5	0
9	ST	2	19	SU	103	0
10	CA	3	20	TN	13	0
11	AD	101				
12	ST	3				
13	SU	102				
14	TN	1				
15						

Fig. 3.8   Vector example.

how these are done with floating-point operations, assume that the arithmetic in this particular case is done in a fixed-point mode. Note that out of the 14 commands which must be executed for each component in the vector, only three of these perform "direct labor" in the computation. All the rest are "white-collar workers" which are doing book-keeping-type operations.

In the program illustrated on the right-hand side of Fig. 3.8, the first two commands establish the initial value of location 5, which is to play the role of an index register, particularly in commands 13, 14, and 15. The first two commands establish the contents of index register 5 as being 1, so that when commands 13, 14, and 15 are executed they refer to locations 601, 701, and 801 in the memory, and consequently perform the required operation with respect to the first components of the vectors. Commands 16, 17, and 18 increment the contents of the index register 5 by unity, and in 19 a limit is subtracted; in 20 a conditional transfer causes the operation to be repeated if the limit has not been reached.

Note that even more is accomplished by the right-hand program than by the left-hand one. For example, the initial value of the addresses are established, whereas, in the left-hand program it is assumed that the program starts with appropriate initial values. Notice that the number of commands that were executed for each component of the vector was only eight in the case of the right-hand program in contrast to the 14 that were used in the left-hand program. Hence, in the case of the index register system, the ratio of overhead to "direct labor" is much more reasonable.

3.12   Elementary Logical Circuits

Thus far the details of a computing system have been presented in terms of composite circuits, that is, in terms of blocks called registers, memory, or arithmetic circuits. It is the purpose of this section to look into the building blocks from which such composite circuits are made. These building blocks consist of elementary storage units and of gating devices which make it possible to transfer information from one storage unit to another.

Flip-flop Storage. A flip-flop is a device which is capable of storing one bit of information, that is, it can effectively say either "yes" or "no." In a sense it may be compared to a light switch that has two positions, ON or OFF.

In what follows, a "yes" bit of information will be represented by a "1" digit, a "no" bit of information will be represented by a "0" digit. On occasion it may be convenient to refer to high signals meaning "yes" or "1," and to low signals meaning "0" or "no" information.

A flip-flop which stores a binary bit of information is shown in Fig. 3.9.

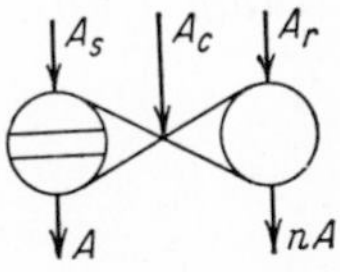

A flip-flop may have three inputs and it may have one or two outputs. The line labeled A in Fig. 3.9 is the primary output and is high if a bit is stored in the flip-flop. If no bits have been stored in the flip-flop, A will be low and will be said to represent a zero. The terminal labeled nA is read "not A," and is high when A is low and is low when A is high. There are three inputs to the flip-flop, labeled A_s, A_c, and A_r. After a signal is received in A_s, the flip-flop is set to store a "1." That is, the output A will be high. After a signal is received in A_r, called the reset input, a zero will be said to be stored in the flip-flop, and the line labeled A will be low. Whenever a

Fig. 3.9   A flip-flop which stores a binary list of information.

signal is received on A_c the contents of the flip-flop will change. That is, if it did store a "1," after A_c it will store a 0, and vice versa. So the effect of a signal on A_c is to change the output A from high to low, or from low to high. A_c is called the change input.

It is convenient to represent the operation of a circuit such as shown in Fig. 3.9 by use of Boolean algebra. Boolean algebra deals with a number system which has two symbols, 0 and 1, and there are two operations, that of addition and multiplication. The rules for addition are as follows: $0 + 0 = 0, 0 + 1 = 1 + 0 = 1 + 1 = 1$. The rules for multiplication are: $0 \cdot 0 = 0 \cdot 1 = 1 \cdot 0 = 0$ and $1 \cdot 1 = 1$.

Some of the characteristics of the flip-flop shown in Fig. 3.9 can be described by making use of Boolean algebra. For example, $A \cdot nA = 0$, $A + nA = 1$. Furthermore, one can write that A at time t, $A(t)$, is equal to 1 if $A_s(t_0)$ equals 1, and $A_r(t) = 0$ for $t \geqslant t_0$.

AND *Gates.* Figure 3.10 shows a three-input AND gate. The operation of this particular circuit is most easily described in terms of Boolean

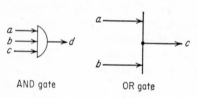

algebra. The output d is equal to the product $a \cdot b \cdot c$. In other words, d is a 1 if and only if all three of a, b, and c are equal to 1.

The second part of Fig. 3.10 shows an OR gate with two inputs. The effect of this is specified by the Boolean equation $c = a + b$.

AND gate   OR gate

Fig. 3.10   AND and OR gates.

The flip-flop storage and the AND and OR gates can be realized in terms of transistor circuits or diode circuits, but it is the purpose of this presentation to consider their aggregation into large-scale devices rather than pursuing the details of their individual structure. Therefore, their properties will be described axiomatically here, and those characteristics pertinent to their logical functions are all that will be considered.

Delay Units. Figure 3.11 shows a delay unit. The length of the

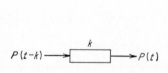

$P(t-k) \longrightarrow \boxed{\quad k \quad} \longrightarrow P(t)$

Fig. 3.11   A delay unit.

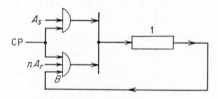

Fig. 3.12   Dynamic flip-flop

delay is k, and the meaning of the circuit is that the signal appearing on the input k units of time ago will be appearing on the output now. This rule is operative for both pulses that might appear on the input or for longer signals which are more nearly direct current in character.

An application of this delay unit is shown in Fig. 3.12, which shows a "dynamic" flip-flop. One of the inputs to the gate shown in Fig. 3.12 is a clock pulse; a clock pulse is defined to be a pulse occurring at a regular interval and is present to keep the operation of the circuits synchronous.

If the length of the delay unit in Fig. 3.12 is exactly the same as the interval between clock pulses, and a pulse is applied at terminal A_s synchronous with the clock pulse, this pulse will pass down the delay and appear at the input to the gate at terminal B in synchronism with the next following clock pulse. If there is no reset signal present, nA_r will be high, so the pulse will pass this gate and will again enter the delay line. Thus, once a pulse is established in the system, it will tend to circulate. The clock pulse is present in order to keep the pulse occurring at a standard time. If a reset signal is applied, then nA_r will be low, the gate will be inhibited, and the recirculation stopped. Consequently, this circuit stores one bit of information and satisfies the general requirements of the circuit described in Fig. 3.9, except that there is no change input, A_c.

Fig. 3.13 Symbol used to represent inverter circuit.

Inverter. It is convenient in logical circuits to derive both the true signal for a given item and the not true signal. This is done by a circuit that is somewhat similar to the flip-flop circuits shown in Fig. 3.9, and is called an inverter. An example of the symbol to represent this circuit is shown in Fig. 3.13. It has one input, labeled A, and there are two outputs which consist of both A and nA. There is a buffering action so that any feedback of signals on the output A has no effect on the input, but from the logical point of view the most important characteristic is that this derives the complement of a particular signal, that is, if A is high, nA will be low and conversely. Generally, this circuit will be assumed to operate instantaneously, that is, whenever the input signal A goes high, the output signal A also goes high, and the signal nA goes low.

3.13 Synchronous and Asynchronous Circuits

After a signal is applied to the terminal A_s in Fig. 3.9 it takes some time for the potential on line A to change from 0 to 1. In terms of vacuum-tube circuitry this time ranges from a few microseconds to a few tenths of a microsecond, depending upon the kind of vacuum tubes used. In terms of using recently developed transistors these transition times have changed from fractions of a microsecond to a few millimicroseconds. In any case, there is a time interval between the application of a signal at A_s and the time at which it is possible to use the signal at terminal A. If a whole sequence of such flip-flops is connected, then there is a transit time between the application of various input signals to the system and the time at which the various outputs reach stability.

In poor design situations it might be possible that the outputs would not reach stability and the whole system would be in a so-called "race" condition.

One approach to the use of such flip-flops in a system design is to operate with a standard clock pulse and agree that the input signals A_s and A_r will have effect only at the time of this clock pulse, and to further agree that the output signal A will not rise fast enough to be operative during the same clock-pulse interval A_s first appeared. This principle makes it possible to hook together large systems of flip-flops separated by gates such as those shown in Fig. 3.10, and to have reliable operation of the complete system. The design principle, of course, is to make sure that the gating occurring between successive flip-flops is never such as to cause a delay in signal of more than half a clock-pulse interval. Systems designed on this principle are called synchronous systems.

Instead of applying the clock-pulse criterion at all inputs to flip-flops, the clock pulse may be applied to only some flip-flops. This would lead to a hybrid system. The other extreme is not to apply a clock to any set of inputs to a flip-flop and then after any disturbance in the system all the flip-flops will change back and forth in a complicated way, but will finally reach a stable situation. Circuits designed in this last form are called asynchronous systems. Most computers are either completely synchronous in operation, or are a combination of asynchronous and synchronous techniques.

3.14   Serial and Parallel Circuits

In a data-processing system which handles units of information, called "words," a number of bits must be used to represent each word. For example, a 10-decimal digit number might actually require 40 bits of information to represent it. This would correspond to using 4 bits to represent each decimal digit. In a strictly binary number system a number with equivalent significance could be represented with fewer than 40 binary bits. Actually, about 32 binary bits are sufficient to represent numbers with 10 significant decimal digits. In the data-processing design discussed in Figs. 3.1 through 3.4 it was noted that there was a transfer of words of information from the memory to the memory buffer, and from the memory buffer to the arithmetic unit or to the control unit. The transfer of the bits of information representing either numbers or commands might be done on various channels, or they might take place as a pulse train on a single channel. In a completely parallel system there would be a channel for each bit in the word, and if the numbers were ten-decimal digits with a binary-decimal representation, then there might be 40 channels, and there would be gates on each channel. Thus, there would be a tremendous number of gates in the corresponding circuitry that would represent the data-processing unit shown in Figs. 3.1 through 3.4. On the other hand, information might be stored in such a way that all the bits representing a particular word passed as a time sequence of pulses over a single wire. In this case one gate would control the transfer of information, and the signal that allowed transfer of information would be a relatively d-c signal persisting for the full length of the word time.

The memory system described above as a dynamic flip-flop and illustrated in Fig. 3.12 can be modified to store more than one bit of information. The operation of this device would not be substantially more complicated than that of the circuit in Fig. 3.12. In fact, with the same amount of control circuitry hundreds of pulses could be stored in the delay line. Actually, in a delay line storing hundreds of pulses there might be more attenuation of signal. Consequently, an amplifier would be required to restore the size of the output signals and perhaps their shape. Such a memory system is shown in Fig. 3.14. The delay unit is K clock pulses long. The inputs to this circuit are a channel for the input information, a line representing input control, and another line representing the clock pulses which keep the information in proper synchronism. One output is shown with a gate activated by an output signal. Such a unit might represent a one-word register, if K was the number of bits in one word, or it might be a memory storage unit for many words. In actual computing systems as many as 32 words have been stored in a particular memory line. Delay systems such as shown in Fig. 3.14 have been built with many thousands of pulses in the delay line, operating at frequencies above 1 megacycle.

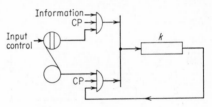

Fig. 3.14 Delay memory.

Parallel memory systems have been built using Williams tube storage and finally, in recent years, magnetic storage. Generally, these are substantially more costly than the type of storage represented by Fig. 3.14. On the other hand, information is essentially immediately available, whereas, in the recirculating system one may have to wait until the proper word appears at the output. For example, core memories are being built with a few microseconds access time, whereas, recirculating memories may have access times that range up to several milliseconds. The recirculating memory system in Fig. 3.14 can be used in building a serial accumulator. Such a circuit is illustrated in Fig. 3.15. Note, that there are three inputs to this system: An additive input, a CLEAR and ADD, and an information channel, called MB, coming from the memory buffer. If the proper signal is applied to the AD line, then information from the memory buffer (which might be a recirculating memory unit such as that shown in Fig. 3.14) passes through gate 1 and through the OR circuit to a binary adder labeled "3." The output of the binary adder, which is the sum of the number coming from the memory buffer and the number coming from the delay line, is sent back into the delay line. In case the CLEAR and ADD line is energized, again information from the memory buffer passes gate 1, and the CLEAR and ADD signal through the inverter inhibits gate 5 so that there is only the information from the memory buffer passing into the binary adder. At the end of the word time the number that was in the memory buffer is now stored in the delay line of the accumulator, and at the end of this word the CLEAR and ADD signal can be removed, causing gate 5 to open and the recirculating path to be reestablished.

3.15 Subtraction

In designing an accumulator there is considerable incentive to make it capable of doing subtraction by adding a minimum of extra equipment to the basic circuit shown in Fig. 3.15. Consider the decimal example of subtraction as shown in Fig. 3.16. Instead of performing the subtraction in the usual fashion column by column and borrowing where necessary, another technique is to add the appropriate power of 10 to the column of figures, such that the "1" is just off the left-hand end of the register. This 10 can actually be split into two numbers, one of which is 999 as illustrated in Fig. 3.16, and the other number is unity. Now it is possible to perform the subtraction from 999 and never have to borrow. This operation is sometimes referred to as taking the 9s complement; for example, in the illustration, the 9s complement of the number 246 is 753.

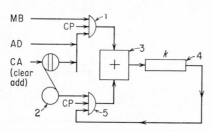

Fig. 3.15   Serial accumulator.

If one buys a low-priced desk calculator which does not have a subtract key on it, then in many cases the keys carry two numbers on them; the bottom number is the regular number for this key and the upper digit is the corresponding 9s complement digit. This is there in case the operator has difficulty in subtracting his digits from 9. After this complement operation the complete result is obtained by adding the figures as shown in the right-hand side of Fig. 3.16, giving a result of 586. The 1 (labeled small a in Fig. 3.16) is sometimes referred to as a corrective one. Note, that in performing this addition there is a carry-off at the end of the register which does not disturb the result.

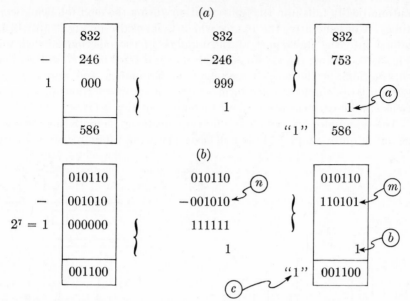

Fig. 3.16 (*a*) Decimal subtraction using complements. (*b*) Binary subtraction using complements.

Consider now the situation in dealing with binary numbers (see the bottom part of Fig. 3.16). Suppose it is desired to subtract a binary number 001010 from the binary number 010110. As in the case of the decimal example, a power of 2 can be added, which in the example is 2^7, such that the answer will not be affected. Again, the 2^7 can be split into two parts, part of it, $2^7 - 1$, consists of ones in every column in the example and the other "one" is shown in the line below. Now, the next step is to subtract the number n from the number which consists of all ones. As in the decimal example this can be done without borrowing. In fact, it is even simpler here since, in effect, one interchanges zeros and ones. After this operation it is a matter of adding the original operand to the complement (m) and adding on the corrective one (b). As in the decimal example there is a carry-off at the end of the register producing a 1 which does not affect the result. Now it just happens that the inverter of Fig. 3.13 does exactly the 1s complement operation which converts the number n into the number m. The incorporation of this as an input to the adder circuit of Fig. 3.15 is shown in Fig. 3.17. The information coming from the memory buffer passes through an inverter to produce the 1s complement of the operand. If a subtract signal is present, this 1s complement is added to the previous contents of the accumulator. Note, that no special circuitry has been added to account for the corrective one. In this example of an arithmetic unit it just happens that a CARRY beyond the more significant end of the register automatically falls into the units position during the next following word time. Consequently, the CARRY which is labeled c in Fig. 3.16 will be added into the units part of the number in the position labeled b in Fig. 3.16. Thus, the arithmetic circuits shown in Fig. 3.17 will perform subtractions in the correct manner, and if numbers are stored in this appropriate complementary form, any sequence of additions or subtractions can be performed by use of the circuit of Fig. 3.17.

The design of a MULTIPLY or a DIVIDE unit using recirculating registers, again, is quite simple. It is not necessary to use four registers, one to

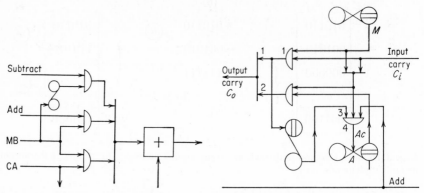

Fig. **3.17** Subtraction.

Fig. **3.18** Stage of a parallel adder. $A_c = (M + C_i) \cdot n(M \cdot C_i)$. Add $= (M \cdot nC_i + nM \cdot C_i)$. ADD $C_o = M \cdot C_i + A \cdot (C_i + M)$.

store the multiplicand, another one for the multiplier, and perhaps two registers to store the product. By careful design one of these registers can be eliminated so that the whole double-precision product can be performed using only three one-word registers. The same type of circuit can perform division by a repeated subtract operation.

Figure 3.18 shows one stage of a parallel binary adder. Note that there is a bit storage in the memory buffer that is represented by the flip-flop at the top of the diagram and there is an A flip-flop at the bottom of the adder circuit to represent the storage of the bit in the accumulator register. Another input to the circuit is the CARRY input from the next less significant position and there is a CARRY output going over into the next more significant position.

In comparing the circuits shown in Figs. 3.15 and 3.18 it is true that each of these circuits has approximately the same number of unit logical circuits. That is, they have approximately the same number of gates and inverters. However, the circuit of Fig. 3.15 takes care of a complete word of information, whereas, the circuit of Fig. 3.18 processes only one bit in a word of information, and in the case of 40 bit numbers there would have to be 40 circuits such as that shown in Fig. 3.18.

It is perhaps easier to check the operation of the circuits shown in Fig. 3.18 by first translating it into Boolean algebra terms. First, consider the signal which changes the A flip-flop A_c. This signal is derived from a three-input AND gate 4 in which one input, 3, is equal to $n[M \cdot C_i]$ as developed by gate 1. Another input comes from an OR gate and is the sum of M and C_i. This can be simplified to $[M \cdot nC_i + nM \cdot C_i] \cdot$ ADD. The CARRY output is a combination from two OR gates, numbers 1 and 2. Gate 1 develops the product $M \cdot C_i$. Gate 2 is the product $A \cdot [C_i + M]$. In thinking about binary addition, one notes that there will be a CARRY output C_o whenever two or more of the three input quantities are equal to 1. That is, if two or more of A, M, and C_i are equal to 1, then there should be a carry output. It is easy to check the Boolean equation for C_o and see if this is true. In checking the addition operation, one notes that in this kind of binary addition where the result is stored in the same register as one of the operands, that the only case in which the result register will change is when a single "one" is added to it. If two ones are added to it the effect is that it changes and then changes back again, and this particular circuit detects the situation and does not change the A flip-flop at all. The expression for A_c detects the situation when M and C_i are different, that is, when one of them is a one and the other is a zero.

Note, that whenever a number has been established in the accumulator register A and in the memory buffer register, a CARRY signal will propagate. This takes place in all the addition circuits that make up the complete arithmetic unit, so this might propagate through 40 stages. Any time that the CARRY circuits have stabilized it is possible to "fire" in the ADD pulse and change the contents of the accumulator into the answer. The moment this change takes place, a new "carry" signal will propagate, but no use is made of this fact. This circuit illustrates both synchronous and asynchronous characteristics of design. The propagation of the CARRY is an asynchronous phenomenon, whereas, the actual addition is a synchronous phenomenon. The process of adding one word in the accumulator of Fig. 3.15 depends upon the spacing between the clock pulses and the number of bits in a word; whereas, the speed of operation in Fig. 3.18 depends only on the time it takes to propagate the CARRY. Computers have been built using vacuum tubes in which the CARRY propagation time through about 40 stages is approximately 5μsec. By using high-speed transistor circuitry, this time can be very substantially reduced. Using comparable techniques a word time in the serial accumulator might be at least 20μsec; but, in the same speed circuitry (the circuit of Fig. 3.18) a CARRY time might be 5μsec. Consequently, the relative speed of addition is a factor of 4 or 5 to 1. This factor is less in proportion than in the operations of multiplication and division. Multiplications consist of a whole sequence of repeated additions. This time differential becomes a very substantial factor in the over-all time for the arithmetic operation.

The conclusion to be drawn is that if one desires extremely high-speed data-processing equipment, the parallel method of design should be used. On the other hand, if one desires low-priced, simpler data-processing equipment then the serial method of design should be used.

However, in terms of the present state of the art, it is true that the smaller the unit cost of computation, the larger and faster is the computing machine. This means, of course, that one must have a sufficient load to keep the large machine busy. If it is kept busy, then the cost of doing a problem is smallest in the largest machine.

3.16   In Conclusion

On any computer such as has been described here, (for example, on one that is only able to deal with numbers which are less than one in absolute value), it is possible to write a program which makes the computer behave as if it had index registers, and which makes it behave as if the arithmetic was done in floating-point decimal. This particular characteristic was proved as a theorem by Turing. This means that one can never expect to have computers which can do things that present computers cannot do, except insofar as they have a larger memory. On the other hand, there is a real difference in efficiency with which some operations can be programmed on certain computers. In many computers the speed of doing floating-point operations is so much less than the fixed-point operations that most people use it only in the fixed-point mode, even though this makes problems much more difficult because of scaling requirements. In contrast to this, other computers have been built in which the ease of doing floating point, and the speed of floating point, is such that this differential is much smaller. Consequently, many people use these computers in a floating-point decimal mode instead of the fixed-point binary mode.

The recent trend is to take computers such as have been described in the above sections and arrange a program in the computer which makes it possible to put in information in algebraic formula form, and to obtain as an output a machine language code which can be run at some subsequent time to produce the numerical answers. This can be done in two different ways. One is an interpretive mode which allows one to actually do the computation as the formula is fed into the computer. The other is to run in a compiling mode, in which case the computation is done at some later time.

This means that the speed of computers is such, and the difficulty of programming is such, that there is considerable incentive to use the computer itself to do as much of the coding job as is possible. It seems certain that the next generation of computers will be designed in such a way that such compilation of programs will be easier to do. One of the difficulties in designing compilers is the problem of temporary storage of results. For example, in the formula $a \cdot b + c \cdot d = e$, it is necessary to store the product $a \cdot b$ while the product $c \cdot d$ is obtained. Also, if parentheses are involved in the formula it is necessary to perform these parenthetical expressions first, and this, again, may cause a need to store temporarily the results that are in the accumulator. One interesting approach to this type of problem is to make use of a parenthesis-free (Polish) notation.

All of the commercially available computers at the present time still have the basic logical structure illustrated in Table 3.2. However, in most cases programmers have built up systems making it possible to use these computing devices and input information directly in algebraic form. In other words, formulas may be typed directly into the system, even though that is not the way the basic design of the device works. Considering that the computers in existence today are all less than ten years old it is hard to guess what will happen in the next 10 years, but very likely designs will evolve which will make it easier to insert formulas directly into the computing devices.

Recent developments in components bring promise of being able to build extremely large-scale machines in the next 10 years, perhaps units with as many as 10^{10}, or 10^{12}, logical elements in 1 cu in. If this occurs it will be impossible for the logical designer to specify the details of the design, or for the programmer to provide commands to utilize this many locations in memory. Therefore, if these engineers are successful in their component developments, or even if they are optimistic by a factor of 1,000, there will be need to develop systems which will develop other systems which in turn may design these machines. Hence, to utilize that sort of memory space, multistage programming developments will be needed.

4

Digital-computer Circuitry Design Techniques

ROBERT C. MINNICK

SENIOR RESEARCH ENGINEER

STANFORD RESEARCH INSTITUTE, MENLO PARK, CALIFORNIA

4.1 Introduction

In the previous chapters it was shown that digital computers have evolved from fairly simple beginnings in the nineteenth century to the very complicated devices of today. In order to describe a computer at all adequately, it has been found necessary to divide it into several somewhat smaller functional *units*, such as *arithmetic units* and *storage units*, and to consider the design of these units separately.

But for most computer systems, the units are still involved enough that it usually is too difficult to consider the design of a unit as a single problem. Rather, the usual practice is to decompose the units into somewhat smaller *circuits*, examples of which are *flip-flops* and *diode* AND *gates*.

Stated in considerably oversimplified form, the task of the computer circuit designer—given the over-all system requirements—is to choose a set of basic circuits from which to assemble the units which in turn are assembled into the computer system. In order to do this with any facility, the designer must know more than the methods by which these basic circuits may be interconnected. He must know such facts as the speed, reliability, cost, size, life, environmental effects, ease of repair, and innumerable others. Furthermore, the designer occasionally must use his knowledge of existing circuits to invent new ones to meet special system requirements.

This chapter is divided into two sections. The first is a nonrigorous exposition of the way that a unit may be specified by a set of logical statements. The second is a survey of some of the electronic circuits for performing digital operations as specified by the logical statements.

58

4.2   Computer Logic[9,10]

It is evident from the discussions of the previous two chapters that most digital computers may be considered as being composed of four basic units: (1) an *arithmetic unit* for performing the various computations, such as *add* or *multiply*, (2) a *storage unit* for retaining the data associated with the computation, (3) an *input-output unit* for communication between the computer and the outside world, and finally (4) a *control unit* which interconnects the other three units appropriate to the computation being performed.

As an illustration, an attempt will be made to show how an arithmetic unit might be specified logically. In order to keep this example within bounds, it will be necessary to make drastic simplifications. Specifically, it will be assumed that the function of this arithmetic unit is, upon receipt of a signal, to accumulate a 3-bit parallel binary number with the 3-bit binary number stored in the accumulator, and to store the sum in the accumulator. This unit may be organized in many alternative ways, one of which is indicated in Fig. 4.1. In this arrangement there are six 1-bit storage circuits—for instance, flip-flops—and three identical add circuits. The number stored in the accumulator is on the bottom row (stores 23, 22, and 21), and the number to be accumulated is presented at the inputs 3, 2, and 1. Furthermore, the binary carry from the sum in the next least significant column constitutes a third input to each add circuit. Each add circuit then delivers the

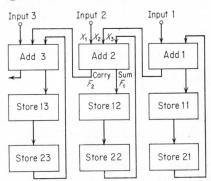

Fig. 4.1   A three-bit parallel accumulator.

binary sum of the three binary inputs to the storage circuit on the second row (stores 13, 12, and 11), and the binary carry to the next most significant add circuit. At a later time the information in the storage circuits 13, 12, and 11 is transferred to storage circuits 23, 22, and 21, respectively.

Once the simplified arithmetic unit has been organized in the block fashion shown in the illustration, it is necessary to make a sufficient number of logical statements about the blocks, so they may be reduced to circuitry. For this example, the six storage circuits each may be a flip-flop, and so there is no need to study them further. The only complexity comes in the three identical add circuits. In the case of add circuit number 2, it is convenient to treat it as being composed of two parts—one for the sum F_1 and one for the carry F_2. Furthermore, the inputs are given the symbols x_1, x_2, and x_3. Each add circuit consists then of the two boxes shown in Fig. 4.2a.

Each of the three inputs to these two circuits is binary; that is, it may take on only one of two possible values. Furthermore, the outputs F_1 and F_2 are binary. Considered collectively, all three inputs may assume only 2^3 or 8 distinct states. These states are indicated in the first three columns of Fig. 4.2b. For each of these states it is possible to specify, in terms of the requirements for the unit, the binary value of the outputs F_1 and F_2. This is done in the columns under F_1 and F_2 in Fig. 4.2b for the present example.

Such tables are known as *truth tables*. They consist of an exhaustive listing of the output state of a given circuit for each of the possible input states. Before continuing with this example, it will be of value to generalize these concepts. In the design of a computer unit, it is usually possible to distinguish a group of circuits which may be termed *switching circuits*. In general, a switching circuit may be considered as having n binary inputs, x_1, x_2, . . . , x_n, and a single binary output F. The desired circuit may be completely specified in terms of a truth table having 2^n rows.

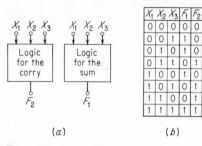

x_1	x_2	x_3	F_1	F_2
0	0	0	0	0
0	0	1	1	0
0	1	0	1	0
0	1	1	0	1
1	0	0	1	0
1	0	1	0	1
1	1	0	0	1
1	1	1	1	1

(a)   (b)

Fig. 4.2 (a) Adder components. (b) Adder truth table.

Even assuming that it has been possible to construct a truth table for a desired switching circuit, the circuit itself is yet to be determined. To do this, it usually is convenient first to convert the truth table into an algebraic statement which uses a group of primitive operations. The AND operation is represented by

$$z = x_1 x_2 . . . x_n$$

Here, z is 'true' if all of the x_1 are 'true.' The OR operation is represented by

$$z = x_1 + x_2 + \cdots + x_n$$

Here z is 'true' if any one or more of the x_1 are 'true.' Finally the NOT operation is

$$z = x'$$

z is 'true' if x is 'false.' 'True' and 'false' are associated with 1 and 0, respectively, in the truth table.

Using these three primitive operations of AND, OR, and NOT, it is now possible to write an algebraic expression for F_1 and F_2. It is seen from Fig. 4.2b that F_1 is 'true' for x_3 'false,' and x_2 'false' and x_1 'true,' or for x_3

'false' and x_2 'true' and x_1 'false,' or for x_3 'true' and x_2 'false' and x_1 'false,' or for x_3 'true' and x_2 'true' and x_1 'true.' In terms of the primitive operations introduced above, it is possible to write this as

$$F_1 = x_3' x_2' x_1 + x_3' x_2 x_1' + x_3 x_2' x_1' + x_3 x_2 x_1 \tag{4.1}$$

and similarly

$$F_2 = x_3' x_2 x_1 + x_3 x_2' x_1 + x_3 x_2 x_1' + x_3 x_2 x_1 \tag{4.2}$$

Recapitulating, it is seen that after having given a word description of a unit, a block diagram was drawn for this unit in terms of a number of circuits, some of which may be called *storage circuits*, and some of which may be called *switching circuits*. Next it was implied that the design of the storage circuits will not create too great a problem, while the design of the switching circuits will be somewhat more involved. The switching circuits were expressed in terms of truth tables, and the truth tables were then converted into algebraic expressions.

Now the algebraic expressions which have been considered are in terms of the primitive operations of AND, OR, and NOT. There are many alternative primitive operations which may be used. A set of primitive operations will be termed *complete* if any switching circuit may be stated using operations of the set. Thus the AND-OR-NOT set is *complete*. Another *complete* set of primitive operations consists of the single operation, NOT-AND. This operation is defined for n variables as

$$z = (x_1 x_2 \ldots x_n)'$$

To show that NOT-AND constitutes a *complete* set of primitive operations, it is necessary only to show that the operations of AND, OR, and NOT may be produced from it. First, it is easily seen that NOT is producible by degenerating the NOT-AND to one variable. Thus $z = x_1'$. The AND may be obtained by applying the NOT operation to the NOT-AND. Thus

$$z_1 = (x_1 x_2 \ldots x_n)'$$
$$z_2 = z_1' = x_1 x_2 \ldots x_n$$

Finally, for the OR operation, it is possible to show that

$$z = (x_1 x_2 \ldots x_n)' = x_1' + x_2' + \cdots + x_n'$$

If the NOT operation is applied first to each of the inputs, the OR is obtained. Thus

$$y_1 = x_1', \quad y_2 = x_2', \ldots, y_n = x_n'$$
$$z = (y_1 y_2 \cdots y_n)' = y_1' + y_2' + \cdots + y_n' = x_1 + x_2 + \cdots + x_n$$

As an example, Eq. (4.1) may be written alternatively as

$$F_1 = [(x_3' x_2' x_1)'(x_3' x_2 x_1')'(x_3 x_2' x_1')'(x_3 x_2 x_1)']' \tag{4.3}$$

This is not an idle exercise in Boolean algebra. The results mean that if a circuit can be formed which produces the NOT-AND operation, then any switching circuit may be composed of these circuits only.

The circuits which will be considered later produce various primitive functions; therefore, if a set of circuits corresponding to a complete primitive set is selected, it is possible to synthesize all required switching functions.

Consider again the algebraic expression for the switching function F_2 in Eq. (4.2)

$$F_2 = x_3'x_2x_1 + x_3x_2'x_1 + x_3x_2x_1' + x_3x_2x_1$$

The first and fourth terms may be written as

$$x_3'x_2x_1 + x_3x_2x_1 = (x_3' + x_3)x_2x_1$$

This says F_2 is true if x_2 and x_1 are true, and simultaneously either x_3 or NOT x_3 is true. However, one of x_3 or x_3' is always true, and so $x_3 + x_3' = 1$. Therefore the above expression reduces to

$$x_3'x_2x_1 + x_3x_2x_1 = x_2x_1$$

Similarly, terms 3 and 4 reduce to x_3x_2, while terms 2 and 4 reduce to x_3x_1. Thus F_2 may be written as

$$F_2 = x_2x_1 + x_3x_1 + x_3x_2$$

This example illustrates that it often is possible to simplify the algebraic statements, and it is reasonable to expect that often a simple algebraic statement leads to a simple circuit. Because of the limitations of space, it will not be possible to develop the techniques for manipulating and simplifying these forms, but such techniques do exist in many variations. The proper use of the methods for simplifying algebraic statements constitutes a significant part of the design problem.

4.3   Diode Circuits[3,5]

In the circuit of Fig. 4.3a, each input $x_1, x_2, \ldots, x_n$ is a voltage which may take on one of two values V_0 or V_1, where $E_0 < V_0 < V_1$. Suppose all the diodes are connected to V_0 volts. As $E_0 < V_0$, the diodes conduct in the forward direction. If R_0 is much larger than the forward resistance of the diodes, the output voltage F_a is essentially V_0. Suppose now some one or more of the inputs are connected to V_0 and some to $V_1 > V_0$. It is clear in this case the output is essentially V_1.

If the true (or 1) binary state is associated with voltage V_1 and the false (or 0) state with V_0, the logical statement for F_a is

$$F_a = x_1 + x_2 + \cdots + x_n$$

That is to say, it produces an OR of the inputs. By a similar analysis of the circuit in Fig. 4.3b, for which $V_0 < V_1 < E_1$, and using the same voltage associations, it is found that

$$F_b = x_1 x_2 . . . x_n$$

Thus the circuit to the right produces an AND of the inputs.

The association among the binary states and the voltages V_0 and V_1 is quite arbitrary. If the inverse association is made, the circuit of Fig. 4.3a becomes an AND, while that of Fig. 4.3b becomes an OR. However, in order to avoid undue confusion, the former convention will be used henceforth.

As diode circuits have now been shown for the production of AND and OR, it should be possible, by the addition of NOT circuits, to synthesize

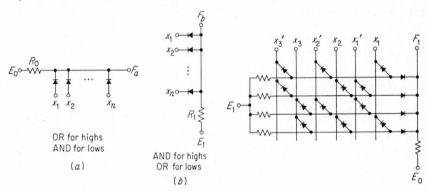

Fig. 4.3   (a) Diode OR or AND circuit.   Fig. 4.4   A two-level circuit.
(b) Alternative diode OR or AND circuit.

switching circuits from those of Fig. 4.3.   As an example, consider the switching function F_1 for the sum of three binary inputs.   The algebraic expression was given as Eq. (4.1) and is repeated here for convenience.

$$F_1 = x_3' x_2' x_1 + x_3' x_2 x_1' + x_3 x_2' x_1' + x_3 x_2 x_1 \qquad (4.4)$$

Considering Fig. 4.4, it is seen that the top horizontal produces the AND operation $x_3' x_2' x_1$, and similarly for the other three horizontals.   Each of these terms constitutes an input to the OR circuit to the right.

The algebraic expression for a switching circuit may be written in a number of alternative ways.   As an illustration, Eq. (4.4) may be written in an equivalent form as

$$F_1 = (x_3' + x_2' + x_1)(x_3' + x_2 + x_1')(x_3 + x_2' + x_1')(x_3 + x_2 + x_1) \qquad (4.5)$$

The reader may wish to verify the equivalence of Eqs. (4.4) and (4.5) and to draw the diode circuit for Eq. (4.5).

Circuits such as that shown in Fig. 4.4 are known as *two-level circuits*, the first level being the four AND circuits, and the second level the single OR circuit.   It is possible to build diode-switching circuits of this type having more than two levels. In such cases the successive levels alternate between AND and OR. Such multilevel circuits may be derived from still other variations in the form of the algebraic expression. The number of levels in diode-switching circuits cannot be extended indefinitely because of the passive nature of the diodes, since after a certain number of levels the signal is degraded to the extent that it becomes unusable. Therefore, the signals in diode-switching circuits must be amplified and reshaped periodically. Furthermore, referring again to Fig. 4.4, it is seen that the inverse of each input was assumed to be an input. This means that external to the diode circuit shown there must be transistor inverters or other devices to provide the operation of NOT.

4.4   Transistor Circuits[8,14]

Probably transistors are the most important elements used in computer circuits at the present time. In many respects they are similar to vacuum

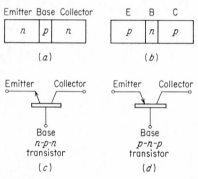

Fig. 4.5 Junction transistor schematic representation.

tubes, but have the advantage of very low power requirements, small size and weight, and—probably of greatest importance—high reliability and long life. The most successful and universally accepted transistor to date is the *junction transistor*. It consists of a piece of semiconductor, usually germanium or silicon, with three adjacent regions in either of the forms shown in Fig. 4.5a and b. The symbols n and p refer to the type of charge carrier in the region: n for negative electrons, and p for positive holes. The end regions are termed *emitter* and *collector*, while the central region is called the *base*. In Fig. 4.5c and d are shown the standard symbols for the two types of transistors.

Considering a *p-n-p* transistor, if the emitter is made more positive than the base, holes are injected into the base region. Given sufficient time, these holes will combine with the electrons of the base and disappear. However, if the transistor is properly designed and if the collector is at a more negative potential, almost all the holes enter the collector region. A measure of the current amplification, which must be less than 1, is termed α, where

$$\alpha = \frac{\Delta i_{\text{collector}}}{\Delta i_{\text{emitter}}} = \frac{\Delta i_c}{\Delta i_e}$$

Since the transistor output impedance is higher than the input impedance in the connection just described, voltage and power amplification are possible. The same arguments obtain for the n-p-n transistor, provided that reference be made to electrons rather than holes, and the polarity of all voltages be reversed.

Current amplification may be obtained in junction transistors providing the input is considered to be at the base rather than at the emitter. For this purpose, a new quantity β is defined as

$$\beta = \frac{\Delta i_{\text{collector}}}{\Delta i_{\text{base}}} = \frac{\Delta i_c}{\Delta i_b}$$

It is easily shown that

$$\beta = \frac{\alpha}{1 - \alpha}$$

Thus if $\alpha = 0.95$, which is easily obtained, $\beta = 20$, and current amplification has been obtained from the base to the collector.

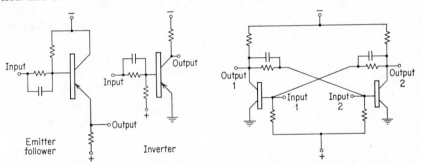

Fig. 4.6 Emitter follower and inverter circuits.

Fig. 4.7 A transistor flip-flop.

The two simplest transistor circuits are the *emitter follower* and the *inverter* shown in Fig. 4.6. These, as well as the remainder of the transistor circuits, have been drawn for p-n-p transistors. The emitter follower may be considered as an analog of the vacuum-tube cathode follower, while the transistor inverter is equivalent to the triode inverter. Indeed, the emitter may be associated with the cathode, the base with the grid, and the collector with the plate. Bearing in mind that the charge carriers in a p-n-p transistor are positive holes rather than negative electrons, the analogy of these transistor circuits with the vacuum-tube cathode follower and the triode inverter is striking.

Circuits of these two kinds may be used in conjunction with the diode circuits considered before. The inverter may be used to provide the inverse of the inputs where they are needed, while the emitter follower may be used for amplifying and reshaping purposes.

Another important transistor circuit is the flip-flop, which is shown in a simple form in Fig. 4.7. The similarity of this circuit with the vacuum-tube flip-flop is evident. Suppose the left transistor is conducting. Then its base is negative with respect to ground. Due to the conduction voltage drop in the left collector resistor, and the voltage divider to the right base, the right base is positive with respect to ground, thus holding the right transistor nonconducting. A negative signal on input 2 serves to change the flip-flop to its opposite state.

The flip-flop may be used in conjunction with the diode circuits considered before to accomplish both reshaping and the inverting functions. In this arrangement, the output of the diode circuit is used to set a flip-flop. The two outputs of the flip-flop constitute an input and its inverse for further diode networks. A reset signal to the opposite input is used to clear the flip-flop.

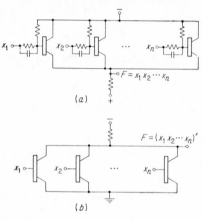

(a)

(b)

Fig. 4.8 (a) Transistor AND circuit. (b) Transistor NOT-AND circuit.

Diode-transistor circuits, in either of the forms just described or in one of many other variations, are one of the most popular means for performing computer logic at present. In addition, however, complete logical systems may be built with transistors and no diodes. For instance, the emitter follower and inverter circuits considered earlier may be generalized to produce several primitive operations. The circuit of Fig. 4.8a consists of a number of emitter followers sharing a common emitter resistor. For this circuit the output is 'true' (or at a high voltage) if no transistors conduct, and this is so if all inputs are 'true' (or at a high voltage). This is equivalent to

$$F = x_1 x_2 . \ . \ .x_n$$

So this circuit produces the primitive of AND. In a similar fashion the circuit of Fig. 4.8b consists of a group of inverters sharing a common collector resistor. The output here is 'false' (or at a low voltage) only if all the transistors are nonconducting, or if all inputs are 'true.' Thus

$$F = (x_1 x_2 . \ . \ .x_n)'$$

Therefore, this circuit produces the NOT-AND primitive. It has already been shown that a suitable grouping of NOT-AND circuits permits the synthesis of any switching function.

In this generalized inverter circuitry, the various transistors are interconnected by means of voltage-dividing resistors as well as by capacitors. By the use of a special type of transistor, known as a *surface-barrier transistor*, it is possible to eliminate these interconnecting networks.

Such transistors have a very low emitter-to-collector voltage drop, and furthermore, they may be rendered nonconducting even though the base potential is slightly less than that of the emitter. Systems of transistor switching circuits of this class are known as *direct-coupled transistor logic*, or DCTL.

Two fundamental DCTL circuits are shown in Fig. 4.9. The circuit of Fig. 4.9a produces an output which is 'false' (or at a low voltage) only if no transistors are conducting. This is so providing all inputs are 'true' (or at a high voltage). Thus the circuit provides the primitive of NOT-AND. In the circuit of Fig. 4.9b the output is 'false' providing there is no voltage drop in the collector resistor. This is so providing any one or more of the transistors is nonconducting; thus the corresponding input is 'true.' This is equivalent to saying that the switching function is

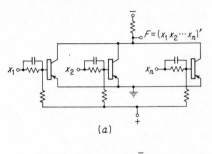

(a)

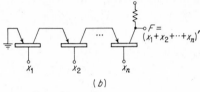

(b)

Fig. 4.9 (a) DCTL NOT-AND circuit. (b) DCTL NOT-OR circuit.

$$F = (x_1 + x_2 + \cdots + x_n)'$$

which may be termed NOT-OR. It is possible to show that NOT-OR alone constitutes a complete primitive set.

It is important to note that there are no coupling networks needed for these DCTL circuits. This simplicity constitutes one of their major advantages.

To conclude the discussion of transistor computer circuits, an inexpensive circuit for producing switching functions is shown in Fig. 4.10.

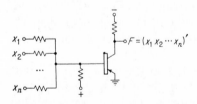

Fig. 4.10 Resistor transistor logic circuit.

The output of this circuit is 'false,' or the collector voltage is low, providing the transistor is nonconducting. This is so providing all inputs are 'true' (or at a high voltage). Should any one or more inputs be 'false,' or low, the resistor sizes are so chosen as to make the base negative enough for the transistor to conduct and thus produce a high output. Therefore, the function produced is the NOT-AND, and as has already been shown, any switching function may be synthesized using circuits of this type alone. The number of inputs which is allowed to circuits of this type is considerably less than the number for transistor-diode circuits, but the principal advantage of the present circuit, which is known as *resistor-transistor logic*, or RTL, is that of economy.

4.5 Magnetic-core Circuits[4,7,13]

Magnetic cores have recently become very popular for information storage in computers, and to a somewhat smaller extent to produce switching circuits. The magnetic cores used in these applications usually exhibit a high degree of nonlinearity of B-versus-H and have a ratio of remanent flux density to saturation flux density of nearly unity. Because of these *rectangular hysteresis-loop* properties, the material is fashioned in the shape of a toroid so as to reduce the demagnetizing fields which tend to decrease the degree of nonlinearity and consequently to move the two remanent flux states toward one another. The two types of magnetic material most often used are the nickel-iron tapes, and the magnetic ferrites.

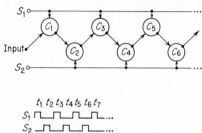

Fig. 4.11 A magnetic-core two-phase shift register.

The *shift register* is a circuit in which binary information may be introduced sequentially at one point and stored in terms of the remanent states of magnetic cores. This information is shifted down a series of cores by the application of shift pulses. Figure 4.11 illustrates the connections of a two-phase shift register. It is called 'two-phase' because of the two shift pulses S_1 and S_2.

Referring to the illustration, let the binary information be represented by the presence or absence of current pulses at the input. Furthermore, suppose this information arrives at the input simultaneously with the application of S_2. Now assuming the register initially stores all zeros, then at time t_2, the first bit of information arrives at C_1. At t_3 the bit in C_1 is shifted to C_2 by S_1, and at t_4 the bit in C_2 is shifted to C_3 by S_2. Simultaneously with this last shift, the second bit is introduced in C_1. By continuing this process, it is clear that a shift register of $2n$ cores can be made to store n bits of information.

Several problems in the design of a shift register are evident. First, information must be made to flow in only one direction upon application of the shift pulses; second, there must be no attenuation as information is shifted down the register; and third, adjacent information bits must not interfere with one another. The solutions of all these problems lie in the design of the networks interconnecting adjacent cores. Three of the most popular interconnecting networks are shown in Fig. 4.12. On this and the following two figures use is made of *mirror notation*, in which the double vertical bars constitute cores, while the diagonal short lines are windings.   The slopes of the diagonal lines indicate the winding polarities.   They may be considered as mirrors in which the input current is 'reflected' into a state of magnetization (up or down).   The inverse of a change in magnetization reflects in the mirrors to determine the currents in the various output windings.

In the circuit shown in Fig. 4.12a, assume the left core stores a ONE (represented by the upward state of magnetization) while the right core is in the reset or downward state. Upon application of S_1, the left core is magnetized downward, causing a current in the forward direction of D_1, but the voltage is such that D_2 does not conduct. If N_1/N_2 is sufficiently large, the second core is magnetized upward.   The diode D_1 in the *next* interconnecting link prevents the switching of the right core from causing any disturbance further down the line, while the diode D_2 in the *previous* link prevents the switching of the left core from causing any disturbance in previous cores.

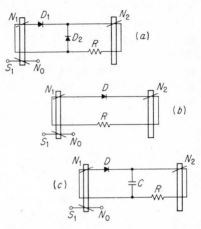

Fig. 4.12   Magnetic-core shift register interconnecting networks.

The circuit of Fig. 4.12a may be simplified to that of Fig. 4.12b by removing diode D_2, and increasing the turns ratio N_1/N_2.   The increased turns ratio effectively prevents interfering with previous cores.

If the interconnecting circuit of Fig. 4.12c is used, information in the left core is stored temporarily in the capacitor.   Upon removal of the shift pulse, the capacitor discharges into core C_2.   With this circuit, n bits may be stored in n cores, and a single-phase shift pulse may be used.

Consider one stage of a shift register, with the binary input designated as x.   The binary output then may be considered as a degenerate switching function, namely $F = x$.   This simple circuit, which uses the single diode network of Fig. 4.12b, is shown in Fig. 4.13a.   This may easily be made nontrivial by replacing the single winding x with n windings as shown in Fig. 4.13b.   In this circuit the inputs x_i and the shift pulse S_1 are assumed to occur alternately, just as was the case in the shift register. If any one or more of the inputs are 'true' (that is, a current pulse occurs at the input), the core will be magnetized upward.   Upon application of S_1 a 'true' signal (or current pulse) will be delivered at the output.   Thus the primitive function produced by the circuit is the OR.

Another magnetic switching circuit is shown in Fig. 4.13c.   For this circuit, F is true providing that x_0 is true and simultaneously none of

$x_1, x_2, \ldots, x_n$ are true. Stated algebraically, this is

$$F = x_0(x_1 + x_2 + \cdots + x_n)'$$
$$= x_0/x_1'x_2'. \ldots x_n$$

The primitive function produced here is essentially the NOT-OR. Therefore, any switching function may be produced using circuits exclusively of the type shown in Fig. 4.13c; however, since the circuit of Fig. 4.13b is a better circuit technologically, often switching functions are made up of circuits of both these types.

These primitive magnetic switching circuits have been drawn for one of the three interconnecting networks of Fig. 4.12. Clearly any of these interconnecting networks, or others which have not been mentioned, may be used.

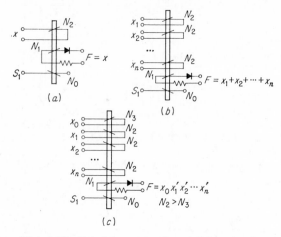

Fig. 4.13 Primitive magnetic switching circuits.

The shift-register interconnecting networks which have been considered all operate on the principle of a transformer which has a coupling coefficient dependent on the initial state of magnetization. Another class of coupling network exists for which the voltage across a winding on a switching core is used to steer the shift current in the proper path. One of several possible circuits is shown in Fig. 4.14. Suppose the inputs to core C_1 produce the function F, and the inputs to C_2 produce F', in a fashion similar to the magnetic circuits just considered. Then, upon application of the shift pulse S_1, one or the other—but not both—of C_1 and C_2 will switch. Assuming C_1 switches, D_1 is forward-biased, and the shift current at point a preferentially is delivered to the output F. Since $N_0 > N_4$, the resultant magnetomotive force is downward as required.

Magnetic-core shift registers and the related switching circuits constitute an important use for magnetic cores in computers, but at present by far the most important use for cores is in *coincident-current storage*.

The two systems having the greatest popularity are the *one-dimensional read* and the *two-dimensional read* systems.

In Fig. 4.15 is shown a 4×6 array of toroidal cores. The bits may be considered to be organized as four 6-bit words, each word in a vertical column. As in the case of the shift register, the remanent flux of the various cores indicates the stored information.

Suppose it is desired to know the word stored in column 3 of the array. A pulse of current sufficient to establish a field in excess of $2H_1$ is applied to the x_3 wire. The polarity is such as to tend to magnetize all cores to the ZERO state. The cores which initially stored ONES will therefore develop substantial voltages on their wires S_1. These voltages may be sensed by appropriate amplifiers.

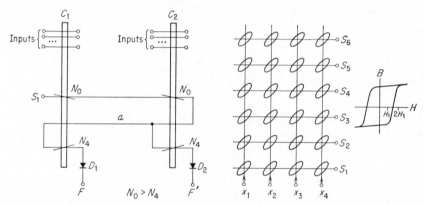

Fig. 4.14 Current steering coupling networks.

Fig. 4.15 A magnetic-core memory array.

Once a *read* operation, such as has just been described, has been performed, all the cores associated with the word which was read store ZERO; therefore, the read is said to be destructive. Following each read operation, it is conventional to perform a *write* operation in which either the word which was just read, or alternatively a new word, is stored in the same location as the previous read. In order to write a word, for instance in column 3 in the storage system shown in the figure, a current sufficient to establish a magnetomotive force H_1 and with a polarity which tends to set the cores to the ONE state is applied to wire x_3. A similar current is applied to those horizontal lines for which it is desired to write a ONE, while no current is applied to the horizontal lines for which it is desired to write a ZERO. By examination of the hysteresis loop in the illustration, it is seen that only those cores which receive a magnetomotive force of $2H_1$ will be switched to the ONE state.

It is apparent from this example that a one-dimensional read system of N words requires N access wires such as the x_i wires in Fig. 4.15. The number of access wires may be reduced by various methods, the most common of which is to use a two-dimensional read system, as is shown in Fig. 4.16. This example consists of 16 words, each of 4 bits. To read a word, a magnetomotive force H_1 which tends to write ZERO is

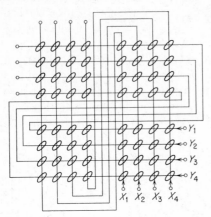

applied to one of the X_i wires and to one of the Y_i wires. This serves to apply $2H_1$ to one core in the same position of each of the small arrays of 16 cores; therefore, the 4 bits of the selected word are available to output amplifiers at the terminals S_i. Note that noise signals are also present on the S_i wires, due to the 24 cores which receive a magnetomotive force H_1. By proper design these noise voltages may be kept low. Writing is accomplished by applying currents of the opposite polarity to one of the X_i wires and to one of the Y_i wires. Simultaneously, an

Fig. 4.16 A two-dimensional READ system magnetic-core memory.

inhibiting magnetomotive force H_1 is applied on the S_i wires for which it is desired to write ZERO, and no current is applied to the S_i wires for which it is desired to write ONE.

In a two-dimensional READ system of N words, if it is assumed there is an equal number of X_i and Y_i wires (which often is the case in practice) only $2(N)^{1/2}$ access wires are required. While this is far from the theoretical minimum of $\log_2 N$ access wires, it is a considerable saving over the one-dimensional read system.

4.6   New Computer Circuits[1,2,6,9,11]

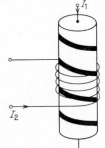

One of the most interesting new magnetic circuits is the *twistor*, which is shown in Fig. 4.17. It consists of a copper wire, shown vertically, wrapped with a helix of rectangular hysteresis-loop magnetic tape. The simultaneous application of a current I_1 down the center conductor and a current I_2 through the solenoid results in a helical magnetic field sufficient to switch the magnetic material under the solenoid. With a proper choice of materials the application of

Fig. 4.17 The twistor.

either current alone is insufficient to switch the magnetic material. Therefore, this device may be used in a way very similar to the coincident-current matrix arrays considered previously. One of the most important features of the twistor is that it should be possible to reduce considerably the manufacturing cost of such a matrix array.

Cryogenic circuits are being intensively investigated in a number of laboratories. The earliest such circuit, known as the *cryotron*, is shown in Fig. 4.18. The cryotron relies on the fact that a superconducting material in the presence of a sufficiently large magnetic field becomes resistive. By constructing a circuit from two superconducting materials, one of which loses its superconductivity at relatively low field intensities (such as tantalum) and the other at relatively high field intensities (such as niobium), a flip-flop results. In the circuit shown in the figure, suppose all the current is delivered to output 1. This current establishes sufficient field on the left tantalum gate to block current to output 2. Similarly, if the current is delivered to output 2,

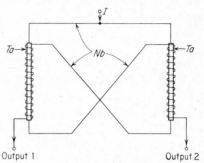

Fig. 4.18 The cryotron.

the circuit is held in that state. By the use of appropriate additional cryogenic circuits, the flip-flop may be switched from one state to the other.

Another effect used in cryogenic circuits is that once a current is established in a superconducting ring, it persists indefinitely. Circuits of this type are currently being investigated for possible application to computer storage.

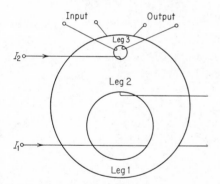

Fig. 4.19 The transfluxor.

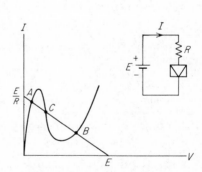

Fig. 4.20 The tunnel diode.

Multiaperture magnetic cores, such as the *transfluxor* shown in Fig. 4.19, may be used for both storage and switching applications in a computer. If a sufficiently large current I_1 is applied, the flux in legs 2 and 3 is clockwise. In this state the application of a current of either polarity to the input winding—as long as it is of insufficient amplitude to exceed the coercive force in leg 1—results in no flux change in legs 2 and 3. Therefore, a negligible signal is observed at the output. If, following the application of I_1, a current I_2 is applied, the flux in leg 2 is counterclockwise, while that in leg 3 remains clockwise. In this case, a current in the input winding reverses the polarity of the flux in legs 2 and 3, resulting in a large output signal.

The *tunnel diode* is a two-terminal device having a current-voltage characteristic such as shown in Fig. 4.20. By adding a resistor and a voltage source as is indicated in the figure, a device results which has two stable states, *A* and *B*, and one unstable state, *C*. It should be evident that such a circuit has a potentiality for storage. Furthermore, tunnel diodes may be arranged to perform switching. Much research effort is being spent on tunnel diodes at the present time in that they are capable of switching at speeds of 10^{-9} seconds or faster.

Another promising new field for computer circuits is that of *microelectronics*. The workers in this field essentially are attempting to extend the miniaturization of electronic circuits to the limit. One approach is to "machine" the electronic circuits by using an electron microscope. It is estimated that 10^{11} active switching or storage elements produced by these methods would fit into 1 cubic inch of space; although to obtain such densities many research problems remain to be solved.

REFERENCES

1. Bobeck, A. H.: A New Storage Element for Large-sized Memory Arrays: The Twistor, *Bell System Tech. J.*, vol. 36, pp. 1319–1340, November, 1957.
2. Buck, D. A.: The Cryotron: A Superconductive Computer Component, *Proc. IRE*, vol. 44, pp. 482–493, April, 1956.
3. Chen, T. C.: Diode Coincidence and Mixing Circuits in Digital Computers, *Proc. IRE*, vol. 38, pp. 511–514, May, 1950.
4. Forrester, J. W.: Digital Information Storage in Three Dimensions Using Magnetic Cores, *J. Appl. Physics*, vol. 22, pp. 44–48, January, 1951.
5. Gluck, S. E., H. J. Gray, C. T. Leondes, and M. Rubinoff: The Design of Logical OR-AND-OR Pyramids for Digital Computers, *Proc. IRE*, vol. 41, pp. 1388–1392, October, 1953.
6. Goto, E., K. Murata, K. Nakazawa, K. Nakagawa, T. Motooka, Y. Matsuoka, Y. Ishibashi, H. Ishida, T. Soma, and E. Wada: "Esaki Diode High-speed Logical Circuits," *IRE Trans. on Electronic Computers*, vol. EC-9, pp. 25–29, March, 1960.
7. Karnaugh, M.: Pulse-switching Circuits Using Magnetic Cores, *Proc. IRE*, vol. 43, pp. 570–584, May, 1955.
8. Kudlich, R. A.: A Set of Transistor Circuits for Asynchronous Direct-coupled Computers, *Proc. Western Joint Computer Conf.*, pp. 124–129, March, 1955.
9. Rajchman, J. A., and A. W. Lo: The Transfluxor: A Magnetic Gate with Stored Variable Setting, *R C A Rev.*, vol. 16, pp. 303–311, June, 1955.
10. Richards, R. K.: "Digital Computer Components and Circuits," D. Van Nostrand Company, Inc., Princeton, N.J., 1957.
11. Shoulders, K. R.: "On Microelectronic Components, Interconnections, and System Fabrication," *Proc. Western Joint Computer Conf.*, pp. 251–258, May 3–5, 1960.
12. Staff of the Harvard Computation Laboratory: "Synthesis of Electronic Computing and Control Circuits," Harvard University Press, Cambridge, Mass., 1951.
13. Wang, A., and W. D. Woo: Static Magnetic Storage and Delay Line, *J. Appl. Phys.*, vol. 21, pp. 49–54, January, 1950.
14. Wanlass, C. L.: Transistor Circuitry for Digital Computers, *IRE Trans. on Electronic Computers*, vol. EC-4, pp. 11–16, March, 1955.

5

Special Topics in Digital-computer Theory

GERALD ESTRIN

PROFESSOR OF ENGINEERING
UNIVERSITY OF CALIFORNIA, LOS ANGELES

5.1 Introduction

The preceding chapters have focused the reader's attention on the structure of a digital computer, on the manner in which it can be made to execute simple functions through sequences of its basic operations, and on the character of the physical elements which store and combine the binary states of the data and control channels. This chapter concerns itself primarily with relations between man and the digital machine.

Following characterization of the digital machine, some simple computations are used to highlight significant aspects of problem analysis and programming processes. The evolution of higher machine languages is discussed, and the relations between the user and the evolved machine-plus-machine-language system are explored.

5.2 Characterization of the Machine

The block diagram of a conventional digital-computer system is illustrated in Fig. 5.1. The range of characteristics of existing electronic general-purpose computers may be described as follows:

1. The control circuitry is capable of decoding and sequencing from 10 to 1,000 instructions.

2. The internal memory has a capacity sufficient to store from 256 to 32,000 binary coded numbers. Each of these binary numbers is equivalent to numbers having about ten decimal places.

3. The input-output systems have essentially unlimited capacity through extendable media such as magnetic tape, punched tape and cards, keyboards, and automatic character-sensing devices.

4. The basic operations on the numbers require operation times from 1 μsec to tens of milliseconds.

5. The initial dollar cost of individual computer installations ranges from tens of thousands to millions.

Two fundamental characteristics which make these modern computers different from desk calculators are the stored-program and the automatic-decision or branching operations discussed in previous chapters.   There are many systems where the universality of the general-purpose computer

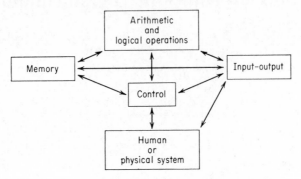

Fig. 5.1 Conventional digital-computer organization.

is not required.   For such applications a special-purpose computer may usually be designed which is more efficient by some criteria such as cost, speed, weight, temperature range, etc.

The newest digital computers are attempting to depart from the simple, one operation at a time, restriction of earlier systems.

The diagram of Fig. 5.2 emphasizes the link between man and the machine.   A common form of application of digital computers will have

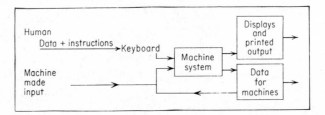

Fig. 5.2   The link between man and machine

instructions and initial data placed on one of the machine's input-output media through a keyboard.   Either the computational procedure will have been translated into a basic machine language before entry, or an intermediate language will have been defined and incorporated within the machine system.   In either case no indeterminacy is allowed. Data for any problem may enter the system without human intervention if it has been generated by other machine systems or by the same machine system at an earlier time and stored on a compatible physical medium with compatible coding of information.   If any of the output is intended for human observation it should be stored on a medium compatible with the human senses and have a defined format and coding.

5.3 Computational Characteristics—Errors

A fundamental property of the digital computer is its ability to carry out computations to any desired precision. In the course of computation there can be millions of operations involving binary digits. An error resulting from operation on a single bit may have negligible effect or catastrophic effect depending upon where and when the error occurs in the system. If an error occurs in a low-order bit of a product and is rounded off, it has no effect on the result of computation. If an error

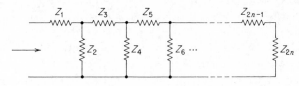

Fig. 5.3 A ladder network.

occurs such that the address of a transfer operation is modified, it is conceivable for it to invalidate the result of the entire computation.

In the following, sources of error and means for detecting them are discussed. As a vehicle for discussion, it is assumed that a computer program is calculating the input impedance of the ladder network of Fig. 5.3, represented by the continued fraction

$$Z_{in} = Z_1 + \cfrac{1}{\cfrac{1}{Z_2} + \cfrac{1}{Z_3 + \cfrac{1}{\cfrac{1}{Z_4} + \cfrac{1}{Z_5 + \cfrac{1}{\cfrac{1}{Z_6} + \cdots}}}}} \tag{5.1}$$

$$Z_{2n-1} + \cfrac{1}{\cfrac{1}{Z_{2n}}}$$

Physical Sources of Error. Errors which are introduced because a physical phenomenon is inadequately represented by the mathematical model used for computation or because measured input data are limited in precision may be classed as physical sources of error.

Let us consider two such cases referred to the network computation illustrated in Fig. 5.3.

1. The impedances Z_1, Z_2, . . . , Z_{2n} may actually be nonlinear functions of current amplitude. Consider a case in which it simplifies the problem to assume linearity and the Z's are introduced as quantities independent of current. An error is therefore introduced into the mathematical model and may become apparent in the results of computation if they are compared with physical measurement.

2. The impedances are measured quantities. The significance of the computational results are limited by the significance of the measured values regardless of the level of computational precision.

Many writers consider these sources of error to be outside the realm of computational problems and prefer to deal only with a problem as stated to the computer. However it is reasonable to include a form of detection for the class of error described in case 1 above. The assumption of linearity may be valid over some specified range of current. If this assumption is included in the model, the computed current may be compared with the assumed range and error recorded. In both cases 1 and 2, sensitivity to the errors introduced may be tested by recomputing with small changes in the data and determining the error amplification through the computation.

Mathematical Errors. Errors which are introduced as a result of the finiteness of the computations are generally called mathematical errors and in turn divided into two types, round-off and truncation errors. The manner in which these generated errors are amplified as they propagate through a computation is one of the central problems of numerical analysis.

Let us once again refer to the network of Fig. 5.3 for specific examples.

Round-off errors are introduced whenever significant figures must be discarded because of the limited number of digits which may economically be retained in the computation. Assume that the values of the input impedances have been determined from idealized calculations. If more digits are retained during computation than are normally used in a given machine (i.e., multiple-precision arithmetic) the computation time is considerably increased. Therefore unless they are essential the abnormal digits are discarded and the least significant digit of the retained quantity is altered or not according to a statistically unbiased round-off rule. Every time a division is executed during evaluation of the terminating continued fraction in Eq. (5.1), a round-off rule is active. Every time a multiplication occurs, the number of retainable digits doubles, and a round-off rule is applied to limit that process. In fixed-radix-point arithmetic no round-off questions are introduced in addition or subtraction. However, automatic-floating-point arithmetic requires round-off rules for every arithmetic operation.

Truncation errors may be introduced, for example, if the impedances represent transmission lines and are calculated as logarithmic functions of assumed dimensions. If the logarithmic function is approximated by means of an infinite power series, the decision to terminate the power-series evaluation after a finite number of terms introduces an error called the truncation error.

The manner in which the round-off and truncation errors affect the final result depends upon the sequence of operations. Thus, for example, the evaluation of Z_{in} expressed in Eq. (5.1) could be effected by an entirely different sequence of elementary operations by first combining the terms to represent the input impedance by a quotient of two polynomials

$$Z_{in} = \frac{P(Z)}{Q(Z)}$$

In general, algebraically equivalent statements will not be numerically equivalent.

Computational Checks. In some cases problem analysis will provide a prior estimate of the significance of computational results. Even in such cases it is desirable to incorporate checks in the automatic computation to determine failure of the model, the human preparation, the computational process or the machine itself. Some typical checks are outlined below.

1. A part of the actual computation is precomputed and the result incorporated in the routine as a test of the automatic computation. This may serve as a check on the machine if executed periodically or may serve as a check on error accumulation or errors in the code itself. Thus, for example, if the input impedance of the network of Fig. 5.3 were to be calculated for a range of values of the individual impedances, a single set might be selected for precomputation on a desk calculator.

2. The physical problem being studied may require that some computed quantity never change sign. Thus it may be required that the input impedance of the ladder network in Fig. 5.3 always have a positive real part. This test could be made every time Z_{in} were computed.

3. The mathematical formulation of a problem may lead to the requirement that a dependent variable be a monotonic function of some independent variable. In that case a test could be included to observe the difference between sequentially computed values of the dependent variable.

4. Allowable minimum or maximum values of quantities such as current, voltage, or dissipation would suggest a test of the range of the numbers produced by the machine.

5. In a real-time problem it is often necessary to keep track of allowable time. Excessive computation time may be a sign of machine difficulty or computational instability, or it may be used to decide to use a previously computed result rather than wait for a new more accurate result to be achieved.

5.4 Computational Characteristics—User Requirements

In this section let us fix our attention on the problem-solver and try to properly locate the techniques of digital computation in his arsenal of tools. It should however be obvious that it is not possible to usefully define a fixed set of rules to any greater extent than the process of problem solving itself is defined.

Users of classical methods of analysis take a problem and try to form a representative mathematical model for which dependent variables may be expressed in terms of elementary functions. Rarely is this possible without introduction of simplifying assumptions about the conditions in the original problem statement. The great power of the analytical solution is that under those conditions for which the simplifying assumptions are valid, it is possible to describe general properties of the behavior of dependent variables through accumulated knowledge about the elementary functions. However most problems are intractable in this sense, and solutions are guessed at by rule of thumb or by laboratory experiment. Digital-computer techniques may be powerfully applied in a manner similar to the laboratory measurement.

Given a model which requires no more than a defined set of simple arithmetic and logical operations to determine the approximate value of dependent variables corresponding to any given set of independent variables, it is possible to conduct carefully controlled numerical experiments. The independent variables may be assigned sets of numerical values, and the values of the dependent variables may be determined. It is a simple matter to hold all but one of the independent variables fixed. Unlike most other experiments, the numerical experiments are exactly reproducible as long as they are unambiguously described.

Classical analysis makes strong use of the analyst's ability to recognize the formulation of the mathematical model and to apply known powerful techniques to that model. For those problems which do not allow analytic solution but which, for example, may be investigated by means of numerical solution of sets of simultaneous equations, by the determination of eigenvalues, by the determination of roots of polynomials, or by the evaluation of statistical properties of sets of data—for such problems it is advantageous to know the time, effort, and expense associated with performance of the numerical "measurements." One type of numerical operation which it is difficult to duplicate in a laboratory is the capability of a computer to use a gradient method to lead itself to at least a locally optimized solution of a design problem.

Formulation of the Question. The control system engineer may be faced with problems from all spheres of science and engineering. The first step in control system engineering is always soberly underlined as, "*Understand the process you want to control!*"

Thus if a body in outer space is to be controlled, it may be necessary to deal with ballistic computational problems further complicated by the thrust required to leave the atmosphere; it may be necessary to deal with orbital calculations of the planetary bodies; it may be necessary to deal with calculations to determine static and dynamic forces on the structure of the body to be controlled; and it may be necessary to deal with computational reduction of data received from the body to determine its position in space.

The control of a body in the atmosphere or in the oceans may require the solution of the partial differential equations describing fluid flow past a moving body or those describing the motion of the atmosphere and ocean themselves.

The control of electric power systems may require the solution of sets of equations to describe the distribution of currents and voltages in a large network.

The control of a plant may require computational investigation of chemical equilibrium problems, thermodynamic properties of gases, heat flow, and combustion.

The control of a reactor may require computations describing neutron generation, diffusion, and absorption using different materials and geometries. These in turn require understanding of atomic and molecular structure.

The control of a business may require the processing of vast quantities of data and the optimization of assignment of production equipment, personnel, inventory, and transportation.

In many of the cases mentioned above there exist reasonably familiar mathematical models of the processes. There are however many extremely complex processes, such as traffic control, which are described only through a set of rules governing the elements. In such cases it is often desirable to be able to numerically simulate the process such that controlled experiments may be effected at a high rate of speed.

All of the cases above have been considered with relation to computation outside the process itself providing information about significant parameters. Another class of computation requires the use of digital techniques within the process and needs "real-time" computing speeds. The required speeds are determined by the arrival rate of input information and the rate of output information necessary to properly control the process. Thus a guidance computer may be forced to complete trajectory calculations in flight and sufficiently fast to effect proper control before the conditions described by its input data change too drastically.

Form of Output. In real-time applications the results of computation are required to effect changes in valve positions, motor speeds, temperature controls, or other such devices, and the numbers calculated are directly converted into a form with sufficient power to execute those

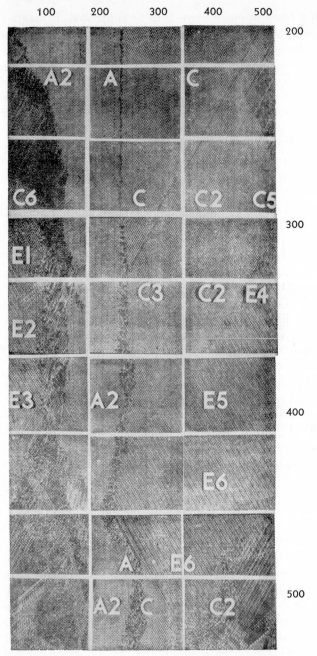

Fig. 5.4 Results of machine experiments in the numerical simulation of evolution processes.

activities.   Most other computations produce outputs meant for human observation and often for reinsertion into further computational processes after human decisions or operations.   The natural products of digital computation are lists of numbers.   A number focuses attention on the detailed representation of a process quantity under special conditions. Information about the special conditions is usually carried in the format which attempts to group related lists of numbers.   In fact, the number is a very poor output form if there is any need to attempt generalization of computed results.   The human being has great capacity to observe patterns, and graphical display of computational results should be planned wherever possible.

One unconventional use of digital-computer output is illustrated in Fig. 5.4 taken from an article by Nils Aall Barricelli[1] describing machine experiments in the numerical simulation of evolution processes.   Genes and organisms are represented by horizontal patterns of ones and zeros or light and dark areas.   They interact by prescribed genetic rules and produce new generations of genes and organisms as time progresses in the downward direction.   The over-all pattern permits gross observations while more microscopic inspection of particular areas of interest may be made at any time.

Description of the Computation.   The detailed program for a computation is itself a listing of numbers or coded words and is unnatural to the human trained in communication with other humans through sound, text, and pictures.   In order to plan complex experiments in which the human may alter computational parameters, to permit other humans to understand the process such that the programming effort need not be reexpended, to enable users of different machines to attempt a similar computation, and to facilitate determination of an error in programming or computation, it is desirable to describe the computational process in a form intelligible to humans.

This problem is being alleviated by the development of more natural programming languages.   Meanwhile common aids are the original programmer, formulated prose description, and the flow chart.   The flow chart displays the information paths which may be used during the computational process.   There are a number of conventions for drawing flow charts, but the most important requirements are symbols which indicate branching in the process as a result of transfers conditional on the state of some computed quantity (the branch point may be converging or diverging), which indicate places in the program where indices or addresses of operations are altered in the course of computation, which indicate places and conditions associated with machine stops, and which indicate places where key parameters are stored.

Figure 5.5 illustrates a simple flow chart for the computation of the input impedance of the network of Fig. 5.3.   Note that the flow chart does not give the explicit sequence in which the branches are used.   Most often such sequences have a complicated dependence upon the numbers being produced in the course of the computation.   The flow chart can also serve as an index to the detailed code listing if numbers defining the locations of leading instructions are appended to the boxes.

The parameters in this particular flow chart are as follows:

Z^*, the input impedance to the ladder network as it is systematically lengthened from a single rightmost rung to its full size.

i, the subscript identifying the individual ladder impedances.   When i is odd, z_i is a series impedance; when i is even, z_i is a shunt impedance.

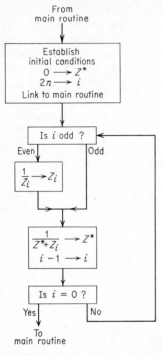

From
main routine

Establish
initial conditions
$0 \longrightarrow Z^*$
$2n \longrightarrow i$
Link to main routine

Is i odd ?

Even   Odd

$\dfrac{1}{Z_i} \longrightarrow Z_i$

$\dfrac{1}{Z^*+Z_i} \longrightarrow Z^*$
$i-1 \longrightarrow i$

Is $i = 0$?

Yes   No

To
main routine

Fig. 5.5 Simple flow chart for the computation of the input impedance of the network of Fig. 5.3.

5.5 Computational Characteristics— Sample Programs

Let us consider in this section numerical methods which are of direct interest in the analysis and synthesis of control systems.

The Roots of Polynomials.[2,3] Determination of the roots of polynomials is a process which arises frequently in the analysis of stability of a control system or the synthesis of a stable control system.

Consider a characteristic equation in the form of

$$f(x) = a_n x^n + a_{n-1}x^{n-1} + \cdots + a_0 = 0 \qquad a_n \neq 0$$

The coefficients a_i may in general be complex.   The roots are the n values of x which make $f(x) = 0$.   The roots $\alpha_1, \alpha_2, \ldots, \alpha_n$ may in general be complex.

If the kth estimate to the ith root is denoted by $x_i{}^k$, then we can seek to improve on that estimate by Newton's method, i.e., let

$$x_i{}^{k+1} = x_i{}^k + \Delta_i{}^k$$

and expand $f(x_i{}^k + \Delta_i{}^k)$ in powers of $\Delta_i{}^k$ to obtain

$$f(x_i{}^k + \Delta_i{}^k) = f(x_i{}^k) + \Delta_i{}^k f'(x_i{}^k) + \frac{\Delta_i{}^{k2}}{2} f''(x_i{}^k) + \cdots$$

For small Δ we may neglect terms beyond the linear one and set

$$f(x_i{}^k + \Delta) = f(x_i{}^k) + \Delta_i{}^k f'(x_i{}^k) = 0$$

giving

$$\Delta_i{}^k = -\frac{f(x_i{}^k)}{f'(x_i{}^k)}$$

Hence after k steps

$$x_i{}^{k+1} = x_i{}^0 + \Delta_i{}^0 + \Delta_i{}^1 + \cdots + \Delta_i{}^k$$

Once an approximation is found close enough to the value of the root, convergence is very rapid.

A subroutine for calculating the roots of a polynomial was developed by R. Johnson of Lockheed Aircraft Corporation and distributed to IBM 704–709 users through the SHARE[4] organization. The subroutine description in its entirety is reproduced in the appendix to this chapter. It gives the reader an opportunity to carry out analysis of a significant subroutine containing many examples of programming art. The character of the calling sequence and explanation of coding conventions may be found in IBM reference manuals.[5]

Root Locus. A common tool in the study of stability of feedback control systems is the root-locus method.[6] The drudgery involved in determination of points in the locus of roots has provoked the development of many mechanical aids. Although the precision of the digital computer is not generally required, the amount of manipulation is sufficient to have motivated the development of a special computer program[7] for generating the locus of roots.

The program deals with the characteristic equation for a system in the form

$$
\begin{aligned}
A_n s^n + A_{n-1} s^{n-1} + \cdots &+ A_i s^i + \cdots + A_0 \\
+ K(B_m s^m + B_{m-1} s^{m-1} + \cdots &+ B_j s^j + \cdots + B_1 s + B_0) = 0 \quad (5.2)
\end{aligned}
$$

where the B polynomial represents the zeros and the A polynomial represents the poles of the open-loop transfer function. This equation is solved for a series of values of the gain K.

The initial data required in the IBM 704 program are listed in Table 5.1. The memory location at which data storage begins is symbolically defined as D so that this program may more readily be incorporated within some larger program.

The computer must be supplied with the $n + m + 2$ coefficients A_i, B_j contained in the characteristic equation (5.2). The fact that 31 locations are provided for each of them limits the system complexity to 3 th order. The initial value of the gain K_0 is prescribed and defines the starting point of the locus of roots. The locus may be stopped at a specified gain in the unstable region by prescribing the constant K_A. The initial value of gain K_0 may be incremented N_A times with an increment I_A and then

Table 5.1   Data Required for Root- and Gain-locus Program

Storage locations (IBM 704)	Description	Octal point Fixed	Octal point Floating
D to $D + 30$	Coefficients of polynomial N of poles—constant term first		X
$D + 31$ to $D + 61$	Coefficients of polynomial M of zeros—constant term first		X
$D + 62$	K_o, initial gain (start of root locus)		X
$D + 63$	K_A, limiting gain (secondary stop for iteration)		X
$D + 64$	I_A, first increment to gain		X
$D + 65$	I_B, second increment to gain		X
$D + 67$	N_A, number of times first increment is used	X	
$D + 68$	N_B, number of times second increment is used	X	
$D + 69$ to $D + 128$	J, trial roots if any (complex form)		X X
$D + 130$	*Zero* for real coefficients *one* for complex coefficients (not used for root locus)		
$D + 131$	S, one to seven, usually four (number of octal places of accuracy)	X	
$D + 132$	N, order of polynomial N	X	
$D + 133$	M, order of polynomial M	X	
$D + 134$	I_C, third increment to gain		X
$D + 135$	N_C, number of times third increment is used	X	

SOURCE: C. J. Doda, *Control Engineering*, p. 103, May, 1958.

N_B times with an increment I_B and then N_C times with an increment I_C. The increment parameters permit varying resolutions to be specified in different regions of the root locus.

The desired accuracy of the roots, the order of the polynomials, and a set of trial roots complete the set of data provided to the machine. For a 30th-order system the total list requires the specification of 134 data items in addition to the set of instructions themselves. The right-hand column of Table 5.1 indicates whether the data are inserted in a standardized fixed- or floating-point representation.

A simplified flow chart for Doda's simplest root-locus program is displayed in Fig. 5.6. We see here that the program for extracting the roots of a polynomial is included as a subroutine within the root-locus program. Figures 5.7, 5.8, and 5.9 are examples of the computer output which demonstrate the effectiveness of the change in resolution in regions where accuracy may be significant.

In characteristic evolution of more powerful programs, Doda also reports on a later program which calculates both phase-angle and gain loci. The phase-angle loci are calculated by raising the original open-loop transform to an integral power and then calculating the normal root locus for the cases of positive and negative gain. The limit to the fineness of the phase angle is determined by the nonavailability of programs for extraction of the roots of polynomials above the 97th order.

Let us consider for a moment the significance of such a program. The program for the usual root and gain locus requires of the order of minutes

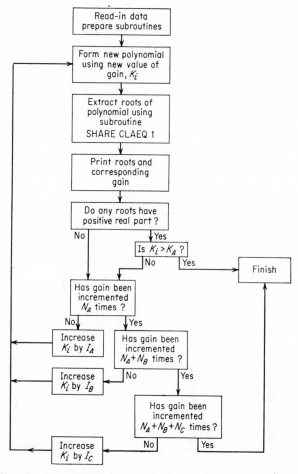

Fig. 5.6 Gross flow chart for root- and gain-locus program.

of computing time on the IBM 704. The phase-angle loci are more time-consuming because of the higher-order polynomial root extraction. Let us assume that the loci would take of the order of the hour in computation and the same order of time to prepare the input data properly. One usually finds the root-locus method described as a very powerful analysis and synthesis tool, limited by the tediousness of construction but very useful even in a somewhat qualitative fashion. Thus one learns

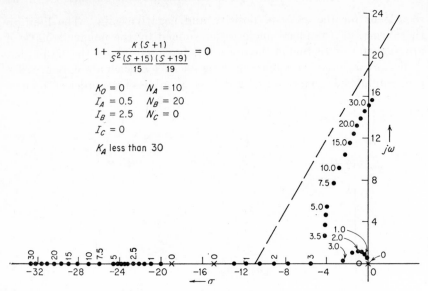

Fig. 5.7 Root-locus plot for values of K incremented as shown, starting from $K = 0$. All points computed are plotted.   Note need for more detail between $K = 3$ and $K = 3.5$.   (*From C. J. Doda.*[7])

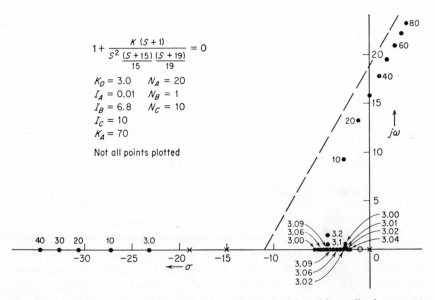

Fig. 5.8 Root-locus plot of same equation as Fig. 5.7, with much smaller increments in K used to obtain accurate curve at break-away point.   (*From C. J. Doda.*[7])

that it is possible to look at the characteristic equation, sketch in the root locus, and demonstrate the effect of other poles and zeros added to the system.

In fact, in a synthesis procedure, when a man is working with pencil and scratch pad, guessing at good solutions, and testing their crucial

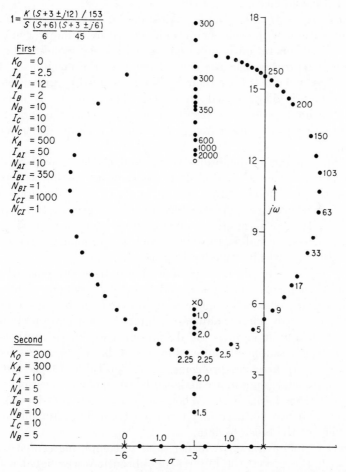

Fig. 5.9 Root-locus plot of digital-computer results shows how second computation was used to fill in precise location of locus between $K = 200$ and $K = 350$. (*From C. J. Doda.*[7])

properties, the very thought of formally translating into detailed, precise input data lists is enough to inhibit the procedure. The obvious power of such a digital program is the ability to carry out detailed analysis of a proposed design much more deeply than would be otherwise possible. Moreover where an initial design fails, it is often possible to instruct the machine to systematically vary parameters of the system.

5.6   Computational Characteristics—Programming and Coding

In the previous section we have discussed particular properties of some fairly complex routines.   In the following we shall consider some general characteristics of programs and trends in the evolution of more effective man-machine languages.

Relative versus Absolute Coding.   Most digital computers have a defined set of operations with each operation identified by a unique combination of digits.   An operation is initiated when the corresponding digit combination is represented in the control organ of the machine.   Memory cells in these machines have their locations specified by unique combinations of binary digits called addresses.   The machine is directed to operate on information at a particular address when the corresponding digit combination is represented in an address register of the machine's control.

Absolute coding is the primitive method of numerical specification of the location of each piece of data and each instruction as a program is written.   Any modification in the interior of the program implies extensive renumbering.   Any coding error may propagate far into the program.   The entire approach of absolute coding treats each problem as separate and excludes properties which would enhance the inclusion of that program within some larger program.

Relative coding breaks a program down into basic subsequences.   The location of each subsequence is established by a symbolic identifier and then each of the elements is numerically ordered within the subsequence. Not only does this relative addressing limit the propagation of effects of modification, but it permits the definition of executive routines which are capable of assigning absolute addresses to the subsequences according to the needs of particular problems.   Thus in Table 5.1 the input data for the root-locus program are assigned to 136 memory locations starting at some memory location D.   When the phase-angle root-locus program was written, it was not necessary to be constrained by previous arbitrary assignment of the block of data.

Library of Subroutines.   A higher stage of computing center evolution came with the growth of libraries of subroutines associated with each machine type.   Those programs which might be incorporated in more extensive computations were relatively coded and provided with systematic procedures for linking the routine with other routines.   In general this linking process means prescription of the location of operands and results for the subroutine and prescription of the return point in the main program after completion of the subroutine.   The first stage of evolution saw the development of local libraries containing routines such as special function evaluation, interpolation, integration, number conversion, and input-output operations.

Pseudo Codes. In order to permit programming in languages more natural to the computer user and programmer, many new codes were designed which then required translation into the actual machine language. In some cases the pseudo code consisted merely of renaming, in mnemonic form, the original machine instructions. Following that step, translation routines then effected a word-for-word translation. In other cases, completely new instruction lists were defined, with each pseudo instruction requiring translation into a sequence of machine language instructions.

The routines used to effect the translation fall into two main classes; interpreters and compilers.

Interpretive Routines. An interpretive routine is in constant use throughout a machine computation. The pseudo-coded instructions in the source program are observed in sequence. The interpretive routine decodes and translates them into equivalent sets of machine language operations. The machine language operations are executed on proper data and then the next pseudo-code instruction is called up. This process is iterated until completion of the program. The computing time is generally increased by between one and two orders of magnitude over the equivalent machine language program.

Compiler Routines. The compiler takes a pseudo code and translates it into another code *prior* to computation.

The primary goal of a compiler is to increase programming effectiveness by permitting the programmer to formulate his problem in as natural a language as possible. The design of a compiler attempts to allocate to the machine those tasks for which it is more efficient and error-free. In order to satisfy the latter criterion it is necessary to introduce a set of constraints to control the design of the pseudo code. In particular, this means removing the ambiguity of natural language and relieving the compiler of the burden of analyzing the programmer.

A standard definition[8] of a compiler ascribes to it the possible tasks of decoding, number representation conversion, selection of required subroutines from the library, generation of subroutines from given skeletal codes and parameters, allocation of storage addresses, assembly of subroutines into the main routine, and recording of the original code and the compiled code or its main characteristics.

5.7 Multilanguage Structures

The demonstrated effectiveness of the digital computer and technological achievements permitting their mass production highlighted the bottleneck of programming skill required for their use. Machine users organizations were formed to cooperatively pool their programming efforts. Machine manufacturers competitively realized that any generalized programs which reduced customer programming time and skill requirements were as much a part of their machine system as the power supplies. They invested hundreds of man years in the generation of user-oriented languages. Inevitably the latter languages contained characteristics designed for each manufacturer's machine. Investigators at university and research establishments added another level in the hierarchy of machine languages by designing translator programs to take, as input, programs written for one type of machine and produce, as output, programs usable by another type of machine. Through professional societies, the same investigators initiated the development of internationally standardized languages to foster more intelligent description and application of problems. Although most of the programs are general-purpose-problem oriented, a number of special-purpose programs

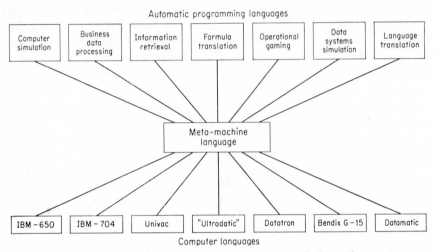

Fig. 5.10 Language schematic. (*From W. F. Bauer.*[9])

for commercial data processing have been produced. The general-purpose languages are oriented to scientific and engineering calculations. The design of special-purpose-problem-oriented languages seeks to make a more direct conceptual link between the computation and the nature of the input information in a particular problem domain.

Despite the apparent higher relative efficiency of a program which would translate a special-purpose-problem-oriented language directly into machine language, these developments have tended to translate into the "nearest"-problem-oriented language and then permit the previously developed processes to carry on from there to actual machine language. The schematic of Fig. 5.10 displays the multilevel character which has evolved among higher languages and some of the existing machines.[9]

Algebraic Compilers. FORTRAN[10,11] is the best known of existing compiler systems. It was designed for the IBM 704, and modifications of it have been produced for the IBM 709, 650, 1620, and 1401 machines. The IT (Internal Translator) code made it possible to translate codes written in FORTRAN to machine language codes of other machines. Thus the FORTRAN code may be read by the IBM 650 and the statements in the FORTRAN changed to equivalent IT statements. Then the IT statements are read by the IBM 650 and translated into a code

C For comment Statement number 1 5	Continuation 6	7 72
3		DIMENSION $X(10)$, $Z(20)$
4		FORMAT $(5F14.4)$
5		READ 4, X, Y, Z
6		SUMA = 0.0
7		DO 12 I = 1, 10
8		IF(ABS$F(X(I))$ − ABS$F(Y(I))$) 9, 12, 11
9		SUMA = SUMA + $X(I)$ + $Y(I)$**2
10		GO to 12
11		SUMA = SUMA + $X(I)$**2 + $Y(I)$
12		CONTINUE
13		SUMZ = 0.0
14		DO 15 J = 1, 20
15		SUMZ = SUMZ + $Z(J)$
16		PROD = SUMA*SUMZ
17		PRINT 4, SUMA, SUMZ, PROD
18		STOP

in the symbolic language of SOAP (Symbolic Optimizing Assembly Program).   The SOAP output is then read by the IBM 650 and is assembled producing a machine language program ready to be executed by the 650.   Each of these three phases of translation requires machine time, and it is obvious that there is a crossover point where the cost of machine time is greater than the cost of skilled programming required to bypass the higher languages.

The closeness of FORTRAN language to user requirements is exemplified by the sample program below, taken from the "FORTRAN Primer."[11]

The problem is

Given X_i, Y_i, Z_j for $i = 1, \ldots, 10$ and $j = 1, \ldots, 20$, compute:

$$\text{PROD} = \sum_{i=1}^{10} A_i \sum_{j=1}^{20} Z_j$$

where
$$
\begin{aligned}
A_i &= X_i^2 + Y_i & \text{if } |X_i| > |Y_i| \\
A_i &= X_i + Y_i^2 & \text{if } |X_i| < |Y_i| \\
A_i &= 0 & \text{if } |X_i| = |Y_i|
\end{aligned}
$$

A possible FORTRAN program is shown on page 93.

The DIMENSION statement sets aside storage locations for the input data. Statement 4 specifies the input and output data as fixed-point numbers having four decimal places.   The READ statement reads the input data from cards into the 704.   Statement 6 sets the quantity SUMA to zero.   Statements 8–12, under control of the DO statement 7, compute $\sum_{i=1}^{10} A_i$.   Statement 15 computes $\sum_{j=1}^{20} Z_j$ under the control of DO statement 14.   The following statements compute and print PROD.   Statement 12, CONTINUE, serves as a common reference point; and since it is the last statement in the range of the DO, I is increased after its completion, and the next repetition is begun.

On the other hand the unnatural constraints of the language are exemplified by some of the rules from the FORTRAN master check list:

1. The basic characters which may be used in writing a FORTRAN statement are
    a. A, B, C, . . . , Z (26 alphabetic characters)
    b. 0, 1, 2, . . . , 9 (10 numerical characters)
    c. + (plus), − (minus), * (asterisk), / (slash), ((left parenthesis),) (right parenthesis), , (comma), = (equal sign), and . (decimal point). . . .
4. A variable symbol can consist of six or less characters.   It must satisfy the following conditions:
    a. The first character must be alphabetic.
    b. The first character cannot be I, J, K, L, M, or N, unless the symbol is an integer variable; if the symbol is an integer variable, the first character must be I, J, K, L, M, or N.

c. Any character following the first may be alphabetic or numerical, but not one of the special characters.

d. The names of all functions defined in the program or appearing on the computing center list, as well as these names with the terminal F removed, must not be used as variable symbols. For example, if SINF is used as the name of a function, neither SINF nor SIN can be used as a variable symbol.

e. If a subscripted variable has four or more characters in its name, the last of these must not be an F. For example, SIN$F(I)$ cannot be used as a subscripted variable, regardless of whether SINF is used as the name of a function.

5. The name used for a function in programming must agree exactly with the name appearing in the list of functions. . . .

7. If a function has more than one argument, the arguments are separated by commas; e.g., SINF (X, Y, Z). . . .

9. Never omit the operation symbol between two quantities; e.g., do not write AB for $A*B$.

10. Never have two operation symbols in a row; e.g., do not write $A* - B$ for $A*(-B)$. The exponentiation symbol ** may appear to be an exception, but it is regarded as a single symbol. . . .

16. Numbers to be printed by means of a PRINT 1 statement should not exceed 999,999.99999. . . .

18. All subscripted variables must appear in a DIMENSION statement, which must appear in the program before reference is made to the variables.

20. Subscripting of subscripts is not permitted.

37. FORMAT statements for output must be so written so that the first character of the first field is a blank.

The UNIVAC MATH-MATIC (U1568) is a similar algebraic compiler. A sample program[12] permits comparison of the languages.

. . . the following problem is to be solved:

$$Y = \frac{X^3(2 + X)}{3 \, \mathrm{Cos} \, A} - \sqrt[4]{3P}$$

for P running from 0.2 to 0.8 in increments of 0.2, A running from 0.35 to 1.05 in increments of 0.175, and X running from 1.8 to 3.8 in increments of 0.5.

A Math-Matic Code statement of this problem is as follows:

1. VARY P 0.2(0.2)0.8 SENTENCES 2 THRU 5.
2. VARY A 0.35(0.175)1.05 SENTENCES 3 THRU 5.
3. VARY X 1.8(0.5)3.8 SENTENCES 4 THRU 5.
4. $Y = X^3*$ $(2X)/(3*$ COS $A) - $4ROOT $(3*P)$.
5. WRITE AND EDIT Y X A P.
6. STOP.

Sentence 1 will set P to its initial value, 0.2, and will insert following sentence 5 a control operation which will add the increment, 0.2, to P and return control to sentence 2. When P exceeds its limit value of 0.8, control will jump to the next operation. Sentences 2 and 3 will perform similar functions for A and X. The range components in these three sentences indicate that sentence 3 lies within the range of sentence 2, and sentence 2 lies within the range of sentence 1. This nesting of loops means that X, the variable of the innermost loop, will take on all of its values, for each value of A and P. When the value of X exceeds its limit value, A will be incremented and X will be reset to its initial value. P will be incremented and A and X will be reset, each time A exceeds its limit. In this way 100 values of Y will be computed and written. Sentence 6 will supply the necessary sentinels for the output and stop the program.

Special-purpose Compilers. In the previous section it was observed in one case that automatic programming evolution had produced three levels of language translation. The DYANA (Dynamics Analyzer) program[13] developed at General Motors introduces a fourth level whose goal is enhanced application of digital computers to the analysis of dynamical systems.

The objectives in setting up DYANA were:
1. To permit an easy description of dynamical systems to a computer.
2. To provide an automatic analysis by a computer to establish the mathematical model of the behavior of the system.
3. To prepare a complete computer program to numerically solve the mathematical model.

The computer program produced by DYANA is a complete FORTRAN program punched out on cards and ready to be run with the requisite set of numerical data. In addition to the program deck of punched cards a printed listing of the resultant FORTRAN program is produced along with an input data plan, or map, describing the input data that is needed and the format in which it must be punched on input data cards. . . .

The user of DYANA will be able to specify any one of three different kinds of solution for his particular problem. He may ask for a program to compute the natural frequencies and associated modes of vibration of a system. He may ask for a program to compute the frequency response of a system. Finally, he may ask for a program which will give him a time-sensitive description of all displacements and velocities in a system. In this latter case nonlinear elements may be described in the system as well as any arbitrary excitations at any coordinate points. In all three cases branched systems may be described, examples of which would be trains of gears in rotational systems, interconnected levers in translational systems, or transformers in electrical systems.

Coincident with the addition of special-purpose programming language is the effort to design more universal programming languages. In particular a cooperative effort between the U.S. Association for Computing Machinery and the European GAMM (*Gesellschaft för Angewand ter Mathematik und Mechanik*) has produced a first-draft proposal for an algorithmic language, ALGOL.[14,15]

Their decision was to focus attention on a practical problem-oriented, common language for scientific numerical calculation. The main objectives of such a language were defined as

I. The new language should be as close as possible to standard mathematical notation and be readable with little further explanation.

II. It should be possible to use it for the description of computing processes in publications.

III. The new language should be mechanically translatable into machine programs.

To meet these objectives, it was proposed that three levels of language be defined.

The *reference language* is established for the language designers. Hence this reference language does not have to have its characters determined by the need to communicate to nondesigners or the requirements of particular machine languages. It must however provide guides sufficient to permit mechanical transliteration between the other two levels.

The *publication language* is established for uniform statement and description of problems and to permit variation of the reference language according to local usage. Whatever local variations are permitted cannot exceed a one-to-one correspondence between characters in the two languages.

The *hardware representation* is the ALGOL language associated with a particular computer. The constraints of the hardware, i.e., number and types of characters, force a condensation of the reference language.

The eventual development of one or more universal languages will provide additional motivation to workers developing special-purpose-problem-oriented programs because the danger of program obsolescence will be reduced.

The goals of the automatic programming effort have always been to have all calculation decisions under control of the programmer and to have the human machine operator function only where the physical properties of the equipment demand it. The special-purpose languages seek then to make it more possible for the problem-solver to be the programmer and still be able to think in a language which has evolved with his problem.

The deficiencies in the results of this program display themselves in the cost of multilevel translation between languages and the need for a universal language such that problem-oriented programs may be used on many different machines and be improved by virtue of intelligible description in publications. Moreover we are still faced with the extensive mismatch between the formulation of a problem and the high-speed manipulation of the machine. The time-consuming clerical work which must be used to prepare data and instructions for the computer and extreme limitations in means of presenting results to the human are very serious drawbacks to more extended use of automatic computers. Finally, and most significant, is our lack of good mathematical models and lack of understanding of numerical methods which presumably represent the models and therefore our lack of confidence in the results of computation.

5.8   Automatic Communication with Computers

The development of methods for pattern recognition by machines has been receiving increasing attention as a result of multiple motivation.

An economically effective motivation to the development of working devices for automatic character recognition stems from the needs in business data processing. The advent of high-speed low-cost-per-computation processors made it economical in many cases to execute bookkeeping procedures automatically if the documents, i.e., invoices, checks, etc., could be machine-read. A proper mixture of motivation, money, ingenuity, and engineering has produced a number of reliable devices based on the use of limited alphabet, stylized characters, and special-purpose digital computers. Both optical reading and magnetic recording and reading have been successfully developed.

A second motivation is the desire to at least imitate with synthetic devices every one of the activities of the human being. This problem is sufficiently challenging to guarantee invention after working hours.

Let us consider now those aspects of communication between man and computer which are retarding technology of machine application.

Automatic Reading of Printed and Handwritten Text. A problem of information search and retrieval may be characterized as the search of recorded past history for information pertinent to the answer to a question. Most of recorded history is in the form of printed text using many different alphabets, type fonts, inks, paper; produced by machines in many different states of operability; and aged under many different conditions. Moreover the great preponderance of present recording may be described in the same way. The crucial problem of information search is of course not a device problem but rather one of predicting the questions which will be asked and organizing recorded information such that it is reasonable to effect a search. However, at least the tremendous inertia provided by the mass of information to be handled may be overcome by a device if it can automatically reduce textual data to a coded form that can be processed at high speed.

Pattern Recognition in Process Control. Many complicated processes have evolved which require the use of human judgment in manipulation of the control variables. Complex qualitative parameters such as odor, color, shape, and homogeneity may serve as criteria for the state of a process. Even assuming a proper physical and mathematical model it might require an impracticable amount of analysis to establish criteria equivalent to the recognition of patterns in parameters such as those mentioned above.

Other advances in technology, such as high-speed or high-altitude flight, result in environments which incapacitate the human as a reliable control element. This problem leads to situations where human decisions have to be made entirely on the basis of instrument measurements and other cases where the human may not be able to participate in the decision process at all.

Thus by pattern recognition there may be implied the development of measures for as yet unmeasured composite qualities of objects, whether it be shape in two or three dimensions, molecular composition and mobility of a mixture of gases, or distribution of particle sizes in a mixture.

For special application it may be possible to constrain the permissible patterns such that relatively inexpensive deterministic approaches will suffice. Such an evolution has taken place in character recognition devices for commercial data processing. However where it is not possible or desirable to constrain the patterns, it will be necessary to devise adaptive devices which can process data from the environment which they will be asked to observe, which can be given success and failure motivation during a training period and which are then capable of readjusting decision criteria or of defining transducers such that the desired pattern recognition will take place with high reliability.

APPENDIX SHARE SUBROUTINE

Identification

Roots of a Polynomial, CL AEQ2; R. Johnson, 3-14-57; Lockheed Aircraft Corporation, California Division.

Purpose

Calculates the n roots of the polynomial

$$F(x) = a_n x^n = a_{n-1} x^{n-1} + a_{n-2} x^{n-2} + \cdots + a_1 x + a_0$$

where the coefficients a_i are either real or complex, by the Newton-Raphson method.

Restrictions

If a coefficient or a root is complex, the imaginary part must be stored immediately following its real part. The estimates of the roots must be in complex form.

Method

See the section below entitled "Description of the Method."

This subroutine differs from Subroutine CL AEQ1 in that the number of figures of convergence is not specified by the programmer.*

* F. B. Hildebrand, "Introduction to Numerical Analysis," sec. 10.9, McGraw-Hill Book Company, Inc., New York, 1956.

Usage

The calling sequence is as shown in Table A.1.

Table A.1

Location	Operation code	Address	Tag	Decrement
L	TSX	ALG	4	
$L + 1$	PZE	A	j	n
$L + 2$	PZE	X	...	G
$L + 3$	PZE	C		
$L + 4$	Error return			
$L + 5$	Normal return			

A = core location a_n. The remaining coefficients must be stored consecutive to a_n, i.e., a_n, a_{n-1}, a_{n-2}, . . . , a_0. If the coefficients are complex, the imaginary part must be stored immediately following its corresponding real part, i.e., $R(a_n)$, $I(a_n)$, $R(a_{n-1})$, $I(a_{n-1})$, . . . , $R(a_0)$, $I(a_0)$.

j = 0 or 1; set j = 0 if the coefficients are real; set j = 1 if the coefficients are complex.

n = the degree of the polynomial.

X = core location where the real part of the first root will be stored. All roots are assumed to be complex and are stored consecutively with the imaginary part of a root immediately following the real part of this root.

G = core location of the first estimate in the set of estimates of the roots. Estimates *must* be in complex form even though the coefficients are real and must be stored consecutively with the imaginary part of an estimate immediately following the real part. If G is set equal to 0, the routine assumes $0.01 + 0.01i$ to be the first estimate for all roots. The programmer should give complex estimates unless he is certain all roots are real.

C = the first location of a block of $4n + 2$ consecutive storage locations which must be reserved by the programmer.

Error Return. This occurs for one of two reasons:

1. If the sign of the AC is plus, an overflow has occurred. See "Overflow Error Return" under "Description of Method."

2. If the sign of the AC is minus, a root or roots failed to converge to four octal figures. In this case the number m in the AC is to be interpreted as follows: (*a*) If $m = -8$, $r - 1$ roots have converged to four octal figures; $r \leq n$, where $r - 1$ is the number of roots which have been stored. (*b*) If $m \neq -8$, at least one root failed to converge to four octal figures on iteration with the polynomial. The number of binary zeros located to the right of position 8 and to the left of the first nonzero bit

in the AC is equal to the number of bits convergence obtained for the worst root. The number of roots stored is the number that converged in the original iterations.

See "Improving the Roots and Error Returns" in "Description of Method."

Storage Required. $429 + 4n + 2$ words plus $COMMON$ through $COMMON + 26$.

Coding Information

Upon an error return, index register 4 contains $-L + 1$. The following constants at the indicated locations are used unless they are changed by the programmer as described under "Description of Method."

$\$+1$	1 floating-point decimal
$\$+2$	.01 floating-point decimal
$\$+3$	DEC 120
$\$+8$	10^{-15} floating-point decimal
$\$+11$	OCT 77777

Timing. $0.036n^2 + 1.032n + 2.436$ msec for setup, plus $3.504(n - p) + 4.272$ msec/iteration on the pth root; $p = 1(1)n$.

Description of the Method

The programmer has the option of supplying first estimates of the roots or letting the routine supply its own estimates. From the first estimate, the routine obtains better estimates of a root by a series of Newton-Raphson iterations. When the root has converged to at least four octal figures, the polynomial is reduced to a polynomial of one degree less and the process is then repeated for the next root. When the n roots have been obtained, they are improved by using each of them in turn in iterations upon the original polynomial.

If an rth root fails to converge within a certain number of iterations specified by the routine, the routine repeats the iterations for this root by using its own second first estimate of this root. If the root now converges, the routine solves for the next root beginning with the estimate specified by the programmer. If, however, the rth root still fails to converge to at least four octal figures, the solving for roots is terminated and the $r - 1$ roots are improved by using each of them in turn in iterations upon the original polynomial.

The programmer may change the number of octal figures convergence specified by this subroutine by changing the mask in location $\$+11$. If S is the number of figures desired, the mask must contain $9 - S$ sevens.

Underflow. Underflows are set equal to zero. Any part, real or imaginary, of a number which is less in magnitude than 10^{-15} is set equal to zero. If both the real and imaginary parts are less than 10^{-15} in magnitude, only the smaller of the two magnitudes is set equal to zero. The limitation, 10^{-15}, can be changed by changing the constant in location \$+8 to the desired number in floating point.

Original Iterations for a Root. If $X_i{}^k$ is the kth estimate of the ith root, the routine uses the Newton-Raphson method for finding the next best estimate, $X_i{}^{k+1}$. This consists of iterations on the formula

$$X_i{}^{k+1} = X_i{}^k - \frac{F(X_i{}^k)}{F'(X_i{}^k)}$$

where F' means the first derivative of F. The first estimate, $X_i{}^1$, is the programmer's estimate if $G \neq 0$ in the calling sequence, or, $0.01 + 0.01i$ if $G = 0$. The latter can be changed to any estimate $a + ai$ by changing the constant at location \$+2 to floating point a.

Termination of Original Iterations. If a root converges to four octal figures, the iteration process is terminated upon the kth iteration where

$$|R(X_i{}^{k-1}) - R(X_i{}^k)| + |I(X_i{}^{k-1}) - I(X_i{}^k)|$$
$$\geq |R(X_i{}^{k-1}) - R(X_i{}^{k-2})| + |I(X_i{}^{k-1}) - I(X_i{}^{k-2})|$$

where R and I denote the real and imaginary parts, respectively, of the result of the iteration. $X_i{}^{k-1}$ is accepted as the root and is then improved as explained under "Improving the Roots and Error Returns."

Roots Failing to Converge. If, (1) a root fails to converge after 120 iterations, or, (2) the real or imaginary part of $F(X_i{}^k)$ or $F'(X_i{}^k)$ overflows, or, (3) $F'(X_i{}^k) = 0$ but $F(X_i{}^k) \neq 0$, the routine will repeat the iteration process using $1 + i$ as a new first estimate of that root. If again any of the three conditions above are met, the subroutine discontinues solving for roots, improves the roots already obtained as explained later, and transfers control to the error return. The number of iterations may be changed by changing the address part of location \$+3 to the number desired. In repeating the iteration process, the new first estimate, $1 + i$, can be changed to any number $a + ai$ by changing the constant in location \$+1 to floating point a. When $F'(X) = 0$ and $F(X) = 0$, the routine assumes the multiple root has converged.

Obtaining the Next Root. When the pth root converges, the polynomial has been reduced to degree $n - p$ by synthetic division. The previously explained process is then repeated for the $(p + 1)$th root. However, if the coefficients of the polynomial are real and the pth root was complex, the conjugate of the pth root instead of the programmer's estimate is used as the first estimate of the $(p + 1)$th root, provided that (1) the absolute value of the imaginary part of the pth root is greater than 10^{-15} and (2) the first estimate of the pth root was not the conjugate of the $(p - 1)$th root. If 1 and 2 do not hold, the first estimate used will be that specified by the programmer.

Table A.2

Location	Operation code	Address, tag, decrement	Comments	Identification
CLAEQ2	REM	419		
ALG	SXD	COMMON, 1	SAVE IR	AEQ2 0001
	SXD	COMMON + 1, 2		AEQ2 0002
	SXD	COMMON + 2, 4		AEQ2 0003
	CLS	ALG + 0359		AEQ2 0004
	STO	COMMON + 24	-9 IN COM + 24	AEQ2 0005
	CAL	1, 4	N IN DECR	AEQ2 0006
	ANA	ALG + 0361		AEQ2 0007
	ARS	18	N IN ADDRESS	AEQ2 0008
	STD	ALG + 0284	0 IN DEC W25	AEQ2 0009
	ADD	ALG + 0352	$N + 1$ IN ADD	AEQ2 0010
	SLW	COMMON + 15		AEQ2 0011
	ADM	1, 4	$A + N + 1$	AEQ2 0012
	STA	ALG + 0086		AEQ2 0013
	ADM	COMMON + 15	$A + 2N + 2$	AEQ2 0014
	STA	ALG + 0081		AEQ2 0015
	ANA	ALG + 0361	N IN DECR	AEQ2 0016
	ADM	1, 4	$2N$ IN DECR	AEQ2 0017
	LRS	18		AEQ2 0018
	SLW	COMMON + 16		AEQ2 0019
	ADM	2, 4	$X + 2N$	AEQ2 0020
	STA	ALG + 0074		AEQ2 0021
	STA	ALG + 0279		AEQ2 0022
	STA	ALG + 0115		AEQ2 0023
	ADD	ALG + 0352	$X + 2N + 1$	AEQ2 0024
	STA	ALG + 0281	$X + 2N + 1$	AEQ2 0025
	STA	ALG + 0117		AEQ2 0026
	SUB	ALG + 0356	$X + 2N - 1$	AEQ2 0027
	STA	ALG + 0122		AEQ2 0028
	SUB	ALG + 0352	$X + 2N - 2$	AEQ2 0029
	STA	ALG + 0120		AEQ2 0030
	CLM			AEQ2 0031
	LLS	3	J IN AC	AEQ2 0032
	SLW	COMMON + 10		AEQ2 0033
	CAL	2, 4		AEQ2 0034
	ALS	4	SHIFT OUT PREFIX	AEQ2 0035
	LRS	22		AEQ2 0036
	SLW	COMMON + 9	G	AEQ2 0037
	ADD	COMMON + 16	$G + 2N$	AEQ2 0038
	STA	ALG + 0104		AEQ2 0039
	ADD	ALG + 0352	$G + 2N + 1$	AEQ2 0040
	STA	ALG + 0106		AEQ2 0041
	CAL	COMMON + 16	$2N$ IN ADD	AEQ2 0042
	ADD	ALG + 0356		AEQ2 0043
	STO	COMMON + 17	$2N + 2$	AEQ2 0044
	ALS	18	$2N + 2$ IN DEC	AEQ2 0045
	ADD	COMMON + 16	$2N + 2$ IN DEC, $2N$ IN ADDR	AEQ2 0046
	STO	COMMON + 3		AEQ2 0047
	CAL	3, 4	C	AEQ2 0048
	STA	ALG + 0130		AEQ2 0049
	STA	ALG + 0163		AEQ2 0050
	ADD	ALG + 0352	$C + 1$	AEQ2 0051
	STA	ALG + 0132		AEQ2 0052
	STA	ALG + 0165		AEQ2 0053
	ADM	COMMON + 17	$C + 2N + 3$	AEQ2 0054
	STA	ALG + 0089		AEQ2 0055

Table A.2 (*Continued*)

Location	Operation code	Address, tag, decrement	Comments	Identification
	STA	ALG + 0136		AEQ2 0056
	SUB	ALG + 0352	$C + 2N + 2$	AEQ2 0057
	STA	ALG + 0082		AEQ2 0058
	STA	ALG + 0087		AEQ2 0059
	STA	ALG + 0148		AEQ2 0060
	STA	ALG + 0302		AEQ2 0061
	ADD	COMMON + 16	$C + 4N + 2$	AEQ2 0062
	STA	ALG + 0155		AEQ2 0063
	ADD	ALG + 0352	$C + 4N + 3$	AEQ2 0064
	STA	ALG + 0146		AEQ2 0065
	SUB	ALG + 0362	$C + 4N$	AEQ2 0066
	TOV	ALG + 0067	TURN OFF OV	AEQ2 0067
	STA	ALG + 0301		AEQ2 0068
	STA	ALG + 0180		AEQ2 0069
	ADD	ALG + 0352		AEQ2 0070
	STA	ALG + 0169	$C + 4N + 1$	AEQ2 0071
	LXA	COMMON + 3, 1	$2N$ IN $IR1$	AEQ2 0072
	CLM			AEQ2 0073
	SLW	COMMON + 25	$+0$ IN COMMON + 25	AEQ2 0074
	SLW	0, 1	SET ALL X ZERO	AEQ2 0075
	TIX	ALG + 0074, 1, 1		AEQ2 0076
	SLW	COMMON + 4	SET REITERATE FLAG	AEQ2 0077
	SLW	COMMON + 6	SET CONJUGATE FLAG	AEQ2 0078
	LXD	COMMON + 3, 1	$C(IR1) = 2N + 2$, ENTER RERUN	AEQ2 0079
	CLA	COMMON + 10	J IN AC	AEQ2 0080
	TZE	ALG + 0085		AEQ2 0081
	CLA	0, 1	PUT COMPLEX COEF	AEQ2 0082
	STO	0, 1	IN C	AEQ2 0083
	TIX	ALG + 0081, 1, 1		AEQ2 0084
	TRA	ALG + 0092		AEQ2 0085
	LXA	COMMON + 15, 2	$N + 1$ IN $IR2$	AEQ2 0086
	CLA	0, 2	PUT REAL COEF	AEQ2 0087
	STO	0, 1	IN C	AEQ2 0088
	CLM			AEQ2 0089
	STO	0, 1		AEQ2 0090
	TNX	ALG + 0092, 1, 2		AEQ2 0091
	TIX	ALG + 0086, 2, 1		AEQ2 0092
	LXD	COMMON + 3, 1	$2N + 2$ TO $IR1$	AEQ2 0093
	LXA	COMMON + 3, 2	$2N$ TO $IR2$	AEQ2 0094
	SXD	COMMON + 15, 1		AEQ2 0095
	LXD	COMMON + 15, 1	ENTER NEXT ROOT, FIRST RUN	AEQ2 0096
	TNX	ALG + 0328, 1, 2	$2N$ IN $IR1$	AEQ2 0097
	SXD	COMMON + 15, 1	$2N$ IN COM + 15	AEQ2 0098
	CLA	COMMON + 4	RERUN FLAG	AEQ2 0099
	TMI	ALG + 0115	TRA ON RERUN	AEQ2 0100
	CLA	COMMON + 6	CONJUGATE FLAG	AEQ2 0101
	TMI	ALG + 0120		AEQ2 0102
	CLA	COMMON + 9	G IN AC	AEQ2 0103
	TZE	ALG + 0111	TRA IF USING PROG GUESS	AEQ2 0104
	CLA	0, 2	CUSTOMER'S REAL GUESS	AEQ2 0105
	STO	COMMON + 7		AEQ2 0106
	CLA	0, 2		AEQ2 0107
	TNZ	ALG + 0109		AEQ2 0108
	CLA	ALG + 0354		AEQ2 0109
	STO	COMMON + 8		AEQ2 0110
	TRA	ALG + 0124		AEQ2 0111

Table A.2 (*Continued*)

Location	Operation code	Address, tag, decrement	Comments	Identification
	CLA	ALG + 0354	PROGRAM	AEQ2 0112
	STO	COMMON + 7		AEQ2 0113
	STO	COMMON + 8		AEQ2 0114
	TRA	ALG + 0124		AEQ2 0115
	CLA	0, 2	ENTER NEXT ROOT, ON RERUN	AEQ2 0116
	STO	COMMON + 7		AEQ2 0117
	CLA	0, 2		AEQ2 0118
	STO	COMMON + 8		AEQ2 0119
	TRA	ALG + 0124		AEQ2 0120
	CLA	0, 2	$R(X(I - 1))$ FIRST GUESS	AEQ2 0121
	STO	COMMON + 7	CONJUGATE	AEQ2 0122
	CLS	0, 2	$-I(X(I - 1))$	AEQ2 0123
	STO	COMMON + 8		AEQ2 0124
	CLM			AEQ2 0125
	SLW	COMMON + 5	SET FIRST GUESS FLAG	AEQ2 0126
	LXA	ALG + 0355, 4	ENTER SECOND GUESS	AEQ2 0127
	CLM			AEQ2 0128
	SLW	COMMON + 11		AEQ2 0129
	LXD	COMMON + 15, 1	ENTER NEXT ITER	AEQ2 0130
	CLA		$R(AN)$, SET UP LEAD COEF	AEQ2 0131
	STO	COMMON + 12		AEQ2 0132
	CLA		$I(AN)$	AEQ2 0133
	STO	COMMON + 13		AEQ2 0134
	SXD	COMMON + 16, 4	SAVE $IR4$	AEQ2 0135
	TSX	ALG + 0379, 4	AN TIMES X	AEQ2 0136
	CLA	0, 1	$A(N - 1)$, IMAG	AEQ2 0137
	TNZ	ALG + 0140	TRA NONZERO	AEQ2 0138
	CLA	COMMON + 13	SKIP FAD IF ZERO	AEQ2 0139
	TRA	ALG + 0146		AEQ2 0140
	FAD	COMMON + 13	$A(N - 1) + I(XA)$, IMAG	AEQ2 0141
	TNO	ALG + 0146		AEQ2 0142
	ARS	1		AEQ2 0143
	PBT			AEQ2 0144
	TRA	ALG + 0349	PUT FOR NEXT GUESS	AEQ2 0145
	CLM			AEQ2 0146
	STO	0, 1	STORE COEF DERIVATIVE	AEQ2 0147
	STO	COMMON + 13		AEQ2 0148
	CLA	0, 1	REAL, $A(N - 1)$	AEQ2 0149
	FAD	COMMON + 12	REAL, $A(N - 1) + R(XA)$	AEQ2 0150
	TNO	ALG + 0155		AEQ2 0151
	ARS	1		AEQ2 0152
	PBT			AEQ2 0153
	TRA	ALG + 0349		AEQ2 0154
	CLM			AEQ2 0155
	STO	0, 1	STORE COEF DERIVATIVE	AEQ2 0156
	STO	COMMON + 12		AEQ2 0157
	TIX	ALG + 0135, 1, 2	RETURN NEXT COEF	AEQ2 0158
	CLA	COMMON + 12		AEQ2 0159
	STO	COMMON + 17	STORE $F(X)$	AEQ2 0160
	CLA	COMMON + 13		AEQ2 0161
	STO	COMMON + 18		AEQ2 0162
	LXD	COMMON + 15, 1	$2N - 2$ FW $IR1$	AEQ2 0163
	CLA		LEADING COEF, REAL	AEQ2 0164
	STO	COMMON + 12		AEQ2 0165
	CLA		LEADING COEF, IMAG	AEQ2 0166
	STO	COMMON + 13		AEQ2 0167

Table A.2 (*Continued*)

Location	Operation code	Address, tag, decrement	Comments	Identification
	TNX	ALG + 0189, 1, 2		AEQ2 0168
	TSX	ALG + 0379, 4	*AN* TIMES *X*	AEQ2 0169
	CLA	0, 1	IMAG DERIVATIVE COEF	AEQ2 0170
	TNZ	ALG + 0173	TRA NONZERO	AEQ2 0171
	CLA	COMMON + 13	SKIP FAD IF ZERO	AEQ2 0172
	TRA	ALG + 0179		AEQ2 0173
	FAD	COMMON + 13	ADD $I(XA)$	AEQ2 0174
	TNO	ALG + 0179		AEQ2 0175
	ARS	1		AEQ2 0176
	PBT			AEQ2 0177
	TRA	ALG + 0349		AEQ2 0178
	CLM			AEQ2 0179
	STO	COMMON + 13	IMAG PART DERV	AEQ2 0180
	CLA	0, 1	REAL COEF DERIVATIVE	AEQ2 0181
	FAD	COMMON + 12		AEQ2 0182
	TNO	ALG + 0187		AEQ2 0183
	ARS	1		AEQ2 0184
	PBT			AEQ2 0185
	TRA	ALG + 0349		AEQ2 0186
	CLM			AEQ2 0187
	STO	COMMON + 12	REAL PART DERV	AEQ2 0188
	TIX	ALG + 0168, 1, 2	RETURN NEXT COEF DERIV	AEQ2 0189
	CLA	COMMON + 9, 1	ROOT	AEQ2 0190
	LDQ	COMMON + 14, 1	DERIVATIVE $F(X)$	AEQ2 0191
	STQ	COMMON + 21, 1	STORE DERIVATIVE $F(X)$	AEQ2 0192
	STO	COMMON + 23, 1	STORE AND SAVE ROOT	AEQ2 0193
	CLA	COMMON + 19, 1	$F(X)$	AEQ2 0194
	STO	COMMON + 9, 1	STORE $F(X)$, SET FOR MULT	AEQ2 0195
	TIX	ALG + 0189, 1, 1	RETURN IMAG PART	AEQ2 0196
	CLA	COMMON + 12	REAL PART DERIVATIVE $F(X)$	AEQ2 0197
	LLS		PUT SIGN REAL PART SAME IMAG PART	AEQ2 0198
	FAD	COMMON + 13		AEQ2 0199
	TOV	ALG + 0349	ADD IMAG PART	AEQ2 0200
	STO	COMMON + 26	APPROX MOD DERIVATIVE $F(X)$	AEQ2 0201
	TZE	ALG + 0220	MOD ZERO, TRA	AEQ2 0202
	LXA	ALG + 0362, 4		AEQ2 0203
	LXA	ALG + 0356, 1		AEQ2 0204
	TQO	ALG + 0205		AEQ2 0205
	CLA	COMMON + 14, 1		AEQ2 0206
	FDP	COMMON + 26	DIV MOD	AEQ2 0207
	TQO	ALG + 0424		AEQ2 0208
	STQ	COMMON + 14, 1		AEQ2 0209
	TIX	ALG + 0205, 1, 1	RETURN IMAG	AEQ2 0210
	TOV	ALG + 0211		AEQ2 0211
	TNX	ALG + 0233, 4, 1	TRA SECOND RUN	AEQ2 0212
	LXA	ALG + 0356, 1	BEGIN CALC MOD	AEQ2 0213
	STO	COMMON + 14		AEQ2 0214
	LDQ	COMMON + 21, 1		AEQ2 0215
	FMP	COMMON + 14, 1		AEQ2 0216
	TNO	ALG + 0218		AEQ2 0217
	CLM			AEQ2 0218
	TIX	ALG + 0213, 1, 1	RETURN IMAG	AEQ2 0219
	FAD	COMMON + 14		AEQ2 0220
	TNZ	ALG + 0226		AEQ2 0221
	CLA	COMMON + 17		AEQ2 0222

Table A.2 (*Continued*)

Location	Operation code	Address, tag, decrement	Comments	Identification
	TNZ	ALG + 0349		AEQ2 0223
	CLA	COMMON + 18		AEQ2 0224
	TNZ	ALG + 0349		AEQ2 0225
	LXA	ALG + 0352, 4	$F(X) = 0$ ROOT	AEQ2 0226
	STO	COMMON + 26	STORE MOD	AEQ2 0227
	CLS	COMMON + 13	CHANGE SIGN $I(F1)$	AEQ2 0228
	STO	COMMON + 13	STORE CONJ	AEQ2 0229
	SXD	COMMON + 17, 4	MULT CONJ OF	AEQ2 0230
	TSX	ALG + 0379, 4	DERIVATIVE $F(X)$ BY $F(X)$	AEQ2 0231
	LXD	COMMON + 17, 4		AEQ2 0232
	TIX	ALG + 0203, 4, 1	RETURN FOR DIV	AEQ2 0233
	LXA	ALG + 0356, 1	2 IN $IR1$	AEQ2 0234
	CLA	COMMON + 23, 1	ROOT	AEQ2 0235
	FSB	COMMON + 14, 1	ROOT + DELTA ROOT	AEQ2 0236
	TNO	ALG + 0241		AEQ2 0237
	ARS	1		AEQ2 0238
	PBT			AEQ2 0239
	TRA	ALG + 0349		AEQ2 0240
	CLM			AEQ2 0241
	STO	COMMON + 9, 1	STORE NEW ROOT	AEQ2 0242
	TIX	ALG + 0234, 1, 1	RETURN IMAG	AEQ2 0243
	CLA	COMMON + 7	R(ROOT)	AEQ2 0244
	LDQ	COMMON + 8	I(ROOT)	AEQ2 0245
	SSP			AEQ2 0246
	LRS			AEQ2 0247
	LXA	ALG + 0356, 1	2 TO $IR1$, PICK REAL	AEQ2 0248
	TLQ	ALG + 0250	COMPARE ABSOLUTE VALUE	AEQ2 0249
	LXA	ALG + 0352, 1	1 TO $IR1$, PICK IMAG	AEQ2 0250
	CLA	COMMON + 9, 1	LARGEST ROOT	AEQ2 0251
	UFS	COMMON + 23, 1	SUB LAST ITER	AEQ2 0252
	ANA	ALG + 0364		AEQ2 0253
	STO	COMMON + 25	DEGREE OF CONV	AEQ2 0254
	LDQ	ALG + 0363		AEQ2 0255
	TLQ	ALG + 0270	TRA IF ROOT NOT CONV	AEQ2 0256
	CLA	COMMON + 7	4 OCTITS	AEQ2 0257
	FSB	COMMON + 21	$R(XI) - RX(I - 1)$	AEQ2 0258
	SSP		SSP	AEQ2 0259
	STO	COMMON + 23		AEQ2 0260
	CLA	COMMON + 8	$I(XI) - IX(I - 1)$	AEQ2 0261
	FSB	COMMON + 22		AEQ2 0262
	SSP			AEQ2 0263
	FAD	COMMON + 23	ABSOLUTE SPREAD OF	AEQ2 0264
	CAS	COMMON + 11		AEQ2 0265
	TRA	ALG + 0273		AEQ2 0266
	TRA	ALG + 0365		AEQ2 0267
	TZE	ALG + 0365		AEQ2 0268
	STO	COMMON + 11		AEQ2 0269
	TRA	ALG + 0315	STILL CONV NEXT ITER	AEQ2 0270
	CLA	COMMON + 11		AEQ2 0271
	TNZ	ALG + 0365	OUT AS ROOT NOT CONV	AEQ2 0272
	TRA	ALG + 0315	NEXT ITER	AEQ2 0273
	LRS	35		AEQ2 0274
	CLA	COMMON + 11		AEQ2 0275
	TNZ	ALG + 0365		AEQ2 0276
	STQ	COMMON + 11		AEQ2 0277
	TRA	ALG + 0315	CONV OBTAINED	AEQ2 0278

Table A.2 (*Continued*)

Location	Operation code	Address, tag, decrement	Comments	Identification
	CLA	COMMON + 21	SMALL PART CONV	AEQ2 0279
	STO	0, 2	STORE	AEQ2 0280
	CLA	COMMON + 22		AEQ2 0281
	STO	0, 2	STORE I(ROOT)	AEQ2 0282
	CLA	COMMON + 4		AEQ2 0283
	TPL	ALG + 0299	TRA FIRST RUN	AEQ2 0284
	TXL	ALG + 0286, 2, 0	SKIP ROOTS NOT CONV FIRST RUN	AEQ2 0285
	TIX	ALG + 0115, 2, 2	GET NEXT ROOT SECOND RUN	AEQ2 0286
	LXD	COMMON + 2, 4	ALL ROOT CONV	AEQ2 0287
	CLA	COMMON + 24	$IF - 9$ NO ERRORS	AEQ2 0288
	ADD	ALG + 0359	IF NOT ZERO, NOT ALL ROOT CONV	AEQ2 0289
	TNZ	ALG + 0293	TRA IF ERROR RETURN	AEQ2 0290
	LXD	COMMON, 1	RESTORE IR	AEQ2 0291
	LXD	COMMON + 1, 2		AEQ2 0292
	TRA	5, 4	NORMAL RETURN	AEQ2 0293
	CLA	COMMON + 24	LEAST NUM DIGITS CONV	AEQ2 0294
	CAS	ALG + 0359		AEQ2 0295
	SSM			AEQ2 0296
	TXI	ALG + 0290, 4, 1		AEQ2 0297
	SSM			AEQ2 0298
	TXI	ALG + 0290, 4, 1	ERROR RETURN	AEQ2 0299
	LXD	ALG + 0352, 1	0 IN $IR1$, ROOT CONV	AEQ2 0300
	TNX	ALG + 0328, 3, 2	$2N - 2$ IN $IR1$, $IR2$, FIRST RUN	AEQ2 0301
	CLA	0, 1	TRA COEF POLY	AEQ2 0302
	STO	0, 1	NEXT LOWER DEGREE	AEQ2 0303
	TIX	ALG + 0301, 1, 1		AEQ2 0304
	CLA	COMMON + 10	IMAG	AEQ2 0305
	TNZ	ALG + 0095	RETURN FOR NEXT ROOT	AEQ2 0306
	CLA	COMMON + 6	CONJ FLAG	AEQ2 0307
	TMI	ALG + 0376	TRA LAST GUESS CONJ	AEQ2 0308
	LDQ	COMMON + 8	I(ROOT)	AEQ2 0309
	CLA	ALG + 0358	$1E - 5$ IN AC	AEQ2 0310
	LRS		ABS VALUE I(ROOT) IN MQ	AEQ2 0311
	TLQ	ALG + 0095	TRA REAL ROOT	AEQ2 0312
	SSM		SET CONJ FLAG MINUS	AEQ2 0313
	STO	COMMON + 6		AEQ2 0314
	TRA	ALG + 0095	RETURN WITH CONJ ROOT	AEQ2 0315
	LXD	COMMON + 16, 4		AEQ2 0316
	STO	COMMON + 25		AEQ2 0317
	TIX	ALG + 0129, 4, 1	NEXT ITER	AEQ2 0318
	CLA	COMMON + 11		AEQ2 0319
	TNZ	ALG + 0365	OUT ROOT CONV AT LEAST	AEQ2 0320
	CLA	COMMON + 4	4 OCTITS	AEQ2 0321
	TMI	ALG + 0338	TRA ON SECOND RUN	AEQ2 0322
	CLA	COMMON + 5		AEQ2 0323
	TPL	ALG + 0332	TRA TO SET UP SECOND GUESS	AEQ2 0324
	CLS	ALG + 0359	-9, THIS CAUSES ERROR RETURN	AEQ2 0325
	ADD	ALG + 0352	-8, SET CONV 8 DIGITS RERUN	AEQ2 0326
	STO	COMMON + 24	STORE AMOUNT OF CONV	AEQ2 0327
	SXD	ALG + 0284, 2	SET TO REDO ONLY ROOTS DONE	AEQ2 0328
	SSM			AEQ2 0329
	STO	COMMON + 4	SET FLAG FOR SECOND RUN	AEQ2 0330

Table A.2 (*Continued*)

Location	Operation code	Address, tag, decrement	Comments	Identification
	CLM		SET CONJ FLAG PLUS	AEQ2 0331
	TRA	ALG + 0077	REITERATE	AEQ2 0332
	SSM			AEQ2 0333
	STO	COMMON + 5	SET FLAG ON SECOND GUESS	AEQ2 0334
	CLA	ALG + 0353	1	AEQ2 0335
	STO	COMMON + 7	TAKE SECOND GUESS $1 + I$	AEQ2 0336
	STO	COMMON + 8		AEQ2 0337
	TRA	ALG + 0126	ENTER SECOND GUESS	AEQ2 0338
	CLA	COMMON + 24		AEQ2 0339
	ALS	6		AEQ2 0340
	TNZ	ALG + 0343		AEQ2 0341
	CLA	COMMON + 25		AEQ2 0342
	STO	COMMON + 24		AEQ2 0343
	CLA	COMMON + 25		AEQ2 0344
	LDQ	COMMON + 24		AEQ2 0345
	TLQ	ALG + 0347		AEQ2 0346
	CLA	COMMON + 24		AEQ2 0347
	STO	COMMON + 24	KEEP RECORD OF CONV	AEQ2 0348
	TRA	ALG + 0284	NEXT ROOT	AEQ2 0349
	CLA	ALG + 0359		AEQ2 0350
	STO	COMMON + 25		AEQ2 0351
	TRA	ALG + 0318		AEQ2 0352
	DEC	1, 1., .01, 120, 2, 17314086911, .00001, 9		AEQ2 0353
	DEC	.00000000000001, 8589672448, 3		AEQ2 0354
	OCT	77777, 777777777		AEQ2 0355
	CLA	COMMON + 4	ROOT ASSUMED CONV	AEQ2 0356
	TPL	ALG + 0278	AFTER 10 CYCLES WITH	AEQ2 0357
	LDQ	ALG + 0360	LARGER PART CONV	AEQ2 0358
	LXA	ALG + 0356, 1	2 IN $IR1$	AEQ2 0359
	CLA	COMMON + 23, 1	ROOT	AEQ2 0360
	LLS		ABS VALUE ROOT	AEQ2 0361
	TLQ	ALG + 0374	ROOT GREATER $1E - 15$	AEQ2 0362
	CLM		SET ROOT LESS $1E - 15$ TO ZERO	AEQ2 0363
	STO	COMMON + 23, 1		AEQ2 0364
	TIX	ALG + 0369, 1, 1	RETURN IMAG	AEQ2 0365
	TRA	ALG + 0278		AEQ2 0366
	SSP		SET CONJ FLAG PLUS	AEQ2 0367
	STO	COMMON + 6		AEQ2 0368
	TRA	ALG + 0095	NEXT ROOT	AEQ2 0369
	LDQ	COMMON + 8	$I(X)$	AEQ2 0370
	FMP	COMMON + 13	$I(X)I(AN)$	AEQ2 0371
	TNO	ALG + 0386		AEQ2 0372
	ARS	1		AEQ2 0373
	PBT			AEQ2 0374
	TRA	ALG + 0349	OV, ERROR	AEQ2 0375
	CLM		SET UNDERFLOW ZERO	AEQ2 0376
	LDQ	COMMON + 7	$R(X)$	AEQ2 0377
	STO	COMMON + 14		AEQ2 0378
	FMP	COMMON + 12	$R(X)R(AN)$	AEQ2 0379
	TNO	ALG + 0394		AEQ2 0380
	ARS	1		AEQ2 0381
	PBT			AEQ2 0382
	TRA	ALG + 0349	OV ERROR	AEQ2 0383
	CLM			AEQ2 0384

Table A.2 (*Continued*)

Location	Operation code	Address, tag, decrement	Comments	Identification
	FSB	COMMON + 14	$R(X)R(AN) - I(X)I(AN) = R(XA)$	AEQ2 0385
	TNO	ALG + 0400		AEQ2 0386
	ARS	1		AEQ2 0387
	PBT			AEQ2 0388
	TRA	ALG + 0349		AEQ2 0389
	CLM			AEQ2 0390
	LDQ	COMMON + 12	$R(XA)$	AEQ2 0391
	STO	COMMON + 12		AEQ2 0392
	FMP	COMMON + 8	$R(AN)I(X)$	AEQ2 0393
	TNO	ALG + 0408		AEQ2 0394
	ARS	1		AEQ2 0395
	PBT			AEQ2 0396
	TRA	ALG + 0349	OV, ERROR	AEQ2 0397
	CLM			AEQ2 0398
	STO	COMMON + 14		AEQ2 0399
	LDQ	COMMON + 13	$I(AN)$	AEQ2 0400
	FMP	COMMON + 7	$I(AN)R(X)$	AEQ2 0401
	TNO	ALG + 0416		AEQ2 0402
	ARS	1		AEQ2 0403
	PBT			AEQ2 0404
	TRA	ALG + 0349	OV, ERROR	AEQ2 0405
	CLM			AEQ2 0406
	FAD	COMMON + 14	$I(AN)R(X) + R(AN)I(X) = I(XA)$	AEQ2 0407
	TNO	ALG + 0422		AEQ2 0408
	ARS	1		AEQ2 0409
	PBT			AEQ2 0410
	TRA	ALG + 0349	ERROR OV	AEQ2 0411
	CLM			AEQ2 0412
	STO	COMMON + 13		AEQ2 0413
	TRA	1, 4		AEQ2 0414
	CLA	ALG + 0357	200777777777	AEQ2 0415
	LRS		SET SIGN MQ PLUS	AEQ2 0416
	TLQ	ALG + 0349	ERROR OV	AEQ2 0417
	LRS	77	MQ = O, UNDERFLOW	AEQ2 0418
	TRA	ALG + 0208		AEQ2 0419

Improving the Roots and Error Returns. When n roots have been obtained to at least four octal figures by the Newton-Raphson method, they are improved by iterating with each of them in turn on the original $F(X)$. The same test, as given under "Termination of Original Iterations," is used to determine when to terminate the iterative process.

If a root fails to converge to at least four octal figures, control is transferred to the error return with a number m in the AC. The value of m indicates whether a root failed to converge in the original iterations or in the iterations on $F(X)$. If an rth root fails to converge in the original iterations, solving for roots is discontinued and the $r - 1$ roots obtained are improved by iteration on $F(X)$. If, when the $r - 1$ roots are improved, they still converge to at least four octal figures, m is set equal to a fixed point -8. The $r - 1$ improved roots are stored.

If any of the $r - 1$ roots, or n roots (in the case where n roots converged in the original iterations) do not converge to at least four octal figures when being improved by iteration on $F(X)$, control goes to the error return with $m \neq -8$. Control, however, is not transferred until an attempt has been made to improve all of the $r - 1$, or n, roots. The number m in this case is the unnormalized difference (with characteristic removed) between the floating-point results of two consecutive iterations for the root with least convergence. The number of bits of convergence obtained in the worst root can then be determined by counting the number of leading binary zeros, excluding the first eight resulting from deleting the characteristic, in m. All the roots, whether converged or not, obtained by iterations on $F(X)$ are stored.

Overflow Error Return. If during the improving of the roots by iteration on $F(X)$, an overflow occurs, the routine will transfer control to the error return. The sign of the AC in this case will be plus. Overflows at any other point in the program will not cause an overflow error return.

REFERENCES

1. Barricelli, Nils Aall: Symbiogenetic Evolution Processes Realized by Artificial Methods, *Estratto Rivista Methodos*, vol. 9, nos. 35-36, 1957.
2. Lanczos, C.: "Applied Analysis," chap 1, Prentice-Hall, Inc., Englewood Cliffs, N.J., 1956.
3. "Modern Computing Methods," Notes on Applied Science no. 16, Her Majesty's Stationery Office, London, 1957.
4. Grabbe, E. M., *et al.*: "Handbook of Automatic Computation and Control," vol. 2, pp. 2-164, John Wiley & Sons, Inc., New York, 1959.
5. "Reference Manual: 704 Data Processing System," International Business Machines Corp., New York, 1958.
6. Evans, W. R.: "Control-system Dynamics," McGraw-Hill Book Company, Inc., New York, 1954.
7. Doda, C. J.: The Digital Computer Makes Root Locus Easy, *Control Eng.*, vol. 5, no. 5, pp. 102-106, May, 1958.
8. Alt, F. L.: "Electronic Digital Computers: Their Use in Science and Engineering," Academic Press, Inc., New York, 1958.
9. Bauer, W. F.: "The Future of Automatic Programming," *Proc. 5th Ann. Computer Applications Symposium*, Armour Research Foundation, Chicago, Oct. 29-30, 1958.
10. Backus, J. W., *et al.*: The FORTRAN Automatic Coding System, *Proc. Western Joint Computer Conf.*, Los Angeles, p. 188, Feb. 26-28, 1957.
11. "Programmer's Primer for FORTRAN," pp. 40-41, 61-62, International Business Machines Corp., New York, 1957.
12. The Mathematicians' Programming System, *Univac Rev.*, vol. 1, no. 2, p. 17, summer, 1958.
13. Theodoroff, T. J., and J. Olsztyn: "Dyana: Dynamics Analyzer-programmer," *Eastern Joint Computer Conf.*, December, 1958.
14. Perlis A. J., and K. Samelson: Report on the Algorithmic Language ALGOL, *Numerische Mathematik*, vol. 1, pp. 41-60, 1959.
15. Naur, Peter, *et al.*: "Report on the Algorithmic Language Communications of the ACM, vol. 3, pp. 299-314, May, 1960.

6

Analog-computer Theory

IRWIN PFEFFER

SENIOR MEMBER OF THE TECHNICAL STAFF
SPACE TECHNOLOGY LABORATORIES, LOS ANGELES

1 ANALOG-COMPUTER OPERATION

6.1 Introduction

The analog computer operates by generation and measurement of physical quantities which represent physical or mathematical variables in the problem being solved. Thus, voltage might be used to represent temperature, current to represent force, or shaft position to represent an abstract variable x. Each variable in the problem appears continuously as a separate voltage, current, or shaft position waveform at the output of a particular element within the computer. All variables are generated simultaneously so that the analog computer is inherently a parallel, rather than a sequential, device.

The most important application of analog computers is in the simulation or control of dynamic systems describable by a set of differential equations. Many analog computers are spoken of as differential analyzers. A unique and very important feature of the analog computer used in the laboratory is its ability to give the operator a physical "feel" for the problem being solved, since the computer behaves in a very real sense just as the dynamic system under investigation.

The analog computer is subject to fundamental limitations in accuracy and speed, since it directly employs the physical properties of computing elements such as amplifiers, capacitors, potentiometers, and gears in the generation of a problem solution. The accuracy and speed obtainable, however, are sufficient for a wide variety of applications in simulation and in control.

6.2 Types of Computers

Figure 6.1 presents a comparison among four basic types of analog computer with respect to accuracy, speed, and method of representation of variables.

112

Analog computer	Accuracy, %	Solution time	Band-width, cps	Independent variable	Dependent variable
1. Mechanical differential analyzer	0.001–0.03	3–60 min	0.2	Shaft position	Shaft position
2. D-c electronic analog computer	0.01–1.0	5–120 sec	10	Time	Voltage
3. A-c electrical analog computer	0.5–10	0.5–120 min	1.0	Time	Voltage
4. Network analyzer	0.5–10	16–200 msec	1000	Time	Voltage, current

Fig. 6.1 Comparison of analog computers.

The mechanical differential analyzer, though very accurate, is slow, delicate, and difficult to program and maintain. Integration is performed by means of a wheel and disk (or in some cases a ball and disk) integrator,

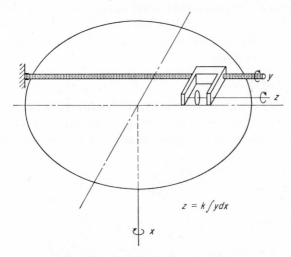

$$z = k \int y \, dx$$

Fig. 6.2 Wheel and disk integrator.

shown in Fig. 6.2, which permits integration of any problem variable with respect to any other variable. Addition is performed with differential gears. General multiplication is performed, using two integrators and a differential gear, according to

$$uv = \int u \, dv + \int v \, du \tag{6.1}$$

The mechanical differential analyzer, because of its lack of speed and its difficulty of operation and maintenance, is rapidly falling out of use. It has an important place, however, in the historical evolution of analog computers.

The d-c electronic analog computer is reasonably fast, easy to maintain, and capable of very good accuracy. It is by far the most popular analog computer for laboratory use and will be discussed later in detail. A close relative of this computer is the repetitive electronic analog computer which is less accurate but much faster.

The a-c electrical analog computer or electromechanical computer is less accurate, slower, and in some respects less versatile than the d-c electronic computer, but is simpler and more rugged, and is well adapted to many control system applications such as air-borne fire control. It is almost never used in the computing laboratory, however. Variables are represented by the envelope amplitude of a modulated a-c carrier. Integration is performed by means of a servo with tachometer feedback. This is less accurate than electronic integration used with the d-c computer, and also results in a lower bandwidth. However, the a-c computer is free of the drift problem which is inherent in a d-c computer.

The network analyzer, or direct analog computer, uses the properties of linear passive electrical elements—resistors, inductors, and capacitors— to solve high-order linear differential equations. It is very fast but has only moderate accuracy. It is most useful in the study of electrical-distribution systems and for many structural and vibration problems, both static and dynamic.

6.3   Method of Solution

Figure 6.3 shows the general method of solution of linear differential equations on the mechanical, d-c, or a-c computer. A linear, nth order, ordinary differential equation with constant coefficients may be written as

$$\sum_{k=0}^{n} a_k \frac{d^k y}{dt^k} = f(t) \tag{6.2}$$

with initial conditions

$$\frac{d^k y(0)}{dt^k} = b_k \qquad k = 0, 1, \ldots, (n-1) \tag{6.3}$$

Equation (6.2) is rewritten for the computer as

$$\frac{d^n y}{dt^n} = \frac{f(t)}{a_n} - \sum_{k=0}^{n-1} \frac{a_k}{a_n} \frac{d^k y}{dt^k} \tag{6.4}$$

The computer is connected to solve for the highest-order derivative at the output of the summing element. A process of repeated integration is used to generate all lower-order derivatives, including y itself. These derivatives, and the forcing function, are multiplied by suitable constants according to Eq. (6.4) and summed to provide the highest-order derivative. The procedure gives rise to a closed-loop block diagram for the interconnection of the computer elements, similar to a servo diagram. Initial conditions are applied to each integrator in various ways, depending upon the computer used.

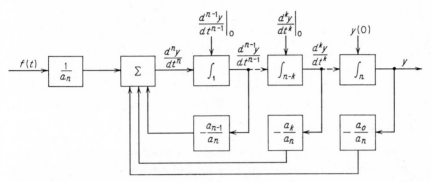

Fig. 6.3 Solution of ordinary linear differential equation with constant coefficients.

A dual procedure involving repeated differentiation, though equally acceptable mathematically, is rejected for practical use, since differentiation tends to magnify high-frequency noise present in all electronic and mechanical equipment. This results in noisy solutions at best, or saturation of a computer element with grossly incorrect solutions.

The operations required to solve ordinary linear differential equations with constant coefficients are shown in Table 6.1, part A. An additional

Table 6.1 Operations Required to Solve Ordinary Differential Equations

   A. Linear constant-coefficient equations
      1. Summation
      2. Integration
      3. Sign inversion
      4. Multiplication of variable by positive constant coefficient
      5. Function generation of function of independent variable
   B. Linear variable-coefficient equations
      6. Multiplication of variable by a variable
   C. Nonlinear equations
      7. Function generation of function of dependent variable(s)

operation, that of multiplication of two variables, is required for linear variable-coefficient equations. Still another, that of generation of a function of an arbitrary variable, is required for nonlinear equations. Each operation is performed by a particular computing element. However, operation 4 can obviously be performed by an element designed for operation 6; likewise 5 by 7. In the d-c electronic analog computer, operations 1 through 3 may all be performed by a single generic device, the operational amplifier with feedback, by suitable selection of the feedback and input circuitry.

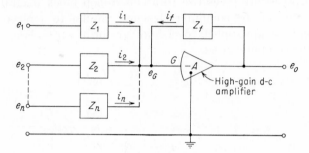

Fig. 6.4   D-c operational amplifier with feedback.

6.4   Operational Amplifier

Figure 6.4 shows the d-c operational amplifier with feedback and with several inputs. The basic equations of this circuit are

$$e_o = -A e_G \tag{6.5}$$

$$i_f + \sum_{k=1}^{n} i_k = 0 \tag{6.6}$$

$$i_f = \frac{e_o - e_G}{Z_f} \tag{6.7}$$

$$i_k = \frac{e_k - e_G}{Z_k} \qquad k = 1, 2, \ldots, n \tag{6.8}$$

Solving for the output voltage e_o yields

$$e_o = -\frac{Z_f \sum_{k=1}^{n} \dfrac{e_k}{Z_k}}{1 + \dfrac{(1 + K)}{A}} \tag{6.9}$$

where

$$K = Z_f \sum_{k=1}^{n} \frac{1}{Z_k} \tag{6.10}$$

If the amplifier gain A is very large, Eq. (6.9) becomes

$$e_o \cong -Z_f \sum_{k=1}^{n} \frac{e_k}{Z_k} \tag{6.11}$$

Equation (6.11) shows that, by suitable selection of the feedback impedance Z_f and the input impedances Z_k the d-c operational amplifier is
capable of performing the operations of sign inversion, summation, and
integration, as well as multiplication by a real or complex constant.   The
relationship between output and inputs, moreover, depends only upon
the impedance ratios of passive electrical elements, which can be made
quite accurate.   It should be noted that a sign inversion is always
obtained with an operational amplifier as a result of the negative feedback
which is used.

Figure 6.5 shows how feedback and input networks are used to provide
several different operations.   In this figure, it is clear that only the
inverter and summer are also applicable to an a-c computer.   For the

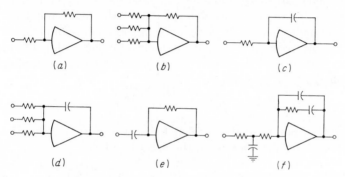

Fig. 6.5   Applications of d-c operational amplifiers.   (a) Inverter.   (b) Summer.
(c) Integrator.   (d) Summing integrator.   (e) Differentiator.   (f) General transfer
function.

a-c computer, integration is provided by a servo with tachometer feedback; complex transfer functions require RLC networks.

6.5   Drift Correction

A most severe difficulty in d-c analog computers is drift—the appearance
at an amplifier output of a spurious voltage, very slowly changing with
time, even when there is no input.   Drift is due to long-term variations
in tube characteristics, power-supply voltages, and circuit resistance
values.   Drift, particularly when it is integrated open-ended by subsequent amplifiers, can give rise to large errors in d-c analog computer
solutions.

Drift may be characterized, for purposes of analysis, as a spurious
battery voltage appearing at the first grid of the amplifier, as shown in
Fig. 6.6.   From this figure, the amplifier output, without the auxiliary
amplifier A', is readily determined to be

$$e_o = -\frac{Z_f}{Z_i} e_i - \left(1 + \frac{Z_f}{Z_i}\right) e_d \qquad (6.12)$$

where the last term represents the drift voltage seen at the output terminals. This term may easily be 0.05 to 0.25 per cent of the full-scale voltage of the computer, seriously degrading the computer accuracy.

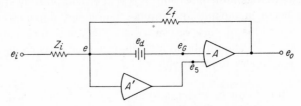

Fig. 6.6   Use of auxiliary amplifier for drift correction.

An auxiliary drift-free amplifier A', used as shown in Fig. 6.6, can dramatically reduce the drift voltage out of the main amplifier. The auxiliary amplifier output is introduced into the main amplifier in addition to the direct input from the summing junction e, thus producing a high-gain loop around the source of the drift. The main amplifier output becomes

$$e_o = -\frac{Z_f}{Z_i}e_i - \frac{[1 + (Z_f/Z_i)]}{1 + A'}e_d \qquad (6.13)$$

The useful output term is unaffected, but the drift is reduced by the factor $(1 + A')$ which may be in the order of 1,000.

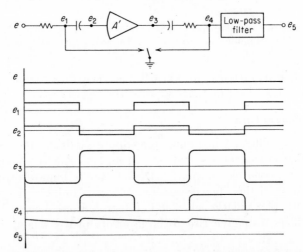

Fig. 6.7   Operation of auxiliary (chopper) amplifier.

The auxiliary amplifier must itself be drift-free, so that a d-c amplifier cannot be used for this purpose. Instead, an a-c amplifier is used in conjunction with a vibrating relay (chopper) which modulates the input signal e and demodulates the output signal, which is then filtered to reject the carrier component at the chopper frequency. The result, between points e and e_5, is a high-gain, driftless amplifier with a very limited bandwidth.   The circuit and waveforms are shown in Fig. 6.7.

6.6   Transfer Functions

Frequently in control system simulation it is necessary to represent complex transfer functions on the analog computer.   This may arise in the representation of electromechanical or hydraulic subsystems, sensing elements, or compensation networks.   One method of representing complex transfer functions involves use of a single operational amplifier

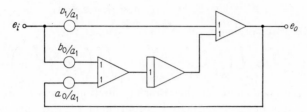

Fig. 6.8   Generation of first-order transfer function.

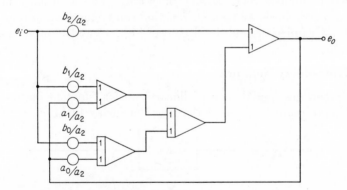

Fig. 6.9   Generation of second-order transfer function.

with complex input and feedback impedances, and has already been shown in Fig. 6.5f.   This method is sometimes awkward in that it is difficult to vary the impedance elements which determine the transfer function parameters.

Another method, based upon solution of the differential equation represented by the given transfer function, is frequently more satisfactory, though more expensive in terms of equipment required.   Summing amplifiers, integrating amplifiers, and potentiometers are used as shown in Figs. 6.8 and 6.9.   In these figures, the standard notation of a circle for potentiometer, a triangle for a summing amplifier, and a triangle with a rectangle for an integrating amplifier, is used.

In Fig. 6.8, the first-order transfer function

$$Y_1(s) = \frac{E_o(s)}{E_i(s)} = -\frac{b_1 s + b_0}{a_1 s + a_0} \tag{6.14}$$

is mechanized by connecting the computer elements to solve the equation

$$e_o = -\frac{b_1}{a_1} e_i - \int \left(\frac{b_0}{a_1} e_i + \frac{a_0}{a_1} e_o \right) dt \tag{6.15}$$

In Fig. 6.9, the second-order transfer function

$$Y_2(s) = \frac{E_o(s)}{E_i(s)} = -\frac{b_2 s^2 + b_1 s + b_0}{a_2 s^2 + a_1 s + a_0} \tag{6.16}$$

is mechanized by solving

$$e_o = -\frac{b_2}{a_2} e_i - \int \left(\frac{b_1}{a_2} e_i + \frac{a_1}{a_2} e_o \right) dt - \iint \left(\frac{b_0}{a_2} e_i + \frac{a_0}{a_2} e_o \right) dt^2 \tag{6.17}$$

Note that the coefficients of the transfer functions are set into the computer by means of easily adjusted potentiometers, thus providing very good accuracy and flexibility. The method shown may be further extended to higher-order transfer functions. This is usually unnecessary, however, since any transfer function can be factored into first- and second-order functions and the circuits of Figs. 6.8 and 6.9 used repeatedly in cascade.

6.7   Time-delay Network

An important special case of linear transfer function occurs in the approximate representation of the true time-delay function, $e^{-s\tau}$, shown

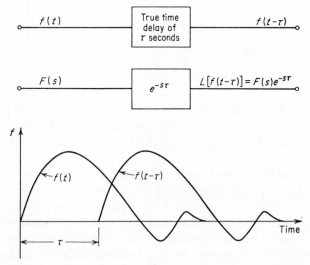

Fig. 6.10   The true time delay (transportation lag or true time lag).

in Fig. 6.10. The Padé approximation of e^x, shown in Fig. 6.11, is excellent for this purpose and leads to an easily mechanized second- or fourth-order transfer function. The transfer functions resulting are all-pass and have pole-zero configurations as shown in the figure.

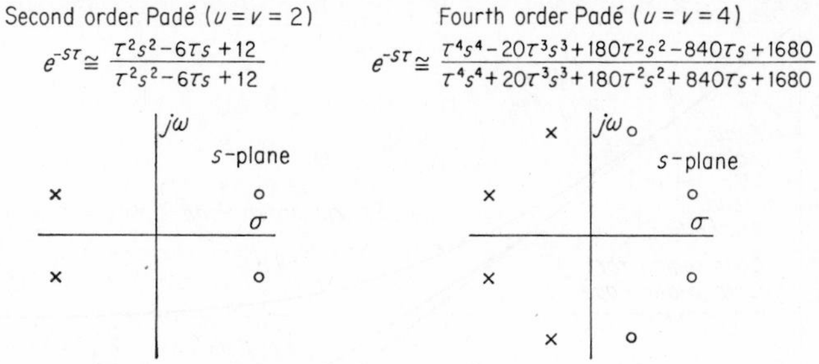

Second order Padé ($u = v = 2$)

$$e^{-s\tau} \cong \frac{\tau^2 s^2 - 6\tau s + 12}{\tau^2 s^2 - 6\tau s + 12}$$

Fourth order Padé ($u = v = 4$)

$$e^{-s\tau} \cong \frac{\tau^4 s^4 - 20\tau^3 s^3 + 180\tau^2 s^2 - 840\tau s + 1680}{\tau^4 s^4 + 20\tau^3 s^3 + 180\tau^2 s^2 + 840\tau s + 1680}$$

Fig. 6.11   Padé approximations of $e^{-s\tau}$.

(1)   Padé approximation: $e^x = \lim_{(u+v) \to \infty} \dfrac{F_{u,v}(x)}{G_{u,v}(x)}$

(2) where

$$F_{u,v}(x) = 1 + \frac{vx}{(u+v) \cdot 1!} + \cdots + \frac{v(v-1) \cdots 1 \cdot x^v}{(u+v)(u+v-1) \cdots (u+1) \cdot v!}$$

(3) and

$$G_{u,v}(x) = 1 - \frac{ux}{(v+u) \cdot 1!} + \cdots + (-1)^u \frac{u(u-1) \cdots 1 \cdot x^u}{(v+u)(v+u-1) \cdots (v+1) \cdot u!}$$

Figure 6.12, which shows a computer mechanization of the second order Padé network, is actually a special case of the network of Fig. 6.9.

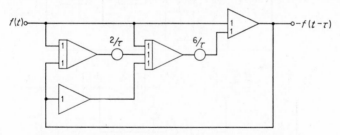

Fig. 6.12   Mechanization of second-order Padé network.

Figure 6.13 shows the phase-shift characteristics of the second- and fourth-order Padé networks. Over a limited frequency range, the approximation to a true time delay is quite good, particularly for the fourth-order network.

6.8   Representation of Typical Servo

Figure 6.14 shows the representation on an analog computer of a typical, though simple, servo system having position and rate feedback. The important thing to note is the striking resemblance between the servo block diagram and the computer diagram. Each element of the servo system has an easily identifiable counterpart in the computer, and each variable of the servo system, ϵ, $\dot{\theta}$, etc., is generated explicitly as a voltage at the output of a computer element. System parameters are

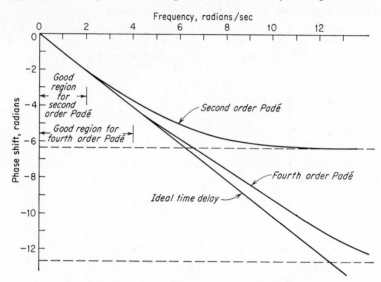

Fig. 6.13   Phase-shift characteristic of Padé networks.

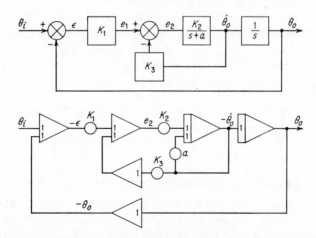

Fig. 6.14   Analog-computer mechanization of servo with position and rate feedback.

easily varied by changing potentiometer settings. A remarkable "feel" for system performance is quickly established.

6.9   Analytic Function Generation

Frequently, in analog computer work, it is necessary to generate certain analytical functions. For example, an exponential function of altitude may be desired for approximating atmospheric density in the solution of aerodynamic problems. Or, a sinusoidal function of an Euler angle may be needed for a coordinate system rotation, or for resolving a vector into rectangular components. A general method of providing such functions is by solution of the differential equation(s) satisfied by the desired function. Figure 6.15 shows the computer diagram for a generation of sin θ and cos θ by solution of the equations

$$\frac{d(\sin \theta)}{dt} = \dot{\theta} \cos \theta \tag{6.18}$$

$$\frac{d(\cos \theta)}{dt} = -\dot{\theta} \cos \theta \tag{6.19}$$

It is assumed that the variable $\dot{\theta}$ is available at the output of some other element in the computer. This will frequently be the case. If $\dot{\theta}$ is not

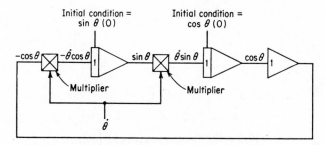

Fig. 6.15   Generation of sin θ and cos θ.

available but θ is, an approximate differentiation technique could be used to generate $\dot{\theta}$ for use in this circuit. In Fig. 6.15, note that if $\dot{\theta}$ is not constant, multipliers capable of multiplying a variable by a variable are required. For the case of $\dot{\theta} = \omega$, a constant, the circuit generates sin ωt and cos ωt. These functions often appear in control system work, so that the circuit of Fig. 6.15 is frequently used.

6.10   Multiplication

For solution of nonlinear differential equations and linear time-varying equations, a computer element for multiplying a variable by another variable is needed. Three commonly used multipliers in d-c analog computers are the servomultiplier, the quarter-square multiplier, and the time-division multiplier.

The servomultiplier, shown in Fig. 6.16, is the oldest in use historically, and is the only one suitable for use with an a-c analog computer. However, it has the poorest frequency response, poorest accuracy, and is the hardest to maintain. It is gradually being replaced by the newer all-electronic multipliers.

One variable, x, positions the arm of a feedback potentiometer by conventional servo action.   The arms of several other potentiometers, called the multiplying potentiometers, are ganged mechanically to the arm of the feedback potentiometer.   A voltage proportional to the other variable y is placed across a multiplying potentiometer, whose output is a

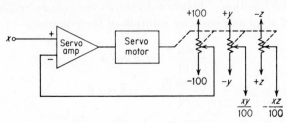

Fig. 6.16   Servomultiplier.

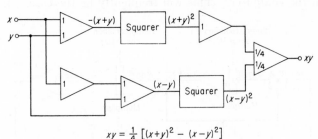

$$xy = \frac{1}{4}\left[(x+y)^2 - (x-y)^2\right]$$

Fig. 6.17   Quarter-square multiplier.

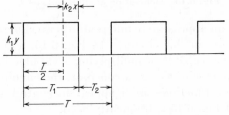

Fig. 6.18   Time-division multiplier operation.

voltage proportional to the desired product xy.   In like manner, a second multiplying potentiometer can be used to generate xz, etc.

Two commonly used all-electronic multipliers are shown in Figs. 6.17 and 6.18.   The quarter-square multiplier takes its name from the equation governing its operation

$$xy = \frac{1}{4}\left[(x+y)^2 - (x-y^2)\right] \tag{6.20}$$

and requires two function generators for generating accurate square-law functions.   This device has the best frequency response of the commonly used multipliers and has good accuracy.

The time-division multiplier of Fig. 6.18 makes use of the fact that the area of a rectangle is the product of its height and width. The pulse amplitude is made proportional to y, and the pulse duration is made equal to

$$T_1 = \frac{T}{2} + k_2 x \tag{6.21}$$

where $f = 1/T$ is the pulse repetition frequency and must be high compared with the frequencies in either x or y. The pulse train is passed through a low-pass filter to remove the carrier. The low-frequency output of this filter is

$$\bar{e} = \frac{T_1 k_1 y}{T} \tag{6.22}$$

A signal proportional to y is subtracted from this to provide

$$e_o = \bar{e} - \frac{k_1 y}{2} \tag{6.23}$$

$$= \frac{k_1 k_2}{T} xy$$

$$= k_3 xy$$

The static accuracy of the time-division multiplier is very good, but the filter phase shift limits the useful frequency range to a small fraction of the pulse repetition frequency. The frequency response is intermediate between the servomultiplier and the quarter-square multiplier.

6.11 Division

A method of division using a servomultiplier is shown in Fig. 6.19. The servo position is proportional to the divisor y. The output of the

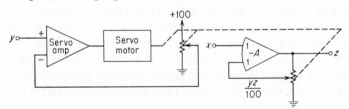

Fig. 6.19 Implicit division using servomultiplier.

multiplying potentiometer is then $yz/100$, where z is the output of a high-gain amplifier of gain $-A$. Then

$$z = -A\left(x + \frac{yz}{100}\right) \tag{6.24}$$

Solving,

$$z = -\frac{100x}{y + 100/A} \cong -100\,\frac{x}{y} \tag{6.25}$$

For a sufficiently high gain, it is seen that the amplifier output is the desired quotient. This division method, which can also be used with electronic multipliers, is actually a special case of a general method of

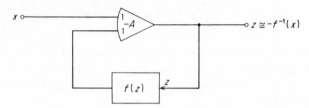

Fig. 6.20   Implicit function generation.

function generation called implicit function generation, shown in Fig. 6.20. The governing equation is

$$[x + f(z)] = -\frac{z}{A} \cong 0 \qquad \text{for } A \gg 1 \qquad (6.26)$$

from which
$$z \cong -f^{-1}(x) \qquad (6.27)$$

Many functions difficult to generate directly can be easily generated implicitly, providing the inverse function may be generated conveniently. Arcsin x and $\sqrt{x}$ are good examples of this.

6.12   Function Generators

In the study of linear constant-coefficient systems, one often wishes to evaluate the system response to an arbitrary forcing function, $f(t)$, of Eq. (6.2). In the study of linear variable-coefficient systems, the coefficients a_k of Eq. (6.2) are themselves arbitrary functions of the independent variable. In the study of nonlinear systems, it is often necessary to generate arbitrary functions of a dependent variable.

For all these purposes, one has need of a function generator to generate arbitrary functions of any argument. Many devices and methods exist for doing this in special cases, but one of the most generally satisfactory is the diode function generator. This device approximates arbitrary, single-valued, continuous functions of single argument by means of a number of straight-line segments as shown in Fig. 6.21. The line segment approximation $f_L(x)$ will typically crisscross the desired function as shown. It may be expressed as the sum of a number of ramp-type functions

$$f_L(x) = a + \sum_{k=0}^{n} r_k(x) \qquad (6.28)$$

as may be seen by examination of Fig. 6.21. A diode circuit may be used to generate each $r_k(x)$, and by adding the output of each circuit, the line segment function is generated. A simplified version of the circuitry employed is shown in Fig. 6.22.

In control systems and in many dynamic systems, certain nonlinear functions appear so frequently that special names have been given to them, and special analog computer circuits have been devised to represent them. Limiting, full-wave rectification, backlash, and dead space are

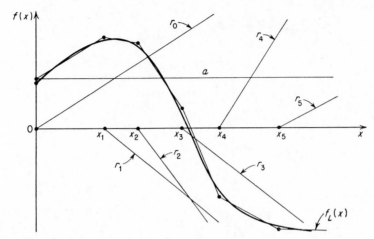

Fig. 6.21   Representation of arbitrary function as sum of straight-line segments.

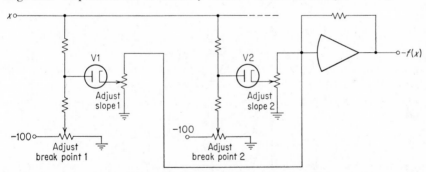

Fig. 6.22   Diode function generator.

among these functions, and the circuits used to represent them are shown in Figs. 6.23 to 6.26. These circuits employ the nonlinear properties of either diodes or relays to provide the desired nonlinear functions. [In Fig. 6.26, the operation of a differential relay amplifier is to select contact K if $(G - G') \geq 0$; otherwise, K' is selected.]

Circuits using diodes have good frequency response but often exhibit a small lack of sharpness, or rounding, at points of discontinuity as a result of the nonideal characteristic of an actual diode. Circuits with relays usually have a very sharp static characteristic but are poorer in frequency response than the diode circuits.

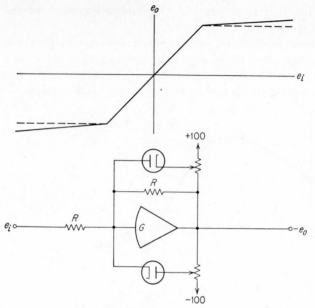

Fig. 6.23   Diode limiter circuit.

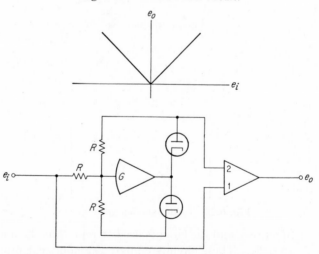

Fig. 6.24   Full-wave rectification circuit using diodes.

The backlash characteristic of Fig. 6.25 differs from the others shown in that it has memory—i.e., the output is a function of the past values of input as well as the present value.   The capacitor is the circuit element providing this memory.   In general, it is difficult to generate a quantity which is a function of past as well as present values of an argument; fortunately, such functions rarely appear in the problems for which analog computers are most often used.

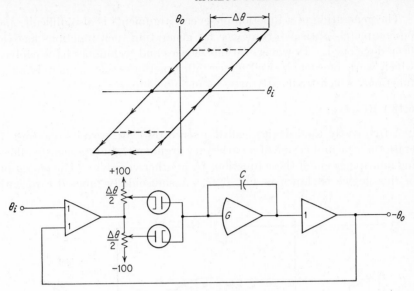

Fig. 6.25 Backlash circuit using diodes.

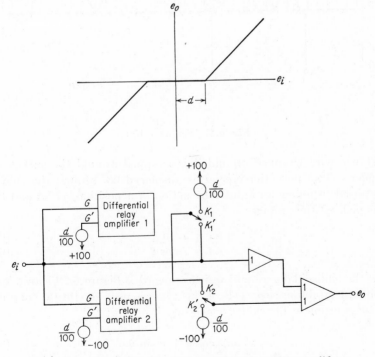

Fig. 6.26 Dead-space circuit using differential relay amplifiers.

The generation of a function of several arguments is also difficult, and no completely satisfactory device for generating such functions has yet been developed. However, various devices and techniques have evolved which work reasonably well for certain functions, such as aerodynamic functions, which frequently arise in analog-computer work.

6.13 Resolvers

A frequently used device, called a servo resolver, permits one to generate the sine and cosine of an arbitrary argument, simultaneously allowing multiplication of these functions by another variable. The operation of this device is shown in Fig. 6.27. A sinusoidally tapered card with

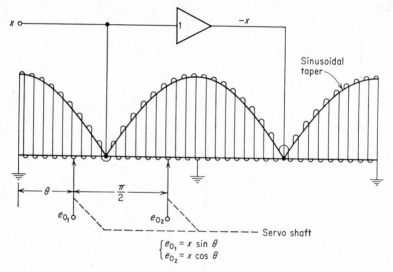

Fig. 6.27 Servo resolver.

resistance wire wrapped around it is wrapped around the surface of a cylinder. Two potentiometer arms, displaced 90° around the cylinder, are caused to follow an input θ by action of a position servo; and these arms pick off the voltages

$$e_{o1} = x \sin \theta \qquad (6.29)$$
$$e_{o2} = x \cos \theta \qquad (6.30)$$

from the sinusoidally wound resistance card. Figure 6.28 shows how a resolver, containing two cards of this type, is used to effect a coordinate system rotation. The equations of operation are:

$$x' = x \cos \theta + y \sin \theta \qquad (6.31)$$
$$y' = -x \sin \theta + y \cos \theta \qquad (6.32)$$

Three rotations of this kind, in accordance with the well-known Euler angles, permit one to resolve rotational motion in any desired coordinate system.

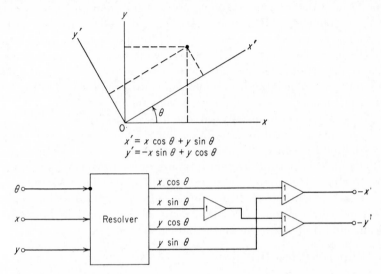

$$x' = x \cos \theta + y \sin \theta$$
$$y' = -x \sin \theta + y \cos \theta$$

Fig. 6.28 Coordinate transformation using resolver.

6.14 Output Devices

Two types of output devices, both graphical, are most frequently used with analog computers. One is the galvanometer recorder, also called a strip chart recorder. Multichannels are usually used, so that the behavior of several dependent variables, plotted as functions of the independent variable, may be observed. The other device is the xy plotter, or servo-driven recorder, in which the x and y channels consist of separately driven servos. This device presents a large-scale plot of any dependent variable versus any other dependent variable.

2 LINEAR TIME-VARYING SYSTEMS AND THE ADJOINT METHOD

6.15 Introduction

An area in which the analog computer has been particularly useful in recent years is the study of the behavior of control systems subjected to random inputs. For nonlinear systems, analytical methods are almost useless in all but the simplest cases. The analog computer permits effective, though laborious, evaluation of system response by means of a direct Monte Carlo approach. The system is simulated on the computer, and the random input is introduced by using an electronic noise generator.

Many runs are made under identical circumstances, save for the input noise sample, permitting the statistics of the system response to be compiled.

For linear time-varying systems, analytical techniques are available, but are extremely cumbersome when the order of the system is high. The analog computer, by means of a technique known as the adjoint method,[1] can compute the mean-square value of the response (usually the most important statistic) at one particular instant with but a single computer run.   The adjoint method is of considerable value in the study of fire-control and missile-guidance systems for three reasons:

1. These systems are usually subjected to noise inputs.

2. These systems are usually either linear time varying or else closely approximated by a linear time-varying system.

3. The most important system response, miss distance, is generally of interest at just one particular instant, the nominal time of impact.

A somewhat heuristic treatment of the adjoint method is offered as the subject of this section.   The treatment deals essentially with block diagrams and minimizes the mathematical aspects.

6.16 Superposition Integral

The weighting function of a linear time-varying system is defined as

$h(t_2,t_1)$ = system response observed at time $t = t_2$ due to unit impulse applied to input at time $t = t_1$

The weighting function is, of course, a function of both the time of application of the impulse and the time of observation of the response.   For a constant-coefficient system, the weighting function is merely a function of the single variable $\tau = t_2 - t_1$.

The response at any time t_2, due to an arbitrary input $x(t)$, is given by the superposition integral

$$y(t_2) = \int_{-\infty}^{t_2} x(t_1)h(t_2,t_1)\, dt_1 \qquad (6.33)$$

If the input is white Gaussian noise with no mean value and a spectral density $W(t)$ over positive frequencies only, the ensemble mean-square response at time t_2 is given by superposition as

$$\overline{y^2(t_2)} = \frac{1}{2} \int_{-\infty}^{t_2} W(t_1)h^2(t_2,t_1)\, dt_1 \qquad (6.34)$$

For stationary white noise, the mean-square response at time t_2 is

$$\overline{y^2(t_2)} = \frac{W}{2} \int_{-\infty}^{t_2} h^2(t_2,t_1)\, dt_1 \qquad (6.35)$$

---

[1] J. H. Laning, Jr., and R. H. Battin, "On an Application of the Use of Analog Computers to Methods of Statistical Analysis," *Project Cyclone Symposium* II, Reeves Instrument Corp., New York, 1952.

Before proceeding, it is important to note that no significant loss of generality is suffered by restricting the analysis to systems with stationary-white-noise input.

For example, consider a system subjected to stationary Gaussian noise of spectral density $W(\omega)$. Its response is equal to that of a combined system subjected to white noise. The combined system consists of the original system with a shaping filter added in front of its input terminal.[1] The shaping filter shapes the input white noise to the spectrum $W(\omega)$ required at the input terminal of the original system. If this filter can be realized, the combined system may then be simulated, and no loss of generality results.

Similarly, if the actual input is white but nonstationary, a filter with time-varying gain can be added. If the actual input is neither white nor stationary, a suitable shaping filter can still be found in principal, but may be difficult to realize.

Thus, the time-domain integration of Eq. (6.35) may be used with great generality to determine the response of linear time-varying systems to noise. The fundamental difficulty with Eq. (6.35) is that it cannot be evaluated on an analog computer, since the integration is carried out with respect to t_1, the time of application of the impulse. An analog computer, which must operate in real time, is only capable of integration with respect to time of observation t_2. Stated differently, an analog computer is only capable of generating $h(t_2,t_1)$ as a function of the time of observation t_2, with the time of impulse application fixed at some particular instant t_1.

Consider, for example, the simple time-varying system of Fig. 6.29, consisting of a switch and an RC circuit. The weighting functions which may be observed by direct experiment, or on an analog computer, are shown in Fig. 6.29b. The weighting function of Fig. 6.29c is the one required for Eq. (6.35). This function is, in general, different from any of those of Fig. 6.29b and cannot be generated *directly* by the system in

---

[1] The shaping filter is defined by

$$|H_f(j\omega)|^2 = W(\omega) \tag{6.36}$$

and its weighting function is

$$h_f(t) = \mathcal{L}^{-1}[H_f(s)] \tag{6.37}$$

The combined system-weighting function is

$$h_c(t_2,t_1) = \int_{t_1}^{t_2} h_f(u - t_1)h(t_2,u)\ du \tag{6.38}$$

and the mean-square response of the original system to noise of spectral density $W(\omega)$ is

$$\overline{y^2(t_2)} = \frac{1}{2} \int_{t_1}^{t_2} h_c{}^2(t_2,t_1)\ dt_1 \tag{6.39}$$

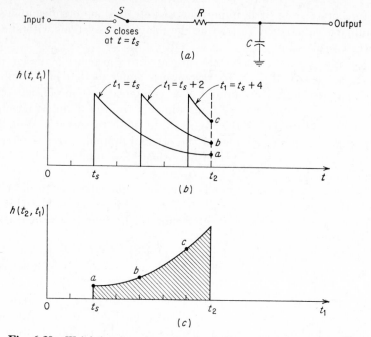

Fig. 6.29   Weighting functions of a simple linear time-varying system.

question.   What is needed is some method of generating $h(t_2,t_1)$ as a running function of t_1, with t_2 held fixed at some desired value.

6.17   The Adjoint System

For each linear time-varying system, we seek a related system, called the adjoint system, whose weighting function plotted against time of observation for a given time of application is a mirror image of the weighting function of the original system plotted against time of application for a given time of observation.   Stated mathematically, the adjoint system is to have a weighting function $h^*(t_2^*,t_1^*)$, such that

$$h^*(t_2^*,t_1^*) = h(t_2,t_1) \tag{6.40}$$

where $h^*(t_2^*,t_1^*)$ = adjoint system response observed at time $t^* = t_2^*$ due to unit impulse applied to input at time $t^* = t_1^*$

$$t_2^* = t_0 - t_1 \tag{6.41}$$
$$t_1^* = t_0 - t_2 \tag{6.42}$$

It is convenient to allow the reference time t_0 to be equal to t_2.   Then $t_1^* = 0$, i.e., the impulse is applied at time zero in the adjoint system. Moreover, t_2^*, the running time of observation in the adjoint system, represents $(t_2 - t_1)$, the interval between application and observation in the original system.   It is permissible to drop the subscript in t_2^* if it is remembered that the first argument in the weighting function refers to observation time. $h^*(t^*,0)$ is then the adjoint system-weighting function corresponding to a particular time of observation t_2 in the original system.

If the adjoint system can be physically realized on the analog computer, h^* may be generated, and Eq. (6.35) evaluated. A straightforward method of realizing the adjoint system from the original system block diagram is presented next. This method is attributable to R. R. Bennett.[1]

6.18 Elementary Operators

It is first noted that any linear time-varying system can be decomposed into blocks of elementary operators, each having a single input and output, suitably connected together. The elementary operators are of two types:

a. Those multiplying the input by a constant-coefficient operator, $F(s)$

b. Those multiplying the input by a function of time, $\phi(t)$

The truth of the above statement, though not immediately obvious, may be demonstrated by reference to Fig. 6.3. For a time-varying system, the a_k's are functions of time, and the operators which multiply by a_k/a_n are of type b. The integrators shown are of type a. A more complicated system, containing more than one dependent variable, can likewise be decomposed. Consider, for example, the system of Fig. 6.9, containing two dependent variables e_i and e_o. This system is time varying if the coefficients of Eq. (6.16) are time dependent. By slight rearrangement, Fig. 6.9 can be redrawn so that all the potentiometers are operators of type b; all integrators operators of type a.

For operators of type a, one has

$$h_a(t_2,t_1) = h_a(t_2 - t_1) = h_a(\tau) \tag{6.43}$$

The adjoint of this operator must also be constant coefficient; thus

$$
\begin{aligned}
h_a^*(t^*,0) &= h_a^*(t^*) \\
&= h_a^*(t_2 - t_1) \\
&= h_a^*(\tau)
\end{aligned}
\tag{6.44}
$$

But the adjoint operator must satisfy the defining equation (6.40)

$$h_a^*(t^*,0) = h_a(t_2,t_1) \tag{6.45}$$

so that
$$h_a^*(\tau) = h_a(\tau) \tag{6.46}$$

which proves that the adjoint of operator a is identical with a. A constant-coefficient operator is said to be self-adjoint.

For operators of type b, one has

$$h_b(t_2,t_1) = \phi(t_1) \cdot \delta(t_2 - t_1) \tag{6.47}$$

[1] R. R. Bennett: Analog Computing Applied to Noise Studies, *Proc. IRE*, October, 1953.

The adjoint operator obeys

$$h_b^*(t^*,0) = \phi^*(t^*) \cdot \delta(t^*) \tag{6.48}$$
$$= \phi^*(t^*) \cdot \delta(t_2 - t_1)$$

Again, by virtue of Eq. (6.40), there results

$$\phi^*(t^*) = \phi(t_1) \tag{6.49}$$

or

$$\phi^*(t^*) = \phi(t_2 - t^*) \tag{6.50}$$

The mirror image relationship between ϕ^* and ϕ is shown in Fig. 6.30.

Having determined the adjoints of the two elementary operators, it remains only to determine the manner of connection of the adjoint operators to obtain the block diagram of the adjoint system.

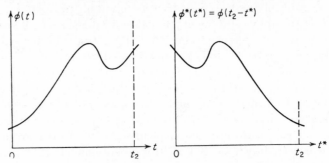

Fig. 6.30 Multiplication by a function of time.

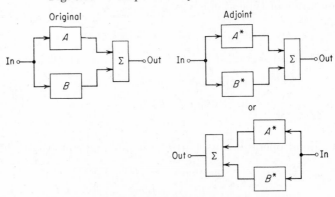

Fig. 6.31 Adjoint of blocks in parallel (adding).

6.19 Blocks in Parallel Paths

Consider two blocks A and B in parallel as shown in Fig. 6.31. These blocks may be elementary operators or more complex subsystems. In either event, assume the adjoint of A is A^* and of B is B^*, and that both are known. The weighting function of the parallel combination of A and B is clearly

$$h_{AB}(t_2,t_1) = h_A(t_2,t_1) + h_B(t_2,t_1) \tag{6.51}$$

The weighting function of the parallel combination of A^* and B^* is

$$
\begin{aligned}
h_{AB}^*(t^*,0) &= h_A^*(t^*,0) + h_B^*(t^*,0) \\
&= h_A(t_2,t_1) + h_B(t_2,t_1) \\
&= h_{AB}(t_2,t_1)
\end{aligned}
\tag{6.52}
$$

which proves that the parallel combination of adjoint blocks is the adjoint of the parallel combination of the original blocks. This rule, of course, applies to any number of paths in parallel.

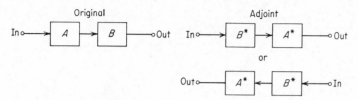

Fig. 6.32 Adjoint of blocks in cascade.

6.20 Blocks in Cascade

Next, consider two blocks A and B in cascade as shown in Fig. 6.32. The weighting function of the combination is

$$
h_{AB}(t_2,t_1) = \int_{t_1}^{t_2} h_A(u,t_1) h_B(t_2,u)\ du
\tag{6.53}
$$

For the adjoint blocks A^* and B^* connected in reverse order as shown, the weighting function is

$$
h_{AB}^*(t^*,0) = \int_0^{t^*} h_B^*(v,0) h_A^*(t^*,v)\ dv
\tag{6.54}
$$

Since B^* is the adjoint of B, and recalling that $t_0 = t_2$ in Eqs. (6.41) and (6.42), one has

$$
\begin{aligned}
h_B^*(v,0) &= h_B(t_2 - 0,\ t_2 - v) \\
&= h_B(t_2,\ t_2 - v)
\end{aligned}
\tag{6.55}
$$

Likewise

$$
\begin{aligned}
h_A^*(t^*,v) &= h_A(t_2 - v,\ t_2 - t^*) \\
&= h_A(t_2 - v,\ t_1)
\end{aligned}
\tag{6.56}
$$

Thus

$$
h_{AB}^*(t^*,0) = \int_0^{t_2-t_1} h_B(t_2,\ t_2 - v) h_A(t_2 - v,\ t_1)\ dv
\tag{6.57}
$$

Making the formal substitution, $v = t_2 - u$, in Eq. (6.57) results in

$$
h_{AB}^*(t^*,0) = - \int_{t_2}^{t_1} h_A(u,t_1) h_B(t_2,u)\ du
\tag{6.58}
$$

Comparing Eqs. (6.53) and (6.58) yields

$$
h_{AB}^*(t^*,0) = h_{AB}(t_2,t_1)
\tag{6.59}
$$

which proves that the two adjoint blocks, in reverse cascade order, form

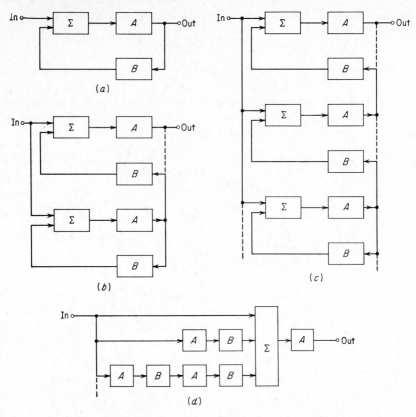

Fig. 6.33   Decomposition of basic closed-loop system.

the adjoint of the two original blocks in cascade.   This result is easily extended to the case of many blocks in cascade.

6.21   Basic Closed Loop

The results obtained for parallel and cascade connections of blocks may be used to derive the adjoint of the basic single-loop–closed-loop block diagram.   The construction of Fig. 6.33a, b, c, and d transforms the closed-loop system into an equivalent infinite open-end structure of parallel paths.   The adjoint of this structure is obtained in Fig. 6.34a from the previous results, and transformed, by an inverse construction to that of Fig. 6.33, to the closed-loop system of Fig. 6.34d.   One notes that the adjoint system is identical in form to the original system, merely replacing the blocks A and B with their adjoints.   Note in Figs. 6.31, 6.32, and 6.34 that the alternate form of the adjoint system leaves the blocks in their original order, but reverses the direction of signal flow through them, and reverses the roles of input and output of the system.

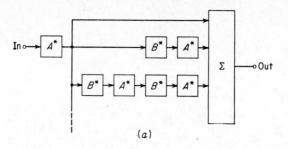

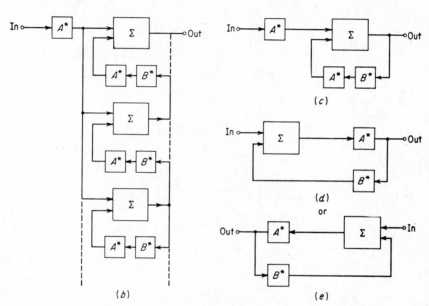

Fig. 6.34 Development of adjoint of basic closed-loop system.

6.22 General System

A set of rules for generating the adjoint system from any given block diagram can now be stated:

1. Redraw the given block diagram so that all blocks are elementary operators.

2. Reverse the direction of signal flow everywhere in the diagram. This includes reversing the roles of the input and output of the system.

3. In the case of a multiple output from a block, these outputs become inputs to a summer whose output is applied to the input of the given block.

4. Replace each block by its adjoint.

The resulting block diagram is the desired adjoint system.

6.23   Example

As a simple example of the application of the adjoint technique, consider again the system of the switch and RC circuit in cascade. The original and adjoint systems and their weighting functions are shown in Fig. 6.35. The adjoint system weighting function is the mirror image of

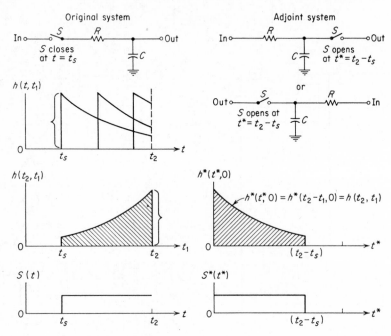

Fig. 6.35   Adjoint of a simple linear time-varying system.

the original system weighting function, plotted as a function of t_1 for a fixed t_2. The time-varying switching functions $S(t)$ and $S^*(t^*)$ are also shown.

By squaring the impulse response of the adjoint system and integrating with respect to t^*, the mean-square noise response of the original system at a particular time is evaluated by a single computer run.

7

Analog and Digital Techniques Combined

WALTER J. KARPLUS

ASSOCIATE PROFESSOR OF ENGINEERING
UNIVERSITY OF CALIFORNIA, LOS ANGELES

7.1 Toward a Unified Approach

In the preceding chapters the design and operating principles of the two main types of automatic computer have been reviewed. The development of analog and digital computers was accelerated tremendously by military requirements during World War II. During the years immediately following the war, there followed a period of intense activity in both fields during which progressively more elegant and more widely applicable computers were designed and in which computing techniques were extended to new areas of science and engineering. As a by-product of this rapid period of expansion during which computer technology matured to fill a vacuum which had existed up to that time, there appeared a rather unfortunate specialization of interest and skills on the part of computer engineers. So many new devices and techniques were being introduced, and so much work had to be done, that engineers in general tended to devote themselves exclusively to digital or to analog computation. A number of factors contributed subsequently to the reinforcement of this type of specialization:

Once an engineer or scientist had become familiar with a specific computer, and the early models of both analog and digital machinery required considerable detailed familiarity, it was natural that he should prefer to attempt to apply this computer to all types of problems that came his way, rather than invest additional time in the study of another type of machine. Many industrial and university organizations acquired either an analog or a digital computer, and in this way cast their lot with one or the other of the two major approaches to general-purpose computations. Similarly, many design groups developed a facility in the design of either analog or digital circuits and then preferred to integrate these circuits in their large systems. Finally, a number of companies manufacturing computers of one type or another recognized a financial stake in the popularization of their approach and therefore encouraged the application of their computers to as wide a variety of problems as possible. In time there arose a wide-open competition between proponents of digital and analog computers, with each side having enthusiastic adherents and opponents.

It is to be hoped that this type of competition represents merely a passing phase in a young field, and that the time will soon be at hand when it will be possible to apply well-tested criteria for determining which computer approach is the most practical for a specific problem. At present few such general criteria exist. It is the purpose of this chapter to demonstrate the desirability of breaking down the boundary lines between the analog and digital fields by examining and systematizing the ways in which analog and digital techniques have been combined in engineering systems to optimize the operation of a laboratory simulator or of complex control systems.

For the purpose of the present discussion, the chief distinction between analog and digital computers is taken to lie in the manner in which the dependent variable is handled within the computer. In analog machines the dependent variable, though not necessarily the independent variable (such as a space variable in partial differential equations), appears everywhere in continuous form and may be recorded with as many significant figures as the quality of available output equipment permits. In digital computers on the other hand, the dependent variable is everywhere in discretized form and is limited therefore to a finite number of digits. The number of significant figures which are manipulated and recorded as the output of the digital computer depends upon the number of digits carried throughout the solution and is directly related to the capacity of the computer memory cells.

As a direct result of this difference in the handling of data within the machine, the basic organization or logic of analog and digital computers developed along radically different lines. The analog computers described in the preceding chapter employ separate electronic units to perform each mathematical operation for the solution of a problem, and all operations are performed simultaneously. This is termed parallel operation. A typical analog computer has available a wide variety of operational units to be interconnected and utilized as the specific problem demands. Among the operational units commonly available are integrators, multipliers, trigonometric resolvers, nonlinear function generators, adders, sign changers, etc. In digital computers, as described in Chap. 3, on the other hand, the computations occur in a program sequence, only one computation taking place at any specific instant of time.   This is termed serial operation.   The mathematical operations required for the solution of the problem are performed by utilizing a relatively small number of arithmetic operations available in the computer.   Complex mathematical tasks are performed by utilizing the basic logical circuits in accordance with a prescribed code.

Since the accuracy of the digital computer is limited only by the number of significant figures carried in the solution, while the accuracy of the analog computer is limited by the quality of its components and associated instruments (the accuracy of analog computers is limited to approximately 0.01 per cent at best), the digital computer must be regarded as the more widely applicable device for general-purpose calculations.   On the other hand, since all mathematical operations in an analog computer occur simultaneously, for most problems of interest to control engineers, the analog computer provides solutions more rapidly, and is in particular better adapted to provide solutions and control signals at the same rate as they occur or are required in control systems; that is, it is better adapted to real-time operations.

Required accuracy and solution time are therefore two considerations upon which a decision to use either digital or analog techniques can be based.   Other important considerations include the types of input data available and the types of output data preferred—that is, are they in continuous form or are they in discrete or digitized form?   In seeking methods of combining analog and digital techniques, it is advantageous to examine each phase or task of the over-all simulation or system design to determine which of these considerations is the most important.

There are a number of ways in which analog and digital techniques can be combined to advantage.   These include:

1. The use of analog techniques in a digital computer; that is, to employ the operational approach in what is essentially a digital machine

2. The application of digital units in analog computers to increase the accuracy or facilitate certain types of computational operations

3. The development of hybrid systems which employ both analog and digital computers simultaneously to solve large problems or to constitute complex control systems

In this chapter each of these possibilities is considered in turn.   In a final section the subject of analog-to-digital and digital-to-analog conversion is reviewed.

7.2 Operational Techniques in Digital Computations—Serial Operation

One of the features of general-purpose electronic analog computers, which have led to the wide acceptance of this type of computer for control system analysis, is the facility with which they lend themselves to an operational or unitized approach.   In analyzing a complex system or in solving a complex set of linear or nonlinear equations, a convenient first step is to draw a flow chart indicating in block form the system operation or the mathematical operations necessary for solution, such that each block represents a linear or nonlinear mathematical operation.   In control system engineering the governing equations are generally differential equations, so that such a typical block may specify an operation of integration, lead-lag, multiplication, limiting, etc.

As described in the preceding chapter, an electronic analog computer has precisely such operational units available.   So in order to program a problem on an analog computer, it is only necessary to employ plug-in connectors to fashion and interconnect these units in the manner specified by the block diagram.   Closed-loop methods are then used to solve differential equations by integrating a variable several times and then feeding this integral quantity back to the input of the loop.   Such an approach has merit because it enables the engineer to visualize clearly what is going on in the computer system and what the voltage at each point in the computer loops represents in terms of the physical system. Furthermore such a setup makes it easy to vary any of the system parameters, which usually appear in the computer in the form of potentiometer settings, and to observe at once the effect of such a variation upon the entire system.

In an effort to combine the advantages of the operational approach with the high accuracy of digital computers, a new type of calculator termed the digital differential analyzer was introduced in the early 1950s.   Considerable development work of systems employing incremental computations had preceded this advance in computer technology. The digital differential analyzer, commonly abbreviated DDA, is a truly digital machine, containing a memory, gating and switching circuits, and processes all data in discretized, binary form.   It differs from the general-purpose digital machines in that it is designed specifically for the solution of ordinary linear or nonlinear differential equations or sets of such equations.   This restriction upon the capabilities of the computer permitted the designers to simplify tremendously the over-all machine. The DDAs described in Ref. 1 are roughly comparable in capability to a 30–40 amplifier electronic analog computer and occupy a space of less than 2 cu ft and weigh less than 100 lb.   Moreover, the internal electronic circuits are designed so as to facilitate the programming of the computer using the operational approach.

In the digital differential analyzer the basic "component" is a digital integrator.   Unlike electronic analog computers, in which integrators exist as distinct units, digital integrators exist only as portions of the surface of a magnetic drum memory, arranged so as to be capable of processing data in accordance with the rules of numerical integration.

By programming suitable commands these integrators, varying in number from 20 to 60 depending upon the type of machine, are capable of being interconnected in a manner similar to that of the analog computers. The mathematical operations are performed sequentially, however, so that the over-all operation is essentially of the serial type. Real-time operation is therefore generally not feasible. The description of the operation of digital differential analyzers presented below is based upon the Litton[1] DDA, the most compact and convenient machine of this type to appear on the market to date, but is equally applicable to other types of digital differential analyzers. The operation of a typical digital integrator will be described first; then the "interconnection" of such integrator units for the solution of a differential equation will be discussed.

A typical integrator[2] in a differential analyzer consists of two registers—spaces along the periphery of the magnetic drum or other memory device which are assigned specifically to retain information pertinent to that integrator. A block diagram of a unit suitable for obtaining $\int y\,dx$ is shown in Fig. 7.1. Increments of the variable y are accumulated periodically (for example, 60 times/sec) in the Y register and are added to the quantity already stored there. The content of this register therefore corresponds at any instant of time to the variable

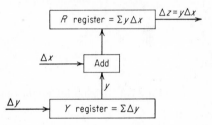

Fig. 7.1 Block diagram of digital integrator.

y. At the same time, the number contained in the Y register is added algebraically to the R register at a rate determined by the increments of a second variable Δx. This process can be visualized as a gating operation such that each time a pulse Δx comes along, the gate is opened, and the entire contents of the Y register are applied to the R register. The content of the R register is therefore $\Sigma y\,\Delta x$.

The content of any memory device is limited to a specific number of significant figures. The R register of the integrator is therefore soon filled to capacity and "overflows." This overflow $y\,\Delta x$ is applied as it occurs to the Y register of another integrator. The quantity contained in the Y register of this second integrator then constitutes the most significant portion of $\int y\,dx$. The less significant portion of this integral, that part which has not overflowed yet, remains in the R register and may be considered a remainder of the incremental operation. The overflow of the R register can be applied to more than one other integrator as shown in Fig. 7.2. It is apparent that the output of the integrator is itself only an incremental value, and that the full result of the integration operation does not appear in the integrator in which this operation is performed, but rather in the Y registers of other integrators.

Each integrator therefore receives two incremental inputs, which themselves may be outputs of other integrators or periodic pulses generated within the machine. Schematically, such an integrator may be represented as shown in Fig. 7.3a. In some of the more modern DDAs, it is possible to specify that the output be either plus or minus the integral. An integrator with a negative output is shown schematically in Fig. 7.3b.

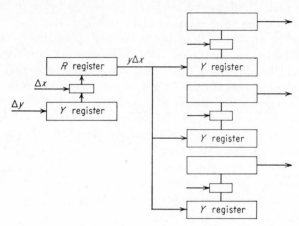

Fig. 7.2 Digital integrator connected to other digital integrators.

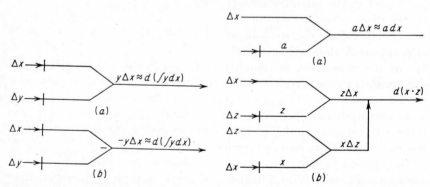

Fig. 7.3 (a) Schematic notation for digital integrator with positive output. (b) Integrator with negative output.

Fig. 7.4 (a) Digital multiplication by a constant. (b) Digital multiplication of two variables.

The multiplication of a variable by a constant is accomplished as shown in Fig. 7.4a. The Y register of the integrator is given an initial value a which remains unchanged throughout the computation. The output of the integrator is therefore $a \Delta x$, and the quantity ax is accumulated in the Y register of another integrator. The operation of constant multiplication is therefore more complex in the DDA than it is in electronic differential analyzers in which a simple potentiometer can do the whole job. The multiplication of two variables by each other is less of a problem in the case of a DDA than it is in electronic analog computers. Here one can employ the relationship

$$xz = \int z\,dx + \int x\,dz$$

so that a two-integrator circuit as shown in Fig. 7.4b can be employed. This mechanization is feasible because in a DDA, integration with respect to any variable can readily be accomplished, whereas in an electronic analog computer the independent variable must necessarily be time. The generation of various nonlinear analytic functions can proceed in a manner essentially similar to that described for electronic analog computers.

As an example of the application of the DDA to the solution of a simple equation, consider

$$\frac{d^2y}{dt^2} + a\frac{dy}{dt} + by = 0$$

In accordance with the procedure discussed in the preceding chapter, this equation may be rearranged as

$$\ddot{y} = -a\dot{y} - by$$

where
$$\ddot{y} = \frac{d^2y}{dt} \text{ and } \dot{y} = \frac{dy}{dt}$$

or
$$d\dot{y} = -a\dot{y}\,dt - by\,dt$$

A program is now constructed so that the terms on the right side of this equation are constructed from the term on the left side by successive integrations.   One approach to the determination of such a program is to assume that the highest-order differential is already available in the system.   The two terms $-a\dot{y}\,dt$ and $-by\,dt$ are then constructed by suitable integrations and constant multiplications.   Figure 7.5 illus-

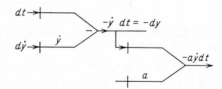

Fig. 7.5   Generation of the term $-a\dot{y}\,dt$.

trates how the term $-a\dot{y}\,dt$ is generated.   The second term $-by\,dt$ is then constructed by the use of two more integrators as shown in Fig. 7.6. The two outputs of this circuit are then summed and fed back by connecting both of them to the input point of the first integrator.   The over-all circuit then has the appearance shown in Fig. 7.7.   The Y registers of integrators 1 and 2 are filled to initial values in accordance with the initial conditions specified for the problems.   The Y registers of integrators 3 and 4 are initially filled to values corresponding to a and b respectively. A periodic time signal to constitute the inputs "dt" for integrators 1 and 2 is generated within the machine.   The desired output, i.e., a plot of y

versus t, is obtained by connecting the output of integrator 2 to a suitable digital plotter.

Digital graph plotters are available as output devices for digital differential analyzers. These are capable of plotting the output of any integrator as a function of time or as the function of the output of any other integrator. The plotter is a two-coordinate graph plotter and is purely digital in that both the abscissa and the ordinate motion are incremental or stepwise. Typically, the magnitude of such steps is of the order of 0.01 in. so that the plotted curve appears to be reasonably smooth. By substituting a follower-head for the pen in a two-coordinate

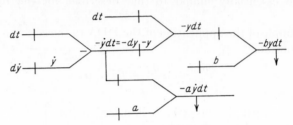

Fig. 7.6 Generation of the term $-by\,dt$.

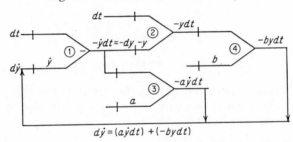

Fig. 7.7 DDA circuit for the solution of a linear second-order differential equation $\ddot{y} + a\dot{y} + by = 0$.

plotter, the output device can be converted into a curve follower to permit arbitrary functions, plotted on graph paper to serve as transient input data for the computer.

On a DDA it is possible to sacrifice solution time or rapidity for the sake of increased accuracy and vice versa. If one is willing to wait a sufficiently long time for the solution, very high accuracies are obtainable with this type of machine. The DDA therefore makes it possible to attain the high-accuracy characteristics of general-purpose digital computers.

7.3 Operational Techniques in Digital Computation— Parallel Operation

One of the chief disadvantages of the digital differential analyzers described in the preceding section is that they are incapable of operating

Table 7.1 Computer Building Blocks

Element	Diagrammatic representation	Function
Gate (AND)	a, b → c	Coincidence device—yields a signal output at c when input signals are simultaneously present at a and b.
Buffer (OR)	a, b → c	Combining unit—yields a signal output at c when signals are present at a or b or both.
Flip-flop (HOLD)	a, b; S FF R	Holding device—excites output(s) at a and b for a period starting with the arrival of a signal at input S (set) and ending with the arrival of a signal at input R (reset).
Binary counter	a, b; C_2	Commutating device—alternately changes state of output(s) at a and b with each input signal.
Forward-backward counter	F, B	Integrating device—accumulates net count of number of signals arriving at F (forward) input and B (backward) input.
Preset counter	a → PC_n → Carry; n	Anticipation device—provides a signal (CARRY) at output after n input signals have been received. n is preset.
Scaler	a → $n:m$ → b	Scaling device—provides m signals at output b for each n signal received at input a.
Synchronizer	a → S → c; b	Synchronizing device—for each randomly occurring signal at a provides one and only one signal at c timed according to pulse train at b.
Shift register	a → SR SR SR SR → b; S	Storage and transfer device—accepts and stores binary data received either as a serial pulse train or as simultaneous inputs to each element.
Shaft-to-digital converter	SDC	Conversion device—converter shaft position to binary or decimal coded representation.
Voltage-to-digital converter	VDC	Conversion device—as above, but accepts input voltage.

Table 7.1   Computer Building Blocks (*Continued*)

Element	Diagrammatic representation	Function
Digital-to-voltage converter	DVC	Conversion device—accepts digitally coded input data and yields appropriate representative output voltage.
Binary rate multiplier	$f \rightarrow$ BM $\rightarrow fx$	Rate multiplying device—accepts average input rate f and binary code x to yield new average output rate fx.
Function table	FT $\rightarrow Y$	Translational device—supplies a unique output function Y for each condition of input function X.

SOURCE: B. M. Gordon.[3]

in real time.   By virtue of the fact that all mathematical operations are performed sequentially, as the magnetic drum memory rotates past the recording and reading heads, the solution of any given problem takes an amount of time dependent upon the required solution accuracy.   This generally makes it impossible to employ digital differential analyzers in systems in which computer outputs must be continuously available to furnish control signals or to constitute inputs to other portions of a large computer system.   The so-called "operational digital computers" are designed to combine the high accuracy of digital equipment with the real-time advantages of the analog method.   In essence such an operational digital computer contains mathematical units such as adders, subtractors, multipliers, dividers, etc., just as an electronic analog computer, but the data within the machine are carried everywhere in digital or discretized form rather than as continuous information.   The basic building blocks of such a device described in considerable detail by Gordon[3,4] are described on pages 149 and 150 (see Table 7-1).

Data within an operational digital computer may be carried either as a unitary weighted pulse train or in binary code.   In a unitary pulse train a specific number is represented by a corresponding number of pulses, so that, for example, the number 365 is represented by a train of 365 pulses.   This type of data representation has the advantage that frequently input data from physical processes are readily available in this form.   Binary techniques are employed in other portions of the system since they permit the representation of data in compact form with elements which need to attain only two discrete stable states, i.e., 1 and 0. Table 7.1 lists the basic building blocks with which it is possible to instrument most digital control or measurement systems.

The most powerful member of the family of operational digital devices is the so-called binary rate multiplier. This unit accepts a train of pulses as one input and information in binary code as the other input, and yields as an output a pulse train containing a number of pulses equal to the product of the two inputs. Such a unit is shown in Fig. 7.8 and is composed of binary scalers, gating circuits, and buffers.

Referring to Fig. 7.8, a pulse train f_{av} is applied to the first binary scaler C_2—a device that yields one output pulse for every two input pulses. In the binary rate multiplier shown, eight such scaling circuits are connected in cascade. The first scaler will therefore yield an output after every two inputs; the second scaling circuit yields an output after every two inputs from the first scaler, that is after four impulse pulses

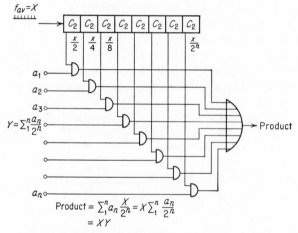

Fig. 7.8   Schematic diagram of binary-rate multiplier.   (*From Gordon.*[3])

from f_{av}; the third scaler will yield one output for every eight input pulses; etc. The outputs of each scaling circuit are applied to a separate gating circuit which is opened or closed in accordance with a binary code determined by the other input y. The output of each scaler is only passed on through the unit if the associated gate circuit is open. The outputs of all the gating circuits are combined by the buffer to yield a train of pulses corresponding to the desired product. By using a sufficient number of scalers and gating circuits, any degree of accuracy can be achieved. As an example, the use of 10 scalers and 10 gating circuits provides an accuracy of 1 part in 2,000. Suitable phase-shifting circuits must be employed to prevent the outputs of two or more scalers from occurring simultaneously. By taking advantage of advanced circuit techniques including the use of magnetic amplifiers and transistors, highly compact and reliable multiplier units can be fashioned. As an example, a multiplier of this type containing 10 scaling-gating units can be constructed as a plug-in unit occupying approximately 2 cu in.

Addition of data represented in pulse-train form may be accomplished by the circuit shown in Fig. 7.9.   To add two pulse trains, it is only

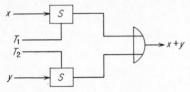

necessary to assure that the pulses of the two inputs do not occur at the same time.   In the circuit shown in the figure, the two pulse trains, whose pulses may occur randomly, are synchronized to clock pulse times T_1 and T_2 whose pulses are made to occur out of phase. The resultant two pulse trains, which

Fig. 7.9 Operational addition circuit. (*From Gordon.*[3])

are now always out of phase, are then combined to form an output pulse train which is the sum of the two inputs.

The subtraction operation illustrated in Fig. 7.10 is more complicated. In the figure it is assumed that the pulse train Y is to be subtracted from the pulse train X.   Timing pulses t_1 and t_2 are first employed to assure that the pulses in the two input pulse trains do not occur simultaneously. The two trains are then applied to the forward input and the backward

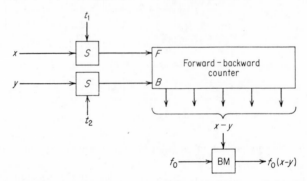

Fig. 7.10 Operational subtraction circuit. (*From Gordon.*[3])

input of a reversible counter.   The output of such a counter is at all times the net difference between these two inputs.   This output can be applied in turn to a binary-rate multiplier whose other input is a pulse train of a fixed rate f_0.   The output of this multiplier will then be the quantity $f_0(x - y)$.

The operation of division can be accomplished by employing three binary-rate multipliers and one forward-backward counter as shown in Fig. 7.11.   Assume that both the divisor and the dividend, x and y, are in binary form.   The x input is applied to a multiplier BM_1 to produce an output pulse train proportional to x.   This pulse train is applied as the forward input of the forward-backward counter.   The output z of this counter is applied to a second multiplier BM_2 to produce a pulse train proportional to z.   This pulse train in turn becomes one input of binary multiplier BM_3 whose other input is the variable y.   The output of BM_3 is a pulse train proportional to zy and is applied as a backward input to the forward-backward counter.   A closed loop is thereby formed, and the system will seek an equilibrium condition in which as many forward pulses per unit time are applied to the counter as are backward pulses.   The system will therefore be in equilibrium when

$$f_0 x = f_0 yz$$

or
$$z = \frac{x}{y}$$

If the variables x and y are initially available as weighted pulse trains, the division circuit becomes even simpler requiring only one multiplier

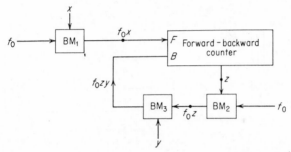

Fig. 7.11   Operational division circuit.   (*From Gordon.*[3])

and the counter.   The x train is then applied directly to the counter, and the y pulse train is multiplied by z, the output of the counter, and then fed back to comprise the backward input of the counter.

The closed-loop approach, used for the generation of a quotient, can be applied as well to the realization of a wide variety of analytic functions of a dependent variable.   In this respect the application of operational digital techniques is very similar to the implicit function generation methods used with electronic analog circuits.   An an example, consider the generation of sines and cosines of angles.   In the circuit shown in Fig. 7.12, the operational digital computer acts as a resolver, translating the angular displacement data of a motion-detecting device into binary numbers proportional to $\sin \theta$ and $\cos \theta$.   The incremental motion $\Delta\theta$ is translated into a pulse train by the pickup device, such that each pulse represents a given amount of incremental angular displacement.   Two forward-backward counters are shown in the figure (for simplicity the necessary control gating circuits for each of these counters have been omitted).   If now the counts in the forward-backward counters are given initial values corresponding to $\sin \theta$ and $\cos \theta$ at the commencement of the computer run, the output pulse trains of the two binary-rate multipliers will be $\sin \theta \, \Delta\theta$ and $\cos \theta \, \Delta\theta$, respectively.   These pulse trains are then fed back to the forward-backward counters as shown, so that two interlaced closed loops are formed. In effect these two loops seek equilibrium conditions such that

$$- \cos \theta = \Sigma \sin \theta \, \Delta\theta$$
$$\sin \theta = \Sigma \cos \theta \, \Delta\theta$$

so that the required trigonometric functions are generated continuously. In this circuit the forward-backward counters act effectively as digital integrators.

A different approach to the performance of digital mathematical computations in parallel was employed by Packard-Bell Computer Corporation in designing the TRICE computer.[10] This device is a

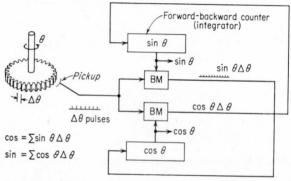

Fig. 7.12 Trigonometric resolution using digital operational methods. (*From Gordon.*[3])

digital differential analyzer, which is similar in some respects to that described in the preceding section, but which uses separate memory units for each integrator, rather than a single magnetic drum memory. The integrators operate at 100,000 iterations/sec, and all integrators are operative all the time. It is therefore possible with this type of a computer, to operate in real time and still retain the accuracy advantages of digital operation. A price in complexity of equipment and initial cost must of course be paid for these advantages.

Each of the operational units are constructed on an etched board which plugs into an etched bussing system. The memory registers are recirculating 30-bit delay lines employing standard delay cable. In addition to the incremental integrators, this system includes digital servo units which have an output only when $-\frac{1}{2} \leq y < +\frac{1}{2}$. Such units make it possible to generate a number of analytic functions by implicit function techniques. A multiplier which generates Δxy from inputs Δx and Δy is also available. A Δy summer is available for accepting as many as six Δy inputs and generating the binary representation of this sum.   Separate constant multipliers are provided for multiplying a variable by a constant.   A control unit consisting of a clock generator, a counter to provide timing pulses within each iteration, a number of control flip-flops, and an overflow detector is also required.

More recently, a number of investigators including Wortzman[11] have described the integration of analog-type operational amplifiers in large digital computers to permit a limited amount of parallel computation.

7.4 Digital Techniques in Analog Computers

On frequent occasions it has been found advantageous to incorporate digital computing elements in an analog computing system.   This approach is profitable in the generation of functions and in the performance of mathematical operations, which would be impossible or extremely

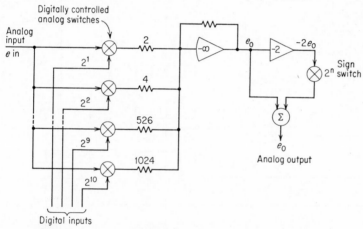

Fig. 7.13 Digital-analog multiplier.   (*From Hurney.*[5])

expensive to realize with sufficient accuracy by means of conventional analog techniques.   Occasionally, some of the input data for the analog computer is in digital form, and the application of digital computing units makes it possible to dispense with the digital-analog converters which would ordinarily be required.   Several digital units of this type are briefly considered below to serve as examples of this approach to combined analog-digital computation.

Hurney[5] describes a digital multiplier as well as a digital function generator suitable for use with electronic analog computers.   These two units are also illustrative of two possible approaches to the digital generation of functions.   In the case of the multiplier the relationship between the input and the output signals is stored as a series of instructions in the digital program; the function generators, on the other hand, have stored all the relationships between the input and the output for the specific function to be generated.   In the multiplier shown in Fig. 7.13, the analog input is first converted into a digital number by an analog-digital converter. The multiplication operation is then performed on the input number in accordance with instructions programmed in the unit. Basically, the multiplier consists of ten parallel conductances arranged in binary ratios. These conductances are switched into the circuit in accordance with programmed commands. The 10 digitally controlled switches and the 10 conductances can be made to assume 1,028

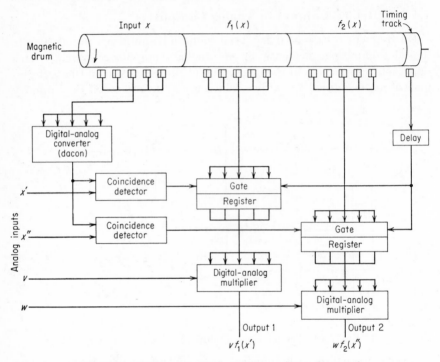

Fig. 7.14   Digital function generator.   (*From Hurney.*[5])

different values of total conductance. These conductances combine to constitute the input resistance of the operational amplifier, so that the gain of this amplifier can assume incremental values between 0 and 1 depending upon the condition of the switches.

The digital function generator for the generation of arbitrary nonlinear functions of a dependent variable is shown in Fig. 7.14. The basic element of this system is the storage device, a magnetic drum. Columns of tabulated numbers, for example tables of trigonometric functions, are stored on this drum. In the first column the values of the dependent variable are stored. Corresponding functions of this variable are stored in adjacent sections of the magnetic drum memory. As the drum is rotated, the first column (the input column) is scanned, and when the desired input value is reached, the appropriate functions of this input are read from the adjacent columns.   The digital numbers representing the output are converted by suitable digital-analog converters into analog voltages.

Bekey[6] describes a generalized integration method employing digital techniques.   Since electronic analog integrators necessarily integrate only with respect to time, considerable additional effort is necessary to generate integrals of dependent variables.   Bekey's method makes use of the numerical relationship

$$F = \int_{x_1}^{x_2} y \, dx = \lim_{\Delta x \to 0} \sum_{i=1}^{n} y_i \, \Delta x$$

If Δx is small

$$F \cong \Delta x \sum_{i=1}^{n} y_i$$

The evaluation of the integral therefore requires the summation of a series of values of the integrand y which are obtained by sampling at

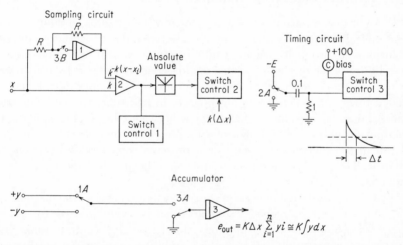

Fig. 7.15   Circuit for integration by a dependent variable.   (*From Bekey.*[6])

constant intervals in the variable x.   This is accomplished with the circuits shown in Fig. 7.15.

Integrator 1 is connected as a "sample-hold" device; that is, its output represents the value of x at the last sample x_i.   Sampling is performed when $|x - x_i| = \Delta x$, the preset width of the sampling interval.   The sampled values of y are summed in integrator 3 which acts as an accumulator by integrating the input voltages for a fixed period of time Δt.   If Δt is sufficiently small, y can be assumed to remain constant so that the output of the accumulator consists of a staircase of integrated inputs. A separate timing circuit is employed to generate clipped pulses of controllable width to determine the integrating time Δt. To permit x and y to assume either positive or negative values, sampling switch control 1 is employed to select either $+y$ or $-y$ depending on whether $(x - x_i)$ is positive or negative. The actual sampling is, however, performed by switch control 2 which is activated by the absolute value of this quantity.

Digital techniques have also been found useful in analog computer work to facilitate the input and output of data to computer systems. Thus in large-scale analog computers the settings of all potentiometers, initial conditions on all capacitors, and other data pertinent to a specific problem can be recorded on punched tape or punch cards. The computer is then freed for other problem work. At a later date the punched tape or punch cards are employed, together with associated switching and servomechanisms, to automatically program the computer for the original problem. In this way the time required to set up a problem can be reduced considerably, and the inevitable mistakes which occur in such a setup procedure can be minimized.

7.5 Hybrid Computing Systems

A hybrid computing system is one in which analog computer units and digital computer units are interconnected and act together to provide solutions to problems which would be more difficult or impossible to handle by other methods. Since analog computers operate in real time with continuous data, while digital computers carry data in discrete and coded form and generally do not operate in real time, special conversion units must be used at each interface between the analog and digital computing units. The design of suitable converters, discussed in some detail in the following section, often presents considerable instrumentation problems. This additional effort may be justified for a number of reasons:

1. In the simulation of certain control systems, some of the mathematical operations required may be more easily accomplished by analog methods, while others may be more suited to digital computation. For example, it may be desired to make a stability analysis of a portion of a large system containing both analog and digital components. The investigation of closed-loop behavior proceeds more easily on an analog computer where potentiometer settings can be varied readily and the resulting effect upon the system behavior noted at once; if the over-all operation of the system is determined by operations which require memory and high accuracy, a digital computer may be required to simulate the rest of the system.

2. Frequently in the simulation of large systems it is desirable to include in the simulating system a number of the actual units or components which occur in the prototype system. For example, it may be desirable to interconnect the autopilot, which is used in the actual guided

missile being simulated, with computers which simulate the rest of the missile performance. If such a unit operates in analog form, and if accuracy requirements demand that much of the computation be performed digitally, it may be desirable to employ a hybrid system to accomplish certain of the computations by analog means and others by digital means.

3. For various applications in control as well as in simulation it may be necessary to operate in real time. Since mathematical operations are processed sequentially in a digital computer, the speed with which such a computer makes data available is limited. The digital computer is therefore able to follow only the relatively slowly varying components of the system transients. Under these conditions it may be advantageous to employ digital computers to process the slowly changing data with high accuracy, while an analog computer is used to perform mathematical operations on the rapidly changing components of the transients. By combining the results of the two computers, it is possible to attain real-time operation with an accuracy higher than could be obtained with either the digital computer or the analog computer working separately.

4. Some of the input channels to a large-scale control system or simulator may provide information in analog form, while other channels transmit data digitally. Such a condition often arises when the computer is located a considerable distance away from other portions of the system. The transmission of data over noisy information channels is generally accomplished with great reliability by digital communications. Instruments in the vicinity of the computing section however may provide data in analog form. To optimize the data-processing operations, it may then be of advantage to employ a hybrid installation.

The ways in which analog and digital computer installations can be used together can be classified into two broad categories: unilateral operation, in which information flows across the interface between the analog and digital sections in only one direction, and bilateral operation, in which the flow across this interface is in both directions. Both methods require conversion equipment at the interface. In the case of unilateral operations however, this conversion equipment is generally much simpler and the instrumentation problems much less severe than in the case of bilateral operation.

In unilateral operation the analog or the digital computing section of the over-all system may be viewed merely as comprising highly complex input or output devices for the rest of the system. Several possible unilateral arrangements are illustrated in block diagram form in Fig. 7.16. In such systems a flow chart is first prepared to indicate all the mathematical operations for the solution of the problem. Each operation is then analyzed to determine whether it is better performed by analog or by digital techniques. The location of the interface between the analog and the digital system is then selected so as to optimize the over-all system operation.

In the case of bilateral operation, there exists a wide variety of ways in which the analog computer, the digital computer, and possibly the system to be controlled can be interconnected. Figure 7.17 illustrates a system in which the slowly varying portions of the system transients,

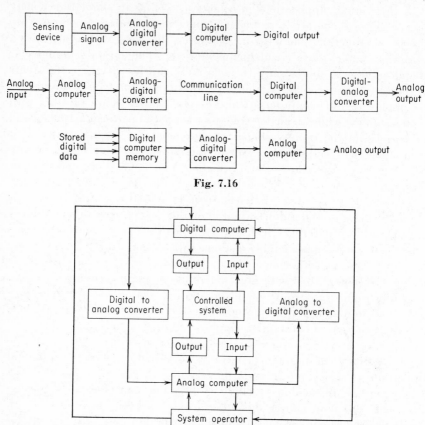

Fig. 7.16

Fig. 7.17 Block diagram of hybrid control system including human operator. (*From Leondes.*[2])

which require high-accuracy data processing, are handled by a digital computer, while the rapidly varying components are treated by an analog computer. This permits real-time operation of the over-all system. Additional analog-to-digital and digital-to-analog converters may be required to adapt the control system inputs and outputs to the computers.

In some complex control systems, the dynamic requirements in one part of the system may differ considerably from those in other parts of the system. Some of the information can be processed rather slowly

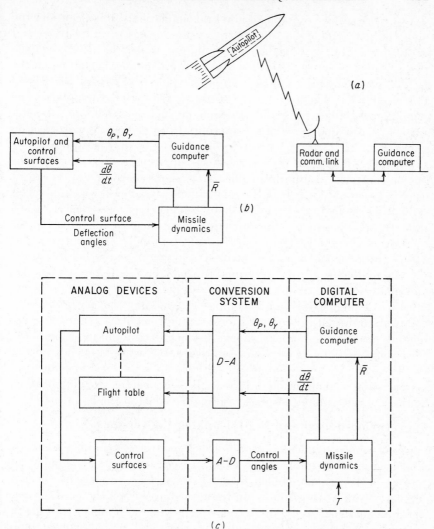

Fig. 7.18 Example of application of hybrid system. (*a*) Missile controlled by guidance computer via ground radar. (*b*) System diagram. (*c*) Combined analog-digital computer simulation. (*From Leger.*[7])

and can be handled successfully and efficiently by means of a digital computer. Control loops within the system, which may contain a human operator, may require much faster solution rates than are possible with digital equipment. The latter portion of the system may be constructed using analog computing techniques, and the digital and analog portions of the system interconnected by means of suitable conversion equipment.

As a more specific example of a hybrid simulation system, consider the simulation of a guided-missile control system as described by Leger and Greenstein.[7] The system, as shown in Fig. 7.18a, includes a missile whose flight trajectory is to be controlled, a radar tracking station on the ground, and a digital guidance computer. The radar tracks the missile and reports the position of the missile to the digital computer. The computer determines whether the missile has departed from its prescribed course and determines appropriate pitch and yaw correction signals θ_p and θ_y. These correction signals are transmitted to the missile autopilot. The autopilot in turn effects appropriate deflections of the missile controls. As shown in Fig. 7.18b, the system simulation can be broken down into three parts: (1) missile dynamics, which involves simulating the motion of the missile by solving equations of acceleration, velocity, and position; (2) guidance computation, which involves the solution of the guidance equation; and (3) autopilot and control. The actual autopilot and missile control system can be employed as part of the simulation to make "dry runs" during the over-all system design and analysis. The missile dynamics and guidance computer are simulated on a high-speed digital computer to permit the performance of complex mathematical computations with the required accuracy. The over-all simulation system is shown in block diagram form in Fig. 7.18c. Occasionally it may be necessary to process the higher-frequency portion of the missile dynamics in the analog computer in order to reduce the computation load on the digital computer. Numerous other applications of this hybridization concept have been described in the literature.[12]

7.6 Analog-digital and Digital-analog Conversion

Conversion equipment is required in a control system or a simulator whenever it is desirable or necessary to employ digital techniques to process or display data which occur in analog form either at the system inputs or within the system. In the preceding section the need for conversion equipment in hybrid systems employing both analog and digital computers has been pointed out. Another, and probably even more important, application of converters is to transform the analog signals generated by physical measuring instruments and associated transducers into digital signals which can be transmitted over communication links and which can be processed by digital computers. In order to permit the results of the digital computation to be employed to control the system, it is often necessary to reconvert the data to analog form.

Analog-digital converters are instruments which are designed to accept data, usually electrical voltages or mechanical shaft rotations, in analog form, to sample this data at periodic intervals, and to translate the magnitude of the analog function at the sampling times into a digital code, for example, binary, binary-decimal, etc. For this reason these devices

are frequently termed encoders or more simply coders.   Digital-analog
converters perform the reverse operation and accept data in binary or
other digitally coded form and furnish an electrical voltage or a mechanical shaft rotation which is proportional in magnitude to the input quantity.   Devices of this type are frequently termed decoders.   Excellent
summaries of coding and decoding techniques and equipment have been
presented by Susskind[8] and Bower.[9]   (The latter reference includes a
tabulation of over 50 commercially available encoders.)   Analog-digital
converters can be classified according to whether they accept electrical
voltages or mechanical displacements as the input variable.   Similarly,
some digital-analog computers provide an electrical output while others
provide a mechanical output signal.   The design principles of some of
the more widely used types of converters are briefly summarized below.

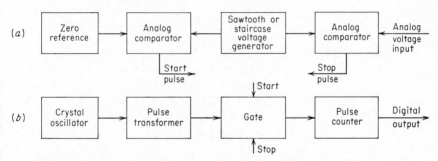

Fig. 7.19   Elements of time interval analog-digital converter.   (*a*) Voltage-to-time
interval transformer.   (*b*) Time interval measuring device.

    One important class of analog-digital converter accepts an analog
input in the form of a transient voltage, translates the input signal into
a series of time intervals whose lengths are proportional to the magnitude
of the applied voltage, and then measures the lengths of these time intervals.   Block diagrams of the circuit used to convert voltage into time
intervals and the circuit used to measure the lengths of this time interval
are shown in Fig. 7.19.   A block diagram of a complete system operating
on this principle is shown in Fig. 7.20.   The time interval is initiated
by a start pulse which also causes a saw-tooth voltage generator or a
staircase voltage generator to apply linearly increasing voltages to an
analog comparator.   The other input of this analog comparator is the
analog voltage to be converted.   The action of the comparator circuit
is such that it emits a pulse the instant that the voltage from the linear
voltage generator is equal in magnitude to the analog input voltage.
This output pulse acts to end the time interval.   Since the output of the
voltage generator is a linear function of time, the length of the time
interval is directly proportional to the magnitude of the input voltage.

A carefully calibrated master oscillator (generally a crystal oscillator) is employed to measure the length of the time interval. The output of this oscillator is passed through an electronic gate circuit and applied to a digital counter. The gate is opened by the start pulse and closed by the stop pulse from the analog comparator. The number of pulses which

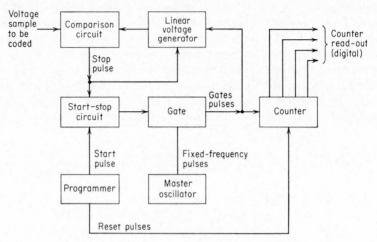

Fig. 7.20 Block diagram of complete analog-digital converter.

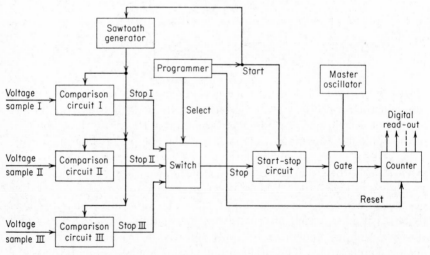

Fig. 7.21 Multiplexed-sawtooth-comparison circuit. (*From Susskind.*[8])

pass through the gate while open are therefore directly proportional to the time interval and hence to the magnitude of the analog input voltage. A digital counter is employed to accumulate incoming pulses and translate them into the desired digital code. A major advantage of this approach to analog-digital conversion is the ease with which it lends itself to multiplexing, i.e., the handling of several channels of signal inputs. A typical multiplex system, capable of handling simultaneously three channels of input information, is shown in Fig. 7.21. Notice that all major components of the converter, with the exception of the comparison circuit, are shared by all three channels, so that little additional equipment is required.

A second approach to analog-digital conversion is based upon the comparison of the input voltage in analog form with a voltage generated inside the converter. The internally generated voltage is adjusted by a control circuit until the two voltages are equal in magnitude. The magnitude of this internally generated voltage, which is adjusted in discrete steps, is then read out in digital form. A block diagram of a typical converter of this type is shown in Fig. 7.22. It can be seen that

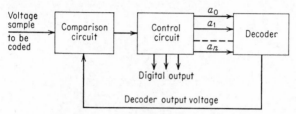

Fig. 7.22 Block diagram of comparison-type analog-digital converter.

a closed loop is formed through the comparator, the control circuit, and the analog-digital converter.

In another type of encoder, the analog voltage signal is made to control the frequency of an internally generated pulse train. These pulses pass through a gate which is open for a fixed time interval. The number of pulses passing through the gate are then proportional to the magnitude of the analog voltage.

A number of techniques are available for converting mechanical shaft rotations or linear displacements into digitally coded information. One large class of devices employs mechanical to electrical transducers to first translate the mechanical analog signal into an electrical signal. The electrical analog-digital converters described above can then be employed. In these devices the errors inherent in the transducer are added to the errors present in the conversion scheme. For high accuracies, this intermediate step is omitted, and the mechanical motion is subdivided into incremental mechanical signals. These increments either can be counted directly or can themselves be in the form of a digital code. Typical of the latter category is the binary coded disk shown in Fig. 7.23. A disk is divided into a large number of equal angular sectors, in accordance with the desired precision. Concentric annular rings are then fixed onto this wheel in such a way that certain areas in each ring are made opaque if an optical readout is intended or are made electrically conductive for electrical brush readout. The combination of opaque or conductive areas in each of the angular sectors of the disk corresponds to an angular position in binary or other digital codes.

The conversion of digital information into an analog signal is generally much simpler than the reverse operation. One frequently used technique is to store the digital number in a memory register. The content of this register memory then controls the application of electrical sources to a ladder network. The network is so arranged that the output voltage generated is directly proportional to the digital number to be converted. Decoding can also be accomplished by an intermediate conversion to a

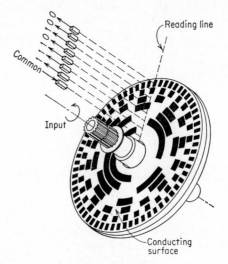

Fig. 7.23   Coded disk for converting analog shaft rotations into digital codes.

time interval. The digital number is first converted into a pulse-width modulated signal, that is, a time interval proportional to the digital number, and this time interval is then converted directly into proportional analog voltage. The output voltage can also be generated by applying a pulse train to a capacitor. If the number of pulses is proportional to the time interval (and hence to the digital input), the capacitor will integrate the pulse train to provide an output voltage proportional to the number of pulses.

REFERENCES

1. "Manual of Programming and Operation of the Litton Digital Differential Analyzer and Associated Equipment," Litton Industries, Beverly Hills, Calif., 1956.
2. Leondes, C. T.: Digital Techniques in Analog Computation, chap. 28 of "Handbook of Automatic Computation and Control," vol. 2, John Wiley & Sons, Inc., New York, 1959.

3. Gordon, B. M.: Adapting Digital Techniques for Automatic Control, *Elec. Mfg.*, vol. 54, part 2, pp. 136–143, 332, November, 1954.

4. Gordon, B. M., and J. F. La Fontaine: Operational Digital Technique, chap. 29 of "Handbook of Automatic Computation and Control," vol. 2, John Wiley & Sons, Inc., New York, 1959.

5. Hurney, P. A., Jr.: Combined Analog and Digital Techniques for the Solution of Differential Equations, *Proc. Western Joint Computer Conf.*, San Francisco, pp. 64–68, February, 1956.

6. Bekey, G. A.: Generalized Integration on the Analog Computer, paper presented at the National Simulation Conference, Dallas, October, 1958.

7. Leger, R. M., and J. L. Greenstein: Simulate Digitally or by Combining Analog and Digital Computing Facilities, *Control Eng.*, vol. 3, pp. 145–153, September, 1956.

8. Susskind, A. K.: "Notes on Analog-digital Conversion Techniques," The Technology Press, MIT, Cambridge, Mass., 1957.

9. Bower, G. C.: Analog-to-digital Converters, *Control Eng.*, vol. 4, no. 4, pp. 107–118, 1957.

10. Ruhman, S., and J. Mitchell: The TRICE, A High Speed Incremental Computer, *IRE Natl. Conv. Record*, part 4, pp. 206–216, 1958.

11. Wortzman, D.: Use of a Digital/Analog Arithmetic Unit within a Digital Computer, *Proc. Eastern Joint Computer Conf.*, New York, pp. 269–282, December, 1960.

12. "Proceedings of the Combined Analog Digital Computer Systems Symposium," Simulation Councils, Inc. and General Electric, Philadelphia, December, 1960.

8

System Error Analysis in Computation

CHARLES B. TOMPKINS

PROFESSOR OF MATHEMATICS AND DIRECTOR OF
NUMERICAL ANALYSIS RESEARCH
UNIVERSITY OF CALIFORNIA, LOS ANGELES

8.1 The Problem

The problems of control are largely problems of ordinary differential equations, difference equations, or difference-differential equations. This is true because control usually involves application of some force-like influence to some system with inertia to overcome some undesired deviation from an optimal position. If the system is a truly mechanical one, it is governed by Newton's laws of motion, and the problem is exactly a differential equation or a set of differential equations with initial conditions. If there is a lag between measurement of the deviation and the application of force, the problem may involve both differences and derivatives, but it is still likely to be an initial-value problem, as these problems are defined below. If the analogy is stretched so that, say, some inventory replaces mass in a mechanical system, and the corrective process is the decision to replenish stock or to move material, the system may vary from a purely differential-equation system to a purely difference-equation system depending on the problem studied, but the essential feature of a system solvable from initial conditions remains.

The discussion here will be limited to a discussion of solutions of systems of ordinary differential equations in an independent variable which will always be treated as time (although this is not essential). Specifically, let t be this independent variable and $x:(x_1, \ldots, x_n)$ be a finite set of dependent variables. Here all these variables will be considered to be real numbers. The type of problem which will be considered is to find (at least approximately) functions x depending on t such that

$$x' = f(x,t) \qquad x(0) = \alpha \qquad (8.1)$$

where x' denotes the derivative of x with respect to t. The system (8.1) is to be considered as a set of n differential equations and n initial

168

conditions.   There are n functions f given in advance, and there are n initial values α given in advance.   Each of the functions f involves (potentially) all the numbers x as arguments.   In all this, indexes which might be common elsewhere running from 1 through n are suppressed as being inessential and cumbersome.

It is essential to note that (8.1) represents a *differential-equation problem*, not just a set of differential equations for which some general solution is sought.   This distinction will always be made, and it lies in the inclusion of the initial conditions in setting the problem.   The attempt is to set the problem so that if the problem itself is completely specified (so that no undetermined parameters appear in the specification), then the solution will be completely specified without requirement of determining any further parameters.   Control problems are usually problems set in this fashion, this type of setting is frequently essential to productive computational attack, and it is most convenient for purposes of mathematical discussion.   An approximate statement of the most useful theorem governing problems of this type will be given here; an accurate statement of one such theorem may be found in almost any textbook on differential equations or in the book by G. A. Bliss.[1]

Theorem.   For sufficiently smooth functions $f(x,t)$ there is exactly one solution to problem (8.1).   This solution depends as smoothly as is plausible on the initial values α and on any parameters different from x and t occurring in the definition of the functions f.

The essential part of the discussion here will be a study of how solution of problems (differential-equation problems, difference-equation problems, or mixed problems) may respond to slight variations in f or in α under an assumption of a theorem similar to that above concerning the uniqueness of solutions and their general behavior as functions of the parameters defining the problem.   To this end, it will be necessary to look in more detail at the smoothness of the dependence of the solution on these parameters.   In the accurate statements of the theorem, this smoothness is stated in terms of the number of times the solution can be differentiated with respect to the parameter under consideration.   However, examples to be solved in the next section indicate that this is not a sufficiently accurate measure for system-error analysis.

The analysis here can be extended by analogy to systems which are analogous to differential-equation problems.   It should also be noted that the form of (8.1) involving several equations of first order does not exclude consideration of equations of higher order.   Indeed, if a system of equations is such that the system can be solved for the derivative of highest order of each dependent variable, and if initial values are given for each of the variables and each of the derivatives except those of highest order, then an equivalent problem of the type of (8.1) can be written.   The systematic method of doing this will be clear from an example with a single dependent variable.   Consider the problem

$$u''' - tu'' - (1 - t^2)u' - u^2 \quad \cos 3t = 0$$
$$u(0) = 1 \qquad u'(0) = 5 \qquad u''(0) = 4$$

Now formally replace u by x_1, u' by x_2 (so that $x_2 = x_1'$, etc.), and u'' by x_3.   The problem becomes

$$x_1' = x_2 \qquad x_2' = x_3 \qquad x_3' = tx_3 + (1 - t^2)x_2 + x_1{}^2 \cos 3t$$
$$x_1(0) = 1 \qquad x_2(0) = 5 \qquad x_3(0) = 4$$

This is clearly of the form of Eq. (8.1).

It should also be noted that the uniqueness theorem above is almost certainly valid for any problem arising naturally from a physical system, but it may not be valid for most reasonable-looking problems set up artificially.   If the problem is set in a single variable x so that $x' = x^{2/3}$ with $x(0) = 0$, two solutions are seen immediately: these are $x = 0$ and $x = t^3/27$.   (That each of these solves the problem may be determined by substitution into the problem.)   The failure of the conclusion of the theorem here may be laid to the lack of smoothness of the function $x^{2/3}$ at the initial value $x = 0$; it has no finite derivative at this point, and this behavior is sufficient to violate the usually imposed smoothness conditions in the hypothesis of the theorem.

Control systems may lead to problems which depart from the ideal indicated in the problem of Eq. (8.1).   While it is likely that (under current assumptions of physics and mechanics) the problem can be stated in this form, the initial values may have been measured and hence be subject to inaccuracy, the restoring forces may be generated mechanically and hence also subject to some inaccuracy, the functions f may not be precisely known for other reasons, and finally errors may be introduced by machinery used in an attempt to solve the problem numerically. The nature of the machine errors introduced in computation need not be discussed here in any detail, for they and their occurrence are discussed elsewhere for both digital and analog machines, but it should be emphasized that they are not mistakes in setting the problem up but natural inaccuracies stemming from the limited precision of machines and (for digital machines) from the impossibility of carrying out limiting processes on the machine.

The view to be taken here is that the problem actually solved by the machine is a problem only approximating (8.1).   It will be assumed that the solution has been carried out, and a backward look at the solution and the errors it may contain will be attempted.   If this point of view is taken, it may be stated that some deviation existed at each time, and independently of the cause or the mechanics of this deviation it could have been written as a function of time by an omniscient and perfectly precise observer. Thus, even though a solution of the problem of Eq. (8.1) is desired, what is obtained is a solution of another problem which may be stated

$$x' = f(x,t) + r$$
$$x(0) = \alpha + \rho$$

(8.2)

where the functions r are error functions, probably random in nature and mechanically influenced by various variables possibly including t, x, and various parameters; the numbers ρ are also random errors. However, for purposes of the study here, the hindsight point of view will be used, and the functions r will be treated as functions of time t.

The problem to be attacked is the estimation of the error resulting in the solution of the whole system by virtue of the introduction of the functions r and the errors ρ. This system error is not necessarily determined simply by the nature of the local error introduced; in particular, there is no safe over-all estimate of the system error introduced by a computing error of, say, 1 part in 1,000 without taking into account in a careful way the nature of the problem to be solved—in particular, its stability. The problem is made more difficult by the fact that any assumption of independence between values of one or more error functions may be unjustified, either because round-off of neighboring numbers may be similarly biased on a digital machine or because departures from ideal behavior are likely to persist on an analog machine.

8.2 Some Examples

Three simple examples will be solved here to serve as illustrations for some of the statements to follow. In each case the solution is well known; however, the solution will be given in detail for reasons of illustration and in order to minimize the requirements for further reference by the reader.

The first example to be treated will be the differential-equation problem

$$x' = -x + r \qquad x(0) = \alpha + \rho \tag{8.3}$$

The second will be the problem

$$x'' = x + r \qquad x(0) = \alpha + \rho_1 \qquad x'(0) = -\alpha + \rho_2 \tag{8.4}$$

The third will be the problem

$$x'' = -x + r \qquad x(0) = \alpha_1 + \rho_1 \qquad x'(0) = \alpha_2 + \rho_2 \tag{8.5}$$

Each of these last two should be written in an equivalent form involving variables x_1 and x_2 and their first derivatives in order to be perfectly consistent with the notation used throughout this chapter, but the more familiar form above will be retained in the discussion here. Furthermore, the point of view leading to Eqs. (8.2) above will be maintained: the error variables r and the error numbers ρ are unwanted, so that the solutions sought are those for which these variables and numbers are all zero. Under these conditions it should be noted that the solution to (8.3) and the solution to (8.4) are identical, $x = \alpha e^{-t}$; it will become apparent, however, that the presence of the error terms may lead to wide departures from this solution.   (Indeed, with the error terms set equal to zero, one can obtain (8.4) by differentiating (8.3) with respect to t and by combining the resulting equation with the original and its initial condition in an obvious way to eliminate x' and to furnish an initial condition for x'.) In this sense the two problems are equivalent.

We can find solutions of these problems by invoking the superposition principle, which is true (and easily verified) by virtue of the linear nature of the equations involved.   This principle is not valid for nonlinear problems of the type likely to occur in control problems.   Hence it is essential to note that the processes to be used here are not generally applicable in detail.

The superposition principle may be stated as follows:

Theorem. Let $x = u$ and $x = v$ respectively solve problems of the type of (8.1) where the functions $f(x,t)$ are of the type $ax + c$ and $ax + d$ respectively, where a, c, and d are all functions of t to sets of n numbers. Then $x = u + v$ solves a system of the type of (8.1) whose initial value is the sum of the initial values of the problems solved by u and v and whose right member is $ax + c + d$.

It should be noted that this theorem is readily extended (by mathematical induction) to any finite number of similarly related problems and that under reasonable conditions of convergence, it can be extended to infinite sets of problems.   An infinite extension will be used below without explicit proof of the convergence.

The fact that it is easy to write a solution for any of the problems above with zero initial conditions and with r constant over some (short) interval and zero elsewhere may be exploited to provide a general solution to each problem.   In particular, consider the problems with the assumption that in the interval $(0,s)$ (that is, for $0 < t < s$) $r = 0$, in the interval $(s, s + h)$ $r = b$, where b is a constant, in the interval $(s + h, \infty)$ $r = 0$; furthermore, consider the initial conditions to be zero in each case.   The solution in this case is an elementary problem in undergraduate differential equations.   Under these conditions, the solution for each problem is $x = 0$ in the interval $(0,s)$.   In the interval $(s, s + h)$ the solutions are as follows:

For (8.3) $x = b[1 - e^{-(t-s)}]$
For (8.4) $x = b[\cosh (t - s) - 1]$
For (8.5) $x = b[1 - \cos (t - s)]$

(These solutions are obtained in a most elementary way.   One way is by assuming the solution is a linear combination of quantities which might plausibly be involved—a constant and e^{-t} for (8.3), a constant, sinh t and cosh t for (8.4), and a constant, sin t and cos t for (8.5), for example—and then evaluating the coefficients by forcing the assumed functions to satisfy the equations and initial conditions. Various schemes, equivalent to this in the present cases, are presented in elementary texts for the solution of these equations with the given initial conditions.)

The form of the solutions of the problems in the interval $(s + h, \infty)$ is easily written from the superposition principle if it is noticed that the form in the interval $(s, s + h)$ is independent of h. The solution above, then, is correct on the interval (s, ∞) if h is taken to be infinite (or, more properly, if r is set equal to b on the whole interval $t > s$). If a similar solution with $r = -b$ on the interval $t > s + h$ is added to the above solution, the superposition principle states that the sum is the required solution to the stated problem. This gives for the interval $(s + h, \infty)$:

For (8.3) $\qquad x = b[e^{-(t-s-h)} - e^{-(t-s)}]$

For (8.4) $\qquad x = b[\cosh (t - s) - \cosh (t - s - h)]$

For (8.5) $\qquad x = b[\cos (t - s - h) - \cos (t - s)]$

The solution of the problems with zero initial conditions and with arbitrary functions r is now obtained by approximating r by piecewise constant functions and passing to the limit. For this, the interval of definition of the function r is subdivided, r is replaced by a number b constant in each interval and approximating r in that interval, and the limit is taken just as in a Riemann (definite) integral as the length of the intervals in the division goes to zero. In carrying out this process the formulas immediately above are used, where h is the length of one of the intervals of the division of the argument of r, and b is the approximating value. The solutions for all intervals of the division are added in accordance with the superposition principle.

If it is noticed that the quantities in brackets in the expressions immediately above are differences of simple functions (the negative exponential, the hyperbolic cosine, and the cosine, respectively) for arguments differing by h, and if for small h the difference of the functions is approximated by the differential, then the following expressions result:

For (8.3) $\qquad bhe^{-(t-s)}$

For (8.4) $\qquad bh \sinh (t - s)$

For (8.5) $\qquad bh \sin (t - s)$

The limiting process gives for the solutions with zero initial value:

For (8.3) $\qquad x = \int_0^t r(s) e^{-(t-s)} \, ds$

For (8.4) $\qquad x = \int_0^t r(s) \sinh (t - s) \, ds$

For (8.5) $\qquad x = \int_0^t r(s) \sin (t - s) \, ds$

Finally the solutions to the problems with the initial values shown are obtained by adding to the above solutions the classical solutions with $r = 0$ and the stated initial values.   This gives

For (8.3)

$$x = (\alpha + \rho)e^{-t} + \int_0^t r(s)e^{-(t-s)} \, ds \tag{8.6}$$

For (8.4)

$$x = (\alpha + \rho_1) \cosh t + (-\alpha + \rho_2) \sinh t + \int_0^t n(s) \sinh (t - s) \, ds \tag{8.7}$$

For (8.5)

$$x = (\alpha_1 + \rho_1) \cos t + (\alpha_2 + \rho_2) \sin t + \int_0^t r(s) \sin (t - s) \, ds \tag{8.8}$$

It should be noted in (8.7) that $\alpha \cosh t - \alpha \sinh t = \alpha e^{-t}$, so that the solutions of (8.6) and (8.7) do agree except for quantities introduced by the random error functions and the errors in the initial conditions.   However, the errors which are introduced to the solutions in the two cases are radically different.   The purpose of introducing these solutions here was to compare the nature of these errors.   This comparison depends on some of the properties of the functions appearing in the expressions above.   In particular (for fixed s) $e^{-(t-s)}$ approaches 0 as t grows; on the other hand $\sinh (t - s)$ grows without limit as t grows, and for large t it is very nearly equal to $\tfrac{1}{2}e^{(t-s)}$; finally, $\sin (t - s)$ oscillates between extreme values of 1 and -1 as t grows, neither approaching zero nor growing without limit.

It is also important to note several other things about this method of constructing a solution (although the method is not of primary relevance here).   The method is an analytic analog to one of the simplest methods of numerical solution of differential equations (Euler's method), in which the contribution of a constant forcing function over a short period is estimated, somewhat less precisely than was done above.   Secondly, it should be noted that no more than a claim of plausibility of the correctness of the method need be made, for once the answer above is written, it can be checked by direct substitution into the differential equation problem and verified.   Most important for the purposes here, however, is the fact that this method permits a detailed study of the introduction of error to the solution of a differential-equation problem and a study of the effects of errors introduced earlier in the solution process.   In the long run, an estimate of this type is essential to the analysis of the stability of a method of solution to a problem.   The study is usually not as straightforward as that outlined above, for we usually have neither the superposition principle to rely on nor the elementary solutions of the simplified equations.

The most instructive illustrative study which is evident in the above examples is the nature of the survival of error at times later than the time of introduction of the error.

The nature of survival of initial value error is easily evident in the formulas. In (8.6) that portion of the solution which does not depend on the random function r is modified in the simplest and least harmful plausible way by the initial value error; so far as this part of the solution is concerned, if the computing device was unable to distinguish between α and $\alpha + \rho$, then it is not likely to be able to distinguish between these two quantities each multiplied by the same factor e^{-t}, which is less than 1. Hence it is not reasonable to complain about the extent to which the initial error is able to survive. A somewhat similar argument can be applied in the case of (8.8), although the initial error is not attenuated as it is in (8.6); however, in this case the initial errors survive as factors of sine and cosine functions which never exceed 1 in value, and hence the initial errors are never magnified at later times. On the other hand, for (8.7), the initial errors are multiplied by hyperbolic sine and hyperbolic cosine functions, and these functions both behave like $\frac{1}{2}e^t$ for large t. Hence unless an improbable fortuitous cancellation of initial errors occurs, these initial errors will be magnified without limit as t increases, and they will dominate the portion of the solution which does not depend on r.

Thus the seriousness of initial error in the solution of this particular differential equation problem is incomparably greater than it is in the other two problems. This difference in survival or growth potential of the initial error is one of the characteristics which led to the statements in the last paragraph of Sec. 8.1 warning against blind assumptions that errors of, say, 1 part in 1,000 would always retain approximately the same relative size. In the first example above, for example, the initial error decreases absolutely but retains its same relative size when compared with the correct solution; in the second example the error grows absolutely and relatively; in the third example the solution retains its absolute size and its size relative to the correct solution on the average.

A similar comparison of the errors introduced by the random functions r leads to essentially similar conclusions. In the first case the influence of the error function introduced at time s is attenuated at a later time t by a factor $e^{-(t-s)}$. Thus the effect of the function r at any time is transitory. Again the opposite effect is observed in the second example: the effect of the error function introduced at time s is magnified at a later time t by the factor sinh $(t - s)$, which grows without limit as t increases. In the third example the effect of the error function introduced at time s is magnified at a later time t by the factor sin $(t - s)$, whose value oscillates between 1 and -1. However, in this case, because of the well-known resonance phenomenon which can occur with this differential equation, the error due to the function r may build up without bound;

in particular this will happen if the function r has a correlation with $\sin t$ which is bounded away from 0.

The stability phenomena illustrated above do not depend on the order of the differential equation of the problem, but rather on its nature as dissipative or not (as will be described below). Nor is it always convenient to avoid higher-order equations; in some cases they are required, and in some cases they are easier than the lower-order equations to solve. As shown above, it is possible to change a stable problem into one which is analytically equivalent so far as the precise value of the solution is concerned but into one which is unstable with respect to errors introduced. Thus in formulating a computational attack on a problem which is known to be stable in itself, a careless analyst may introduce a new problem which seems to be equivalent to the old but which is actually unstable. Such a change should usually be avoided; it should certainly be recognized as dangerous.

A final remark here might clarify the statement above that the order of a differential equation might be raised as a matter of convenience. One example might be the differential equation of the Weierstrass elliptic function ρ. A solution of the equation

$$(x')^2 = 4x^3 - g_2 x - g_3$$

with a singularity behaving like t^{-2} neighboring $t = 0$ is $x = \rho(t)$. If this equation is differentiated and a common factor x' removed, there results a second-order equation whose solution does not require extraction of square roots:

$$x'' = 12x^2 - g_2$$

(Here both quantities g_2 and g_3 are constants.) The initial conditions may be augmented to make the solution of the second problem equal to that of the first, and in some cases this solution is easier to produce computationally.

A more frequently encountered example is concerned with the use of difference methods in the solution of differential equations. Here some extrapolation scheme is used to estimate the solution, and in order to permit longer steps in the extrapolation use of higher differences in the extrapolation is usual. In devising such a scheme, the worker must be careful not to introduce instability. This question is treated in many textbooks on ordinary differential equations and their numerical solution. For the purposes of the present exposition it need only be remarked that in some cases the introduction of higher differences is equivalent to the simple Euler solution of a higher-order problem with the same solution as the stated problem; in other words, it is somewhat analogous to introducing the second-order equation in the first example above or in the example relating to Weierstrass's elliptic function and then solving by the simplest methods.

In summary, a problem was stated in the first section and illustrated in this section. The problem of error analysis which is pertinent to any computation is not that of estimating the error term introduced at any time to the equation considered but rather the total effect of possible errors on the whole system studied. This effect may be large or small depending on subtle magnifications or attenuations of errors introduced in the past. The problem of system error analysis is the problem of estimating reliable bounds for this error.

8.3 Cumulative and Noncumulative Generation of Error

The solutions (8.6), (8.7), and (8.8) above will here be used to illustrate a type of error analysis which seems originally to have been due to Liapunov. A very short exposition of this theory by Richard Bellman may be found in Beckenbach[2] and a more detailed presentation in Bellman.[3] Additional material is available in Lefschetz[4] and in Liapunov's own publication.[5] No complete exposition is planned here, for the details of the theory seem to the author to require careful study more space-consuming than is feasible in this chapter.

The essence of Liapunov's approach lies in the discovery of an energy-like mathematical function which is dissipated in the system being solved as time increases. This energylike function must faithfully measure the departure of a neighboring solution from a central chosen solution— say the desired correct solution.

The solution (8.6) departs from the desired solution of the stated problem through the presence of the constant ρ and the function r. The difference between this solution and the desired solution αe^{-t} in absolute value satisfies the following relations:

$$
\begin{aligned}
|x - \alpha e^{-t}| &= \left| \rho e^{-t} + \int_0^t r(s) e^{-(t-s)} \, ds \right| \\
&\leq |\rho| + \max |r(s)|
\end{aligned} \tag{8.9}
$$

The right member of (8.9) can be made to be as close to zero as is desired by forcing the number ρ and the function r both to be small in absolute value. Thus, the error in this problem can be made to be arbitrarily small by making the error-generating elements sufficiently small.

No similar argument can be made for the other illustrative problems treated above.

In most cases of real interest a somewhat more involved reasoning is necessary. Generally the process is one of constructing a family of neighborhoods around the desired solution (that is, of proving that there exists such a family around any possible solution of the problem).

The neighborhoods in the family must include some which remain arbitrarily close to the desired solution and have the additional property that limits other than zero can be placed on the absolute value of the error-generating elements so that the error-infested solution will remain in any chosen one of these neighborhoods.

This can be done for the problems illustrated in the section above for bounded time periods or for the one stable problem illustrated there independent of the time span.

The crucial difference is the accumulation of displacement, and the establishment of a system error estimate depends on a control of this accumulation.

In many practical engineering problems the boundaries of the neighborhoods are likely to be chosen as at least approximate contour surfaces of an energy function. If analysis of the type of the Liapunov analysis is quickly possible, it is likely to be through a study of the cumulative effect of the energy introduced by the random error-producing elements. Experts with this method seem most adept at coming forward with suitable functions to show stability.

8.4 Statistical Survival Theory of Errors

A rational descriptive theory of system errors, but not usually a constructively productive one at its present state of development, is attained through the use of a model which imitates birth-death and immigration-emigration processes. In such a model the error existing at any particular time during the solution process or at any particular stage of this process is considered to be a population. This population is subject to changes in size which can be predicted (usually) only probabilistically. This population is subject to birth and death processes in that the existing error may tend to die out (because of the stability of the problem attacked) or may tend to increase (because of lack of stability of the problem), and it is subject to immigration and emigration processes in that the population of error may be increased or decreased by inaccuracies introduced in the calculation (round-off errors, truncation errors, and other errors of the machine, the precision of its numbers or its demand that analytic processes be imitated by finite processes).

A considerable literature on such matters has been built up and is continuing to appear, although scant success has accrued up to date in applications to system error analysis. In fact, the main success lies in the development of a clear language to use in setting forth the principal problem encountered.

More specifically suppose that the error in the solution at a time stage t is known (or assumed) to be (the n numbers) E_t. Based on this we assume that the probability of a particular set of errors E_{t+h} at a given time shortly later, $t + h$, is known. This probability estimate is based on an estimate of the rate at which the assumed error increases or decreases (the birth and death rate of the error population) and on an estimate of the rate with which new error is introduced to the solution. Since any assumption concerning the error present may be used with the solution obtained at that time to give an assumption of the correct answer, this estimate may become difficult to make by virtue of an embarrassing richness of information. This is one of the difficulties involved in applying this stochastic survival technique.

In general some simplifying assumptions are likely to be made, although in principle these are not necessary. In particular, these assumptions are likely to be that the probability of a given change in error is proportional to the length of the time step (plus a number which is small when compared with this major probability if the time step is small), although the probability of a particular change may vary both with the error assumed to exist at the beginning of the time period under study and (almost certainly) with the size of the error change for which the probability is being estimated.

If it is now assumed that the error is not known at the beginning of the time period but that the probability of each plausible error is known, this same process can be used to estimate the probability of any plausible later error. In particular, the probability of any particular set of errors at time $t + h$ is calculated by multiplying the probability of each plausible set of errors at time t by the probability that this set of errors at time t will be transported into the particular errors whose probability is to be estimated at time $t + h$, summing the results.

If such an analysis is actually carried out, there results a set of equations of the general type of difference or differential equations with initial conditions. The dependent variables are the probabilities of various sets of errors and the independent variable is time. If the original differential or difference equations had n dependent variables and if the errors are assumed to be capable of continuous variation, the error-analysis equations would have a family of dependent variables depending on n continuous parameters (the plausible errors) and on time. They would take the general form

$$\frac{\partial}{\partial t}[P(E,t)] = F[P(E,t)]$$

in the most favorable case, and initial values would come from estimates of the probabilities of plausible initial errors. In less favorable cases, the estimate of the probabilities $P(E, t + h)$ would depend on more complicated calculations than that indicated above, but it would still be referred to the probabilities $P(E,t)$. In all cases above the symbol $P(E,t)$ refers to the probability that the set of errors at time t is the n numbers E. The right member of the equation above is some function of $P(E,t)$; in many cases it may be chosen to be a linear function, but it is likely to involve partial derivatives with respect to the various components of E. Thus the equation, while simple in form and in genesis, is likely to be about as hard to solve as a multidimensional heat equation. This discouraging difficulty is inherent in the problem, however, and easier computational attacks must accept a loss in information gained when compared with the total available information which would be gained by complete solution of the equations of stochastic survival of the error population.

In particular, the method of Liapunov, outlined above, simply gives bounds on the maximum error which can be realized. Other methods outlined below also give such bounds or (in a few cases) lead to estimates of the probable error without yielding information concerning the expected probabilistic dispersion of this error around its most probable value. Additional estimates of this probable error could presumably be obtained by standard processes used in stochastic survival theory, but this has not been done systematically. These processes attempt to provide a simple approximate differential equation for the expected population, based on an approximately correct averaging process. This process has been successful in dealing with many attrition processes, particularly in military analyses, but it has not been applied to system error analysis.

8.5 Perturbation Theory and Error Analysis

In this section and the next, two methods which have been directed toward the analysis of errors will be outlined briefly. Both these methods have the strong advantage that they may take into account the approximate solution obtained in the calculation and attempt to estimate how far the correct solution may lie from this approximate solution. In general this is hard to do by using other methods of error analysis, and they usually provide error estimates which are independent of the results of the computation being checked. Thus, these two methods are potentially more sensitive than purely a priori methods.

A perturbation method initially described by K. S. Miller and F. J. Murray[6] has been developed and widely applied with considerable success. The method was designed for use with differential analyzers, and its main applications have been in connection with differential analyzers, but it is also applicable to other calculators.

This perturbation method assumes that the functions $f(x,t)$ in Eqs. (8.1) above are analytic in the variable x. This is a stronger assumption than has been made heretofore in this chapter, and it is necessary for assurance of validity of expansions into power series, on which the method is based. The power series are developed in terms of the parameters upon which it is assumed the errors are based. In the view to be taken in this approach, these errors arise from three different general sources. The first of these is the introduction of higher derivatives than the first into Eqs. (8.1); these higher derivatives might be introduced by inertia in the components of a differential analyzer, for example. A second source of error arises in imprecision in computing the functions $f(x,t)$ of Eqs. (8.1); the assumption to be made is that the machine actually computes some different functions $g(x,t)$ differing slightly from $f(x,t)$ because of imperfections in the computing device. Finally it is assumed that additional errors are introduced in the form of small displacements of the dependent variables x during the course of the calculation; these displacements could be caused by mechanical or electrical disturbances affecting the computing instrument, for example.

Each source of error is parametrized. It is assumed that the true problem is represented by zero values of these parameters, that the actual case is represented by small values of these parameters, and that a solution of a system of increased complexity which includes the computational solution obtained in terms of a power-series expansion in these parameters is theoretically possible (that is, that the power series converges for values of the parameters representing the computational situation actually existing).

Under these assumptions and a realistic but complicated set of additional assumptions, the analysis of the stability of the problem is made to depend on the analysis of a system of linear equations; in some favorable cases the analysis of the linear system can be based on an assumption that coefficients are piecewise constant. In the long run the quantity which is sought and which dominates the stability of the problem is the sign of the exponent in exponential terms occurring in the solution of the linear system. As usual, if the exponent has a negative real part, the problem is stable, and if it has a positive real part, the problem is unstable.

The outline as presented above indicates that the most frequent application of this theory is to find information about the stability of a problem, and this is correct. However, as was indicated in introducing this section, some estimate of the size of the error is possible in some favorable cases by an extension of the perturbation technique to its ultimate limit. The theoretical difficulties of perturbation methods for the solution of differential equations are far from negligible (see, for example, Coddington and Levinson[7]), but these methods have furnished at least plausible solutions in many cases of practical physical or engineering importance when other methods seemed inapplicable. In the present application the requirement would be for an estimate of the maximum absolute value which could be attained by a power series around the solution found by the computer; the variables in the series would be the error parameters, and they would be limited in size by the operator's estimates of the maximum errors of various types which could be introduced to the solution.

Finally it should be pointed out that a sizable literature concerning this type of error analysis has grown up since the work cited above. Much is prepared for use in particular computing establishments. In many cases the stability of particular problems has been analyzed. To a considerable extent this literature is highly specialized, only a little is formally published, and largely it is obtainable from the computing laboratories in which it has been prepared.

8.6   The Schauder-Leray Index

The Schauder-Leray index theory was introduced many years ago and applied to prove the existence of solutions to some of the most complicated elliptic partial differential equations problems which have been successfully attacked. The theory has not yet been widely applied to studies of system errors, but a potential is there. To the extent that the theory could be applied to error analysis it would have attractive features of seeming independence from analyticity restrictions imposed on the functions $f(x,t)$ in the perturbation analysis and of provision of machinery to use the computational solution obtained for the problem in the estimation of the error. Again, this last provision should be given serious consideration, for ultimately one should be able to form a more accurate estimate of error after a computational solution has been obtained than he could based on purely a priori estimates which necessarily use less knowledge.

The basic idea of the index method is simple, and trouble arises only because it must be applied in a space of infinitely many dimensions when dealing with differential equations. (However, it should be noted that the space involved may be one of a finite number of dimensions for difference equations.) The idea will first be illustrated here for a space of two dimensions, where its most significant features are easily perceived.

For purposes of this illustration, consider a problem of finding a complex valued root of a polynomial

$$P(z) = z^n + a_{n-1}z^{n-1} + \cdots + a_1z + a_0$$

Suppose also that the constant term a_0 differs from 0; otherwise, of course, there is an obvious root at $z = 0$. The method depends on an examination of the value attained by $P(z)$ at the points of closed curves in the complex plane of $z = x + iy$, where i is a square root of -1. On a small enough circle surrounding the point $z = 0$, the term a_0 dominates all other terms of the polynomial, and therefore on this small circle the polynomial maintains a value which is almost constant and almost equal to a_0. On the other hand, for a huge circle with center at the origin the term z^n equally dominates the other terms and the value of the polynomial on such a circle is z^n plus some other term which is small when compared with the value of z^n.   As z traverses a circle with center at the origin, z^n attains complex values lying on a circle (in the complex plane) with center at the origin and with radius equal to the nth power of the radius of the z circle.   Furthermore, as z traverses its circle, z^n goes around its circle of values n times, and this is the phenomenon upon which the index method is based.

Specifically, for the small circle $P(z)$ maintains an almost constant value, and if this is plotted as a vector from the origin to the value taken in the complex plane, this vector moves only slightly and certainly does not turn through a complete rotation as z traverses its circle.   On the other hand a similar vector plotted as z traverses its large circle turns through n complete rotations.   These vectors vary continuously as functions of z and hence as functions of the circles on which they are determined.   As the small circle grows, the turning number must change from zero (initially) to n (for a very large circle), and such a change for a continuously varying vector can happen only if the length of the vector becomes 0.   Thus there is assuredly at least one point between the small circle and the large circle at which $P(z)$ takes the value 0.   This illustration actually furnishes one of the standard proofs of the fundamental theorem of algebra—that every polynomial has at least one root in the complex plane.

More to the point here, however, is the observation that if the image vector $P(z)$ makes one or more complete (net) rotations as z traverses any simple closed curve in its complex plane, there must be a root of $P(z)$ inside this curve.   If one has found a root by some computational means, he may assure himself concerning the accuracy of his computation by proving that the turning number of the image vector on a small circle surrounding this root differs from 0.   This might be a useful procedure if the root has been determined so closely that the values attained by the polynomial lie below the precision of the machine; if the circle around the approximate root is chosen to be just large enough to give values to $P(z)$ which are reliably within the precision of the computer, and if the turning number on this circle can be shown to differ from zero, the desired error analysis for this simple problem will have been accomplished.

While the geometry is not quite as clear in more dimensions, a similar argument holds for spaces of finitely many dimensions.   As an illustration consider a difference-equation problem approximating the differential-equation problem of Eq. (8.1).   Suppose for purposes of this illustration that there is a single dependent variable x and that the difference equation is to be solved for N different values of t, say $t_1, t_2, \ldots , t_N$.   The computed solution at each of these values has an error (which may be 0), and the set of these errors is a set of N real numbers; these numbers may be considered to be components of a vector in Euclidean space of N dimensions. Presumably the solution is so good that the values of these numbers are not computable on the device being used for the computation. The solution itself is also a set of N real numbers (the N values of x taken in order), and it may be considered to be represented by a point in the same N-dimensional Euclidean space with the same coordinates used for the error vector.

Now consider a hypersphere in this Euclidean space around the point representing the computed solution. If this sphere is large enough in radius, the error vector corresponding to any of its points will be computable on the machine used; that is, the machine could test any point on the surface of this hypersphere and show that this point is not a solution of the problem being attacked by demonstrating a set of N numbers, sufficiently large to be meaningful in the machine, which are residuals left when the difference equation is tested at each of the N points.   (If, for example, the first difference at some point t_k should be 1.00000 to satisfy the equation for the value of t taken and the value of x assumed and represented by the point in the Euclidean space, and if this value when computed is 0.99990, then the residual at this value of t and for this assumed solution is 0.00010.)

Thus there is generated a vector in N space corresponding to every point on the small hypersphere surrounding the computed solution.   If this error vector sweeps out a nonzero number of complete solid angles in N space as the point on which it depends traverses its hypersphere, then there must be some point within this small hypersphere at which the error vector is 0; that is, there must be a solution of the difference equation inside the small hypersphere.   If this could be shown, the error analysis for the difference-equation problem would be complete.

There are two apparent major difficulties in applying this type of analysis.   The first is the difficulty of calculating the index of the error vector, and the second is the theoretical difficulty of extending the arguments above to a space of infinitely many dimensions—which must be done when continuous rather than discrete problems are analyzed. Some progress has been made in each direction.

J. Schauder did succeed in extending these arguments to spaces of infinitely many dimensions, and with J. Leray he was able to handle problems of considerable complexity in these spaces.   However, much remains to be done.   The chief difficulty lies in the fact that the surface of the hypersphere considered above has dimensionality 1 less than the dimensionality of the Euclidean space in which it lies; the generation of an "($\infty - 1$)-dimensional" hypersphere requires a little care.

The other problem, that of computation of the index, must also be treated with much ingenuity, for the index computation for any space of many dimensions by trying to evaluate the error vector explicitly at a suitably dense set of points would be forbiddingly extensive. However, analytic attacks on some classes of problems might plausibly be made.

REFERENCES

1. Bliss, G. A.: "Lectures on the Calculus of Variations," Appendix, University of Chicago Press, Chicago, 1946.
2. Beckenbach, Edwin F., (ed.): "Modern Mathematics for the Engineer," McGraw-Hill Book Company, Inc., New York, 1956.
3. Bellman, Richard: "Stability Theory of Differential Equations," McGraw-Hill Book Company, Inc., New York, 1953.
4. Lefschetz, S.: "Differential Equations: Geometric Theory," Interscience Publishers, Inc., New York, 1957.
5. Liapunov, A. M.: "Problème général de la stabilité de mouvement," Princeton University Press, Princeton, N.J., 1947.
6. Miller, K. S., and F. J. Murray: A Mathematical Basis for an Error Analysis of Differential Analyzers, *J. Math. and Phys.*, vol. 32, pp. 136–163, 1953.
7. Coddington, E. A., and N. Levinson: "Theory of Ordinary Differential Equations," McGraw-Hill Book Company, Inc., New York, 1955.

PART II
Control Technology

9

Control System Theory

JOHN G. TRUXAL

PROFESSOR AND HEAD OF ELECTRICAL ENGINEERING DEPARTMENT
POLYTECHNIC INSTITUTE OF BROOKLYN

9.1 Introduction

Control Technology, the theme of the following six chapters, broadly deals with the analysis and design of a variety of systems unified by the presence of feedback. In this chapter we consider the fundamental nature of the design problems peculiarly associated with the existence of this feedback and certain of the more important viewpoints and analytical techniques which have proved to be particularly useful when we are dealing with structures possessing feedback. In the following five chapters, a distinguished group of authorities discusses five important, particular aspects in considerably greater depth.

Thus, as background for the later chapters, the present discussion attempts to give at least a partial answer to the following questions:

1. What are the essential characteristics of the feedback or control design problem, or what is the basic design problem which unifies the diverse applications of the broad area of control technology?

2. What methods are available for describing the physical problem and the actual components in terms appropriate for analytical design, evaluation, and testing?

3. What aspects of signal analysis are appropriate—i.e., in what ways may we hope to characterize typical signals?

4. In what ways does the control engineer correlate the answers to the above three questions with analytical techniques in the consideration of actual problems?

Control engineers have given these four aspects of the field the distinguishing titles of (1) feedback theory, (2) model theory, (3) signal theory, and (4) control systems engineering, although none of these terms is free from the customary ambiguity of engineering terminology and nomenclature.

189

This chapter represents an attempt to present the fundamental elements of each of these specific areas: to indicate the basic analytical and design techniques characterizing the area, to delineate the class of problems which can be solved, and to outline the current status of research and certain currently important problems which are not amenable to solution.   Our broad purpose then is to indicate the present state of the art and to report on a few interesting and promising recent developments, while simultaneously presenting a background for the subsequent chapters.

Before we consider each of these areas in more detail, it is appropriate to comment briefly and qualitatively on certain fascinating characteristics of control engineering.   The simplest sort of feedback control system, shown in block diagram form in Fig. 9.1, consists of a process or plant which is to be controlled, an instrument to measure the instantaneous value of the system output, a comparator to generate an error measuring

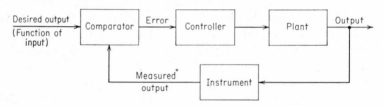

Fig. 9.1   Basic control system.

the deviation of the output signal from the desired value, and a controller which modifies the error and drives the plant in such a way as to reduce the error toward zero.   Such a system can be complicated by inserting additional paths from input to output or alternate feedback paths, by adding inputs and outputs so that the problem becomes one of controlling each of several outputs by operations on several input signals, and by requiring that the system behave properly even when the characteristics of the plant or the nature of the input signal is varying rapidly and radically.   In subsequent sections we consider such complications, but for the moment we can assume that Fig. 9.1 represents the essence of control engineering.

The fascination of control engineering arises primarily from the fact that Fig. 9.1 represents the essential characteristics of an enormous variety of physical situations drawn from all branches of engineering.   Such a configuration represents in simplified form the guidance system of a missile or the aircraft autopilot control system in aeronautical engineering, the unit operation of mixing and dilution control in chemical engineering, the gate control for hydroturbines or throttle control for gasoline engines for regulating speed in mechanical engineering, the automatic control of traffic lights in highway engineering, and the action of a human in a simple control task such as driving a vehicle in human engineering. In other words, control engineering spans the conventional compartmentation of engineering sciences and unifies diverse specialties by the common mathematical and physical principles which underlie the different fields. As another example, a consultant in control engineering recently considered, on successive days, feedback problems associated with the accurate positioning of a large radar antenna, an automatic learning machine, and a system for automatically drawing fiber in a manufacturing process.

Precisely this diversity or breadth of applicability is the primary source of the fascination of control engineering. In a period when the emphasis in so much of engineering is on greater and greater specialization, control engineering presents an opportunity to reverse the trend, to apply the same analytical techniques to diverse fields, and to emphasize the essential unity of many aspects of the various branches of engineering. In order to apply the techniques of linear-system analysis to this span of problems, the control engineer must develop analogous descriptions for physical situations in all the various fields; he must determine descriptions for the dynamics of the plant or process being controlled in a common form of model so that the feedback theory and systems analysis techniques can be applied. In other words, emphasis is directed toward the development of mathematical models for physical situations—models which satisfactorily describe the component dynamics.

Two other aspects of control engineering have contributed markedly to the present-day glamour of the field. First, a large portion of control engineering is concerned with a broad system analysis or evaluation, in which the engineer has an opportunity to utilize the fundamental concepts of the mathematical theories so often developed initially by the communications engineer (e.g., network theory and information theory). Information theory, initially developed in large measure for the evaluation of communication systems, has primarily been carried by the theorist in the direction of establishing erudite theorems on coding theory or channel capacity, and a considerable portion of the literature in the field is readable only by the select group of information theory specialists. The control engineer's interest is in another direction, however—aimed toward the understanding of the characteristics of feedback systems as they relate to the transmission or processing of information. As a specific example, the design of an afc (automatic-frequency-control) system combines feedback theory and the elements of communication or information theory, with the latter establishing required bandwidths and frequency characteristics for individual components and the feedback theory concerned with such questions as stability and dynamic accuracy.

The second important factor in the attractiveness of control engineering is the developing merger with computer technology—a merger which is the theme of this book. As the basic principles of automatic feedback control are extended to more and more complex systems and as the specifications on system performance become more stringent, the controller of Fig. 9.1 becomes a computer in order to achieve the required flexibility. Historically analog computers have been in large measure developed for the solution of complex control problems; now digital and analog computers, operating in real time, become key components of the control system. An ultimate goal of control systems engineering, a system in which the controller is sufficiently "intelligent" or adaptive to design itself for continuously optimum performance, represents an important and exciting apex of computer control technology.

The above introductory comments on the nature of control engineering naturally generate two objections:

1. Such a broad definition of control engineering is obviously presumptive, as we are attempting to make the control engineer envelope all areas of engineering.

2. The main characteristic of a control engineer is then superficiality, as he is an expert in no field, a dabbler in all.

Both reactions can be answered if it is recognized that the province of the control engineer is not specific component development, but rather the analysis and understanding of the interrelation and interaction of specific elements of the over-all system. The mechanical engineer must design the gyros just as the chemical engineer designs the distillation column; the control engineer guides the design (insofar as feasible) to obtain desirable component characteristics, but he is primarily concerned with system design.

Even in the light of this comment, however, the demands on the control engineer are large: he must, above all, be able to communicate intelligently with component engineers in a variety of fields in spite of the greatest semantic difficulties. As control systems become more and more complex, we can only conjecture as to whether technological developments are to be ultimately bounded by the human limitations on the systems engineer.[1]

With the above comments on the sources of the fascination and glamour of control engineering, we turn now to a consideration of the elements of the subject: feedback theory, model theory, signal theory, and (control) systems engineering. In the following sections, an attempt is made to delineate, in each area, the essential analytical and theoretical elements and the current state of the art.

[1] H. H. Goode, "Survey of Operations Research and Systems Engineering," University of Michigan IP-242, September, 1957.

9.2 Feedback Theory

The topic of feedback theory embraces the system characteristics which arise as a direct consequence of the existence of feedback. Figure 9.2 shows a simplified version of the basic system of Fig. 9.1, in which the

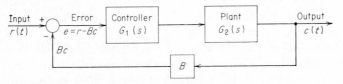

Fig. 9.2 Simple control system

desired output is simply the input $r(t)$, the instrument measuring the output performs perfectly with a gain B, and the comparator is simply a subtractor. For such a system, with $G_1(s)$ and $G_2(s)$ representing the transfer functions of the controller and the plant, the output $c(t)$ is related to the input by the transfer function

$$T(s) \equiv \frac{C}{R}(s) = \frac{G_1(s)G_2(s)}{1 + BG_1(s)G_2(s)} \tag{9.1}$$

Equation (9.1), simple as it is, suggests several important aspects of feedback systems, which could be more fully substantiated in a more detailed treatment. For example, feedback is actually only an analytical tool which we introduce in order to exploit a large body of technical knowledge developed over the last two decades. In analysis, we can view the system as a feedback structure, or we can disregard entirely feedback concepts. For example, in the analysis of the system of Fig. 9.2, we might focus attention on $T(s)$, the over-all transfer function, and treat the system as a single block with this transfer characteristic. If, however, it is possible to distinguish clearly those components

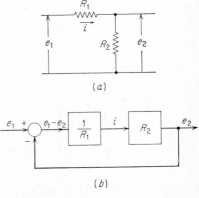

Fig. 9.3 Feedback system. (a) Resistive network (e_1 input, e_2 response). (b) Block diagram.

represented by B, $G_1(s)$, and $G_2(s)$, it is often useful to view the system as a single-loop feedback structure and exploit the analytical technology of feedback theory.

It can be shown, alternatively, that any passive network can be viewed as a feedback system. For example, the analysis of the circuit of Fig. 9.3a can be effected in terms of the two equations

$$i = \frac{1}{R_1}e_1 - \frac{1}{R_1}e_2$$

$$e_2 = R_2 i \qquad\qquad (9.2)$$

which can be represented by the block diagram of Fig. 9.3b. In such a case, we are obviously carrying the feedback concept to a ridiculous extreme.

The question of exactly when the feedback viewpoint is useful in analysis and design, however, is difficult to answer. In general, experience has demonstrated that feedback theory is most useful in the study of systems where these points are true:

1. There is a clear and obvious feeding back of the output signal to an earlier point in the system (in other words, it is convenient to construct a mathematical model in which the output depends upon itself).

2. The system is neither ridiculously simple or depressingly complex. (This constraint is discussed again in the last part of this section.)

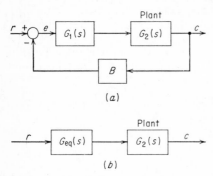

(a)

(b)

Fig. 9.4 Alternate realizations of same $T(s) = C(s)/R(s)$. (a) Feedback structure. (b) Open-loop structure.

Since the feedback concept is most useful when the system possesses an actual, physical transmission of the output back to an earlier point (as in the comparator of Fig. 9.2), what is achieved by the intentional use of such a system? Specifically, what is the advantage of the configuration of Fig. 9.4a over the corresponding open-loop (i.e., non-feedback) configuration of Fig. 9.4b, if we assume the over-all transfer function to be the same in the two cases? The two transmissions are made equivalent by selecting an appropriate value of $G_{eq}(s)$

$$T(s) = \frac{G_1 G_2}{1 + BG_1 G_2} \qquad \text{for feedback configuration} \qquad (9.3)$$

$$T(s) = G_{eq}G_2 \qquad \text{for open-loop configuration} \qquad (9.4)$$

The primary advantage of the feedback realization is the reduced sensitivity of T to changes in the plant characteristics G_2. In the open-loop system, Eq. (9.4), if G_2 changes by 10 per cent, T also changes by the same amount; in the feedback system, Eq. (9.3), however, if

$$|BG_1 G_2| \gg 1 \qquad (9.5)$$

the over-all transmission

$$T \rightarrow \frac{1}{B} \qquad (9.6)$$

and T is essentially independent of G_2. *Feedback permits the design of a satisfactory system even when the plant characteristics change radically during operation or even when the plant characteristics are only vaguely known at the outset of design.*

Thus, Eq. (9.3) demonstrates that feedback makes the system characteristics independent of the plant G_2; Fig. 9.4 indicates that feedback switches the critical element from the high-power level of G_2 to the low-power level of the feedback transducer. For example, if the control system is used to drive a large antenna, G_2 might be an hydraulic or electric motor of many horsepower with parameters depending critically on temperature, signal level, etc., while the instrument B can be a low-power inductosyn, synchro, or potentiometer utilized to generate an electrical signal proportional to antenna position. Such a signal transducer, delivering only negligible energy to the comparator, can be constructed with precision and with characteristics essentially independent of signal level or ambient conditions over wide ranges.

This use of feedback to control sensitivity is directly analogous to the utilization of feedback in the electronic operational amplifier of an analog computer where the essentially infinite forward gain is exploited to guarantee zero grid voltage (i.e., zero error in Fig. 9.2). In the operational amplifier, the result is an over-all transfer function independent of amplifier gain; since the input admittance of the amplifier is zero, the subtracting is effected in terms of Kirchhoff's current law at the amplifier-input node. As another example, the same principle is used in electronic feedback amplifiers: if B is made less than unity, a signal gain $1/B$ greater than unity is obtained effectively independent of the active elements (tubes or transistors).

The detailed evaluation of a feedback configuration demands a quantitative definition of the sensitivity described above. The definition in common use today is, with reference to Fig. 9.4a,

$$S_{G_2}{}^T \equiv \frac{d \ln T}{d \ln G_2} \qquad (9.7)$$

That is, the sensitivity of T with respect to G_2 is the percentage change in T divided by the causative percentage change in G_2 (for incremental changes). Thus, a sensitivity of unity corresponds to an open-loop system, a sensitivity of zero is ideal. With such a definition, the effectiveness of the feedback in Fig. 9.4a is described by

$$S_{G_2}{}^T = \frac{1}{1 + BG_1(s)G_2(s)} \qquad (9.8)$$

The denominator, termed the return difference with reference to G_2, is equal to unity minus the loop gain $(-BG_1G_2)$, the gain all the way around the single feedback loop. Realization of a sensitivity significantly less than the open-loop value of unity requires, then, a loop gain correspondingly greater than unity. In a typical system design problem, $G_2(s)$ is given as the transfer function of the plant to be controlled, B is fixed by the required over-all transmission (since C/R is $1/B$ if the loop gain is large), and hence $G_1(s)$ can be partially determined from the requirement that $|BG_1G_2|$ be at least $1/|S|$ over the frequency band of interest. Any $G_1(s)$ yielding the required $|G_1|$ can be selected.

Framed in the above terms, the feedback system design problem (at least for our single-loop system) is no more difficult than a common amplifier design problem; as usual in attempts to apply engineering design theory, the only real trouble arises from the difficulty in deciding upon quantitative specifications: e.g., how small must the sensitivity be to yield a "satisfactory" system. Unfortunately, as we know from our daily experience with human or sociological feedback systems, a second important difficulty arises (fortunately for the employment situation among control engineers). As the specifications are made more stringent, and the required $|G_1|$ increases, a point is reached beyond which the system oscillates. Design of the feedback system then becomes the problem of selecting the frequency variation $G_1(s)$ in such a way that:

1. $G_1(s)$ can be realized by actual equipment which is feasible on the basis of weight, space, and component limitations.
2. $|G_1|$ is sufficiently large over the frequency band of interest.
3. The over-all system is stable.

Thus, the design of the simple, single-loop system of Fig. 9.4a involves two basic factors, which we term *sensitivity* and *stability*. By *sensitivity*, we signify the realization of a loop gain sufficiently high to permit satisfactory system performance in the face of anticipated variations of plant characteristics (we shall see shortly that such high loop gain also ensures several other system characteristics which are in certain instances of critical importance). *Stability* refers to the tendency of the system to come to rest after the termination of an input signal.[1] System design requires simultaneous realization of specified sensitivity and relative stability.

[1] Rigorous definition of the term "stability" requires, of course, the consideration of nonlinear systems in which the system performance may depend on initial conditions or past history or in which the term "stability" may refer to the ability of a system to maintain an oscillatory mode in the presence of disturbances. In the brief treatment of this chapter, we shall be content to define a stable system as one in which oscillations following a finite-duration signal die out eventually, and a "relatively stable" system (or one possessing suitable "relative stability") as a system in which these oscillations die out *in a reasonable* length of time.

Example of Single-loop System Design. The next chapter discusses in some detail the problems and techniques associated with the design of single-loop systems such as shown in Fig. 9.4a. A single example illustrates a number of the significant factors which are involved in such a design.

1. In the positioning of a mechanical load by an hydraulic motor (with the motor and load constituting the plant), it is desired to realize a positioning control system (usually termed a servomechanism) with the output identical with the input. Hence, the feedback transducer must possess a gain B of unity, and the block diagram reduces to that of Fig. 9.5a.

2. Furthermore, when the input is a ramp function, the output must follow at the same velocity and with an error less than 0.1 per cent of the input velocity amplitude, once steady state is reached. In terms of the characteristics of $G_1(s)$ and $G_2(s)$, if the error is to be bounded when the output increases linearly with time, $G_1(s)G_2(s)$ must involve an integration (i.e., a factor $1/s$). Hence, at low frequencies

$$G_1(s)G_2(s) \rightarrow \frac{K_v}{s} \tag{9.9}$$

where K_v is a constant termed the velocity error coefficient or velocity constant. Under these conditions, the steady-state output is K_v times the integral of the error, or the steady-state error is $1/K_v$ times the output velocity. Hence, K_v must be 1,000 for the accuracy specification.

3. The loop gain must be at least 60 db (1,000) for all frequencies from 0 to 1 rad/sec in order to permit suitable accuracy and insensitivity to changes in the parameters of the hydraulic motor. (Actually the system is to be designed to be competitive with direct mechanical gearing for load positioning.)

4. In order to minimize the effects of noise in the input, we desire to maintain the bandwidth of the system as narrow as possible (a narrow bandwidth might also be required by secondary resonances of the mechanical load and the desire to cut the system off at a frequency well below such resonances in order that vibrations of the load not be magnified by the feedback action). Specifically, the bandwidth should not exceed 10 rad/sec.

The nature of our design problem is now indicated by a consideration of the requirements on the loop gain G_1G_2. Here

$$T(s) = \frac{G_1(s)G_2(s)}{1 + G_1(s)G_2(s)} \tag{9.10}$$

Since $|G_1G_2|$ is greater than 1,000 at all ω less than 1 rad/sec, T is essentially unity in this band. As $|G_1G_2|$ falls off at higher frequencies, the unity in the denominator becomes significant and, at high frequencies where

$$|G_1 G_2| \ll 1 \qquad (9.11)$$

T is essentially just $G_1 G_2$. Hence, the bandwidth of T occurs approximately at the frequency at which $|G_1 G_2| = 1$, if we assume $|G_1 G_2|$ decreases monotonically with ω.

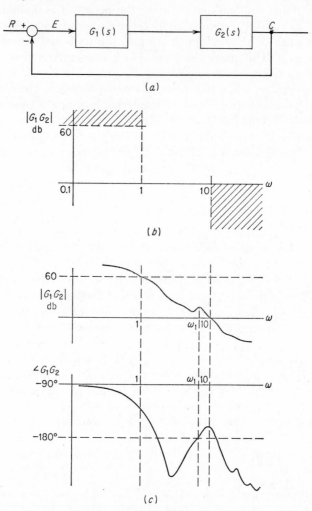

Fig. 9.5 Conditionally stable system. (*a*) Block diagram. (*b*) Required behavior of loop gain. (*c*) Gain and phase characteristics.

Figure 9.5*b* illustrates the nature of the requirements on $|G_1 G_2|$: $|G_1 G_2|$ must lie within the shaded areas. In other words, we must select a $G_1(s)$ [$G_2(s)$ is given] such that $|G_1 G_2|$ falls from 60 to 0 db as ω increases from 1 to 10 rad/sec. Unfortunately, some twenty years ago Bode demonstrated that the rate of change of gain is intimately related to the phase shift: in particular, an average rate of change of gain of 60 db/decade corresponds to a phase shift of $-270°$. In other words, if we design a $G_1(s)G_2(s)$ which has a gain characteristic falling at 60 db/decade of frequency, the same G_1G_2 possesses a phase of $-270°$ which is sufficient to cause the over-all system to oscillate. Alternatively, if the system is not to oscillate, the average rate of change of gain is limited to about -34 db/decade and almost 2 decades are required to cut off the high-gain system (i.e., the bandwidth is nearly 100 rad/sec, instead of the specified 10 rad/sec).

Actually the only requirement for stability of this system is, according to the Nyquist stability criterion, that the phase lag should be less than 180° as the gain passes through 0 db. Consequently, it is theoretically possible to select a $G_1(s)$ which yields the $G_1(s)G_2(s)$ gain and phase characteristics shown in Fig. 9.5c. Here, the gain is dropped rapidly from 60 db at 1 rad/sec through 0 db at 10 rad/sec; the phase lag greatly exceeds 180° beyond $\omega = 1$, but, just as the gain passes through 0 db, the phase rises above $-180°$ for a short interval along the frequency axis.

Such a system is termed *conditionally stable*, since a reduction in the open-loop gain constant (dropping the entire gain curve) can cause instability (as evidenced in the figure by the fact that, if the gain is dropped until 0 db occurs below ω_1, the phase at the frequency of 0-db gain will be below $-180°$). The conditional stability is not, in itself, a particularly undesirable characteristic (indeed, a large number, if not the majority, of complex control systems are conditionally stable), but unfortunately there is no simple, straightforward technique for selecting a realizable $G_1(s)$ which yields the required gain and phase characteristics for the open-loop transfer function G_1G_2.[1] As long as the bandwidth is not reduced by a factor of more than 2 below that achievable in an unconditionally stable system (i.e., below 50 rad/sec in our example), $G_1(s)$ can be chosen by a trial-and-error procedure, based upon the gain and phase characteristics known to be associated with pole and zero factors. When in our example we request a bandwidth of 10 rad/sec., however, the $G_1(s)$ required is quite complex, and the author knows of no rational approach which leads to networks of reasonably near minimum complexity or at least of a simplicity appealing to the control system engineer.

Multiloop Systems. In an attempt to separate the stability and sensitivity problems, various proposals have been made to utilize multi-loop configurations involving more than one feedback loop. In addition, control system design problems often inevitably possess several feedback

[1] J. Oizumi and M. Kimura, Design of Conditionally Stable Feedback Systems, *IRE Trans. on Circuit Theory*, vol. CT-4, pp. 157–166, September, 1957.

paths, for example when the controller of Fig. 9.2 utilizes not only the output, but also several variables existing within the plant as a basis for generating the signal driving the plant. While it is not possible to consider in detail the properties of such multiloop configurations in this chapter, we shall consider two aspects: determination of the over-all transfer function and evaluation of the sensitivity and stability—both in terms of the specific example of Fig. 9.6.

The over-all transfer function,

$$T(s) = \frac{C(s)}{R(s)} \tag{9.12}$$

can be determined by step-by-step simplification and reduction to a single-loop block diagram or by solving the simultaneous equations represented by the original block diagram. Particularly when several transmissions are required (e.g., if there were several inputs or if sensitivities

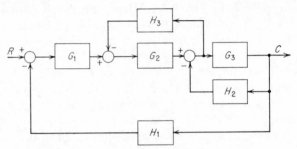

Fig. 9.6 Multiloop feedback control system.

to various elements are desired), it is greatly advantageous as well as mentally satisfying to be able to write $T(s)$ directly by inspection. Exactly such a possibility has been provided by a theorem of S. J. Mason,[1] which states that

$$T(s) = \frac{\Sigma_i P_i \Delta_i}{\Delta} \tag{9.13}$$

where Δ, the diagram determinant, is

$$\Delta = 1 - \Sigma T_e + \Sigma T_j T_k - \Sigma T_i T_j T_k + \cdots \tag{9.14}$$

Here ΣT_e represents the sum of *all* loop gains, $\Sigma T_j T_k$ represents the sum of all products of two loop gains where the two loops are *nontouching*, and $\Sigma T_i T_j T_k$ are the products (three at a time) of all triplets where none of the three loops touch one another; where P_i is the gain of direct path i from input to output; and where Δ_i is Δ evaluated with all loops which touch the path of P_i eliminated.

[1] S. J. Mason, Feedback Theory: Further Properties of Signal-flow-graphs, *Proc. IRE*, vol. 44, pp. 920–936, July, 1956.

The application of Eq. (9.13) is considerably simpler than the explanation. In the system of Fig. 9.6, for example, the terms are evaluated as follows: there are three loops, with the respective loop gains

$$T_1 = -G_2H_3$$
$$T_2 = -G_3H_2 \qquad (9.15)$$
$$T_3 = -G_1G_2G_3H_1$$

Hence

$$\Delta = 1 + [G_3H_2 + G_2H_3 + G_1G_2G_3H_1] \qquad (9.16)$$

since each loop touches each of the other two. There is only one direct path from input to output

$$P_1 = G_1G_2G_3 \qquad (9.17)$$

In the calculation of Δ_1, we eliminate all loops which touch this direct path (hence all feedback loops) and

$$\Delta_1 = 1 \qquad (9.18)$$

Thus, direct substitution in Eq. (9.13) yields

$$T(s) = \frac{G_1G_2G_3}{1 + G_3H_2 + G_2H_3 + G_1G_2G_3H_1} \qquad (9.19)$$

The important aspect of Eq. (9.19) is that the expression for $T(s)$ can be written by inspection of the original block diagram; no labor is involved

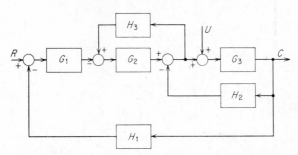

Fig. 9.7 System of Fig. 9.6 with disturbance input $u(t)$.

in an example of this complexity. Furthermore, if we considered the related system of Fig. 9.7, in which $u(t)$, a noise or disturbance input, is added, we could write $\frac{C}{U}(s)$ directly.

$$\frac{C}{U}(s) = \frac{G_3(1 + G_2H_3)}{1 + G_3H_2 + G_2H_3 + G_1G_2G_3H_1} \qquad (9.20)$$

The denominators of Eqs. (9.20) and (9.19) are identical; the numerator of Eq. (9.20) is simply the single direct transmission G_3 multiplied by the corresponding Δ_{G_3} (the loop G_2H_3 not touching the direct transmission path).

In more complex systems enumeration of the various feedback loops (the closed paths in the block diagram) can be effected systematically by breaking all feedback loops by opening the connections at the inputs of as many elements as are required. For example, Fig. 9.8a shows the

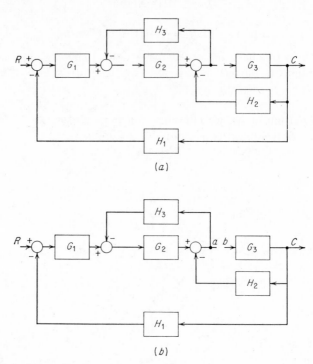

Fig. 9.8 Breaking the feedback loops in Fig. 9.6. (a) Inputs to G_2 and G_3 opened. (b) Input to G_3 opened.

configuration of Fig. 9.6 with the three loops broken by opening paths at the inputs of G_2 and G_3.[1] We now move toward restoration of the original system; if we first close the input to G_2 (Fig. 9.8b), any loops must pass through G_2. By considering all possible ways to return from the output of G_2 to the input, we find there is only one loop with

$$T_1 = -G_2H_3 \tag{9.21}$$

Now closing the input of G_3, any new loops must include G_3; from the output of G_3 we can either pass through H_2 and (-1) to the input or

---

[1] Actually, we can open the output of the last comparator and succeed in breaking all feedback loops at once. The simplification is inconsequential in our present application.

through H_1, (-1), G_1, and G_2 (we do not traverse our previous loops); hence

$$T_2 = -G_3 H_2 \qquad (9.22)$$
$$T_3 = -G_3(H_1 G_1 G_2) \qquad (9.23)$$

This step-by-step approach is general and directly applicable in systems of great complexity. As the complexity increases, of course, we soon reach systems which no sane man would want to analyze theoretically and which can only be studied intelligently with the assistance of computers.

Thus, Mason's theorem permits direct and simple determination of the transfer functions of multiloop feedback configurations; in addition, the theorem also permits rapid calculation of the sensitivity of the over-all transfer function to changes in any particular system parameter. The block diagram is drawn in such a way that the specified parameter appears only once and alone as the gain of an individual block. Under these conditions Bode demonstrated that

$$S_x{}^T = \frac{1}{F}\left(1 - \frac{T_0}{T}\right) \qquad (9.24)$$

is one of several possible relations for the sensitivity.
Here T = over-all transfer function
  x = specified parameter
  T_0 = value of T with $x = 0$
  F = return difference with reference to x, or unity minus the loop gain around x (i.e., total gain from input of x through x and then through all possible paths back to input)
Thus, even in the general case when T_0 in Eq. (9.24) is not 0, evaluation of S requires only the determination of three specific transfer functions from the block diagram.

Figure 9.6 again provides a simple example of Eq. (9.24) if we seek the sensitivity with respect to changes in the power amplifier G_3. In this case $S_{G_3}{}^T$ depends only on F since T_0 is zero (if $G_3 = 0$ there is no transmission from R to C). F_{G_3} is evaluated from Fig. 9.8b as unity minus the transfer function from b to a, or

$$F_{G_3} = 1 - G_3\left[\frac{-H_2 - H_1 G_1 G_2}{1 + G_2 H_3}\right] \qquad (9.25)$$

or

$$S_{G_3}{}^T = \frac{1 + G_2 H_3}{1 + G_2 H_3 + G_3 H_2 + G_1 G_2 G_3 H_1} \qquad (9.26)[1]$$

[1] Equations (9.20) and (9.26) illustrate the important fact that, if feedback reduces the sensitivity with respect to an element, it also reduces the effects of unwanted signals injected at the element. For example, reduction of the effects of variations in antenna drive-motor parameters accompanies reduction of the effects of wind load disturbances in an antenna control system.

The final characteristic of interest in the analysis of multiloop systems is the stability, and once more we illustrate in terms of the specific system of Fig. 9.6. As in any linear system, stability is determined by the poles of the transfer function (the zeros of the Δ of the block diagram). Equation (9.19) [or (9.20)] indicates that the over-all system is stable if the roots of

$$1 + [G_3H_2 + G_2H_3 + G_1G_2G_3H_1] = 0 \qquad (9.27)$$

lie within the right half of the s plane. Substitution of the G and H functions as ratios of polynomials in s permits direct application of any of the conventional stability criteria (Nyquist diagram, Routh test, and so on).

Unfortunately, in the design or evaluation of a system of this nature, it is usually insufficient merely to know that the system is stable with the normal, designed values for the various parameters. In order to establish that the designed system is satisfactory, we must demonstrate that the system will remain stable for normally anticipated variations of critical parameters. For example, in the system of Fig. 9.6, each of the blocks G_1, G_2, and G_3 may involve active elements (signal or power amplifiers). Although we design the over-all system for specified values of K_1, K_2, and K_3 (the multiplying constants involved in G_1, G_2, and G_3), we might logically require that the system be stable for any set of three gain constants, each less than the design value. As a specific example, if K_1 is normally 10, $K_2 = 2$, and $K_3 = 50$, we would require system stability for any set of values satisfying the inequalities

$$0 \leqslant K_1 \leqslant 10$$
$$0 \leqslant K_3 \leqslant 50 \qquad (9.28)$$
$$0 \leqslant K_2 \leqslant 2$$

Determination of the stability as a function of K_1 alone, for example, is a straightforward task on the basis of either the Nyquist diagram plotted with K_1 as the gain or the root loci plotted as a function of K_1. Determination of the stability of the over-all system over the three-dimensional space defined by Eq. (9.28) is in general an important, unsolved theoretical problem. F. Blecher[1] recently presented an extension of the Nyquist graphical test which establishes sufficient (although not necessary) conditions for stability, and which seems to be adequate in a variety of actual problems of practical importance. The amount of work involved in applying Blecher's test becomes prohibitive as the number of dimensions increases, and for problems involving from two to four dimensions, equally satisfactory results can usually be

---

[1] F. Blecher, Transistor Multiple Loop Feedback Amplifiers, *Bell Labs. Record*, 1958.

obtained for control problems with an analog-computer simulation of the system and a programmed scanning of the n-dimensional space.

Systems Intentionally Multiloop. In recent years, as the demands on control system performance have grown, there has been increased interest in systems which are intentionally multiloop. For example, improved control can often be achieved if we measure and feed back not only the output, but secondary signals existing within the plant and load. Such subsidiary feedback paths have long been utilized in the control of nonlinear processes (e.g., if the gear train possesses backlash, it is useful to monitor not only load position, but also motor position), and are being employed increasingly to improve the quality of performance.

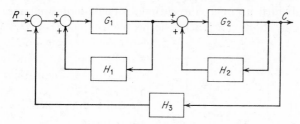

Fig. 9.9   Three-loop structure.

A variety of examples of multiloop feedback structures has been presented in the literature during the last few years; we shall mention here only a few which typify the attainable characteristics. The first important category embraces those systems in which multiple loops are used in an attempt to divorce the stability and sensitivity problems.

Figure 9.9 is a block diagram of a three-loop structure with several fascinating characteristics. Evaluation of the over-all transfer function and the sensitivities with respect to G_1 and G_2 yields the results

$$T(s) = \frac{G_1 G_2}{1 + G_1 G_2 H_3 - G_1 H_1 - G_2 H_2 + G_1 G_2 H_1 H_2} \qquad (9.29)$$

$$S_{G_1}{}^T = \frac{1 - G_2 H_2}{1 + G_1 G_2 H_3 - G_1 H_1 - G_2 H_2 + G_1 G_2 H_1 H_2} \qquad (9.30)$$

$$S_{G_2}{}^T = \frac{1 - G_1 H_1}{1 + G_1 G_2 H_3 - G_1 H_1 - G_2 H_2 + G_1 G_2 H_1 H_2} \qquad (9.31)$$

The interesting situation arises when H_1 and H_2 are selected as the reciprocals of G_1 and G_2, respectively, so that the three equations above reduce to

$$T(s) = \frac{1}{H_3} \qquad (9.32)$$

$$S_{G_1}{}^T = 0 \qquad (9.33)$$

$$S_{G_2}{}^T = 0 \qquad (9.34)$$

In other words, as long as G_1H_1 and G_2H_2 are unity, both sensitivities are zero, and the system characteristics are independent of G_1 and G_2.

Such a utilization of combined positive and negative feedback (with the positive feedback represented by the H_1 and H_2 paths) places an infinite gain in tandem with both G_1 and G_2, and transmission is independent of the power-amplifying stages. Such systems have actually been constructed in transistor amplifiers, although it can be shown that the primary advantage achieved in audio amplifiers derives from the realization of high gain with only a small number of stages (and hence fewer parasitic capacitances and unwanted phase lags and attenuation). Actually, the requirement of matching $1/H_1$ to G_1, for example, is so stringent that the frequency characteristics must be controlled over as wide a bandwidth as in a conventional, single-loop configuration. In control systems, however, where the problem is not the excessive band-

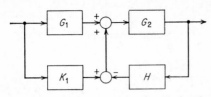

Fig. 9.10 Ham-Lang configuration.

width over which gain and phase must be controlled, but rather the realization of high gain economically and with a smoothly and carefully controlled cutoff, such configurations are widely useful. Essentially the simplicity of the control problem lies in the fact that both transistor and vacuum-tube preamplifiers possess negligible distributed capacitance (or phase lag) within the relatively minute control system bandwidth.

The positive-feedback scheme of Fig. 9.9 requires that H_1 be matched to $1/G_1$; alternate schemes for separating stability and sensitivity have been proposed in which the modeling element is matched directly to the plant. Figure 9.10, showing the basic configuration proposed by Ham and Lang, yields an over-all transmission which is essentially open-loop even though the system still possesses feedback (and hence reduced sensitivity) around the plant G_2. In this system, if the transfer function K_1 is selected as $G_1G_2H_2$,

$$T(s) = G_1G_2 \qquad (9.35)$$

$$S_{G_2}{}^T = \frac{1}{1 + G_2H_2} \qquad (9.36)$$

Realization of the compensation requires construction of a model which *simulates* the plant, at least approximately. A basically similar scheme is described by O. J. M. Smith[1] for lightly damped systems, in which the controller network models only the lightly damped mode and a transcendental transfer function (realized by a delay network) is used to

[1] O. J. M. Smith, "Feedback Control Systems," pp. 331–345, McGraw-Hill Book Company, Inc., New York, 1958.

generate zeros of transmission at the lightly damped poles. Such a scheme is paralleled by oscillation traps used by communication engineers in the transmission of pulsed waveforms through ringing circuits.

The system of Fig. 9.6 is utilized for the partial separation of stability and sensitivity problems. In this system, there are two primary feedback paths from the output C to the input of G_2: one through H_1, (-1), G_1; the other via H_2, (-1), H_3, and (-1). If the signals fed back along the two paths are equal and opposite, i.e., if

$$H_2 H_3 = H_1 G_1 \tag{9.37}$$

there is no net feedback from C to the input of G_2. The only two feedback loops are then those with loop gains $-H_2 G_3$ and $-G_2 H_3$. Therefore, insofar as the over-all transmission is concerned, the configuration satisfying Eq. (9.37) is equivalent to that of Fig. 9.11; from the standpoint of

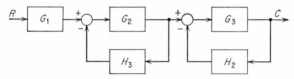

Fig. 9.11   Reduction of the system of Fig. 9.6 if $H_2 H_3 = H_1 G_1$.

stability, we are now dealing with two relatively simple systems in tandem rather than the single, more complex configuration of Fig. 9.6, in which the inherent complexity of the system often tends to make stabilization a difficult procedure.

The system of Fig. 9.11 is particularly useful when the actual signal R is not measurable, but (with $H_1 = 1$) only the error signal E is available (and actually some of G_1 may be prescribed, as when the system represents a tracking radar). Under these conditions, Eq. (9.37) serves to specify H_3.

$$H_3 = \frac{G_1}{H_2} \tag{9.38}$$

If the $G_2 - H_3$ system is constructed as a rapid-response feedback control system, the output of G_2 is a direct follow-up of the input signal R. In terms of the general concept of compensation by models, we essentially are utilizing H_3 to model the $H_1 G_1 / H_2$ system, and the configuration falls into the same pattern as the positive-negative feedback configurations.

Evaluation and comparison of the various multiloop configurations and selection of a configuration for a specific design problem are most difficult tasks. Erection of any sort of general theory is impeded by the following considerations:

1. In terms of linear time-invariant systems in which the plant transfer function is known precisely (including second-order, linear effects such as minor time lags), it is possible to separate stability and sensitivity problems to any desired degree. Any of the configurations described above behave as indicated and are useful improvements over the classical single-loop system.

2. The effects of changes in plant characteristics and of deviation of the actual plant characteristics from anticipated behavior (e.g., in terms of second-order effects) must be evaluated in terms of the specific configuration, transfer functions, and signals.

3. Of even more importance is the unfortunate fact that system performance is often critically related to the existence of seemingly slight nonlinearities. In a system which involves a critical balancing of signals at two different points, slight nonlinearities which destroy the balance may generate distortion signals which tend to be augmented by the feedback action.

The nature of the above difficulties can be illustrated specifically with the configuration of Fig. 9.11, in the simplified case with

$$H_2(s) = 1 \qquad G_2(s) = G_3(s) = \frac{100}{s(s+5)} \qquad G_1 = 1 \qquad (9.39)$$

so that, with H_3 adjusted for simplification of the system, the over-all transfer function is

$$T(s) = \left(\frac{100}{s^2 + 5s + 100}\right)^2 \qquad (9.40)$$

If G_1 (representing, for example, receiver gain) increases by only 6.25 per cent above its normal value of unity, the system becomes oscillatory—in spite of the nearly perfect cancellation of the two feedback signals. This excessive criticalness happens, in this system, to be a consequence of the equal bandwidths of the two simpler feedback systems. If the bandwidths of the G_2-H_3 and the G_3-H_2 systems are in a ratio of 10:1 (in either direction), the over-all system is stable even if G_1 increases by 800 per cent from its normal value, the exact relation for the critical value of G_1 being

$$\frac{G_1}{G_{10}} = 4\zeta^2 - 1 + \frac{\alpha}{\beta} + \frac{\beta}{\alpha} \qquad (9.41)$$

where G_{10} = nominal value of G_1

ζ = relative damping ratio of either the G_2-H_3 or the G_3-H_2 system (we assume the two ζs are equal)

α, β = bandwidths of the two systems

Equation (9.41) is, of course, of little importance in itself; rather, the relation indicates the manner in which the value of the configuration (in

terms of the criticalness of parameter values or the effects of nonlinearities) depends so markedly on the specific details and objectives of the
design problem.

The nature of the above behavior indicates clearly, as well, the importance of an analytical study of the system evaluation and the proper
relation of computer and analytical studies in control-system design.
The analog-computer evaluation of the effects of nonlinearities and
parameter variations is an essential part of system studies; the computer
study alone, however, must be supplemented by analysis of simplified
systems or restricted classes of systems in order that the designer may
acquire an appreciation of the general limitations or possibilities of performance characteristics. A relation such as Eq. (9.41), of such value
in establishing limitations on performance, can only be derived by an
analytical study.

In spite of these disadvantages, the intentionally multiloop configuration is an important and effective tool of the system designer—a tool
which has only been appreciated by feedback engineers during the last
few years (although the advantages of combined positive and negative
feedback, for example, were presented—often erroneously—more than a
decade ago). Important advantages are:

1. Possibility of simplifying the system complexity (as in Fig. 9.11)
to bring the design problem to a realizable state in the light of the quality
of available components.

2. Simplification of the actual, physical realization of required controller characteristics. For example, positive feedback is frequently
useful as a means of realizing high gain with few components (and,
accordingly, few incidental lags to complicate the stability problem).

3. Added flexibility for the designer in the difficult problem of utilizing
available transducers and permissible pickoff points to obtain adequate
feedback control.

Perhaps an equally important advantage of the recent trend toward
this intentional introduction of multipath feedback is the corresponding
expansion in the breadth of the feedback control system design problem.
Not only is it possible to reduce many complex systems to an understand-
able level, but the flexibility and broad range of configuration possibilities
place new emphasis on the ingenuity and imagination of the systems
designer. Control system design, incidentally, becomes that much more
entertaining.

Multidimensional Systems. We conclude our survey of certain of the
interesting aspects of feedback theory with a brief description of a class
of systems of broad importance: multidimensional systems, or systems
in which there exist more than one input or output. Simple examples of
such systems are controllers for curve tracers in which we desire to con-

trol orthogonal velocities in such a way as to follow a two-dimensional curve at a constant speed; vastly more complex examples arise in jet engine and missile control or process control, when many inputs and outputs are involved.

The classical approach to the design of such systems involves diagonalization of the matrix relating j of the outputs to j inputs,[1] even though such a design is intuitively amateurish. It is evident that, if we force each output to be controlled by a single, specified input, much greater variations in control signals are required than if we were to exploit the possibility of allowing correlated control by several inputs. One recent study[2] has investigated the design of the control system on the basis of minimizing the mean-square value of the control signals, while other research efforts have been concerned with the utilization of the flexibility available in a nondiagonalized system to control sensitivity of over-all transfer performance to changes in plant characteristics. The general problem of the logical design of multidimensional systems remains one of the most promising areas of current research.

Other Aspects of Feedback Theory. In the preceding paragraphs, we have attempted to outline the essential elements of feedback theory, with particular emphasis on those aspects which seem to serve as a logical background for the following chapters. We have intentionally slighted those topics, such as nonlinear feedback systems, which are covered in depth in these subsequent chapters. Furthermore, we have rather arbitrarily defined feedback theory as that aspect of control technology which deals with the characteristics derived from the configuration or mode of interconnection of the components. Particular emphasis is placed on the theoretical bounds which can be established on system performance as a result of the configuration. The specific evaluation of the detailed dynamic characteristics of the over-all system depends upon not only the configuration, but also the specific elements comprising the configuration and the signals applied. Thus, we turn now next to the characterization of specific elements.

9.3   Model Theory

By the term model theory, we refer to the available techniques for describing the detailed characteristics of the individual components constituting the configuration: i.e., the individual blocks making up the block diagram. The control engineer exploits extensively four basic representations of physical components as an aid in understanding the behavior of such components as elements of an over-all system:

---

[1] If the number of actual outputs is less than the number of inputs, additional controlled variables can be defined.

[2] R. C. Amara, "The Linear Least Squares Synthesis of Continuous and Sampled Date Multivariable Systems," *SEL Tech. Rept.* 40, Stanford, Calif., 1958.

1. Differential equations (or mathematical relations)
2. Signal-flow diagrams
3. Circuit diagrams
4. Computer simulations

Each representation (i.e., each form of model) contains essentially equivalent information, and we can convert from one form to another without particular difficulty.[1] Which form is most desirable in a specific design problem depends upon both the information required in the design and the attitudes and background of the designer. The control engineer properly exploits all four possibilities.

Each of the four forms is essentially a representation of the mathematical model of the component, and hence the derivation of each depends upon the designer's ability to discriminate between primary and unimportant (or secondary) factors, since any successful design requires, to at least some extent, a focusing of attention on only those factors which contribute significantly to the pertinent component characteristics. Furthermore, in the following discussion we are primarily concerned with deterministic models in which definite mathematical relations (whether analytic or graphical) exist among pertinent system variables. This restriction in the following paragraphs is imposed because of the limitations of space and because of the present state of the art of determination of probabilistic models (in which, for example, probability distributions of various variables are related). Such a limitation is perhaps unfortunate in view of the importance of such probabilistic models both in the quantitative determination of reliability and also in the evaluation of an over-all system in terms of probable accuracy in the presence of random parameter variations and random disturbing signals. Certainly any list of significant current research in the control field must include the work on the development and utilization of probabilistic models, both for analytical studies and for digital- and analog-computer work.

Differential Equations. The classical form of the mathematical model for a dynamical, physical system is a set of differential equations based upon either appropriate physical laws (e.g., Newton's laws, Kirchhoff's laws) or experimental measurement of the mode of interrelation of pertinent system variables. For example, in the characterization of an hydraulic motor, we might write a set of differential equations on the basis of the known laws of mechanics and fluid dynamics; the required parameters (such as valve flow gradient, oil compressibility, inertia) are then determined by static or dynamic measurements or calculated

---

[1] While it is not difficult to convert from one form to any other, it is often exceedingly difficult or demanding on the ingenuity of the engineer if we further demand that the new form be an optimum representation in any sense. For example, from the differential equations we can always find a circuit diagram; to determine the simplest circuit may be impossible or extremely difficult.

from measured dimensions, environmental conditions, and values of known variables (such as supply pressure). Alternatively, the dynamic transfer characteristics of the motor can be measured directly with familiar test signals (steps, ramps, pulses, sinusoids, random noise); the data are then used to determine a transfer function or an impulse response, either equivalent to the differential equation for a linear component.

If the device is nonlinear and the nonlinearity plays a significant role in the transfer characteristics, characterization or identification of the component is vastly more difficult. If the forms of the nonlinearities are known, it is often possible to devise specific test inputs which separate measurements of the linear and nonlinear parts. For example, in the characterization of an a-c servomotor, it is often permissible to assume the only significant nonlinearities are static friction, coulomb friction, and saturation, in which case the frictional nonlinearities can be determined by small-signal inputs, the saturation characteristic from large-signal and high-velocity measurements, and the linear transfer characteristic from the wide range of essentially linear operation. If the specific nature of the nonlinearity is unknown, Wiener has advocated that the system be characterized by its response to random signals, with the possibility in a broad class of systems of representing the linear section by a Laguerre-function filter and the nonlinear section by a zero-memory, amplitude-dependent nonlinearity.[1]

The over-all objectives of the control system designer establish the desirable form for the characterization of the system. As we pointed out in the last section, the system design involves the correlation of component characteristics with configuration properties; hence, we ordinarily seek characterization in terms of a transfer function for substitution in the block diagram. In the study of nonlinear systems, correspondingly, we desire a representation in which the nonlinear element is divorced from the linear parts. For example, if the component is described by the differential equation

$$y''' + (2 + y^2)y'' + 4y' + 3y = x \qquad (9.42)$$

with y the response and x the excitation, it is possible to describe the system as a single nonlinear transfer characteristic as shown in Fig. 9.12a; alternatively, we can in this case separate the nonlinear effect by rewriting Eq. (9.42) in the form

$$y''' + 2y'' + 4y' + 3y = x - \frac{d}{dt}\left(\frac{1}{3} y^3\right) \qquad (9.43)$$

with the representation of Fig. 9.12b.

[1] A. G. Bose, A Theory of Nonlinear Systems, *Mass. Inst. Technol. Research Lab. Electronics Tech, Rept,* 309, May, 1956.

The configuration of Fig. 9.12b has several significant advantages. For example, if this is one component of an over-all feedback system, it is possible to determine stability by considering the characteristics of the linear system seen from the terminals of the single nonlinear element. In particular, it is a simple matter to determine the effect of the non-linearity on stability—i.e., whether the nonlinearity tends to stabilize or destabilize the system, and the extent of such an effect. Such an investigation can be carried out by representing the nonlinear element as a variable gain, with the gain for small signals determined by the slope of the cubic characteristic of Fig. 9.12c and the gain for sinu-soidal signals evaluated by some averaging process over the period (e.g., in the "describing-function" analysis, we obtain the averaging by determining the equivalent gain which minimizes the mean-square error between the actual output and the linearized-system output, with the specific value of the equivalent gain then depending on the signal amplitude). In the same way, the representation of Fig. 9.12b is use-ful in the evaluation of the effects

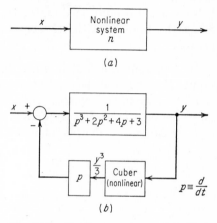

Fig. 9.12 Nonlinear system. (a) $y''' + (2 + y^2)y'' + 4y' + 3y = x$. (b) Alternate representation.

of the nonlinearity on other characteristics of the feedback configuration: sensitivity, susceptibility to noise or extraneous signals, and impedance levels existing throughout the system.

Thus, whether the system be linear or nonlinear, the transfer characteristics are satisfactorily described in terms of a set of simultaneous differential equations or equivalent analytical and graphical representations.

Signal-flow Diagrams. Signal-flow diagrams provide an alternate technique for representing the characteristics of a linear system. Essentially the signal-flow diagram is simply a graphical representation of the simultaneous equations describing the system; the advantages of the signal-flow diagram arise solely from the possibility that a graphical representation may exhibit clearly and obviously important interrelationships among the various system variables.

In order to be more specific, we consider a specific example. A particular component is described by the simultaneous equations

$$Z = AX + BY$$
$$W = CZ \qquad\qquad (9.44)$$
$$V = DW + EX$$

where X and Y are the input signals (or their Laplace transforms); Z, W, and V are dependent signals; and A, B, C, D, and E are transfer functions. The signal-flow diagram is based upon the use of *a node to represent each variable* and *directed branches to represent transfer functions* or transmittances. The diagram is constructed on the basis of these rules:

1. The value of any node is the sum of all incoming signals.
2. The value of a node travels out all outgoing branches (i.e., does not divide).
3. A signal is multiplied by the transmittance of a branch as it travels along the branch (with travel permitted only in the direction of the arrow).

To represent the first of Eqs. (9.44), we need three nodes: the two inputs X and Y and the dependent variable Z. Since Z depends on both X and Y, we have branches from X and Y directed toward Z, and the flow diagram is shown in Fig. 9.13a. Representation of the second equation requires another node W and a single branch of gain C and directed from Z to W (Fig. 9.13b). Finally, the complete set of equations is represented as shown in part (c) of the figure.

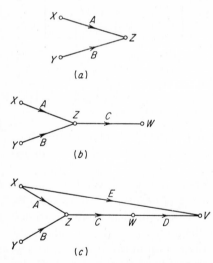

Since Fig. 9.13c is nothing more than a representation of Eqs. (9.44), what are the advantages to be gained from a flow-diagram representation? Basically the advantages lie in having available an alternate form for characterizing components; in a difficult design or analysis problem it is imperative that the engineer utilize all possible approaches or viewpoints which might give added insight. Even the trivial example above, which is really too simple to indicate the power of the flow diagram, demonstrates this possibility of an alternate viewpoint. Figure 9.13c demonstrates clearly, for example, that if $X = 0$, V is simply $BCDY$, since the signal from Y has only one path to V and must pass through successive gains B, C, and D. Alternately, if $Y = 0$, V consists of two terms, EX and $ACDX$. The important feature of the flow graph is the vividness and emphasis with which such relationships are indicated.

Fig. 9.13 Signal-flow diagram for Eqs. (9.44).

The above brief comments hardly suffice as any sort of justification for signal-flow diagrams; the effective exploitation of the signal-flow diagram

depends upon the utilization of feedback theory in the study of the properties of components and in the evaluation of the importance or role
associated with specific parameters (i.e., the ease with which we can
calculate sensitivity, for example, from a flow diagram). It is not
feasible here to expand on feedback theory applied to flow diagrams;
rather, in keeping with the basic motif of the book, we shall consider
one specific application of flow diagrams in connection with the scaling
of analog computer simulations of physical systems.

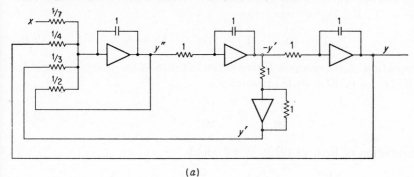

(a)

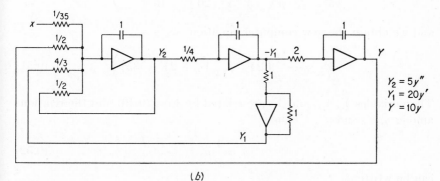

(b)

Fig. 9.14 Scaling in a simple example. (a) Simulation of Eq. (9.46). (b) Simulation of Eq. (9.56).

Once again we utilize a specific example for the presentation of the
basic ideas as we consider simulation of the linear differential equation

$$y''' + 2y'' + 3y' + 4y = -7x \qquad (9.45)$$

where y is the response to be evaluated, x is the excitation given, and the
system is to be assumed initially inert. The computer setup can be
determined by writing the equation in the form

$$y'' = -\frac{1}{p}(2y'' + 3y' + 4y + 7x) \qquad (9.46)$$

in which case the realization of Fig. 9.14a is at once apparent.

Scaling of this simple problem can be carried out in a straightforward manner if we assume the maximum anticipated values of y, y', and y'' are known. To be specific, we assume

$$y < 10 \qquad y' < 5 \qquad y'' < 20 \tag{9.47}$$

If the saturation level of the amplifiers is 100 and the full signal capabilities are to be utilized, the variables to appear in the machine are $10y$, $20y'$, and $5y''$ rather than y, y', and y''. If we define the machine variables as Y, Y_1, Y_2,[1] we can write

$$Y = 10y \qquad Y_1 = 20y' \qquad Y_2 = 5y'' \tag{9.48}$$

Equation (9.46) can now be rewritten in terms of the machine variables with the use of Eqs. (9.48) rewritten as

$$y = \frac{Y}{10} \qquad y' = \frac{Y_1}{20} \qquad y'' = \frac{Y_2}{5} \tag{9.49}$$

Substitution of Eqs. (9.49) in (9.46) yields

$$\frac{Y_2}{5} = -\frac{1}{p}\left(2\frac{Y_2}{5} + 3\frac{Y_1}{20} + 4\frac{Y}{10} + 7x\right) \tag{9.50}$$

and we obtain the new computer equation

$$Y_2 = -\frac{1}{p}\left(2Y_2 + \frac{3}{4}Y_1 + 2Y + 35x\right) \tag{9.51}$$

The variables Y, Y_1, and Y_2 are related by Eqs. (9.49) and the relations among y, y', and y''. Thus

$$y = \frac{1}{p}y' \tag{9.52}$$

can be written

$$\frac{Y}{10} = \frac{1}{p}\frac{Y}{20} \qquad \text{or} \qquad Y = \frac{1}{2p}Y_1 \tag{9.53}$$

Likewise

$$y' = \frac{1}{p}y'' \tag{9.54}$$

corresponds to

$$\frac{Y_1}{20} = \frac{1}{p}\frac{Y_2}{5} \qquad \text{or} \qquad Y_1 = \frac{4}{p}Y_2 \tag{9.55}$$

---

[1] We might use the notation Y, Y', Y'' for the machine variables, but confusion then arises because Y' is not the time derivative of Y. Therefore, in this initial exposition of the method, we use subscripts.

Collection of Eqs. (9.51), (9.53), and (9.55) gives us the relations to be implemented on the computer:

$$Y_2 = -\frac{1}{p}\left(2Y_2 + \frac{3}{4}Y_1 + 2Y + 35x\right)$$

$$Y = \frac{1}{2p}Y_1 \qquad\qquad (9.56)$$

$$Y_1 = \frac{4}{p}Y_2$$

and Fig. 9.14b shows the new computer realization.

Several aspects of the above amplitude scaling are particularly noteworthy. Essentially we have started from a differential equation (9.46) in terms of the dependent variables y'', y', and y; we have replaced these three variables by Y_2, Y_1, and Y, and formulated the new equation (9.51). Instead of a relation among a variable y and its derivatives, we have a relation among three variables (Y_2, Y_1, and Y) which are related by simple differential or integral operations [Eq. (9.56)]. By this process we have simulated the original system with each dependent variable in our simulator having a maximum value which we can select arbitrarily.

Exactly the same procedure can be utilized in the simulation of more complex systems described, for example, by a set of simultaneous nonlinear differential equations. Each of the dependent variables and the derivatives is represented by a distinct machine variable with arbitrarily adjusted amplitude scale factors. In the simulation of more complex systems, however, the analytical approach described above tends to become tedious, time-consuming, and susceptible to algebraic errors; in such cases it is helpful to perform the scaling in terms of a graphical representation of the simulation. The signal-flow diagram for the computer setup provides a convenient basis for the scaling operation.

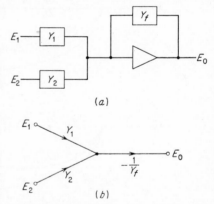

Fig. 9.15 Building blocks for simulator representation. (a) Basic operational amplifier. (b) Canonic flow diagram.

Any given system may be represented by a variety of signal-flow diagrams, corresponding to the numerous ways in which the system equations may be written. When we apply flow-diagram techniques to the study of analog simulators, we are dealing primarily with operational amplifiers, and it is useful to have a *canonic* flow diagram for representation of the operational amplifier of Fig. 9.15a. The equation for this circuit may be written, by summing currents at the amplifier input, as

$$E_o = \frac{Y_1}{Y_f} E_1 - \frac{Y_2}{Y_f} E_2 \qquad (9.57)$$

where the Y's are the admittances indicated in the figure.[1]   We shall

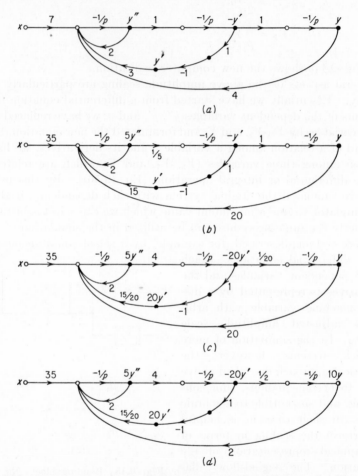

Fig. 9.16 Scaling of example of Fig. 9.14. (*a*) Flow diagram for Fig. 9.14*a*. (*b*) y'' replaced by $5y''$. (*c*) y' replaced by $20y'$. (*d*) y replaced by $10y$.

arbitrarily select the signal-flow diagram of Fig. 9.15*b* as the fundamental model for such a system.   In this flow diagram, the addition involved ⌐ the summing of currents is represented by the three branches entering the one node, while the effect of the feedback element is placed in evidence by the $-1/Y_f$ branch.[1]

On the basis of this very simple representation for the operational amplifier, we can construct the flow diagram for the simulator setup of Fig. 9.14a—if we now return to consideration of our previous example. The signal-flow diagram is shown in Fig. 9.16a, where we have indicated the primary dependent variables (y'', y', y) by a solid dot ● and the secondary dependent variables by a small circle ○. This notation is helpful in emphasizing that it is only the dot variables which are to be scaled in amplitude.

The system can now be scaled directly from the flow diagram, with the technique illustrated in Fig. 9.17a, which shows the scaling of a single variable in a portion of an over-all computer setup. Here we can make the node w represent $10w$ instead by increasing the incoming signals by a factor of 10 (i.e., replacing b by $10b$) and decreasing the gain of all outgoing branches by $\frac{1}{10}$; the result is shown in Fig. 9.17b. The nodes representing v and t are unchanged. If we are willing to change the node v to $10v$, we can multiply a and $c/10$, the branches coming into v, by 10 and divide $10b$ by 10 to obtain the diagram of Fig. 9.17c. Comparison of parts (a) and (c) reveals that we have scaled before and after the feedback loop; we have not changed the feedback loop gain,

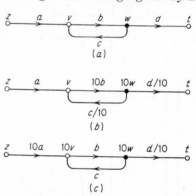

Fig. 9.17 Scaling of a single variable.

but simply increased the signals circulating in the loop by a factor of 10. This transformation from (a) to (c) is the amplitude scaling technique: we multiply all branches entering the node v by any constant and divide all branches leaving the node w by the same constant to scale w.

If we return now to Fig. 9.16a and our previous example, Eq. (9.48) indicates we wish to replace y'' by $5y''$, y' by $20y'$, and y by $10y$. Parts (b), (c), and (d) of Fig. 9.16 show the successive steps in achieving this result:

b. Leaving the feedback loop alone, we multiply other incoming branches by 5 and the outgoing branch from ($5y''$) by $\frac{1}{5}$. The variables y' and y are left undisturbed.

---

[1] The canonic flow diagram we have selected could easily be complicated to demonstrate the effects of nonzero input admittance, nonzero output impedance, or noninfinite gain of the amplifier; such second-order effects are rarely important in scaling and, indeed, ordinarily of no importance in analog-computer work. We desire to consider only first-order effects insofar as possible.

$$\begin{cases} y'' + 2y' + y^3 - z' - z = -2x \\ z'' + 3z' - 2y' - y = 0 \end{cases}$$

$$(a)$$

$$\begin{cases} y' = -\dfrac{1}{p}\left[2y' + y^3 - z' - z + 2x\right] \\ -z' = -\dfrac{1}{p}\left[-3z' + 2y' + y\right] \end{cases}$$

$$(b)$$

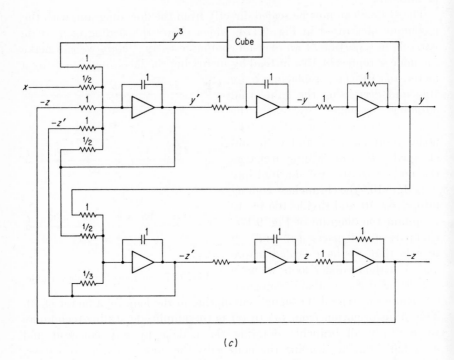

$$(c)$$

We wish to realize $8y'_{,}\ 4y,\ z'_{,}\ 5z,\ \dfrac{1}{2}y^3$

$$(d)$$

Fig. 9.18 Scaling in nonlinear problems. (a) Original equations. (b) Equations (e) Flow-diagram scaling. (f) Final simulation.

c. To realize $20y'$ rather than y', the $\frac{1}{5}$ branch is multiplied by 20 and the branches leaving by $\frac{1}{20}$. The multiplication by $\frac{1}{20}$ is placed at the output of $20y'$ since the variable y' is to be scaled as well as $-y'$.

d. Finally we realize $10y$ in the same manner, to obtain the final configuration of Fig. 9.16d.

From Fig. 9.16d the computer simulation previously shown in Fig. 9.14b can be written by inspection.

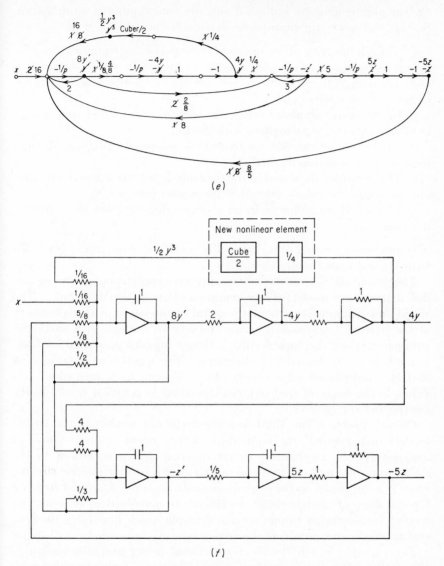

(e)

(f)

written for simulation. (c) Original computer setup. (d) Scaling specifications.

The steps described in detail above and outlined graphically in Fig. 9.16 can, in practice, be carried out directly on the original signal-flow diagram of the unscaled computer program. The signal-flow-diagram representation provides a simple basis for the straightforward insertion of scaling factors. In order to illustrate this simplicity, Fig. 9.18 shows an additional example representing the solution of two simultaneous, nonlinear differential equations, with the successive values of gains in the signal-flow diagram indicated and the final computer setup shown. Several comments are appropriate in connection with Fig. 9.18:

a. The nonlinearity arises in the y^3 term in the first equation.

b. The equations are treated exactly as though they were linear (it is often convenient to alternate the signs in sets of simultaneous equations, as here we solve for y' and $-z'$).

c. In the initial simulator setup, the term y^3 is generated from y by a nonlinear element (e.g., realized with diodes).

d. In the scaling process, we treat y^3 as a separate variable (distinct from y) to be scaled individually.

e. The variables are scaled in the sequence listed; the crossed-out gains are the successive values derived in the scaling process.

f. The scaled computer program is drawn directly from the final flow diagram.

In practice we would of course utilize potentiometers, initial-condition switches and batteries not shown, etc.

The above discussion illustrates only one application of the signal-flow diagram as a model for representation of the system dynamics. The signal-flow diagram is particularly useful in the study of the sensitivity of the over-all transmission or the stability to changes in a particular parameter, when the basic feedback theory initially presented by Bode is applied to the signal-flow diagrams. The signal-flow diagram can also be manipulated with exactly the techniques used with block diagrams in the study of feedback configurations as outlined briefly in the first part of the chapter.

Circuit Models. The third important class of models is the circuit model—in particular, the equivalent electric circuit representation or analogously, the mechanical circuit diagram drawn according to the systematic rules and conventions so well established for electric circuits. Since it is impossible in the brief space available here to consider in detail the extension of electric circuit techniques to nonelectrical systems,[1] we restrict consideration to one specific example which illustrates the general approach and certain of the advantages.

The example is a hydraulic translational power amplifier shown in Fig. 9.19a. The determination of the dynamics of the amplifier with sufficient completeness to permit evaluation of the characteristics of an over-all system in which the amplifier is only one part can be affected by derivation of a circuit model. If we initially assume that a linear approximation is adequate (and this is the customary assumption in order to obtain a rough idea of how the system operates), we can determine a circuit exactly as we would proceed in the study of an electronic circuit.

[1] W. A. Lynch and J. G. Truxal, "Introductory System Analysis," McGraw-Hill Book Company, Inc., New York, 1961.

The hydraulic system operates in the following manner: when the valve rod is moved to the right by the solenoid, oil flows from the high-pressure (P_0) supply through the right port toward the left side of the power piston and from the right side of the power piston through the left valve port to the low-pressure reservoir. Consequently, a pressure differential exists across the piston and a net force acts to the right. The pressure buildup on the left side of the power cylinder is related to the flow into this volume by the compressibility of the oil.

Analysis of the system is conveniently divided into three parts: the mechanical and hydraulic system from the power side of the valve ports to the load, the valve action, and the solenoid action. In the analysis of the power cylinder and the load, it is convenient to work in terms of pressure differentials, comparing the right and left sides of the system. Thus, in Fig. 9.19b, the pressure at A is denoted $P_0/2 + p_v$ and at B, $P_0/2 - p_v$ (with the valve at neutral and the system entirely at rest, we assume sufficient leakage past the valve ports from the pressure supply to the reservoir to maintain the quiescent pressure at both A and B as $P_0/2$).

With this notation, the net pressure differential from A to B is $2p_v$. We likewise denote the net volumetric flow rate as q, with the positive direction as shown. Because of the flow through the lines there is a pressure drop, and the net pressure differential across the power piston is $p_p = p_v - rq$. The net flow q divides into three primary parts:

1. Leakage around the power piston (flow proportional to the pressure differential)
2. Motion of the power piston (flow proportional to the velocity v_p)
3. Compression of the oil (flow proportional to the rate of change of pressure)

Hence, as a first linear approximation, we can write the three terms, respectively, as

$$q = gp_p + Av_p + k\frac{dp_p}{dt} \qquad (9.58)$$

where A is the effective piston area.

The variables p_p and v_p are related by the nature of the specific load on the output. A typical load, shown in Fig. 9.19b, consists of a compliant shaft driving a mass, spring, and damper combination, so that the hydraulic force p_pA is given by

$$p_pA = k(x_p - x_L)$$
$$k(x_p - x_L) = M\frac{d^2x_L}{dt^2} + B\frac{dx_L}{dt} + Kx_L \qquad (9.59)$$

Equations (9.58) and (9.59) describe the "linear" hydraulic and mechanical circuit loading the valve. If we view the valve as the central control

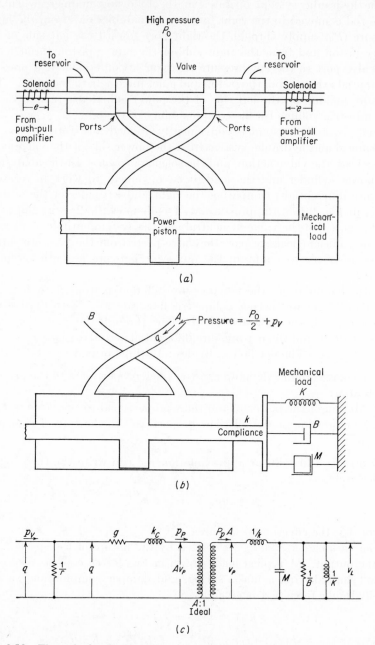

Fig. 9.19 Electrohydraulic amplifier. (*a*) Hydraulic power amplifier. (*b*) Hy- (*d*) Typical value characteristics. (*e*) Linearized value characteristics. (*f*) Circuit representation.

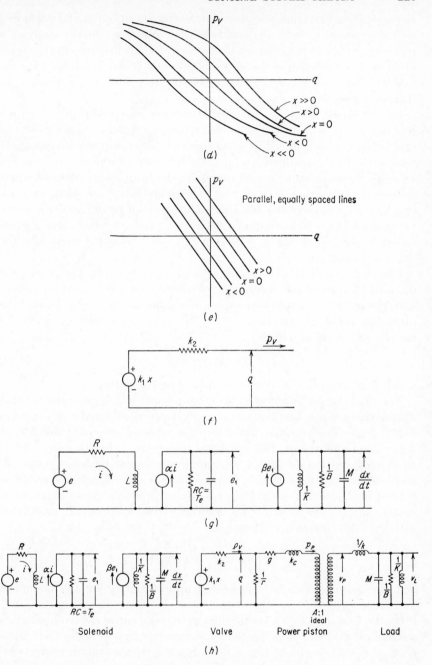

draulic-mechanical system following value. (c) Equivalent circuit for part (b). model for value. (g) Circuit for solenoid representation. (h) Complete circuit

element, these two equations describe the constraints on p_v and q imposed by the external circuit; analysis is exactly analogous to the study of a triode amplifier with a complex load circuit, for our first step in the triode problem is to determine the relation between i_b and e_b imposed by the external circuit. Figure 9.19c emphasizes this analogy by the circuit representation for the two equations.

In the triode analysis, we now determine one additional equation relating i_b and e_b from the tube characteristics; in this step the control grid voltage is introduced as a parameter. Usually it is convenient, at least early in the analysis, to linearize the tube characteristics and use an equivalent-circuit or model representation—although when accuracy is desired, or voltage and current swings are large, we have to work graphically. Exactly the same procedure is used in the analysis of the valve, with the relation imposed between p_v and q by the valve characteristics (illustrated in Fig. 9.19c); in this case the added variable is the valve displacement x.

Linearization of the valve characteristics is shown in Fig. 9.19e (the desirable linearization depending, of course, on the operating region, with the specific example here chosen to emphasize the region around the quiescent point at which $p_v = q = 0$). The linearization yields the parameters of the equation

$$q = k_1 x - k_2 p_v \qquad (9.60)$$

which is represented by the circuit model of Fig. 9.19f.

The final portion of the system is the solenoid which generates a valve displacement x as a function of the applied electrical signal e, as shown in Fig. 9.19a. The transfer dynamics of a solenoid are quite difficult to determine theoretically, but in general the system is fourth order.[1] The mechanical portion is a typical resonant system involving mass, damping, and compliance; there is an L/R time constant describing the buildup or current in the coil when a voltage e is applied; and experimental measurements indicate the need for an additional time constant T_e associated with the eddy currents. Thus

$$\frac{X}{E} = \frac{K}{(T_e s + 1)[(L/R)s + 1](Ms^2 + Bs + K)} \qquad (9.61)$$

and the solenoid can be represented approximately by the circuit of Fig. 9.19g.

On the basis of Eqs. (9.58) through (9.61), the entire electro-hydraulic-mechanical system is represented approximately by the moderately complicated circuit model of Fig. 9.19h. Such a representation neglects all nonlinearities (those in the valve, such as stiction and hysteresis, are

[1] J. G. Truxal (ed.), "Control Engineers' Handbook," pp. 15–48, McGraw-Hill Book Company, Inc., New York, 1958.

often particularly important in determining the characteristics and stability of the over-all control system) and the force reaction of the valve (we assumed above that X/E is independent of p_v and q, although in practice the existence of the fluid dynamic force influences the solenoid displacement just as the input impedance of a transistor modifies the input current). Even with these approximations, however, the model we have constructed often yields answers sufficiently accurate to be a most important and useful guide in design. Consideration of the secondary factors is then postponed in practice until an analog-computer simulation is constructed, since only then are we in a position to analyze the effects of the various nonlinearities.

The above example illustrates two significant aspects of control system engineering:

1. The analysis and design of electromechanical systems in most cases parallels directly the study of electronic systems; the basic techniques of linearization, the utilization of circuit models, and the steps and procedure in analysis are similar.

2. The circuit model is a general pictorial representation of sets of linear integro-differential equations; the talent the electrical engineer has developed for rapid analysis of electric circuits and for simple deduction of pertinent system characteristics from the circuit diagram can be applied directly in the study of nonelectrical systems.

Computer Simulations. The fourth model of importance to the control engineer is the analog-computer simulation. Since analog computers have been discussed in detail in the earlier chapters of this text, we confine our remarks here to a reemphasis of those principles of analog-computer programming which are of special and basic importance when the simulator is to be used as a model for assistance in control system design (i.e., not as an active element of the final control system).

If the computer is to be of maximum utility in guiding system design, the following aspects of the setup are essential:

1. Each isolated section of the system must be represented by an isolated portion of the computer. All too often, programmers in the computer department first convert the data of the control engineer to a set of differential equations, and then the entire system is set up as a unit; if the control system designer is to utilize the computer efficiently, he must be able to recognize separate parts of the system.

2. Simulation should be in the same terms as the original, analytic description insofar as possible: i.e., if the component is described by a transfer function in factored form, the computer realization should be based upon the same form. Such a requirement places severe demands upon the computer engineer, since maximum utilization of the general

operational amplifier form of Fig. 9.20, for example, while maintaining simple correlation between computer potentiometers and variable system parameters, often demands rather elegant network synthesis. Very often the fullest exploitation of the computer requires such elegance.

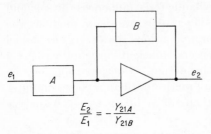

$$\frac{E_2}{E_1} = -\frac{Y_{21A}}{Y_{21B}}$$

Fig. 9.20 Basic operational amplifier configuration (Y_{21} is short-circuit transfer admittance).

3. The computer setup must be sufficiently flexible to permit ready insertion of various types of non-linearities—a requirement which is closely related to point 2 above.

The above comments can be generalized by the statement that the computer program must be developed with the single objective of facilitating the control engineer's interpretation of computer results; such a computer program requires usually unconventional, often ingenious use of operational amplifiers.

9.4 Signal Theory

Previously in this chapter we have considered briefly the topics of feedback theory and model theory, and we have been concerned with the characterization and interconnection of components in feedback systems. The performance of a feedback system depends not only on these factors, but certainly to an equal extent on the types of signals exciting the system. In this section, we attempt to consider very briefly certain important aspects of signal analysis, the topic which encompasses the study of the nature of signals particularly as this nature is important in establishing system performance characteristics.

Control system design techniques ordinarily involve the assumption that the input signals fall into one of a restricted group of classes:

1. Singularity functions and their integrals
2. Sinusoidal functions
3. Exponential functions
4. Random signals

The problem of system design then resolves to the following steps:

1. Typical or actual input signals are interpreted in terms of one of the above classes—e.g., the actual input signal is resolved, at least approximately, into its sinusoidal components.

2. The fundamental characteristics of the feedback system are interpreted in terms of these selected input signals—e.g., the sensitivity of system performance to changes in specified process parameters is evaluated in terms of the components of the input signals.

A simple example illustrates the general technique implied above. If we desire the control system to reproduce accurately a given, typical input signal as in Fig. 9.21a, the bandwidth required for the system is determined by the highest significant frequency of the signal.   Determination of the "frequency content" of such a short-duration signal is not a clear-cut problem; essentially we are dealing with a transient rather than a steady-state situation.   However, an approximate answer for the required bandwidth can be obtained if the given signal is approximated in its interval of most radical variation by a sinusoid, as shown in part (b) of the figure.   Obviously such a criterion for bandwidth selection is undesirably vague, but the difficulties of such vagueness are at least partially compensated by the fact that the designer

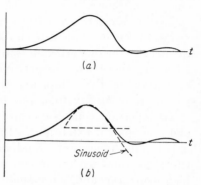

Fig. 9.21   Approximation in region of rapid variation.   (a) Signal input. (b) Approximation.

is seeking only a guide; final design must involve evaluation of the system in actual operation.

The importance of the specific nature of the input signals is indicated by the dependence of the sensitivity on the particular signals.   The sensitivity function, the fundamental evaluation of the effectiveness of the feedback, is given by

$$S_x{}^T \equiv \frac{d \ln T}{d \ln x} = \frac{dT/T}{dx/x} \tag{9.62}$$

and hence measures the percentage change in T (the over-all transmission) resulting from a given percentage change in x (the variable parameter). Even in simple cases, S is a function of the complex frequency s, and hence the interpretation of S depends upon the input signals.

The specific example of Fig. 9.22 illustrates the situation in very simple terms.   In this case, the over-all transmission is, with a assuming the normal value of unity,

$$T = \frac{25}{s^2 + 5s + 25} \tag{9.63}$$

and the sensitivity of T to changes in the parameter a is (again with an a of unity)

$$S_a{}^T = -\frac{s(s + 5)}{(s^2 + 5s + 25)(s + 1)} \tag{9.64}$$

Thus, the sensitivity is 0 when s is either 0 or -5; in other words, as long as the input consists of a sum of step functions or exponentials of the form

$$A\epsilon^{-5t}$$

the over-all transmission is independent of changes in a, at least if these changes are small.

The zero-sensitivity nature of the system of Fig. 9.22 for $s = 0$, -5 is, of course, evident from the block diagram, since at these complex frequencies the forward gain is infinite. In more complex configurations, however, the zeros of the sensitivity function are ordinarily less apparent; evaluation of the complete system requires a detailed study of the pertinent sensitivity functions for each of the components of the input.

An important conclusion can be drawn from even this simple example and its apparent extensions. In many control system design problems, it is totally unnecessary (and wasteful of gain, complexity, and design effort) to approach the design problem from the viewpoint of realizing high loop gain (and hence small sensitivity) over the bandwidth of the

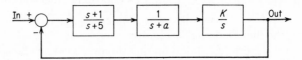

Fig. 9.22 Unity feedback system (normal $a = 1$).

input signals. In other words, the bandwidth characterization of the signals (i.e., the decomposition into sinusoidal components) often places unnecessary constraints on the design. If the signals are decomposed into damped exponential components, the system can be designed to realize insensitivity to these specific components.

The above example illustrates very briefly one implication of signal theory in the over-all theory of the design of feedback control systems. Introductory control and servo texts conventionally treat the subject exclusively in terms of the response of the system to singularity functions or sinusoids, with particular emphasis on the sensitivity function when the input is one of the integrals of the impulse (e.g., a step function or a ramp function). The importance of step and ramp functions as media for characterizing performance has led to the definition of the error coefficients (the position error constant, the velocity constant, the acceleration constant) as measures of the magnitude of the loop gain at very low frequencies. Specifically, in the unity feedback system with G the forward gain, the coefficients are defined by the relations:

$$\text{Position constant} \quad \equiv K_p = \lim_{s \to 0} G(s)$$

$$\text{Velocity constant} \quad \equiv K_v = \lim_{s \to 0} sG(s) \qquad (9.65)$$

$$\text{Acceleration constant} \equiv K_a = \lim_{s \to 0} s^2 G(s)$$

Defined in this way, the error coefficients are rough indications of the magnitude of the loop gain at low frequencies.[1]

Thus, the general area of signal theory provides a foundation for detailed evaluation of the control system in its specific task. In the subsequent chapters, particular aspects of signal theory are discussed in more detail. Just as in communication system studies, where we are just beginning to understand the performance characteristics of specific circuits in terms of specific input signals, the evaluation of control systems, both linear and nonlinear, on the same basis is a relatively unexplored field with a host of important and challenging problems.

9.5 Control Systems Engineering

The final area of control, control systems engineering, represents the combination of feedback theory, model theory, and signal theory in a unified and logical approach to control system design. This control systems engineering is the theme of the following five chapters, first in conventional systems, then in nonlinear and sampled-data systems, and finally in systems in which the input signals are random processes. Thus, in these subsequent chapters, we shall consider the exploitation of the fundamental theories underlying control engineering; our objective will be the design of control systems which, incorporating the specified process elements and adding control elements within the constrained limits of space, weight, and reliability, realize over-all characteristics specified in terms of responses to both input signals and parameter variations.

[1] Fuller treatments of the error coefficients are given in all standard servo texts; *cf.*, for example, John G. Truxal, "Automatic Feedback Control System Synthesis," McGraw-Hill Book Company, Inc., New York, 1955.

10

Control System Synthesis Techniques

JOHN A. ASELTINE

DIRECTOR OF SENSING AND INFORMATION SCIENCES
THE AEROSPACE CORPORATION, LOS ANGELES
AND LECTURER, UNIVERSITY OF CALIFORNIA, LOS ANGELES

10.1 Introduction

We define synthesis as any process which produces a system design having prescribed performance characteristics. If a control system is to be synthesized, there is implied the presence of an element to be controlled—the plant. Our problem is to determine additional elements in an appropriate configuration to yield the desired results.

In this chapter we will examine various methods for synthesizing control systems. As we shall see, the general problem is far from a complete solution. Nevertheless, the methods are applicable in some situations, and more important, represent steps in the direction of a general synthesis technique.

Synthesis Procedure. The first step in control system synthesis is the specification of objectives in useful form. This is probably the most difficult part of the problem. While it is easy to relate performance (transient response, bandwidth, etc.) of a second-order system to its transfer function, the problem rapidly becomes unmanageable for higher-order linear systems. If the system is nonlinear, the problem is even more difficult. Let us suppose, however, that we have arrived at a set of specifications.

Next, we examine our specifications for reasonableness. For example, it is theoretically possible to begin by canceling all plant poles and zeros with a tandem element in order to get a completely fresh start. In general this is an unreasonable thing to do. We often are unable to locate plant singularities accurately; further, they may move around during system operation. Nonlinearities may become important under some operating conditions (this is the reason we can't build an autopilot which will make a large transport fly like a jet fighter). In general,

232

we wish our final design to include simple, economical, and reliable compensation.

Finally, having specified our synthesis criteria, and then determined that what we are seeking is reasonable, we proceed with an appropriate synthesis method. We favor methods which allow retention of some physical feeling for the problem during the design process. We may not always be able to find such a method, and in some complex situations our approach may be largely trial and error, as we shall see.

Synthesis Methods. In the sections to follow we shall discuss the following techniques:

1. *Algebraic synthesis.* If we have written a closed-loop transfer function which meets the synthesis criteria, we can always find compensation which will yield the desired results. The complexity will, however, be high, and degree of physical understanding during design low.

2. *Geometric methods.* These use s-plane geometry, and hence keep the physical situation apparent during design.

3. *Inverse root locus.* This category includes methods which work back to open-loop from closed-loop s-plane singularities.

4. *Truxal's method.* This method yields compensation with real-axis poles. It is partly graphical so that some physical intuition is retained.

5. *Synthesis with transport lags or nonlinearities.* A number of methods based largely on special system configurations are available.

6. *Synthesis with computers.* For sufficiently complex systems we may be led to the systematic use of automatic computers.

10.2 Synthesis Criteria

Before proceeding with discussions of the various synthesis methods, we shall write down some of the criteria which might be used.

1. *Steady-state performance.* This includes specification of maximum errors under constant excitation, as well as amplitude and phase of sine-wave output.

2. *Transient response.* Rise time, overshoot, damping, and frequency are associated with impulse and step response. Response characteristics for other kinds of excitation might be used. For higher-order systems some criterion such as integrated time-multiplied absolute value (ITAE) might be used.

3. *Noise.* The spectral density, mean, mean square, etc. of the output for noise excitation might be specified.

These criteria must, of course, be converted into acceptable transfer functions before synthesis of a linear system can start. For higher-order systems we may be faced with the choice of one among a number of acceptable transfer functions—or we may have difficulty in finding even one. This, as we have said, is a difficult problem, there being no direct path from criteria to transfer function. We are often reduced to cut-

and-try procedures. We will assume in the following sections that a suitable transfer function has been somehow found and that we are ready to proceed.

If the system is nonlinear, we do not even have a transfer function. In general, each case must be examined by itself. We may, for example, specify a maximum amplitude limit cycle permissible. In some cases some of the linear criteria (e.g., rise time) may be applicable. Often we may be satisfied with stability as the only criterion.

In summary, our criterion may reflect any or all of the following:

1. Best dynamic performance
2. Lowest steady-state errors
3. Simplest compensation
4. Greatest reliability
5. Lowest cost
6. Widest tolerances
7. Smallest size

With these goals before us we proceed now to the methods available for achieving them.

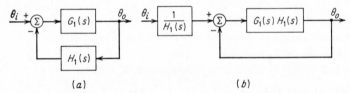

(a)   (b)

Fig. 10.1 (a) Single-loop block diagram. (b) Equivalent diagram with no feedback path block.

10.3   Mathematical Preliminaries

The methods of linear synthesis which we shall investigate in the sections to follow are based on properties of open- and closed-loop transfer functions. These properties will be reviewed here.

Fig. 10.2 General single-loop feedback system.

Transfer Functions. The block diagram of the most general single-loop transfer function is shown in Fig. 10.1. Since parts (a) and (b) are equivalent so far as output and input are concerned, we may treat the system of Fig. 10.2 with no loss of generality.

The transfer function for Fig. 10.2 is:

$$\frac{\theta_o}{\theta_i} = \frac{KG(s)}{1 + KG(s)} \triangleq KY(s) \qquad (10.1)$$

or

$$Y(s) = \frac{G(s)}{1 + KG(s)} \qquad (10.2)$$

Solving for G,

$$G(s) = \frac{Y(s)}{1 - KY(s)} \tag{10.3}$$

$G(s)$ is assumed to be of the form

$$G(s) = \frac{(s - z_1)(s - z_2) \cdots}{(s - p_1)(s - p_2) \cdots} = \frac{s^Z + \cdots}{s^P + \cdots} \tag{10.4}$$

If $P > Z$, $Y(s)$ will have the same form.

A case of special interest occurs when $G(s)$ has one pole at the origin. In this case we write

$$KG(s) = \frac{K(s - z_1)(s - z_2) \cdots}{s(s - p_2)(s - p_3) \cdots}$$
$$\triangleq \frac{K_v(\tau_1 s + 1)(\tau_2 s + 1) \cdots}{s(T_2 s + 1)(T_3 s + 1) \cdots} \tag{10.5}$$

which defines the *velocity constant* K_v.

Poles and Zeros.   From (10.1) and (10.3) the zeros of $Y(s)$ occur at the zeros of $G(s)$, and vice versa.

The closed-loop poles [poles of $Y(s)$] occur at the roots of

$$1 + KG(s) = 0 \tag{10.6}$$

From (10.3) the open-loop poles [poles of $G(s)$] occur at the roots of

$$1 - KY(s) = 0 \tag{10.7}$$

When we write Eqs. (10.6) and (10.7) in polar form, they become statements of the root-locus method of analysis:

At the poles of $Y(s)$ $\angle G(s) = n\pi$ n odd

$$|G(s)| = \frac{1}{K} \tag{10.8}$$

At the poles of $G(s)$ $\angle Y(s) = m\pi$ m even

$$|Y(s)| = \frac{1}{K} \tag{10.9}$$

s-Plane Geometry.   Let us now suppose that $G(s)$ has poles (p_1, p_2, etc.) and zeros (z_1, z_2, etc.) as shown in Fig. 10.3.

A term of (10.4) is identified in the figure.   This term contributes an angle to $G(s)$ as shown.   Referring now to Fig. 10.4, the angle of $G(s)$ is given by:

$$\angle G(s) = \phi_1 + \phi_2 - (\theta_1 + \theta_2 + \theta_3 + \theta_4) \tag{10.10}$$

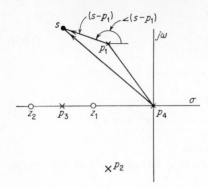

Fig. 10.3 Angle of a term of $G(s)$.

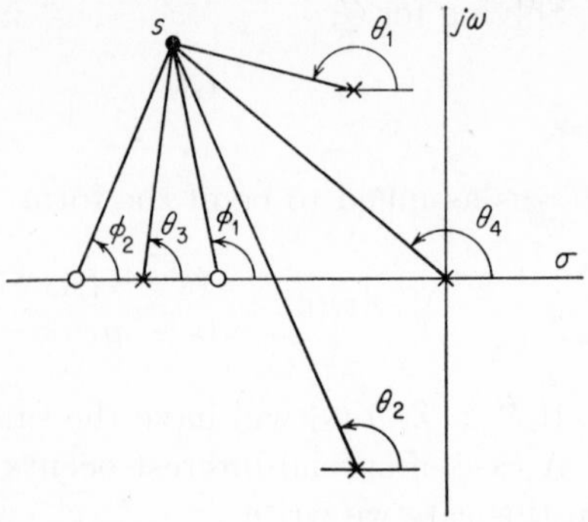

Fig. 10.4 Angles contributing to angle of $G(s)$.

If this angle is an odd multiple of π, then the test point s is a possible pole of $Y(s)$. It *will* be a pole of $Y(s)$ if [from (10.8)]

$$|G(s)| = \frac{\Pi \text{ (distances from zeros to point } s)}{\Pi \text{ (distances from poles to point } s)} = \frac{1}{K} \qquad (10.11)$$

From the similarity of (10.8) and (10.9) it is clear that a similar argument leads to conditions for possible open-loop poles when $Y(s)$ is known. If $Y(s)$ has poles and zeros as in Fig. 10.5,[1] the angle of $Y(s)$ is given by:

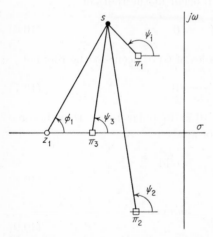

$$\angle Y(s) = \phi_1 - (\psi_1 + \psi_2 + \psi_3)$$

If the result is 0, 2π, 4π, etc., then s is a possible pole of $G(s)$. It *will* be a pole of $G(s)$ if the counterpart for $Y(s)$ of Eq. (10.11) holds.

A knowledge of poles of $Y(s)$ is, of course, the beginning of the synthesis problem. The geometric relation just discussed will be useful in its solution.

Fig. 10.5 Angles contributing to angle of $Y(s)$.

The Gains K and K_v. Let us write down some relations between gains and pole-zero locations which will be useful later. We rewrite from (10.5):

$$KG(s) = \frac{K(s - z_1) \cdots}{s(s - p_2) \cdots} = \frac{K_v(\tau_1 s + 1) \cdots}{s(T_2 s + 1) \cdots} \triangleq \frac{Kp(s)}{q(s)} \qquad (10.12)$$

[1] We will mark open-loop poles $\times$ and closed-loop poles $\square$.

We also write $Y(s)$ to exhibit its poles π_1, π_2, etc.

$$Y(s) \triangleq \frac{(s - z_1)(s - z_2) \cdots}{(s - \pi_1)(s - \pi_2) \cdots} \tag{10.13}$$

First, let us write from (10.2) and (10.12)

$$Y(s) = \frac{G(s)}{1 + KG(s)} = \frac{K_v(\tau_1 s + 1) \cdots / K s(T_2 s + 1) \cdots}{1 + K_v(\tau_1 s + 1) \cdots / s(T_2 s + 1) \cdots} \tag{10.14}$$

We note that

$$Y(0) = \frac{1}{K} \tag{10.15}$$

Next we write by differentiating (10.2)

$$Y'(s) = \frac{G'(s)}{[1 + KG(s)]^2} = \frac{(p/q)'}{\left(1 + K \dfrac{p}{q}\right)^2}$$

$$= \frac{qp' - pq'}{(q + Kp)^2} \tag{10.16}$$

Now from (10.12)

$$p = \frac{K_v}{K} (\tau_1 s + 1) \cdots$$
$$q = s(T_2 s + 1) \cdots$$
$$p' = \frac{K_v}{K} [\tau_1(\tau_2 s + 1) \cdots + \tau_2(\tau_1 s + 1) \cdots + \cdots] \tag{10.17}$$
$$q' = (T_2 s + 1)(T_3 s + 1) \cdots + s[T_2(T_3 s + 1) \cdots + \cdots]$$

and

$$p(0) = \frac{K_v}{K} \qquad p'(0) = \frac{K_v}{K} \sum \tau_i$$
$$q(0) = 0 \qquad q'(0) = 1 \tag{10.18}$$

Then from (10.16)

$$Y'(0) = \frac{-K_v/K}{K_v{}^2} = -\frac{1}{KK_v} \tag{10.19}$$

and finally from (10.15)

$$\frac{Y'(0)}{Y(0)} = -\frac{1}{K_v} \tag{10.20}$$

Now we note that

$$\frac{Y'(0)}{Y(0)} = \left[\frac{d}{ds} \ln Y(s) \right]_{s=0} \tag{10.21}$$

and write from (10.13)

$$\ln Y(s) = \ln (s - z_1) + \ln (s - z_2) + \cdots$$
$$- \ln (s - \pi_1) - \ln (s - \pi_2) - \cdots$$

$$\frac{d}{ds} \ln Y(s) = \frac{1}{s - z_1} + \frac{1}{s - z_2} + \cdots$$
$$- \frac{1}{s - \pi_1} - \frac{1}{s - \pi_2} - \cdots$$

$$\left[\frac{d}{ds} \ln Y(s) \right]_{s=0} = - \sum \frac{1}{z_i} + \sum \frac{1}{\pi_i} \qquad (10.22)$$

Combining (10.22) and (10.2?), we have finally

$$\frac{1}{K_v} = \sum \frac{1}{z_i} - \sum \frac{1}{\pi_i} \qquad (10.23)$$

where $Y(s)$ has zeros at $s = z_i$; poles at $s = \pi_i$.

When complex poles or zeros occur, the pair can be combined into a single term. For example, if a pair of zeros is located at $-\alpha \pm j\beta$, then (10.23) becomes

$$\frac{1}{K_v} = \sum \frac{1}{z_i} + \frac{1}{-\alpha + j\beta} + \frac{1}{-\alpha - j\beta} - \sum \frac{1}{\pi_i}$$
$$= \sum \frac{1}{z_i} - \frac{2\alpha}{\alpha^2 + \beta^2} - \sum \frac{1}{\pi_i} \qquad (10.24)$$

10.4   Algebraic Methods

Perhaps the most straightforward solution of the synthesis problem is the following. We write the closed-loop transfer function:

$$KY(s) = \frac{KG(s)}{1 + KG(s)} \qquad (10.25)$$

Now $Y(s)$ is assumed to be a known rational fraction

$$Y(s) = \frac{(s - z_1)(s - z_2) \cdots}{(s - \pi_1)(s - \pi_2) \cdots} \qquad (10.26)$$

We assume an appropriate form for $G(s)$, substitute in (10.25), equate coefficients of like powers of s, and the problem is solved.

It is true that a solution can be obtained in this way, but there are certain drawbacks which will be brought out presently. Specifically, they are as follows:

1. There is no flexibility in design—the solution appears at the end of the algebraic manipulation with no opportunity for understanding the system under study.

2. A complete specification of $Y(s)$ is required. No advantage is taken of the freedom usually permitted in the choice of pole-zero locations to meet performance requirements.

On the other hand, the algebraic methods appear to have considerable promise for improvement, especially through the use of digital computers.

Algebraic Synthesis. Let us consider the system of Fig. 10.6. We shall now determine the form of $G_c(s)$ required to realize a given closed-loop transfer function $Y(s)$.[1]

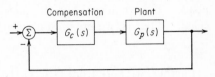

Fig. 10.6 Block diagram.

We assume the following:

1. The system contains certain unalterable elements—the *plant.* $G_p(s)$ has more poles than zeros.

2. The *compensation* transfer function has at most the same number of zeros as poles. None of the zeros of $G_c(s)$ are to be used to cancel plant poles.

Now from Fig. 10.6 we write

$$Y(s) = \frac{G_c(s)G_p(s)}{1 + G_c(s)G_p(s)} \tag{10.27}$$

Solving for $G_c(s)$,

$$G_c(s) = \frac{1}{G_p(s)} \frac{Y(s)}{1 - Y(s)} \tag{10.28}$$

Now we assume forms for the various transfer functions. For the closed loop

$$Y(s) \triangleq \frac{N_y(s)}{D_y(s)} = \frac{s^{Z_y} + a_{Z_y-1}s^{Z_y-1} + \cdots}{s^{P_y} + b_{P_y-1}s^{P_y-1} + \cdots} \tag{10.29}$$

For the plant

$$G_p(s) \triangleq \frac{N_p}{D_p} = \frac{s^{Z_p} + \cdots}{s^{P_p} + \cdots} \tag{10.30}$$

and for the compensation

$$G_c(s) \triangleq \frac{N_c}{D_c} = \frac{a_{Z_c}s^{Z_c} + a_{Z_c-1}s^{Z_c-1} + \cdots}{s^{P_c} + b_{P_c-1}s^{P_c-1} + \cdots} \tag{10.31}$$

From condition 1

$$P_p > Z_p \tag{10.32}$$

and from condition 2

$$P_c \geq Z_c \tag{10.33}$$

[1] The following development is based on work by R. E. Mortensen of Space Technology Laboratories.

Next, we write (10.28)

$$G_c(s) = \frac{D_p}{N_p} \frac{N_y}{D_y - N_y} \tag{10.34}$$

Now from condition 2, G_c contains no zeros which would cancel plant poles. This requires that the factor D_p on the right of (10.34) be canceled. That is, we must be able to write

$$D_y - N_y = D_p b(s) \tag{10.35}$$

Further, we note from (10.27) that zeros of $Y(s)$ are the same as those of $G_c(s)G_p(s)$. Then N_y can be written

$$N_y = N_p a(s) \tag{10.36}$$

Now we write (10.34):

$$G_c(s) = \frac{D_p}{N_p} \frac{N_p a(s)}{D_p b(s)} = \frac{a(s)}{b(s)} \tag{10.37}$$

Now from (10.35) and (10.36)

$$\begin{aligned} D_y &= N_y + D_p b(s) \\ &= N_p a(s) + D_p b(s) \end{aligned} \tag{10.38}$$

Now, finally, we write (10.38)

$$\begin{aligned} s^{P_y} + b_{P_y-1} s^{P_y-1} + \cdots = N_p[a_{z_c} s^{z_c} + \cdots] \\ + D_p[s^{P_c} + b_{P_c-1} s^{P_c-1} + \cdots] \end{aligned} \tag{10.39}$$

On the right-hand side of (10.39) there are $P_c + Z_c + 1$ unknown coefficients. On the left there are P_y known coefficients since $Y(s)$ is specified. We can determine the coefficients on the right [thus determining $G_c(s)$] by equating coefficients if

$$P_c + Z_c + 1 \geqslant P_y \tag{10.40}$$

Another relation is obtained by noting from (10.32) and (10.33) that the degree of the right side is determined by the second term and

$$P_y = P_p + P_c \tag{10.41}$$

Combining (10.40) and (10.41) we can find the number of compensation zeros:

$$\begin{aligned} P_c + Z_c + 1 &\geq P_y \\ P_y - P_p + Z_c + 1 &\geq P_y \\ Z_c &\geq P_p - 1 \end{aligned} \tag{10.42}$$

The minimum number of compensation poles or zeros is thus

$$P_c = Z_c = P_p - 1 \tag{10.43}$$

Finally, the minimum number of closed-loop poles is, from Eq. (10.41),

$$P_y = 2P_p - 1 \qquad (10.44)$$

EXAMPLE.   Let us illustrate by considering the following specifications:

Plant   Poles: 0, $\pm j3$
            Zeros: none

Then
$$P_p = 3$$
$$Z_p = 0$$

and from (10.44)
$$P_y = 5 \qquad (10.45)$$

Closed loop   Required poles: $-3.5 \pm j5,\ -14.2$

Two more poles will result according to (10.45).   We arbitrarily place these on the real axis remote from the required poles:

Additional poles: $-20,\ -30$

Compensation   From (10.43)

$$P_c = Z_c = 2$$

We now write (10.38) to determine the coefficients of the compensation transfer function

$$
\begin{aligned}
D_y &= N_p a(s) + D_p b(s) \\
&= a(s) + s(s^2 + 9)b(s) \\
&= (a_2 s^2 + a_1 s + a_0) + s(s^2 + 9)(s^2 + b_1 s + b_0) \qquad (10.46)
\end{aligned}
$$

but from the specifications

$$D_y = [(s + 3.5)^2 + 25](s + 14.2)(s + 20)(s + 30) \qquad (10.47)$$

Equating (10.46) and (10.47) we write, after expanding,

$$
\begin{aligned}
& s^5 + 71s^4 + 1{,}797s^3 + 20{,}082s^2 + 108{,}438s + 317{,}370 \\
& = s^5 + b_1 s^4 + (b_0 + 9)s^3 + (9b_1 + a_2)s^2 + (9b_0 + a_1)s + a_0 \qquad (10.48)
\end{aligned}
$$

Equating coefficients we have

$$
\begin{array}{ll}
a_2 = 19{,}442 & b_1 = 71 \\
a_1 = 92{,}358 & b_0 = 1{,}788 \\
a_0 = 317{,}370 &
\end{array}
$$

and the compensation is then

$$
\begin{aligned}
G_c(s) &= 19{,}442\,\frac{s^2 + 4.75s + 16.3}{s^2 + 71s + 1{,}788} \\
&= 19{,}442\,\frac{(s + 2.375)^2 + 3.265^2}{(s + 35.6)^2 + 22.95^2} \qquad (10.49)
\end{aligned}
$$

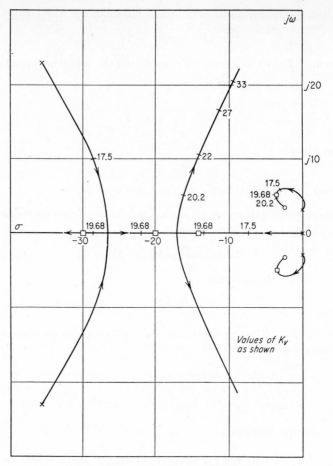

Fig. 10.7 Root-locus verification.

A root-locus plot verifying this result is shown in Fig. 10.7. The behavior of the roots starting at the compensation poles is rather surprising and somewhat troublesome. We make the comments:

1. The compensation poles produced by the algebraic method are complex. We would probably prefer real poles which would be easier to obtain physically.

2. The roots starting at the compensation poles move violently with K_v, and might lead to difficulties if the gain were set too high. The roots starting at $\pm j3$, on the other hand, are insensitive to gain changes.

These comments simply bear out those made at the beginning of this section. The algebraic method may lead to difficulties unforeseen at the beginning of the problem. Other general observations are:

1. The complexity of compensation may be all out of proportion with the desired results. In Sec. 10.9 we shall discuss a system with nine

plant poles. Equation (10.43) would require eight poles and eight zeros for the compensation. In the example of Sec. 10.9, adequate performance is achieved with two poles and one zero.

2. There is no guarantee that compensation poles will lie in the left half-plane, or on the real axis, or meet any other condition required by physical considerations.

The above problems do not appear to be insurmountable, however. The algebraic approach appears to have potential for real usefulness, especially with the use of high-speed computers.

Method of Povejsil and Fuchs. An algebraic method for synthesizing multiple-loop systems has been proposed by Povejsil and Fuchs.[1] The method uses feedback compensation as opposed to the tandem compensation discussed in the previous section.

The method is applied to systems with several "plant" elements. The input to each is modified by the addition of feedback terms chosen to obtain closed-loop poles with favorable positions in the s plane.

As an example, let us consider lateral control of an aircraft. The input variables are rudder deflection δ_r and aileron deflection δ_a. The outputs are roll φ, yaw ψ, and sideslip β. The equations can be written in the form

$$A_{11}\varphi + A_{12}\psi + A_{13}\beta + F_{11}\delta_a + F_{12}\delta_r = 0$$
$$A_{21}\varphi + A_{22}\psi + A_{23}\beta + F_{21}\delta_a + F_{22}\delta_r = 0 \qquad (10.50)$$
$$A_{31}\varphi + A_{32}\psi + A_{33}\beta + F_{31}\delta_a + F_{32}\delta_r = 0$$

or

$$\begin{pmatrix} A_{11} & A_{12} & A_{13} \\ A_{21} & A_{22} & A_{23} \\ A_{31} & A_{32} & A_{33} \end{pmatrix} \begin{pmatrix} \varphi \\ \psi \\ \beta \end{pmatrix} = \begin{pmatrix} -F_{11}\delta_a - F_{12}\delta_r \\ -F_{21}\delta_a - F_{22}\delta_r \\ -F_{31}\delta_a - F_{32}\delta_r \end{pmatrix} \qquad (10.51)$$

The transfer functions for φ, ψ, and β will always contain the A determinant in the denominator. Thus, the roots of $|A|$ are the poles of the system.

Now we can modify this determinant by changing the inputs. For example, the aileron deflection may consist of a command δ_a' plus signals obtained from measured roll and yaw

$$\delta_a = \delta_a' + H_{11}\varphi + H_{21}\psi \qquad (10.52)$$

This has the effect of changing the A matrix in (10.51) which now becomes:

$$\begin{pmatrix} A_{11} + H_{11}F_{11} & A_{12} + H_{21}F_{11} & A_{13} \\ A_{21} + H_{11}F_{21} & A_{22} + H_{21}F_{21} & A_{23} \\ A_{31} + H_{11}F_{31} & A_{32} + H_{21}F_{31} & A_{33} \end{pmatrix} \qquad (10.53)$$

---

[1] D. J. Povejsil and A. M. Fuchs, A Method for the Preliminary Synthesis of a Complex Multiloop Control System, *Trans. AIEE*, pp. 129–134, July, 1955.

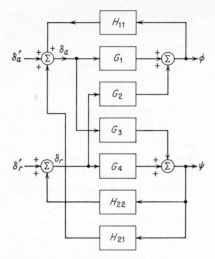

Fig. 10.8 Feedback compensation for aircraft lateral control.

The expansion of the new A determinant is compared with the desired system transfer function denominator as H_{11} and H_{21} are adjusted. Similar modifications to δ_r are made. For any but the simplest systems, machine implementation is desirable.

The final result might be as shown in Fig. 10.8· in this figure G_1, for example, is given by

$$G_1 = \frac{\begin{vmatrix} -F_{11} & A_{12} & A_{13} \\ -F_{21} & A_{22} & A_{23} \\ -F_{31} & A_{32} & A_{33} \end{vmatrix}}{|A|} \quad (10.54)$$

The G's, however, are not used explicitly in determining the form of the H's.

10.5   Geometric Methods

If we plot poles and zeros of $G(s)$ and $Y(s)$, we may be able to use the geometry of the configuration to solve the synthesis problem.

Lead Network.   Let us consider first the use of a lead network in achieving a desired pole location of $Y(s)$.[1]   A pole-zero pair for a lead network is shown in Fig. 10.9. The contribution to the angle at A is $\theta_z - \theta_p$; and this is simply the angle subtended at the point by the pole-zero pair.

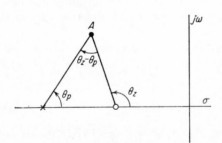

Fig. 10.9 Angle contribution of lead network.

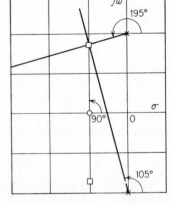

Fig. 10.10 Open- and closed-loop poles.

EXAMPLE.   Suppose we have poles and zero of $G(s)$ as shown in Fig. 10.10   It is desired to increase the damping by moving the imaginary

[1] L. G. Walters, Optimum Lead-controller Synthesis in Feedback-control Systems, *IRE Trans. on Circuit Theory*, vol. CT-1, no. 1, pp. 45–48, 1954.

roots to the places marked □.
The angle measured at the desired
pole locations (□) is

$$-195° - 105° + 90° = -210°$$

A lead network with a contribution
of 30° is needed. One of the possible solutions is shown in Fig. 10.11.

From the example it is apparent
that the angle contribution available from a single lead network is
likely to be limited. Somewhat
more flexibility can be achieved

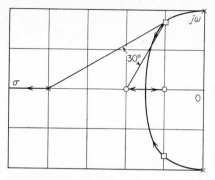

Fig. 10.11 Solution to problem of Fig.
10.10 and root-locus verification.

through the use of bridged- or parallel-T networks having complex zeros.

Complex Zeros.[1] Let us consider the angle contributed at a point in
the s plane by a pair of complex
zeros as shown in Fig. 10-12.

From the figure it is clear that
the angle of the zero pair to the
left is positive and equal to the

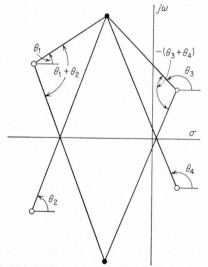

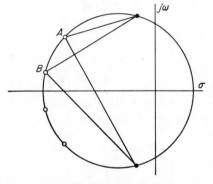

Fig. 10.12 Angle contributed by a pair
of zeros.

Fig. 10.13 Circular locus of zeros contributing same angle at test point.

angle subtended at one of the zeros by the conjugate pair of test points.
For the pair to the right the angle contributed is negative.

Let us now construct a circle through the zeros and test points as
shown in Fig. 10.13. Since the angles at A and B are inscribed in the

[1] Design charts for the use of complex zeros are used by A. H. Zemanian, Further
Effects of the Pole and Zero Locations on the Step Response of Fixed, Linear Systems,
Trans. AIEE, part II, pp. 52–55, March, 1955. The graphical technique was sug-
gested to the author by W. Carpenter of Space Technology Laboratories. See W.
Carpenter, Synthesis of Feedback Systems with Specified Open-loop and Closed-loop
Poles and Zeros, *IRE Trans. on Auto. Control*, vol. AC-4, no. 3, pp. 185–196.

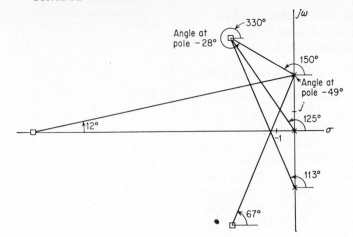

Fig. 10.14   Open- and closed-loop poles.

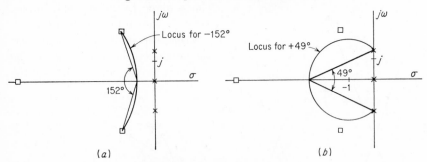

Fig. 10.15   Loci for complex zeros.

same segment, they are equal.   The part of the circle to the left of the test points is the locus of zeros contributing the same angle at the test points—that angle being subtended at a zero by the test points.

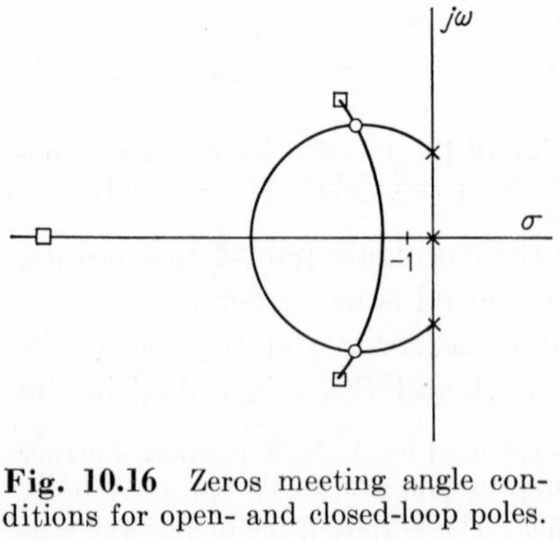

The fact that zeros anywhere on the circular locus to the left of the test points provide the same lead angle provides us with considerable flexibility in synthesis. This will be brought out in the following example:

EXAMPLE.   Suppose open- and closed-loop poles are as shown in Fig. 10.14.   Angles at the poles are as shown.   The steps leading to the complex zero location are shown in Fig. 10.15.   Zeros placed on the locus in part (a) would make the angle 180° at the closed-loop poles, as required by (10.8).   According to (10.9) we also require that the angle at the

Fig. 10.16   Zeros meeting angle conditions for open- and closed-loop poles.

open-loop poles be zero, and this condition is met by the locus in part (b). Both conditions are satisfied by zeros at the intersections of the loci as shown in Fig. 10.16.   The final root locus for verification is shown in Fig. 10.17.   This figure should be compared with Fig. 10.7 where the zeros were obtained by an algebraic method.

It should be pointed out that complex zeros if furnished by a bridged- or twin-T network would be accompanied by a pair of poles not included in the example.   The example was chosen to illustrate the principles of

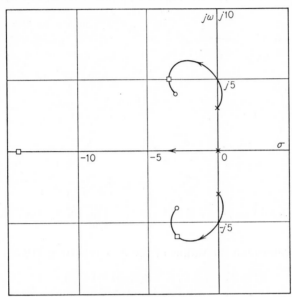

Fig. 10.17   Root-locus verification of example.

geometric synthesis, and not as a realistic design problem.   The method can be extended to more complicated situations, however.   It can also serve as the basis for iterative techniques such as the one we will discuss in detail in the next section.

K_v *with Complex Zeros.*   A technique similar to the one just discussed can be used to fix the velocity constant K_v.   We write from (10.24)

$$\frac{1}{K_v} = \sum_i \frac{1}{z_i} - \frac{2\alpha}{\alpha^2 + \beta^2} - \sum_i \frac{1}{\pi_i} \tag{10.55}$$

To find the locus of zeros for constant K_v we write (10.55) as

$$\frac{2\alpha}{\alpha^2 + \beta^2} = \frac{1}{A} \tag{10.56}$$

or
$$\alpha^2 - 2\alpha A + \beta^2 = 0 \tag{10.57}$$

where
$$\frac{1}{A} = \sum_i \frac{1}{z_i} - \sum_i \frac{1}{\pi_i} - \frac{1}{K_v} \tag{10.58}$$

Completing the square, we have finally

$$\alpha^2 - 2\alpha A + A^2 + \beta^2 = A^2$$
$$(\alpha - A)^2 + \beta^2 = A^2 \tag{10.59}$$

The locus is a circle with radius A and center at $-A$.

EXAMPLE. Suppose we have closed-loop poles as shown in Fig. 10.18. It is required to find a pair of complex zeros which will provide a K_v of 30 and also be consistent with open-loop poles shown in Fig. 10.19.

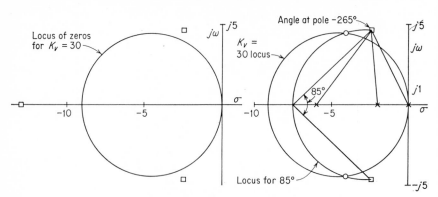

Fig. 10.18　Closed-loop poles and K_v locus for example.　　**Fig. 10.19**　Angle locus construction.

First we determine the radius of the K_v circle from (10.58)

$$\frac{1}{A} = \frac{1}{13} + \frac{2(2.45)}{2.45^2 + 4.65^2} - \frac{1}{30} \tag{10.60}$$

from which $A = 4.5$. The K_v circle is shown in Fig. 10.18.

Next we determine the angle at the closed-loop poles as in Fig. 10.19. The zeros must contribute $+85°$, and hence must lie on the locus shown. The K_v circle is plotted here also, and the required zeros lie at the intersection of the loci as shown.

At this point we know that:

1. A root locus starting with the open-loop poles of Fig. 10.19 will pass through the closed-loop poles of Fig. 10.18.

2. The K_v for the closed-loop poles and complex zeros will be as specified.

However, we *do not* know whether the value of K in the root-locus plot which places poles at the complex points specified will also locate the closed-loop real pole properly. This is seen from the following argument. K_v is completely specified by the closed-loop poles [Eq. (10.55)]. The angle locus of Fig. 10.19 is specified by the open-loop pole positions, but not vice versa. Other combinations of open-loop poles could be found which would have the same angle at the closed-loop pole position. Therefore we are not assured that the open-loop pole configuration specified is the one which will yield the correct closed-loop real pole.

To finish the synthesis, then, we must check by plotting the root locus as shown in Fig. 10.20. In this case the value of K is the same at all closed-loop pole positions. In general, however, this will not be the case, and some compromise is needed. By relaxing the specifications on K_v, on real closed-loop pole position, or on both, we can in most cases iterate to a satisfactory solution, since neither of these is critical in most problems. The procedure would be to choose new values of K_v, say,

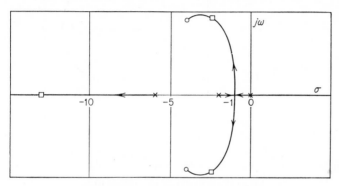

Fig. 10.20 Root locus for example.

and repeat the process just described until the relaxed specifications are met.

Unfortunately, there is no way presently to assure the convergence of this process. In more complicated examples it may be difficult to choose which compromises to make. In the next section we will discuss another iterative method.

10.6 Inverse Root Locus

Just as the root-locus method begins with the open-loop roots and shows where closed-loop roots may be located, the reverse is possible. The inverse root-locus method starts with poles and zeros of $Y(s)$ and shows possible open-loop pole positions.

We write from (10.2) and (10.3)

$$Y(s) = \frac{G(s)}{1 + KG(s)} \tag{10.61}$$

$$G(s) = \frac{Y(s)}{1 - KY(s)} \tag{10.62}$$

and note that the symmetry suggests that the method for plotting direct and inverse root loci should be similar. In fact, the only difference in plotting[1] inverse root loci is that the angle be an even, rather than an odd, multiple of π.

Let us take as an example the situation shown in Fig. 10.21. The inverse root locus is shown in Fig. 10.22. In particular, for a K of $\frac{8}{3}$ the open-loop poles would be as shown.

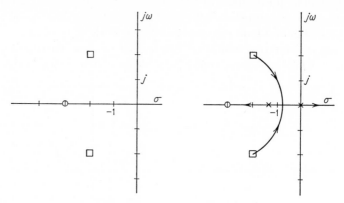

Fig. 10.21 Closed-loop poles and zero.   **Fig. 10.22** Inverse root locus.

A number of comments can be made about the use of inverse root locus:

1. Given closed-loop poles and zeros the method shows where open-loop poles may be located.

2. If prescribed open-loop poles do not lie on the locus, cancellation can be used.

3. The method forms the basis for an iterative method to be described below.

4. The method forms the basis for an algebraic method to be discussed later in this section.

Zaborszky's Method.   Zaborszky[2] has proposed a method of synthesis as follows:

1. An inverse root locus is constructed from closed-loop poles and zeros meeting specifications. Locations of open-loop poles are also specified.

2. Open-loop poles and zeros are located on the locus so that one pole of $G(s)$ or the gain meets the specifications. The other poles are shifted to coincide with nearby required poles; or new poles are added. Zeros are shifted to compensate for changes in pole positions.

3. A direct root locus is plotted. If closed-loop specifications are met the synthesis problem is solved. If not, the process is repeated.

---

[1] For a discussion of plotting inverse root loci, see J. A. Aseltine, Feedback System Synthesis by the Inverse Root-locus Method, *IRE Conv. Record*, part 2, pp. 13–17, 1956.

[2] J. Zaborszky, Integrated *s*-Plane Synthesis Using 2-Way Root Locus, *Trans. AIEE*, part 1, pp. 797–801, January, 1957.

The method may lead, through trial and error, to a satisfactory solution. The convergence of the process when many poles are involved is questionable, however.

Synthesis with Open-loop Constraints. A method for writing equations from the inverse root-locus plot has been proposed by the author.[1] The method is based on the fact that the gain on an inverse root-locus plot must have the same value at all required open-loop poles.

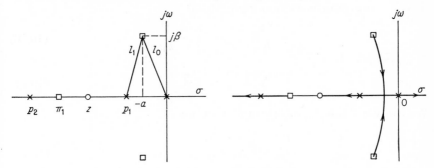

Fig. 10.23   Poles and zeros.   **Fig. 10.24**   Inverse root-locus test of feasibility.

We shall illustrate the method by example. Suppose we require open- and closed-loop poles as shown in Fig. 10.23. Further, suppose that K_v is also specified. The specifications are:

Open loop $$G(s) = \frac{s - z}{s(s - p_1)(s - p_2)} \qquad (10.63)$$

Closed loop $$Y(s) = \frac{s - z}{(s - x_1)[(s + a)^2 + \beta^2]} \qquad (10.64)$$

Compensation $$G_c(s) = \frac{s - z}{s - p_2} \qquad (10.65)$$

Plant $$G_p(s) = \frac{1}{s(s - p_1)} \qquad (10.66)$$

We wish to find z and p_2.

We first verify that the proposed closed-loop transfer function is feasible. This is done by sketching an inverse root-locus plot as in Fig. 10.24. If the gain is the same at each of the open-loop pole positions, the problem is solved. We now proceed to positions z and p_2 to meet this requirement.

Referring now to Fig. 10.23, we use the closed-loop counter part to (10.11) and write at each open-loop pole

$$|Y(s)| = \frac{\Pi \ (\text{distances from zeros to } s)}{\Pi \ (\text{distances from poles to } s)} = \frac{1}{K} \qquad (10.67)$$

[1] J. A. Aseltine, On the Synthesis of Feedback Systems with Open-loop Constraints, *IRE Trans. on Automatic Control*, vol. PGAC-7, 1959.

At the origin, then, we write

$$\frac{1}{K} = \frac{|z|}{l_0^2|\pi_1|} \tag{10.68}$$

and at p_1

$$\frac{1}{K} = \frac{|z - p_1|}{l_1^2|\pi_1 - p_1|} \tag{10.69}$$

The K_v constraint is written from (10.23)

$$\frac{1}{K_v} = \frac{1}{z} + \frac{2\alpha}{l_0^2} - \frac{1}{\pi_1} \tag{10.70}$$

If we define

$$C \triangleq \frac{1}{K_v} - \frac{2\alpha}{l_0^2} \tag{10.71}$$

We can write the three constraint equations

$$\begin{aligned} Kz - l_0^2\pi_1 &= 0 \\ Kz - l_1^2\pi_1 &= p_1(K - l_1^2) \\ z - \pi_1 &= -Cz\pi_1 \end{aligned} \tag{10.72}$$

The third equation is nonlinear. However, if we solve the first two

$$\begin{aligned} z &= \frac{l_0^2 p_1(K - l_1^2)}{K(l_0^2 - l_1^2)} \\ \pi_1 &= \frac{p_1(K - l_1^2)}{l_0^2 - l_1^2} \end{aligned} \tag{10.73}$$

and substitute the result in the third, the resulting equation is linear in K and yields

$$K = \frac{l_0^2[(l_0^2 - l_1^2) - l_1^2 p_1 C]}{(l_0^2 - l_1^2) - l_0^2 p_1 C} \tag{10.74}$$

EXAMPLE. Let us require

1. Poles of $Y(s)$ at $-3 \pm j4$
2. Poles of $G(s)$ at $0, -2$
3. $K_v = 10$

That is,

$$G(s) = \frac{s - z}{s(s + 2)(s - p_2)} \tag{10.75}$$

$$Y(s) = \frac{s - z}{(s - \pi_1)(s^2 + 6s + 25)} \tag{10.76}$$

$$G_c(s) = \frac{s - z}{s - p_2} \tag{10.77}$$

$$G_p(s) = \frac{1}{s(s + 2)} \tag{10.78}$$

We are to find z and p_1.

From the specifications we write

$$l_0 = 5 \qquad p_1 = -2$$
$$l_1 = 4.1 \qquad C = \frac{1}{10} - \frac{6}{25}$$
$$= -0.14$$

From these we obtain

$$\begin{aligned} K &= 81.3 \\ z &= -4.95 \\ \pi_1 &= -16.1 \\ p_2 &= -20.1 \end{aligned} \tag{10.79}$$

The value of p_2 was obtained from (10.5) and (10.75) by writing

$$K_v = \frac{-Kz}{p_1 p_2} \tag{10.80}$$

This method can be applied to systems of up to the fourth order with linear algebra resulting. Its utility for higher-order systems depends on finding additional constraints (like K_v); otherwise there will be more unknowns than equations.

10.7 Truxal's Method

An algebraic method suggested by Guillemin and developed by Truxal[1] will be discussed in this section. The method has the following features:

1. Compensation poles lie on the negative real axis.
2. Plant poles must be canceled by compensation zeros.
3. Compensation poles are determined graphically so that some measure of control over final results is retained.

The method is based on the following development. We write, as in (10.27),

$$Y(s) = \frac{G_c(s)G_p(s)}{1 + G_c(s)G_p(s)} = \frac{N_y}{D_y} \tag{10.81}$$

Next, we write

$$G_c(s)G_p(s) \triangleq \frac{N_0}{D_0} \tag{10.82}$$

so that

$$Y(s) = \frac{N_0}{D_o + N_o} = \frac{N_y}{D_y} \tag{10.83}$$

Now the closed-loop zeros will be the same as those of $G_c(s)G_p(s)$, so

$$N_0 = N_y \tag{10.84}$$

From (10.83) and (10.84)

$$\begin{aligned} D_0 + N_0 &= D_y \\ D_0 &= D_y - N_y \end{aligned} \tag{10.85}$$

[1] John G. Truxal, "Automatic Feedback Control System Synthesis," chap. 5, McGraw-Hill Book Company, Inc., New York, 1955.

Since $Y(s)$ is assumed known, we simply plot its numerator and denominator for real values of s; when the curves intersect, that value of s corresponds to a pole of $G_c(s)G_p(s)$ according to (10.85).

EXAMPLE.   Suppose we have the following specifications:

Plant
$$G_p(s) = \frac{1}{s(s + 2)} \tag{10.86}$$

Closed loop
$$Y(s) = \frac{s - z}{[(s + 3)^2 + 16](s - \pi)} \tag{10.87}$$
$$\text{Velocity constant } K_v \approx 10$$

First we use the K_v condition to locate the zero approximately.   From (10.24)

$$\frac{1}{K_v} = \frac{1}{z} + \frac{2\alpha}{\alpha^2 + \beta^2} - \frac{1}{\pi} \tag{10.88}$$

From (10.87) we have $\alpha = 3$, $\beta = 4$.   If we assume the pole at π is far enough from the origin to have only a minor effect on K_v, we have from (10.88)

$$\frac{1}{10} = \frac{1}{z} + \frac{6}{25}$$
$$z = -\frac{50}{7} \tag{10.89}$$

Actually, π will effect the final value of K_v.   Hence, we move the zero slightly and use the value

$$z = -6.0 \tag{10.90}$$

to try to anticipate the effect of the pole.

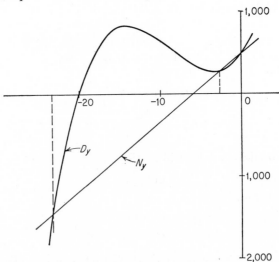

Fig. 10.25   Curve for Truxal's method.

Next a value of π is assumed. Let us try $\pi = -20$. Then, referring to (10.85) we write

$$D_y = [(s + 3)^2 + 16]\,(s + 20) \tag{10.91}$$
$$N_y = K(s + 6) \tag{10.92}$$

Now we plot D_y, as in Fig. 10.25, and note that a K can be chosen to yield an intersection, and hence a pole of the open-loop transfer function, at the origin.

From the figure we write

$$\begin{aligned} N_y &= 83.3\,(s + 6) \\ D_0 &= s(s + 2.6)(s + 23.4) \end{aligned} \tag{10.93}$$

Our final result is

$$Y(s) = \frac{83.3(s + 6)}{[(s + 3)^2 + 16](s + 20)} \tag{10.94}$$

$$G_c(s)G_p(s) = \frac{83.3(s + 6)}{s(s + 2.6)(s + 23.4)} \tag{10.95}$$

$$G_c(s) = \frac{83.3(s + 6)(s + 2.0)}{(s + 2.6)(s + 23.4)} \tag{10.96}$$

$$K_v = 8.2 \tag{10.97}$$

We note that the compensation contains a zero at -2.0 to cancel the plant pole there. The poles are all on the negative real axis, making feasible the use of RC networks in realizing the compensation.

10.8   Synthesis with Transport Lags or Nonlinearities

Here we will give examples of systems which cannot be treated by the methods of the previous sections.

Use of the Model. A design method (not strictly a synthesis method since final performance is not rigidly specified) based on the work of Lang and Ham[1] is applicable to systems with transport lags and nonlinearities.   It is discussed here because the approach may have potential for extension to true synthesis.

A feedback system incorporating a model is shown in Fig. 10.26. So long as the plant response and the model response are the same,

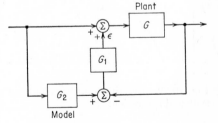

Fig. 10.26   Feedback system with model.

no error signal ε is applied to G.   Thus, the plant tends to respond like the model.   On the other hand, G_1 can be chosen to minimize effects of

[1] G. Lang and J. M. Ham, Conditional Feedback: A New Approach to Feedback Control, *Appl. and Ind.*, no. 19, pp. 152–161, July, 1955.

disturbances. If the system is linear it is equivalent to a feedback system with prefilter as shown in Fig. 10.27.

We will first discuss the application of the model concept to systems in which the plant contains a nonlinearity.

Synthesis with Plant Nonlinearity. With certain types of nonlinearity, a system may be stable under low-level excitation, but go into a limit cycle if excited by larger inputs. Our synthesis criterion here might be adequate dynamic performance without excitation of the limit cycle.

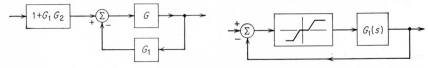

Fig. 10.27 System equivalent to linear model system.

Fig. 10.28 System with possible limit cycle behavior.

An example of a system with this kind of behavior is shown in Fig. 10.28. If the linear part of the plant $G_1(s)$ has sufficient high-frequency attenuation to effectively suppress all but first harmonic at its output, the *describing function* method of analysis applies.[1] The nonlinearity can be regarded as having a gain which is dependent on amplitude of its sinusoidal input. The general shape of the describing function for our example is shown in Fig. 10.29. The condition for existence of a limit cycle is that the equation

$$1 + NG_1(s) = 0 \tag{10.98}$$

have roots on the imaginary axis. Intersection of the $G_1(j\omega)$ and $-1/N$ plots on a Nyquist diagram is a test for imaginary roots of (10.98). Such a plot is shown in Fig. 10.30. Intersection A corresponds to unstable oscillation, the amplitude either decreasing or increasing to stable-equilibrium point B with any small disturbance. It is reasonable from the figure that if input levels are kept small compared to the value of X at point A the limit cycle will not be initiated.

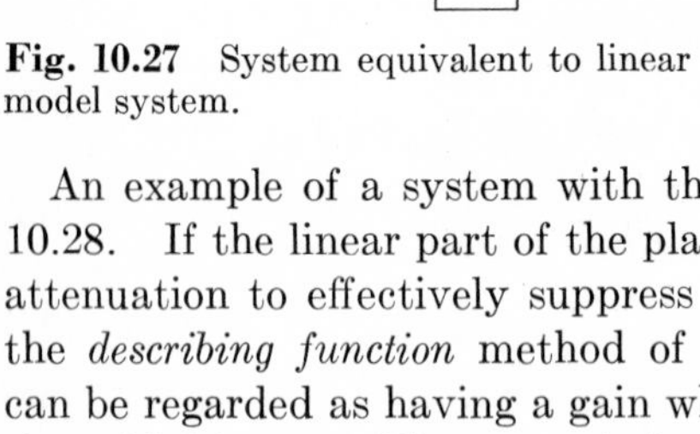

Fig. 10.29 Describing function for dead zone and saturation.

Now let us consider the system of Fig. 10.31. The model includes the same type of nonlinearity as the plant. G_3 has been added to improve system performance. We now argue that so far as signals due to the nonlinearity are concerned, cancellation effectively opens the loop at A

[1] Truxal, *op. cit.*, chap. 10.

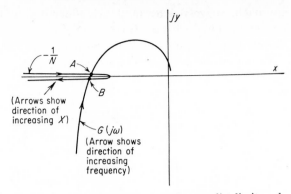

Fig. 10.30 Nyquist diagram used to predict limit cycle.

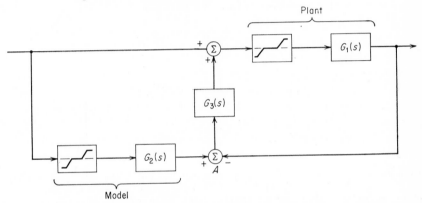

Fig. 10.31 Addition of nonlinearity to model to prevent excitation of limit cycle.

so that the limit cycle cannot be initiated. If this is so, G_3 can be chosen by one of the linear synthesis methods.

The above discussion indicates that deliberate addition of a non-linearity may lead to a system free of limit-cycle behavior. Each case should be examined carefully, how-ever, since the method cannot be considered universally applicable. It does represent a step in the direc-tion of nonlinear synthesis.

Plant with Transport Lag. The idea of a model can be applied to control of a plant containing a

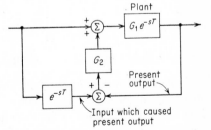

Fig. 10.32 System with transport lag.

transport lag (true time delay). Such a system is shown in Fig. 10.32. Here the error signal is derived from the difference between present out-put and the signal which caused that output. The synthesis for best performance is based on the open-loop transfer function G_1G_2.

Another approach, suggested by O. J. M. Smith,[1] is shown in Fig. 10.33. In part (a) the plant with the transport lag is shown. In part (b) we remove all but the transport lag from the plant and include it in a closed-loop with compensation G_2. This separation of G_1 is in general

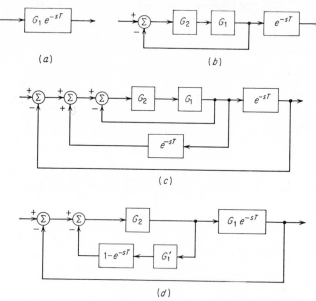

(a)   (b)

(c)

(d)

Fig. 10.33 O. J. M. Smith's method of synthesis. (a) Plant with transport lag. (b) Unrealizable solution for control of plant. (c) System equivalent to part (b) but still unrealizable. (d) Realizable system equivalent to part (b).

not physically realizable. In part (c) we add two parallel loops which cancel one another. One feedback path comes from the measurable plant output. In part (d) we combine loops to obtain a realizable system. G_1' is assumed to be as nearly like the plant as possible.

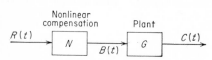

Fig. 10.34 Nonlinear compensation.

Since the final system is equivalent to (b), we synthesize G_1G_2 as we would a system without transport lag.

Experimental Synthesis of Nonlinear System. A method for experimentally determining the characteristics of a nonlinear element to be included in a system for improved performance has been suggested by Lebell.[2]

The proposed control system is shown in Fig. 10.34. N is the non-

[1] Otto J. M. Smith, "Feedback Control Systems," pp. 325–329, McGraw-Hill Book Company, Inc., New York, 1958.

[2] D. Lebell, Nonlinear Compensation of an Aircraft Instrument Servomechanism by Analog Simulation, *Trans. IRE Prof. Group on Automatic Control,* vol. PGAC-1, pp. 10–18, May, 1956.

linear element to be synthesized.   The criterion is that the output $C(t)$ should be equal to the input $R(t)$.

If we impose the condition that $C = R$ we can determine N as shown in Fig. 10.35. B is a test signal supplied externally.

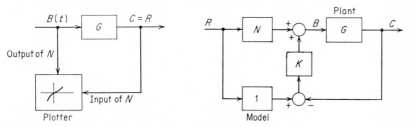

Fig. 10.35   Determination of N.

Fig. 10.36   Final system with nonlinear compensation.

The final system incorporates N in a model system to reduce errors due to uncertainties and tolerances in the plant.   The system is shown in Fig. 10.36.

10.9   Synthesis With the Aid of Digital and Analog Computers

While the methods of the preceding sections are applicable to the synthesis of some systems, they fall short of meeting requirements in more complex situations.   In this section we shall illustrate how a design may be reached by the systematic use of digital and analog computers. All of the calculations that follow were made with computing machinery. Although this technique is not synthesis in the strict sense, it represents a systematic method for achieving desired results.   The emphasis is on the intelligent and systematic use of computers with a minimum of trial and error.

We will consider a hypothetical missile with the following characteristics:

1. The plant has nine poles and six zeros.
2. Cancellation is impractical because of uncertainty in plant pole-zero positions.
3. Reliability requires the simplest possible control system.

In reality the missile treated here is considerably simplified.   The following simplifying assumptions have been made:

1. No aerodynamic forces are present.
2. No propellant sloshing is present.
3. Only the first bending mode is considered.
4. The system is linear.

Our objective will be to synthesize a control system using only a rate gyro for compensation.   Our procedure will be as follows:

1. Open-loop poles and zeros are computed.
2. The open-loop root locus, Bode plot, and Nyquist diagram are computed to see how serious a problem the stabilization will be.

3. These plots are recalculated for extreme values of rate feedback gain.

4. The analog computer is used to make final adjustments of gain values, using the digital computer results as a guide.

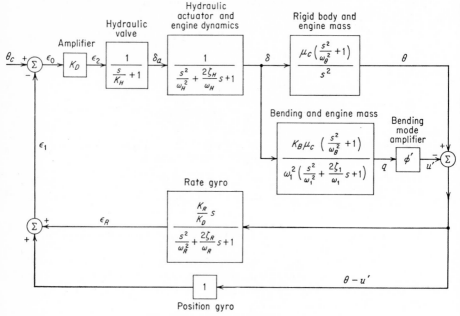

Fig. 10.37   Missile block diagram.

The Missile.[1]   A block diagram of the missile[2] and proposed autopilot loops is shown in Fig. 10.37.   The numerical values assumed for the various parameters are shown in Table 10.1.

Table 10.1   Missile Parameters

$K_H = 30$	$K_B = 10$	$\omega_R = 157$
$\omega_H = 82$	$\varphi' = 0.14$	$\zeta_R = 0.7$
$\zeta_H = 0.1$	$\omega_B = 36.1$	K_D = displacement gain
$\mu_c = 4.72$	$\omega_1 = 30$	K_R = rate gain
$\omega_\theta = 38.9$	$\zeta_1 = 0.01$	

Open-loop Roots.   Because of the parallel paths starting with δ in the block diagram it is necessary to perform some computation to locate the open-loop zeros.   A digital-computer routine designed to find roots of a determinate with polynomial elements was used.   The parameters were substituted in the transfer functions and the matrix equation (10.99) written.

[1] The author is indebted to J. Friedenthal of Space Technology Laboratories for his assistance in formulating this example.

[2] The transfer function between δ and u' is discussed in the appendix to this chapter.

$$
\begin{bmatrix}
(0.033333333s+1) & 0 & 0 & 0 & 0 & K_D \\
-1 & (0.00014872100s^2+0.0024390244s+1) & 0 & 0 & 0 & 0 \\
0 & (-0.0031191969s^2-4.72) & s^2 & 0 & 0 & 0 \\
0 & (-0.0000056339517s^2-0.0073422222) & 0 & (0.0011111111s^2+0.0006666667s+1) & 0 & 0 \\
0 & 0 & -\dfrac{K_R}{K_D}s & \dfrac{K_R}{K_D}s & (0.0000405695597s^2+0.0089171974s+1) & 0 \\
0 & 0 & -1 & 1 & -1 & 1
\end{bmatrix}
\begin{bmatrix}
\delta_a \\ \delta \\ \theta \\ u' \\ \epsilon_R \\ \epsilon_1
\end{bmatrix}
= 0 \qquad (10.99)
$$

The first row of Eq. (10.99) can be written

$$\left(\frac{s}{30} + 1\right)\delta_a + K_D\epsilon_1 = 0 \qquad (10.100)$$

or
$$\frac{\delta_a}{\epsilon_1} = \frac{K_D}{s/30 + 1} \qquad (10.101)$$

Two runs are made after setting up (10.99) on the digital computer to find its roots

1. The term K_D is set to zero in the matrix. The roots can then be thought of as those of the closed-loop system with zero gain, and hence are the *poles* of the open-loop transfer function.

2. The term $(s/30 + 1)$ is replaced by zero in the matrix. This makes the closed-loop gain infinite, and the roots then correspond to open-loop *zeros*.

The result of the computation made for a value of K_D/K_R of 1.0 is the open-loop transfer function.[1]

$$\frac{\epsilon_1}{\epsilon_0} =$$

$$-K \frac{(s + 0.991)(s + 0.041 \pm j35.48)(s + 41.1)(s - 42.2)(s + 24868)}{s^2(s + 0.3 \pm j30.0)(s + 30.0)(s + 8.2 \pm j81.59)(s + 109.9 \pm j112.1)} \qquad (10.102)$$

For $K_D/K_R = 10.0$

$$\frac{\epsilon_1}{\epsilon_0} =$$

$$-K \frac{(s + 9.21)(s + 0.041 \pm j35.48)(s + 41.1)(s - 42.1)(s + 2675.5)}{s^2(s + 0.3 \pm j30.0)(s + 30.0)(s + 8.2 \pm j81.59)(s + 109.9 \pm j112.1)} \qquad (10.103)$$

With only position feedback the transfer function is

$$\frac{\epsilon_1}{\epsilon_0} = -K \frac{(s + 0.04 \pm j35.48)(s + 41.1)(s - 42.1)}{s^2(s + 0.3 \pm j30.0)(s + 30.0)(s + 8.2 \pm j81.59)} \qquad (10.104)$$

We will use the uncompensated transfer function (10.104) as a starting point for our synthesis problem.

Preliminary Analysis. We now make use of digital routines designed to produce root-locus plots, Bode plots, and Nyquist diagrams.

First, to get an idea of the problem we are beginning—the stabilization of a missile—we plot a root locus with position feedback only. This is shown in Fig. 10.38. The poles and zeros were obtained from (10.104). This is actually an inverse root-locus plot,[2] the angles summing to 2π.

---

[1] The K in (10.102) corresponds to K in (10.5) and includes K_D as a factor.

[2] Corresponding to the use of the sign change between ϵ_1 and ϵ_0 at the summing point in Fig. 10.37, in combination with the minus in (10.104).

Direct root locus was not considered because of the positive-real-axis zero which would always produce a pole in the right half-plane. Even so, the inverse plot in Fig. 10.38 is unstable also, and some kind of compensation is needed for stability.

Some features of the system can be noted from the Fig. 10.38:

1. The double pole at the origin due to the rigid body will cause instability for all values of gain.

2. The bending pole pair on the imaginary axis leads to a pole pair with small but positive damping.

3. The hydraulic pole pair increases its damping with K.

The alternate methods of determining behavior—Nyquist and Bode plots—are shown in Figs. 10.39 and 10.40.   In Fig. 10.39 are

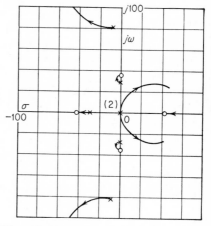

Fig. 10.38 Root locus with position feedback only.

shown details near the origin, as well as a sketch of the complete Nyquist diagram.   It is apparent that two clockwise encirclements resulting from the two rigid body poles in the right half-plane are present. In Fig. 10.40 we see the same information in its alternate form.

Since one of the most important requirements on the final system is simplicity, we now consider compensation consisting only of a rate gyro physically located near the position gyro.   With this configuration we now examine two extremes of rate feedback gain.

Effects of Rate Feedback. We now add rate feedback as shown in Fig. 10.37.   Two ratios of displacement-to-rate gain are considered. The root-locus plots resulting are shown in Figs. 10.41 and 10.42.   It is clear that we have gained rigid body damping at the expense of bending pole damping.

A detailed plot near the origin and near the bending pole is shown in Fig. 10.43.   We comment in passing that the only practical way to get plots like this is with a digital computer.   From this plot the characteristics shown in Table 10.2 can be tabulated.

Table 10.2

Characteristic	$K_D/K_R = 1.0$	$K_D/K_R = 10.0$
$K_D\mu_c$ for instability	9.0	59.0
Compromise gain value	2.0	29.5
Rigid-body damping ratio at compromise value	0.71	0.19
Bending damping ratio at compromise value	0.0051	0.0068

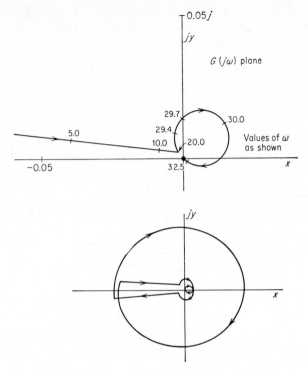

Fig. 10.39   Nyquist diagram with position feedback only.

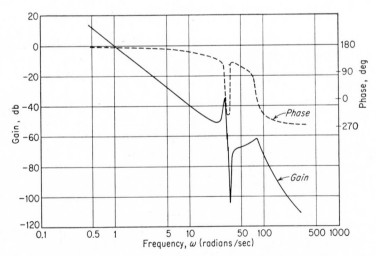

Fig. 10.40   Bode diagram with position feedback only.

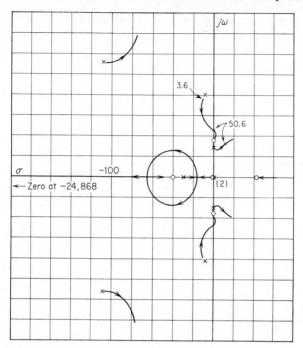

Fig. 10.41   Root locus with $K_D/K_R = 1.0$, values of $K_{D}\mu_C$ as shown.

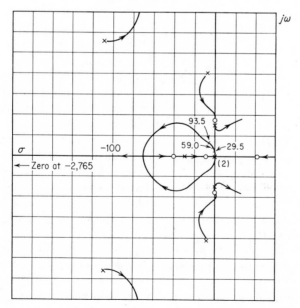

Fig. 10.42   Root locus with $K_D/K_R = 10.0$, values of $K_{D}\mu_C$ as shown.

Evidently we trade rigid-body damping for bending damping as we go from low to high K_D/K_R.

A Nyquist diagram is shown in Fig. 10.44 for $K_D/K_R = 1.0$. The figure shows a sketch of the complete diagram as well as details for positive frequencies. We see that as gain is increased, the following events occur:

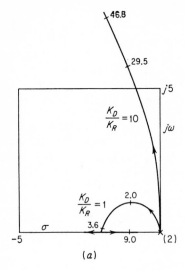

1. No encirclements—stable
2. Two c-w encirclements—bending poles in right half-plane
3. Four c-w encirclements—hydraulic and bending poles in right half-plane
4. Two c-w encirclements—bending poles in right half-plane

These events can be followed in the root-locus Fig. 10.41.

Figure 10.45 compares Bode diagrams for no rate feedback, for $K_D/K_R = 1.0$ and for $K_D/K_R = 10.0$. Since there is always some uncertainty about the exact bending frequency and damping, we are inclined toward the higher value of K_D/K_R which will leave more phase and gain margin. We must remember however that the effect on rigid body motion is unfavorable (see Fig. 10.43). To make the final compromise we will go to the analog computer.

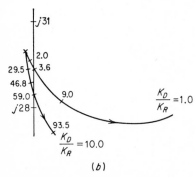

Analog-computer Study. Having determined that stabilization with a rate gyro appears feasible, and further what the effects of parameter changes will be, we are ready to set up the

Fig. 10.43   Details of root-locus plots near origin and bending pole. (*a*) *s* plane near the origin. (*b*) *s* plane near bending pole.

problem on the analog computer. One of the advantages of analog computers is flexibility; it is easy to try different parameter values and observe effects. This flexibility should be used intelligently, however. To avoid a "shotgun" approach, we prepare by studying the system with the less flexible digital machine as we have just done.

An analog machine diagram for the system of Fig. 10.37 is shown in Fig. 10.46. The similarity of the diagrams is characteristic of analog

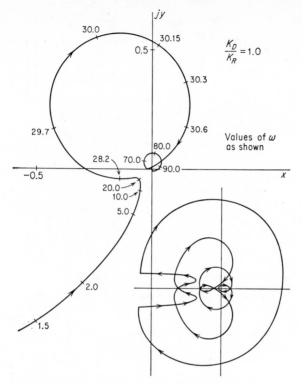

Fig. 10.44 Nyquist diagram for $K_L/K_R = 1.0$.

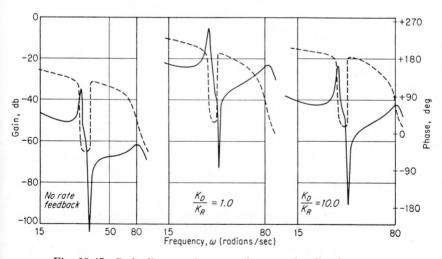

Fig. 10.45 Bode diagrams for comparison near bending frequency.

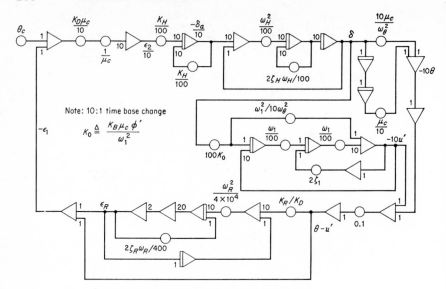

Fig. 10.46 Analog-computer diagram for system.

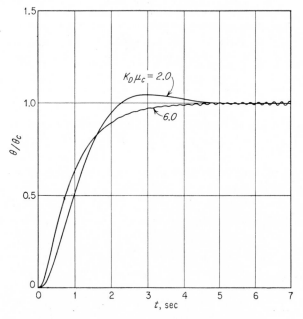

Fig. 10.47 Step response with $K_D/K_R = 1.0$.

work, and makes possible considerable physical feeling for the problem under study.

Figures 10.47 through 10.50 are step responses for various values of K_D/K_R. In each case several values of $K_D\mu_C$ were tried. The best compromise between rise time and damping seems to be $K_D/K_R = 5.0$.

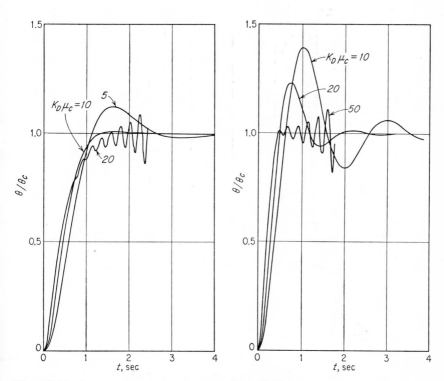

Fig. 10.48 Step response with K_D/K_R = 2.0

Fig. 10.49 Step response with K_D/K_R = 5.0.

The details of engine step response for this value are shown in Fig. 10.51. The oscillations due to hydraulics, rigid body, and bending are all visible in the figure. A value of $K_D\mu_C = 15$ was chosen for its smaller bending oscillation and overshoot.

The behavior of the various variables in the final system is shown in Fig. 10.52.

10.10 Conclusions

For certain relatively simple problems, we have seen that synthesis methods exist. For most situations, however, there is no simple, direct way of achieving desired results. In no case were we able to take into account all of the objectives at the end of Sec. 10.2.

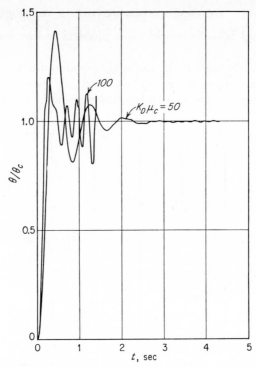

Fig. 10.50   Step response with $K_D/K_R = 10.0$.

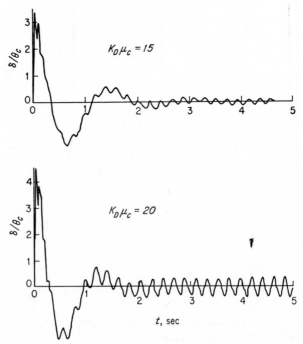

Fig. 10.51   Engine motion with step input and $K_D/K_R = 5.0$.

We need better ways of stating synthesis criteria in usable form. If we had these ways, we would still need more generally applicable methods for synthesizing systems meeting the criteria.

Of particular promise in the latter respect, are machine methods. It seems reasonable to expect that high-speed computation may make

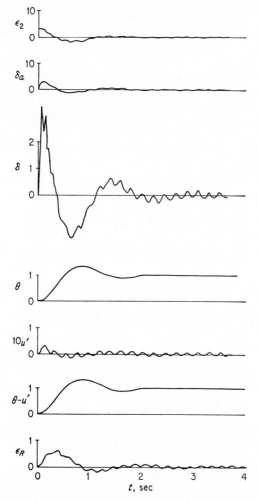

Fig. 10.52 Unit step responses of system variables to θ_c input: $\mu_c K_D = 15$; $K_D/K_R = 5.0$.

possible the synthesis of complex systems meeting realistic requirements. The methods discussed in this chapter ought to be viewed as steps toward better synthesis methods rather than as isolated solutions to special problems. If machines are to be used, they must be used with the insight obtained by analytical understanding.

APPENDIX A TRANSFER FUNCTION FOR A BEAM

In formulating the control problem for a missile in which bending takes place, a transfer function relating applied force to local body angle is needed. Let us suppose for simplicity that the missile can be treated as a uniform beam (EI is constant). The equation relating static bending to applied force for a uniform beam is

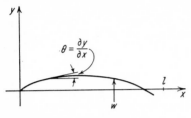

$$EI \frac{\partial^4 y}{\partial x^4} = w \qquad (A.1)$$

Fig. 10.53 Beam coordinates.

where w is force per unit length, and x and y are coordinates as in Fig. 10.53.

The deflection $y(x,t)$ is assumed small; the slope $\partial y / \partial x$ can be taken as the deflection θ.

If we include as part of the applied force the kinetic reaction due to acceleration of each element of mass, the equation becomes

$$EI \frac{\partial^4 y}{\partial x^4} + m \frac{\partial^2 y}{\partial t^2} = w_1 \qquad m = \frac{\text{mass}}{\text{length}} \qquad (A.2)$$

Finally, if the beam is subjected to a unit impulse at $x = 0$, we have

$$EI \frac{\partial^4 y}{\partial x^4} + m \frac{\partial^2 y}{\partial t^2} = \delta(x)\, \delta(t) \qquad (A.3)$$

If the beam is unsupported (free-free) and initially at rest, the boundary conditions for Eq. ($A.3$) are

$$y(x,0) = 0$$
$$\frac{\partial y(x,0)}{\partial t} = 0 \qquad (A.4a)$$

$$\frac{\partial^2 y(0,t)}{\partial x^2} = \frac{\partial^2 y(l,t)}{\partial x^2} = 0 \qquad \text{moment zero}$$
$$\qquad\qquad\qquad\qquad\qquad\qquad\qquad\qquad (A.4b)$$
$$\frac{\partial^3 y(0,t)}{\partial x^3} = \frac{\partial^3 y(l,t)}{\partial x^3} = 0 \qquad \text{shear zero}$$

Let us begin by $\mathcal{L}$-transforming ($A.3$) with respect to t, letting $\mathcal{L}_t y(x,t) \triangleq \bar{y}(x,s)$:

$$EI \frac{d^4 \bar{y}}{dx^4} + ms^2 \bar{y} = \delta(x) \qquad (A.5)$$

Next, let us transform ($A.5$) with respect to x, with $\mathcal{L}_x \bar{y}(x,s) \triangleq Y(\gamma,s)$:

$$EI\gamma^4 Y + ms^2 Y = EI \left[\frac{1}{EI} + \gamma^3 \bar{y}(0,s) + \gamma^2 \bar{y}_x(0,s) \right.$$
$$\left. + \gamma \bar{y}_{xx}(0,s) + \bar{y}_{xxx}(0,s) \right] \qquad (A.6)$$

We note that the impulse function enters the problem exactly as an initial shear, so that instead of solving ($A.5$) with boundary conditions ($A.4b$) we can solve

$$\frac{\partial^4 \bar{y}}{\partial x^4} + \frac{ms^2}{EI}\, \bar{y} = 0 \qquad (A.7)$$

with
$$\bar{y}_{xx}(0,s) = 0$$

$$\bar{y}_{xxx}(0,s) = \frac{1}{EI}$$

$$\bar{y}_{xx}(l,s) = 0$$
$$\bar{y}_{xxx}(l,s) = 0 \qquad (A.8)$$

We will solve this classically, since the two-point boundary conditions ($A.8$) make the use of the $\mathcal{L}$ transform cumbersome. We assume a solution of the form

$$\bar{y}(x,s) = A\cos kx + B\sin kx + C\cosh kx + D\sinh kx \qquad (A.9)$$

where
$$k^4 \triangleq -\frac{ms^2}{EI} \qquad (A.10)$$

If we differentiate ($A.9$) to form $\bar{y}_{xx}$ and $\bar{y}_{xxx}$ and substitute these in ($A.8$), a set of equations which can be solved for A, B, C, and D results:

$$\begin{pmatrix} -1 & 0 & 1 & 0 \\ 0 & -1 & 0 & 1 \\ -\cos kl & -\sin kl & \cosh kl & \sinh kl \\ \sin kl & -\cos kl & \sinh kl & \cosh kl \end{pmatrix} \begin{pmatrix} A \\ B \\ C \\ D \end{pmatrix} = \begin{pmatrix} 0 \\ 1/k^3 EI \\ 0 \\ 0 \end{pmatrix} \qquad (A.11)$$

The determinant of the left-hand matrix is

$$\Delta = 2(1 - \cos kl \cosh kl) \qquad (A.12)$$

Since $\bar{y}(x,s)$ has its singularities at the roots of ($A.12$) we expect that these will define the frequencies of oscillation of the beam. The first three roots are[1]

$$k_0 l = 0$$
$$k_1 l = 4.730 \qquad (A.13)$$
$$k_2 l = 7.853$$

After solving (A.11) we write the transformed beam deflection

$$\bar{y}(x,s) = \frac{1}{2EIk^3(1 - \cos kl \cosh kl)}\, [(\cos kl \sinh kl - \sin kl \cosh kl)$$
$$\times (\cos kx + \cosh kx) + (\cos kl \cosh kl + \sin kl \sinh kl - 1)\sin kx$$
$$+ (\sin kl \sinh kl - \cos kl \cosh kl + 1)\sinh kx] \qquad (A.14)$$

We will next find the terms of a partial fraction expansion of ($A.14$).

---

[1] See S. Timoshenko, "Vibration Problems in Engineering," 3d ed., p. 336, D. Van Nostrand Company, Inc., Princeton, N.J., 1955.

The Pole at 0.   We now examine the terms of $(A.14)$ as $k \to 0$.   If we expand the functions involved in power series, we find

$$(\cos x \sinh x - \sin x \cosh x) \xrightarrow[x \to 0]{} -\frac{2x^3}{3} \qquad (A.15)$$

$$(1 - \cos x \cosh x) \xrightarrow[x \to 0]{} \frac{x^4}{6} \qquad (A.16)$$

Then

$$\bar{y}(x,s) \xrightarrow[k \to 0]{} \frac{1}{2EIk^3(k^4l^4/6)} \left(-\frac{4}{3} k^3l^3 + k^2l^2kx + k^2l^2kx \right) = \frac{4l - 6x}{ml^2s^2} \quad (A.17)$$

It can be verified that $(A.17)$ corresponds to the rigid body motion due to an impulse applied at $x = 0$ for small values of y.

Other Poles.   The expression $(A.14)$ has singularities at the roots of the denominator.   The term

$$g(k) = 1 - \cos kl \cosh kl \qquad (A.18)$$

has a nonvanishing first derivative

$$g'(k) = l \sin kl \cosh kl - l \cos kl \sinh kl \qquad (A.19)$$

Therefore, $\bar{y}(x,s)$ has first-order poles in the k plane.   These occur at $\pm k_n$ and $\pm jk_n$, where k_n is the nth root of $(A.18)$.

The residue of $\bar{y}$ at the poles gives us the coefficients of the terms in a partial fraction expansion of $\bar{y}$

$$\bar{y}(x,s) = \frac{4l - 6x}{ml^2s^2} + \sum_{n=1}^{\infty} \left[\frac{A_n}{k - k_n} + \frac{B_n}{k + k_n} + \frac{C_n}{k - jk_n} + \frac{D_n}{k + jk_n} \right] \quad (A.20)$$

The coefficient A_n, for example, is found from $(A.14)$ by evaluating numerator over derivative of denominator at $k = k_n$.
From $(A.14)$ and $(A.19)$

$$A_n(x) = \frac{1}{2EIk_n{}^3l(\sin k_nl \cosh k_nl - \cos k_nl \sinh k_nl)}$$
$$\times [(\cos k_nl \sinh k_nl - \sin k_nl \cosh k_nl)(\cos k_nx + \cosh k_nx)$$
$$+ \sin k_nl \sinh k_nl(\sin k_nx + \sinh k_nx)] \quad (A.21)$$

Similarly, it is found that

$$B_n = -A_n$$
$$C_n = jA_n$$
$$D_n = -jA_n$$

so that $(A.20)$ can be written

$$\bar{y}(x,s) = \frac{4l - 6x}{ml^2s^2} + \sum_{n=1}^{\infty} \frac{4k_n{}^3A_n(x)}{k^4 - k_n{}^4} \qquad (A.22)$$

Now, from $(A.10)$

$$k^4 = -\frac{ms^2}{EI} \qquad (A.23)$$

So we can write $(A.22)$

$$\bar{y}(x,s) = \frac{4l - 6x}{ml^2s^2} - \sum_{n=1}^{\infty} \frac{4k_n{}^3EI}{m} \frac{A_n(x)}{s^2 + \omega_n{}^2} \qquad (A.24)$$

where

$$\omega_n{}^2 = \frac{EIk_n{}^4}{m}$$

Now from $(A.21)$ we write

$$\bar{y}(x,s) = \frac{4l - 6x}{ml^2s^2} + \frac{2}{ml} \sum_{n=1}^{\infty} \frac{\phi_n(x)}{s^2 + \omega_n{}^2} \qquad (A.25)$$

where

$$\begin{aligned}
\phi_n(x) &= (\cos k_n x + \cosh k_n x) \\
&\quad - \frac{\sin k_n l \sinh k_n l}{\sin k_n l \cosh k_n l - \cos k_n l \sinh k_n l} (\sin k_n x + \sinh k_n x) \\
&= (\cos k_n x + \cosh k_n x) \\
&\quad + \frac{\sin k_n l + \sinh k_n l}{\cos k_n l - \cosh k_n l} (\sin k_n x + \sinh k_n x) \quad (A.26)
\end{aligned}$$

We see that $\bar{y}(x,s)$ has simple poles at $\pm j\omega_n$ in the s plane. From $(A.25)$ we can draw the block diagram shown in Fig. 10.54.

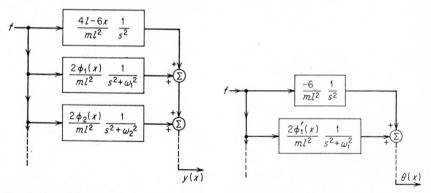

Fig. 10.54 Block diagram from force to beam deflection.

Fig. 10.55 Block diagram for angle.

If we are only concerned with the angle of deflection $\theta = \partial y/\partial x$, our block diagram is as shown in Fig. 10.55.

The functions $\phi(x)$ and $\phi'(x)$ are shown in Figs. 10.56 and 10.57 for the first four modes where $k_1 l = 4.730$, etc., from $(A.13)$. Note that, from $(A.26)$

$$\phi_n(0) = 2$$
$$\phi_n(l) = \pm 2 \qquad (A.27)$$

The transfer function for the missile shown in Fig. 10.37 is based on including only the first body bending mode. Higher bending modes could, of course, be included for purposes of system synthesis, and in

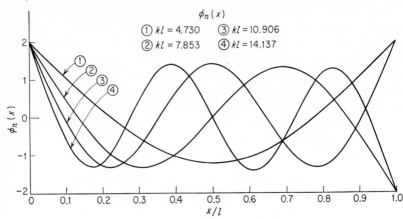

$$\phi_n(x)$$

① $kl = 4.730$ ③ $kl = 10.906$
② $kl = 7.853$ ④ $kl = 14.137$

Fig. 10.56 Plot of $\phi_n(x)$ versus (x/l).

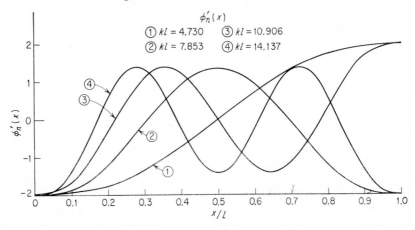

$$\phi'_n(x)$$

① $kl = 4.730$ ③ $kl = 10.906$
② $kl = 7.853$ ④ $kl = 14.137$

Fig. 10.57 Plot of $\phi'_n(x)$ versus (x/l).

practice several additional modes are usually included. For our illustrative purposes, the study of the system with one bending mode is adequate in the interests of focusing attention on basic design techniques.

The damping constant shown as ζ_1 in the transfer function of the first body bending mode in Fig. 10.37 arises from the dissipation of energy in the missile structure. This was ignored in the above derivation of the beam transfer function, but it is extremely important in that it is this damping that results in a stable missile control system design as is shown more specifically in Fig. 10.43b.   It is not too surprising, because of the complexity of ICBM's, that values for ζ are assumed, or "pulled out of the air" so to speak, for the purposes of system synthesis.[1]   This is not an uncommon situation in control system synthesis, particularly when the controlled system or plant is extremely complex and difficult to analyze precisely.

This problem of the uncertainty of location of the poles and zeros of a plant or controlled system and the resultant uncertainty of control system design is one of numerous problems which are leading to an increasing interest in the development of the theory of adaptive[2] or anthropomorphic control systems.   For example, the human body is an extremely versatile control system in spite of a lack of knowledge of an analytical description of its characteristics, and this is due in no small part to its adaptive attributes.

---

[1] An experimental approach to the determination of ξ at various points in missile flight involves the excitation of the missile on a test stand with a sinusoidal test signal.   The rate of decay of the excitation is then observed with the fuel at various levels.   However, the accuracy of these measured values is open to some question.

[2] E. Mishkin and L. Braun, Jr., (eds.), "Adaptive Control Systems," McGraw-Hill Book Company, Inc., New York, 1961.

11

Nonlinear Control System Theory

RICHARD E. KUBA

ASSISTANT DIRECTOR OF RESEARCH

POWER EQUIPMENT COMPANY, COLUMBUS, OHIO

11.1 Introduction

The study of nonlinear control systems is mostly concerned with finding answers to these two questions:

1. How do inherent system nonlinearities affect system behavior?

2. Is it possible to improve system behavior by introducing specific forms of nonlinearities into a proposed control system?

Inherent system nonlinearities constitute such often troublesome phenomena as backlash, saturation, hysteresis, etc. Contactor or switching systems, on the other hand, present inherent nonlinearities which are absolutely essential for the proper functioning of the control scheme.

It has been discovered that certain types of specific nonlinearities—for example, nonlinear damping or nonlinear amplification—when properly introduced into a control system will greatly improve the system's characteristics. The improvements obtained are often dependent on the class of inputs used to stimulate the control system.

11.2 Methods of Attack

There exist two very promising methods for attacking the analysis and synthesis of nonlinear control systems. The phase-space technique is particularly useful when one wishes to learn precisely the nature of the transient behavior exhibited by a control system for various classes of input functions. The phase-space technique is extremely useful for the presentation of all possible modes of system behavior, and the synthesis possibilities of this method indicate a high potential for great exploitation. The phase-space technique is fundamentally a time-domain technique.

The describing function technique is particularly useful in the determination of nonlinear control system stability. Although the describing

278

function method is subject to certain restrictions—which will be discussed subsequently—when properly applied, the technique is easily adapted to the study of higher-order systems without introducing necessary complexities. The describing function technique is a frequency-domain technique.

In the following discussion, the symbol p will be employed to represent the time derivative operation d/dt; thus if $e(t)$ is the error-time function of a control system, then $pe(t) = de(t)/dt$, $p^2e(t) = d^2e(t)/dt^2$, etc.

11.3 Phase-space Analysis

The study of nonlinear control systems is often considerably facilitated through the use of a tool known as phase-space analysis. The behavior of a servomechanism can be described in terms of its error coordinate e, and time derivatives of its error coordinates pe, p^2e, p^3e, etc., considered as independent variables.

Consider a servo described by the nth-order differential equation

$$p^n e = f(t, e, pe, \ldots, p^{n-1}e) \tag{11.1}$$

If now, independent variables, $x_0 = e$, $x_1 = pe$, $\ldots$, $x_{n-1} = p^{n-1}e$ are selected clearly Eq. (11.1) is equivalent to a system of $n + 1$ equations given by the expressions,

$$px_{n-1} = f(t, x_0, x_1, \ldots, x_{n-1}) \tag{11.2}$$
$$x_q = p^q e \qquad q = 0, 1, 2, 3, \ldots, n - 1 \tag{11.3}$$

Now, the independent variables $x_0, x_1, x_2, \ldots, x_{n-1}$ may be considered as the coordinates of a space S of n dimensions known as the phase space. The condition of the system at a particular instant of time t_0 is expressed by the location of a point Q in space S having coordinates $x_0(t_0), x_1(t_0), \ldots, x_{n-1}(t_0)$. As time progresses, (either positively or negatively) the representative point Q will traverse a curve in the phase space called a phase trajectory. A family of such phase trajectories is often referred to as a phase portrait. Thus, the topology of the phase portrait presents all the various possible "phases" or types of system behavior.

The time ΔT which elapses as the representative point moves along a trajectory from point Q_1 having coordinates $x_0(t_1), x_1(t_1), \ldots, x_{n-1}(t_1)$ to point Q_2 having coordinates $x_0(t_2), x_1(t_2), \ldots, x_{n-1}(t_2)$ is given by the equation

$$\Delta T = \int_{t_1}^{t_2} dt = \oint_{x_q(t_1)}^{x_q(t_2)} \frac{dx_q}{x_{q+1}} \qquad q = 0, 1, 2, \ldots, n - 2 \tag{11.4}$$

since
$$\frac{dx_q}{x_{q+1}} = dt \qquad q = 0, 1, 2, \ldots, n - 2 \tag{11.5}$$

Additional properties of phase-space analysis will become apparent as the exposition of the following example progresses.

Consider the continuously second-order, nonlinear servo system illustrated by Fig. 11.1. An error signal e generated from the comparison of an input signal r and an output signal c is fed through an amplifier having a gain K_1, a differentiator having a gain K_2, and a squarer circuit. The outputs of the differentiator and the squarer are multiplied together with a gain K_3/K_2. The outputs of the linear amplifier, differentiator,

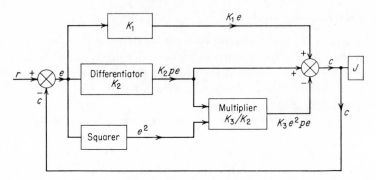

Fig. 11.1   Second-order nonlinear control system.

and multiplier are now combined to form an output torque T given by the equation,

$$T = (K_2 - K_3 e^2)pe + K_1 e \tag{11.6}$$

If J is the moment of inertia of the output element, then

$$T = Jp^2 c \tag{11.7}$$

Now since $c = r - e$, then

$$p^2 c = p^2 r - p^2 e \tag{11.8}$$

If it is assumed that the nature of the inputs is such that $p^2 r = 0$ $(t > 0)$, then the behavior of this servo is described by the second-order, nonlinear differential equation

$$p^2 e + \left(\frac{K_2}{J} - \frac{K_3}{J} e^2\right) pe + \frac{K_1}{J} e = 0 \tag{11.9}$$

Substituting $x_0 = e$ and $x_1 = pe$ in Eq. (11.9) yields the equivalent phase-plane equations

$$px_1 = -\left(\frac{K_2}{J} - \frac{K_3}{J} x_0{}^2\right) x_1 - \frac{K_1}{J} x_0 \tag{11.10}$$

$$px_0 = x_1 \tag{11.11}$$

Dividing Eq. (11.10) by Eq. (11.11) results in the differential equation (11.12) for the phase trajectories of this system in a phase plane having coordinates x_0 and x_1, that is, system error and system-error rate.

$$\frac{dx_1}{dx_0} = -\left(\frac{K_2}{J} - \frac{K_3}{J} x_0^2\right) - \frac{K_1}{J} \frac{x_0}{x_1} \qquad (11.12)$$

The solution of Eq. (11.12) is not known in terms of elementary functions, however, in principle, integration would yield a phase portrait expressed by the equation

$$F(x_0, x_1, A) = 0 \qquad (11.13)$$

Here, A is the arbitrary constant of integration. For the initial conditions $x_{0,0}$ and $x_{1,0}$, a particular value of A, namely A_0, is determined from Eq. (11.13). The insertion of other sets of initial conditions in Eq. (11.13) will result in a family of trajectories which constitute the phase portrait of the servo system.

11.4 Graphical Determination of Trajectories

The phase trajectories of the control system described by Eqs. (11.10) and (11.11) can be determined by a graphical procedure known as the method of isoclines. Returning to Eq. (11.12) and making the substitution

$$S = \frac{dx_1}{dx_0} \qquad (11.14)$$

the equations of the curves along which the slope of the tangent to the phase trajectories is everywhere identical are given by

$$S = -\left(\frac{K_2}{J} - \frac{K_3}{J} x_0^2\right) - \frac{K_1}{J} \frac{x_0}{x_1} \qquad (11.15)$$

These are known as the isoclines. Using various values of S, plots of these curves are constructed as shown in Fig. 11.2. Here, the constants K_1, K_2, K_3, and J were all assumed to be unity. In order to determine a phase trajectory, one selects as a starting point the location in the phase plane corresponding to the initial conditions of the coordinates for the solution desired. Through this point, two straight lines are drawn having slopes corresponding to the values given by the two nearest isoclines (see Fig. 11.2 where a construction is shown on curve CBA). The midpoint of the arc determined by the intersection of these straight lines and the nearest isocline is then used as a next point to continue the graphical construction. The points thus determined are connected by a smooth curve which approximates the phase trajectory. The accuracy of the method increases as the number of isoclines is augmented.

Examination of Eq. (11.4) reveals that for increasing positive values of time, the representative point experiences a clockwise motion along a phase trajectory, hence arrows are used to indicate this motion. A number of phase trajectories have been constructed for this system as shown in Fig. 11.2. The following observations are easily verified.

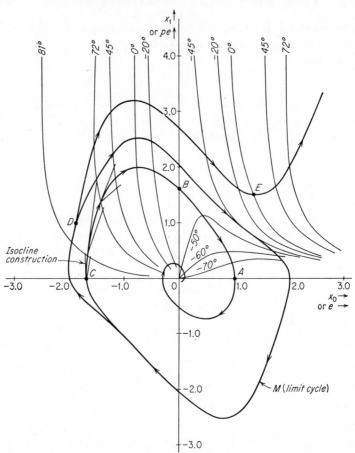

Fig. 11.2   Phase portrait of a second-order nonlinear servo system.

1. The closed curve M divides the phase portrait into two regions; phase trajectories originating inside M have the origin as their terminating point. On the other hand, phase trajectories starting at points outside M spiral outwards. The curve M is known as a limit cycle; it represents a steady-state sustained oscillation of the system. The limit cycle is a phenomenon characteristic of nonlinear systems and is not found in truly linear systems. The limit cycle M is defined as an unstable limit cycle because trajectories originating on either side of M move away from M as positive time increases.

2. The origin of the phase plane is a point of system stability because it is the terminal point of trajectories beginning inside of M. Physically, this means that the nonlinear servo will exhibit stable operation with zero steady-state error provided inputs are such that the system response is characterized by phase trajectories in the x_0,x_1 phase plane which lie wholly within M.

3. The response of the servo to a positive, unit step input of position is described by the curve AO.

4. The servo response for a positive step input of velocity is given by the curve BAO.

5. Sufficiently large inputs will cause the servo to have a phase trajectory such as DE, representing unstable performance.

The topology of phase-plane analysis, therefore, gives an accurate picture of the possible modes of operation of a second-order nonlinear control system.

11.5   Singular Points

The analytical study of differential equations has brought forth an important theorem by Cauchy[1] which states:

There exists a unique analytic solution of the differential equation

$$p^n e = f(t, e, pe, \ldots, p^{n-1}e) \tag{11.16}$$

in the neighborhood of $t = t_0$ such that the function e and its $n - 1$ derivatives acquire for $t = t_0$ the set of prescribed values $e(t_0)$, $pe(t_0)$, $\ldots$, $p^n e(t_0)$, provided $p^n e$ is analytic in the neighborhood of this set of values.

In particular, the phase-plane set of equations

$$px_0 = f(x_0,x_1) \tag{11.17}$$
$$px_1 = g(x_0,x_1) \tag{11.18}$$
$$\frac{dx_0}{dx_1} = \frac{f(x_0,x_1)}{g(x_0,x_1)} \tag{11.19}$$

will, therefore, admit two types of points. These are:

1. A point $(x_{0,0}, x_{1,0})$ for which $f(x_{0,0},x_{1,0}) = 0$ and $g(x_{0,0},x_{1,0}) = 0$ simultaneously, called a singular point.

2. Any point of the phase plane where definition 1 does not apply, called an ordinary point.

At singular points, the slope of the tangent is indeterminate, hence phase trajectories may cross one another at these points. Through ordinary points, however, there will pass one and only one phase trajectory.

There are six types of singular points which may appear in the behavior of a nonlinear system. The nature of the phase trajectories in the neighborhood of these singular points is presented in Fig. 11.3. If all trajectories in the neighborhood of a singular point flow into the singular point, then the singular point is stable.

The stability of a singular point associated with a given nonlinear differential equation may be determined if a linearization of the differential equation is possible in the vicinity of the singular point. To illustrate, consider the nonlinear differential equation

$$p^2 e + f_1(e)pe + b_2 e = 0 \qquad (11.20)$$

which has only one singular point at the origin of its e,pe phase plane. Suppose that $f_1(e)$ is of a nature such that, in the region ($-E_1 \leq e$

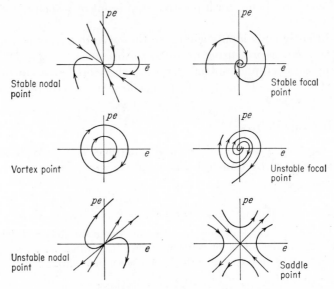

Stable nodal point

Stable focal point

Vortex point

Unstable focal point

Unstable nodal point

Saddle point

Fig. 11.3   Singular points.

$\leq + E_1$), $f_1(e)$ is a continuous function of e, that is, $f_1(e)$ can be represented by the uniformly convergent power series

$$f_1(e) = d_0 + d_1 e + d_2 e^2 + \cdots \qquad -E_1 \leq e \leq + E_1 \quad (11.21)$$

Now for small values of e, $f_1(e) \cong f_1(0) = d_0$. The stability of the singular point can then be determined from the linearized form of Eq. (11.20) given by

$$p^2 e + d_0 pe + b_2 e = 0 \qquad (11.22)$$

Standard methods exist for determining the stability criteria and the degree of stability of linear differential equations of any order. These methods can be applied to the linearized differential equation to obtain the stability of the singular point.

11.6   Nonexistence of Limit Cycles

Bendixson[2] has established a theorem for the nonexistence of limit cycles in second-order systems. The theorem states that if the equations of the phase portrait of a second-order system are given by $px_0 = f(x_0,x_1)$ and $px_1 = g(x_0,x_1)$ where $px_0 = x_1$, then no periodic motions can exist within a domain D of the x_0,x_1 phase plane provided the expression $\partial f/\partial x_0 + \partial g/\partial x_1$ does not change its sign within that domain.

Application of this theorem to Eq. (11.20) reveals that upon placing $x_0 = e$ and $x_1 = pe$ one obtains the equations

$$px_0 = x_1 \quad \text{and} \quad px_1 = -x_1 f_1(x_0) - b_2 x_0$$

and hence

$$\frac{\partial f}{\partial x_0} + \frac{\partial g}{\partial x_1} = -f_1(x_0) = -f_1(e) \tag{11.23}$$

Therefore, if the damping of the system described by Eq. (11.20) does not change sign within a domain of its phase plane, no periodic motions are possible in that domain. Moreover, if the system of Eq. (11.20) exhibits positive damping for all values of e, then the system will be stable for any initial value of error and error rate.

11.7 Piecewise Linear Systems

As one reflects on the properties of servomechanisms, ultimately the question arises as to what constitutes an optimum control system. Usually, the controller element of a servo is limited as to the maximum amount of power it can deliver to the controlled element. These limitations are imposed, for example, by the saturation characteristics of rotating machinery magnetic circuits, the maximum velocities and accelerations at which system elements can safely operate, and the overload capacity of these elements. Since the major objective of the servo is to reduce and maintain the system error below an acceptable minimum without appreciable overshoot in the least possible time, it seems reasonable, therefore, to define an optimum servo as "One which when stimulated by step inputs of position or velocity causes its controller to modulate its output power in such a fashion as to uniformly reduce and maintain the system error below an accepted minimum without appreciable overshoot, in the least possible time subject to the operating limitations of the servo system."

A class of servos to which the adjective *optimum* is often applied is known as contactor servomechanisms. These servos are sometimes called piecewise linear servos because their behavior over any portion of their response is specified by a linear differential equation having constant coefficients. Physically, this type of servo system is characterized by a switching mechanism which allows either maximum positive or maximum negative torque to be applied at its output as a discontinuous function of the system error. Figure 11.4 presents a diagram of this type of device. The system contains a d-c motor as the output element having an armature current which is maintained constant. In addition, a computer is used, activated by the system error, which is able to switch the motor field current from a maximum value in one direction of flow to a maximum value in the opposite direction.   If one neglects the time constant of the motor field and output damping, the system equations are

$$e = r - c \tag{11.24}$$
$$T_m = Jp^2c \tag{11.25}$$

where T_m is the maximum torque available at the motor output.   For inputs of the nature $p^2r = 0$ (that is, step inputs of position or velocity)

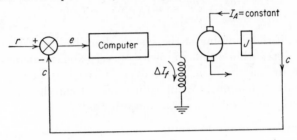

Fig. 11.4   Ideal second-order contactor servo.

the system differential equation becomes

$$p^2e = -\delta \frac{T_m}{J} \tag{11.26}$$

in which δ may take on the value $+1$ or -1.   Making the substitution $x_0 = e$ and $x_1 = pe$, the phase-plane equations become

$$px_1 = -\delta \frac{T_m}{J} \tag{11.27}$$
$$px_0 = x_1 \tag{11.28}$$
$$x_1\, dx_1 = -\delta \frac{T_m}{J}\, dx_0 \tag{11.29}$$

Integration of Eq. (11.29) results in the equations of the phase trajectories of this servo given by

$$\frac{x_1{}^2}{2} = -\delta \frac{T_m}{J} x_0 + K \tag{11.30}$$

where K is the constant of integration.   The phase portrait of this servo consists, therefore, of two families of parabolas all having their vertices on the x_0 axis as shown in Fig. 11.5.

Hopkin[3] has demonstrated that the optimum switching criteria

$$\delta = +1 \text{ for } x_1|x_1| + 2\frac{T_m}{J} x_0 > 0 \tag{11.31}$$

$$\delta = -1 \text{ for } x_1|x_1| + 2\frac{T_m}{J} x_0 < 0 \tag{11.32}$$

will carry the representative point directly into the origin without any overshoot.   The optimum switching curves are shown as A and B on the phase portrait.   The path DCO represents the error, error-rate response of the system to a step input of position, while the path $EDCO$ gives the servo response for a step input of velocity.   Clearly, at most, only one switching operation is necessary for the representative point to reach the origin regardless of its starting position.   The time solutions of this contactor servo are presented in Fig. 11.6 for the case of a step input of

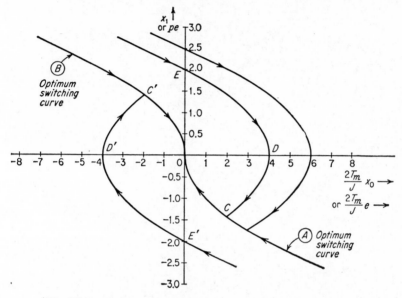

Fig. 11.5   Phase portrait for ideal second-order contactor servo.

position.   Since this servo is operating at maximum acceleration or deceleration at all times, its response will be the optimum for second-order systems.

11.8   Disadvantages of Contactor Servos

Although the contactor servo response characteristics are highly desirable because of their optimum qualities, there are a number of severe practical difficulties encountered in the physical construction of these servo systems.   Since the final optimum, switching phase trajectories for positive or negative output torque always pass through the origin of the phase space, the system at equilibrium finds itself in a state where its output torque is continually being switched back and forth from maximum positive to maximum negative values.   This instability can often be removed by incorporating a dead zone of operation near the region of zero error.   The controller is inactive as long as the state of the system is inside of the dead zone.   However, this solution of the problem results in a system having, in general, large steady-state errors, which is undesirable.

Another method used to cope with the steady-state instability problem is to switch the servo over to a linear mode of operation when in the

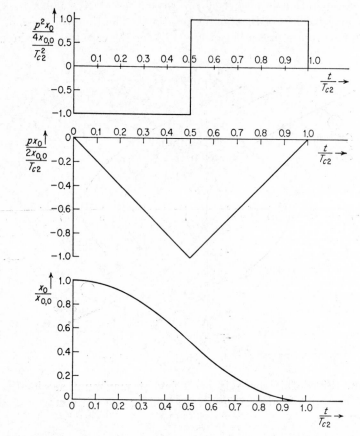

Fig. 11.6   Time solutions for a second-order ideal contactor servomechanism. T_{c2} = response time.

vicinity of the origin of its phase space.   The scheme greatly increases the size, complexity, and cost of the control system.

The switching criteria for higher-order contactor servomechanisms become increasingly complex.   Bogner and Kazda[4] have demonstrated that an nth-order system requires, in general, $n - 1$ switching criteria to reduce its error and the $(n - 1)$st derivatives of error to zero simultaneously.   Computer circuitry of an advanced type is required to continually solve the $n - 1$ differential equations containing involved functions of the system error and its derivatives.   Moreover the switching criteria are functions of the system parameters; small changes in these parameters will introduce errors into the switching program which are magnified as the order of the system increases. For example, small changes in output friction or load inertia will introduce errors into the switching program.

In spite of these practical difficulties, the study of the behavior of contactor servomechanisms is important to the control system engineer because these systems exhibit the optimum response characteristics which the system designer is seeking.

11.9 Compromise Nonlinear Control Systems

A great amount of work has been directed toward obtaining a compromise between the optimum response characteristics exhibited by discontinuous switching systems and the economy of continuously operating linear systems. This can be accomplished by intentionally nonlinearizing a system so that its response characteristics for a specific class of inputs can approach the optimum response of the contactor system. Clearly, a synthesis approach is required in order to determine the quantitative nature which the nonlinearity should possess to achieve the degree of compromise desired. The phase-space approach is particularly useful for synthesis work on nonlinear systems.

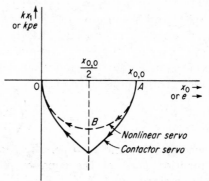

11.10 Phase-space Synthesis

Let us undertake the step-by-step synthesis of a second-order nonlinear servo having a response behavior for step inputs of position which closely approaches that of the optimum second-order contactor system. Figure 11.7 presents the phase trajectories for the optimum contactor servo when sub-

Fig. 11.7 Phase trajectories for optimum contactor servo and nonlinear servo.

jected to a positive step input of position as well as an approximating curve ABO for the nonlinear servo which is to be synthesized. Briefly, the steps in the synthesis process will be these:

1. A desired form of the nonlinear differential equation describing the behavior of the nonlinear servo is selected.

2. The desired phase trajectory of the nonlinear servo is chosen as shown in Fig. 11.7.

3. Sufficient conditions for synthesis are determined so that the specified differential equation can be made to exhibit the desired response characteristics.

4. The nonlinear differential equation is then synthesized, and from it, the control system components determined.

Theorem 1 and its corollary specify sufficient criteria for the synthesis of a second-order servomechanism when responding to step inputs of position.

Theorem 1. If $kx_1 = f(x_0)$, where $x_1 = px_0$, with k a real constant, is continuous in the region $x_{0,0} \geq x_0 \geq x_{0,1}$ with $f(x_{0,0}) = 0$ and has a continuous first derivative in the region $x_{0,0} \geq x_0 \geq x_{0,1}$, then the real constant a_1 and the function $h(x_0)$ can be uniquely determined such that the nonlinear differential equation $p^2 x_0 + h(x_0)px_0 + a_1 x_0 = 0$ has $kx_1 = f(x_0)$ as its phase trajectory in the interval $(x_{0,0} \geq x_0 \geq x_{0,1})$, with $h(x_0)$ a continuous function, except perhaps at points where $x_1 = 0$, provided $\lim\limits_{\substack{x_0 \to x_{0,0} \\ x_1 \to 0}} [x_1 h(x_0)] = 0$ and $\lim\limits_{\substack{x_0 \to x_{0,0} \\ x_1 \to 0}} [x_1 \, dx_1/dx_0]$ exists and is nonzero.

Corollary. The real constant a_1 and the function $h(x_0)$ are given by $a_1 = f_1(x_{0,0}, x_{0,1}, T_{0,1})$ and $h(x_0) = f_2(x_0, x_{0,0}, x_{0,1}, T_{0,1})$ where $T_{0,1}$ is the absolute value of the time elapsed from $x_0 = x_{0,0}$ to $x_0 = x_{0,1}$ provided that

$$\left| \int_{x_{0,0}}^{x_{0,1}} \frac{dx_0}{x_1} \right|$$

exists and is nonzero.

Returning now to Fig. 11.7 the phase-plane coordinates are taken as system error and error rate multiplied by the constant k which gives both coordinates the same physical units. The equation of the nonlinear servo trajectory is given by

$$x_1 = -\frac{1}{k} \sqrt{\left(\frac{x_{0,0}}{2}\right)^2 - \left(x_0 - \frac{x_{0,0}}{2}\right)^2}$$ (11.33)

where $x_0 = e$ and $x_1 = pe$. The constant a_1 and the nonlinear damping function $h(x_0)$ of the equation $p^2 x_0 + h(x_0)px_0 + a_1 x_0 = 0$ are to be determined.

From Eq. (11.33) one obtains by differentiation with respect to x_0,

$$x_1 \frac{dx_1}{dx_0} = -\frac{x_0 - x_{0,0}/2}{k^2}$$ (11.34)

Application of Theorem 1 yields,

$$a_1 = -\frac{1}{x_{0,0}} \lim_{\substack{x_0 \to x_{0,0} \\ x_1 \to 0}} \left[x_1 \frac{dx_1}{dx_0} \right] = \frac{1}{2k^2}$$ (11.35)

and in addition,

$$h(x_0) = -\left(\frac{dx_1}{dx_0} + a_1 \frac{x_0}{x_1}\right) = -\left[\frac{x_1(dx_1/dx_0) + a_1 x_0}{x_1}\right]$$ (11.36)

$$h(x_0) = \frac{1}{2k} \sqrt{\frac{x_{0,0}}{x_0} - 1}$$ (11.37)

Note that $h(x_{0,0}) = 0$ which satisfies the requirement of Theorem 1 that $\lim\limits_{\substack{x_0 \to x_{0,0} \\ x_1 \to 0}} [x_1 h(x_0)] = 0$.

The application of the corollary to Theorem 1 will determine the constant k

$$k = \frac{\Delta T}{\displaystyle\int_{x_{0,0}}^{0} dx_0/kx_1} \tag{11.38}$$

where ΔT is the time required for the system to reach equilibrium when it is excited by step inputs of position. Substituting for x_1 in Eq. (11.38) from Eq. (11.33) and performing the integration results in

$$k = \frac{\Delta T}{\pi} \tag{11.39}$$

The synthesis procedure has now evolved the nonlinear differential equation

$$p^2 x_0 + \left(\frac{\pi}{2\Delta T}\sqrt{\frac{x_{0,0}}{x_0}} - 1\right) p x_0 + \frac{\pi^2}{2(\Delta T)^2} x_0 = 0 \tag{11.40}$$

One of the most pleasing aspects of this result is the nature of the constants which appear in Eq. (11.40), because these constants are the very ones which the design engineer would encounter in his design specifications.

The final step in the synthesis procedure is to adjust the response time ΔT such that the maximum acceleration of the nonlinear servo equals the maximum acceleration of the optimum contactor servo. Inspection of Eq. (11.40) reveals that the nonlinear system attains maximum acceleration at times $t = 0$ and $t = \Delta T$ because of the symmetry required in the acceleration function for a step input of position. The maximum acceleration of the nonlinear system is, therefore,

$$-p^2 x_0 \Big|_{t=0} = \frac{\pi^2 x_{0,0}}{2(\Delta T)^2} \tag{11.41}$$

Now, the maximum acceleration of the optimum contactor servo is given by $4x_{0,0}/T_{c2}^2$ where T_{c2} is the response time of the contactor servo for a step input of position $x_{0,0}$. Hence, the relationship between ΔT and T_{c2} is expressed by

$$\Delta T = \frac{\pi}{2\sqrt{2}} T_{c2} = 1.1111^{+}T_{c2} \tag{11.42}$$

Thus the response time of the nonlinear servo is only 11.11 per cent greater than the response time of the optimum contactor servo.

The Nonlinear Damping Function. The behavior of the nonlinear damping term

$$h(x_0) = \frac{\pi}{2\Delta T} \sqrt{\frac{x_{0,0}}{x_0} - 1} \qquad (11.43)$$

is displayed in Fig. 11.8. The system damping is small when the error magnitude is large and large when the error magnitude is small. Since infinite damping is required at the error magnitude of zero, it is not physically possible to build a servo meeting this requirement. Therefore, in the actual construction of the system, the damping function is approximated as closely as possible in the range $(0 < x_0 \leq x_{0,0})$, and allowed to reach a finite, positive value at $x_0 = 0$.

System Stability. In order to determine the stability of the singular point associated with the nonlinear system described by Eq. (11.40), one linearizes this equation under the assumption that the damping at $x_0 = 0$ is adjusted to be a finite, positive constant A. This results in the linearized equation

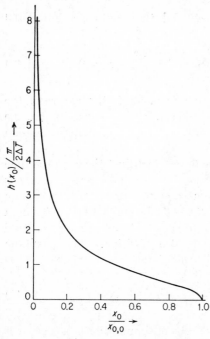

$$p^2 x_0 + \left(\frac{\pi}{2\Delta T} A\right)$$
$$px_0 + \frac{\pi^2}{2(\Delta T)^2} x_0 = 0 \quad (11.44)$$

Clearly, since ΔT is a positive, real quantity, the singular point of the system is stable.

In order to assure the non-existence of limit cycles, it is necessary that the damping function not change sign throughout the entire region of operation. This is true in the region $(0 \leq x_0 \leq x_{0,0})$ because of the nature of the damping function illustrated in Fig. 11.8. Therefore, if the damping function is adjusted by the designer to be positive in the range $(x_{0,0} \leq x_0 < \infty)$, the system will be free of limit cycles.

Fig. 11.8 Plot of the nonlinear damping function $h(x_0) = (\pi/2\Delta T) \sqrt{(x_{0,0}/x_0) - 1}$.

Time Solutions. Very often it is possible, in the phase-space approach, to obtain time solutions of the synthesized nonlinear differential equation. These time solutions are extremely valuable because they reveal the complete transient behavior of the system. In this respect, phase-space synthesis overcomes the great stumbling block which nearly always occurs in nonlinear analysis, namely, that the time solutions of the nonlinear differential equations encountered cannot be obtained.

The time solution of Eq. (11.40) for the interval $(0 \leq t \leq \Delta T)$ will now be obtained starting with the equation

$$\int_0^t dt = \int_{x_{0,0}}^{x_0} \frac{dx_0}{x_1} \tag{11.45}$$

Substituting for x_1 its value as given in Eq. (11.33) along with the value of k obtained in Eq. (11.39) and performing the integration results in the time solution

$$x_0 = \frac{x_{0,0}}{2} \left[1 + \cos \frac{\pi t}{\Delta T} \right] (0 \leq t \leq \Delta T) \tag{11.46}$$

The first and second derivatives of the time solution are given by

$$px_0 = -\frac{\pi x_{0,0}}{2 \Delta T} \sin \frac{\pi t}{\Delta T} \qquad 0 \leq t \leq \Delta T \tag{11.47}$$

$$p^2 x_0 = -\frac{\pi^2 x_{0,0}}{2(\Delta T)^2} \cos \frac{\pi t}{\Delta T} \qquad 0 \leq t \leq \Delta T \tag{11.48}$$

A comparison of the time response characteristics of the synthesized nonlinear servo along with the ideal characteristics of the optimum contactor system are presented in Fig. 11.9.

Adjustment for Magnitude and Sign of Initial Error. The synthesized nonlinear differential equation

$$p^2 e + \left(\frac{\pi}{2 \Delta T} \sqrt{\frac{E_1}{e}} - 1 \right) pe + \frac{\pi^2}{2(\Delta T)^2} e = 0 \tag{11.49}$$

[repeated here in terms of the system error function e, the initial error E_1 (for a step input of position), and the response time ΔT required to reduce the initial error to zero] is not stated in the most convenient form for use in the construction of the physical servo system because the time interval ΔT is not a true constant but depends on the magnitude of the initial error E_1. The equation can be manipulated in the following manner:

Let E_{1m} = maximum initial error imposed on system

T_{c2m} = optimum contactor servo response time when subjected to initial error E_{1m}

Now since the maximum acceleration attained by the optimum contactor servo is the same regardless of the magnitude of the initial error (considered positive), Eq. (11.49) yields the equality

$$\frac{\pi^2 E_1}{2(\Delta T)^2} = \frac{4 E_{1m}}{T_{c2m}^2} \tag{11.50}$$

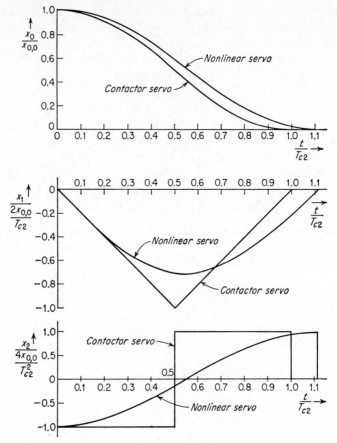

Fig. 11.9 Time solutions for nonlinear and optimum contactor servos: $T_{c2} =$ response time of contactor servo.

solving for ΔT yields

$$\Delta T = T_{c2m} \frac{\pi}{2\sqrt{2}} \sqrt{\frac{E_1}{E_{1m}}} \qquad (11.51)$$

Substituting this result into Eq. (11.49) results in

$$p^2 e + \left(\frac{\sqrt{2}}{T_{c2m}} \sqrt{\frac{E_{1m}}{E_1}} \sqrt{\frac{E_1}{e}} - 1 \right) pe + \frac{4 E_{1m}}{T_{c2m}^2 E_1} e = 0 \qquad (11.52)$$

The practical problem of obtaining identical system response regardless of the algebraic sign of the error can be solved by making the nonlinear damping function an even function of the error; hence Eq. (11.52) can be written as

$$p^2 e + \left(\frac{\sqrt{2}}{T_{c2m}} \sqrt{\frac{E_{1m}}{E_1}} \sqrt{\frac{E_1}{|e|}} - 1 \right) pe + \frac{4 E_{1m}}{T_{c2m}^2 E_1} e = 0 \qquad (11.53)$$

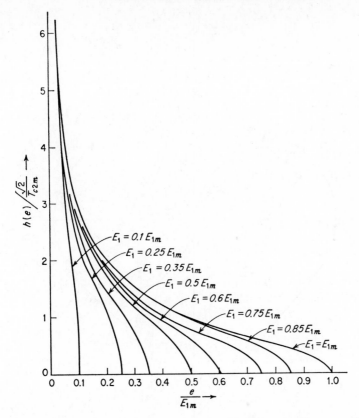

Fig. 11.10 Plot of the nonlinear damping function $h(e) = (\sqrt{2}/T_{c2m}) \sqrt{E_{1m}/E_1} \sqrt{(E_1/|e|) - 1}$.

where E_1 is the initial value of $|e|$ and E_{1m} is the maximum value of E_1. The time solution of Eq. (11.53) takes the form

$$e = \frac{E_1}{2}\left(1 + \cos\frac{2}{T_{c2m}}\sqrt{\frac{2E_{1m}}{E_1}}\,t\right) \qquad 0 \le t \le 1.111\sqrt{\frac{E_1}{E_{1m}}}\,T_{c2m} \quad (11.54)$$

The nonlinear damping function

$$h(e) = \frac{\sqrt{2}}{T_{c2m}}\sqrt{\frac{E_{1m}}{E_1}}\sqrt{\frac{E_1}{|e|} - 1} \qquad (11.55)$$

is plotted in Fig. 11.10 for various values of initial error E_1.

It is evident, that since the nonlinear damping function and the coefficient $4E_{1m}/T_{c2m}^2 E_1$ theoretically approach infinity for zero values of initial error, any practical system must terminate these quantities in finite values at zero initial error. The practical nonlinear servo, there-

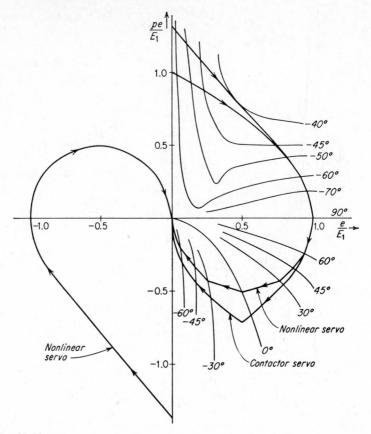

Fig. 11.11   Phase-plane isocline—plot of second-order nonlinear servo system.

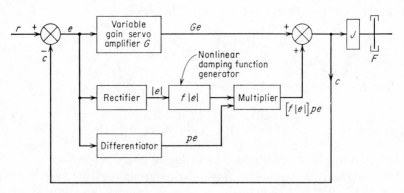

Fig. 11.12   Block diagram of the nonlinear servo.

fore, will have an automatically "built-in" linear mode of operation in the very near vicinity of its phase-space origin.

Phase Portrait. In order to examine the behavior of the synthesized nonlinear system for inputs other than step inputs of position, an isocline plot was constructed, and Fig. 11.11 depicts the results. The phase trajectory of the optimum contactor servo is displayed on the same figure and the behavior of the two systems appears to be quite similar.

Block Diagram of the Physical Servo System. The servo designer is now in a position to build up the nonlinear system such that the differential equation describing its behavior is given by Eq. (11.53). The building blocks must consist of input, output, and error-detecting devices, a variable-gain servo amplifier, an absolute-value device, a differentiating device, a multiplier, and apparatus which will closely approximate the nonlinear function. Figure 11.12 gives a block diagram of the servo system. The equations of the system are

$$e = r - c \tag{11.56}$$
$$Ge + f(|e|)pe = Jp^2c + Fpc \tag{11.57}$$

where F is the coefficient of viscous friction associated with the output device. The combination of Eqs. (11.56) and (11.57) results in

$$p^2e + \left(\frac{f(|e|)}{J} + \frac{F}{J}\right)pe + \frac{G}{J}e = 0 \tag{11.58}$$

assuming inputs such that $p^2r = pr = 0$, that is, step inputs of position. If now, one compares Eq. (11.58) with Eq. (11.53) and equates corresponding quantities, the design equations (11.59) and (11.60) result.

$$G \cong \frac{4JE_{1m}}{T_{c2m}^2 E_1} \tag{11.59}$$

$$f(|e|) = \frac{\sqrt{2}\,J}{T_{c2m}} \sqrt{\frac{E_{1m}}{E_1}} \sqrt{\frac{E_1}{|e|}} - 1 - F \tag{11.60}$$

These equations are written with "approximately equal" signs because at zero error both G and $f(|e|)$ must approach finite constants in a physically realizable system.

For the class of inputs having the characteristic $pr = W$, where W is a constant, that is, a step input of velocity, Eq. (11.58) becomes

$$p^2e + \left[\frac{f(|e|) + F}{J}\right]pe + \frac{G}{J}e = \frac{FW}{J} \tag{11.61}$$

The system now exhibits a maximum steady-state error given by

$$E_{ss}^{\max} = \frac{FWT_{c2m}^2}{4J} \tag{11.62}$$

11.11   Higher-order Systems

The philosophy of synthesis which has been under consideration for a second-order control system can be extended to higher-order systems. Essentially, what one does is to concentrate on the projections of the required phase trajectory onto the coordinate planes which constitute the phase space.   Kuba and Kazda[5] have provided a set of sufficient

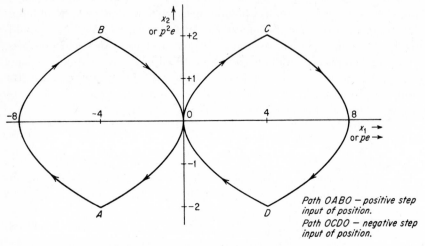

Path OABO — positive step
input of position.
Path OCDO — negative step
input of position.

Fig. 11.13   Projection of phase trajectory onto x_1, x_2 plane—third-order contactor system.

conditions for the synthesis of the nonlinear control system having a differential equation

$$p^n e + h(e)p^{n-1}e + b_{n-2}p^{n-2}e + \cdots + b_1 pe + b_0 e$$
$$= 0 \qquad n \geqslant 2 \quad (11.63)$$

in which equation the function $h(e)$ and the constants $(b_{n-2}, \ldots, b_0)$ are uniquely determined so that the phase-space trajectory of (11.63) closely approximates the optimum contactor phase trajectory.

Synthesis of a Third-order System.   The nonlinear control system to be synthesized will have a differential equation of the form

$$p^3 e + h(e)p^2 e + b_1 pe + b_0 e = 0 \qquad (11.64)$$

The problem is to determine b_0, b_1, and $h(e)$ so that the time response of the nonlinear system approaches the time response of the optimum third-order contactor system.   The optimum contactor system is described by Eq. (11.65)

$$p^3 e = \pm S \qquad (11.65)$$

where S is the switching constant.   The projection of the contactor system phase trajectory onto the x_2,x_1 plane (where $x_2 = p^2e$ and $x_1 = pe$) is shown in Fig. 11.13.

Because of the parabolic nature exhibited by projections on the x_2,x_1 plane of the contactor system phase trajectories, it is evident that an elliptic approximating phase trajectory may be employed for the nonlinear system. Figure 11.14 presents the parabolic phase trajectories of the third-order contactor system along with a typical phase trajectory of the nonlinear system defined by

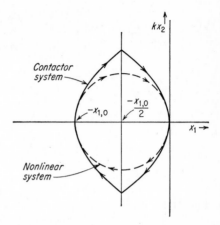

$$\left(x_1 + \frac{x_{1,0}}{2}\right)^2 + k^2 x_2^2 = \left(\frac{x_{1,0}}{2}\right)^2$$

(11.66)

Upon carrying out the synthesis procedure, it is found that $b_1 = 3\pi^2/T_3{}^2$ and $b_0 = 4\pi^2/T_3{}^3$ where T_3 is the time response of the nonlinear servo for a step input of position. The response time T_3 is related to the opti-

Fig. 11.14 Phase trajectories in the kx_2,x_1 plane for third-order contactor and nonlinear systems.

mum contactor servo response time by the equation $T_3 = 1.073T_{c3}$ for equal step input of position functions. Equation (11.64) now becomes

$$p^3e + h(e)p^2e + \frac{3\pi^2}{T_3{}^2}pe + \frac{4\pi^2}{T_3{}^3}e = 0$$

(11.67)

in which the function $h(e)$ is illustrated by Fig. 11.15. The synthesis procedure can now be carried on in a similar manner to what was done in the second-order system to produce a physical system as shown in Fig. 11.16. The time solutions of both the synthesized nonlinear control system and the optimum third-order contactor system are given in Fig. 11.17.

11.12 Advantages of Nonlinear Control Systems

It is worthwhile to point out here that the value of a continuously operating nonlinear control system is closely correlated with the classes of inputs which are most probable for the system. Indeed, if all classes of inputs are equally probable, there is no advantage to a nonlinear system over a well-designed linear system. However, if the probability for a particular class of inputs (e.g., step inputs of position) is very large as compared to other classes of inputs, then the nonlinear servo which is designed to optimize its response when excited by this most probable

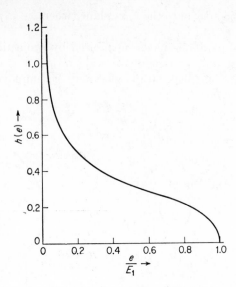

Fig. 11.15   Nonlinear function $h(e)$ versus e/E_1.   Third-order system: E_1 equals the initial error.

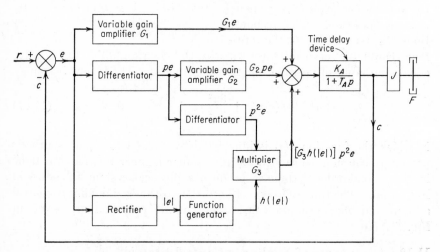

Fig. 11.16   Block diagram of the third-order nonlinear servo.

class of inputs will demonstrate a tremendous advantage over the equivalent linear system.

11.13   Describing-function Method of Analysis

The describing-function technique stems from the desire to extend frequency-response methods of analysis and synthesis commonly used in the study of constant linear systems in order to include nonlinear con-

trol systems.   The basis of the method is the assumption that the nonlinear element when excited by a sinusoidal input will exhibit a response
which can be represented satisfactorily, insofar as the performance of
the entire control system is concerned, by its fundamental Fourier component.   The describing function is defined as the magnitude and phase

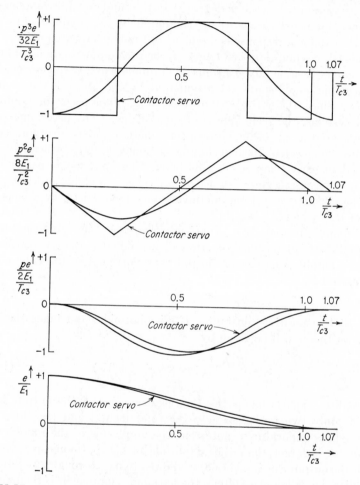

Fig. 11.17   Comparison of time solutions for contactor and nonlinear servos—third-
order systems. T_{c3} = response time of contactor system.

angle of the fundamental response component referred to the assumed
input sinusoid.   Clearly, in order for the fundamental component alone
to describe system behavior accurately, it is necessary that the system
itself possess the property of a low-pass filter which will significantly
attenuate all harmonics associated with the output function of the nonlinear element.   More specifically it is assumed in this technique that:

1. The control system can be separated into several sections, nonlinear sections and linear sections with each nonlinear section followed by a linear section.

2. The linear sections following each nonlinear section behave as low-pass filters, significantly attenuating the harmonics received from the nonlinear section to a greater degree than the fundamental component.

3. The nonlinear section when stimulated by an assumed sinusoidal input will exhibit a response component of fundamental frequency.

If these three conditions are achieved, then the inputs to each nonlinear section can be assumed to be a sinusoid of fundamental frequency because the harmonic components are attenuated by the linear low-pass filter sections. Since these three conditions very often occur in nonlinear control systems, the technique is of great value. The describing function is treated as an ordinary transfer function and is incorporated as such into the powerful linear techniques of analysis and synthesis already described in early chapters of this book. The method is particularly useful in determining the existence of limit cycles in higher-order systems since the effectiveness of the method is not impaired by increasing the order of the system.

Describing Function of a Nonlinear Amplifier. As an example, in determining the describing function of a nonlinear section, consider a nonlinear amplifier having an output v proportional to the cube of the input e, that is,

$$v = K_2 e^3 \tag{11.68}$$

where K_2 is a positive constant. If e is sinusoidal and takes the form $K_1 \cos \omega t$, then v will be given by

$$v = \frac{K_2 K_1^3}{4} (3 \cos \omega t + \cos 3\omega t) \tag{11.69}$$

In reality, Eq. (11.69) is the Fourier expansion of the output which contains only two terms, namely the fundamental and the third harmonic. It is important to note that the amplitude of the fundamental component is larger than the amplitude of the harmonic component. Now if the output v of Eq. (11.69) is allowed to pass through any integrating device (i.e., a low-pass filter), the harmonic component is then greatly attenuated as compared to the fundamental. For example, one integration of Eq. (11.69) yields

$$\int_0^t v \, dt = \frac{K_2 K_1^3}{4} \left(3 \sin \omega t + \frac{1}{3} \sin 3\omega t \right) \tag{11.70}$$

This result clearly shows the effect of low-pass filter action for attenuating harmonic components. It also shows that the effect of derivative operations would be to enhance the harmonic content and perhaps invalidate the use of the describing function technique. In this example, the describing function, a complex quantity in general, is given by

$$G(K_1, j\omega) = \frac{3K_2 K_1^2}{4} + j0 \qquad (11.71)$$

It is important to note that, in general, describing functions are complex quantities which depend on the amplitude of the input sinusoid as well as the frequency. In many cases, however, describing functions depend only on amplitude in contrast to steady-state transfer functions which depend only on frequency. For the purpose of studying control system behavior, describing functions for the nonlinear elements are combined with conventional transfer functions for the linear sections of the system, and the usual techniques are applied.

11.14   Limit Cycles

Consider a feedback control system having a nonlinear section followed by a linear section in its forward path as shown in Fig. 11.18.

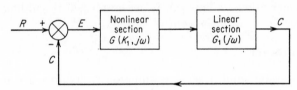

Fig. 11.18 Block diagram of a nonlinear control system composed of one nonlinear and one linear section.

Here $G_1(j\omega)$ is the transfer function of the linear section and $G(K_1, j\omega)$ is the describing function of the nonlinear section. The control system's equations are

$$E = R - C \qquad (11.72)$$
$$C = [G(K_1, j\omega)][G_1(j\omega)]E \qquad (11.73)$$

Thus,
$$\frac{C}{R} = \frac{G(K_1, j\omega)G_1(j\omega)}{1 + G(K_1, j\omega)G_1(j\omega)} \qquad (11.74)$$

Equation (11.74) indicates that self-sustained oscillations may exist when $1 + G(K_1, j\omega)G_1(j\omega) = 0$, or

$$G(K_1, j\omega) = \frac{-1}{G_1(j\omega)} \qquad (11.75)$$

The solution for K_1 and ω can be obtained by:

1. Plotting $G(K_1, j\omega)$ and $-1/G_1(j\omega)$ in the complex plane and noting points of intersection
2. Equating real and imaginary parts of $G(K_1, j\omega)$ and $-1/G_1(j\omega)$ and solving for K_1 and ω

Figure 11.19 illustrates a graphical construction which results in a limit cycle of the form 10 cos 5t. In order to eliminate limit cycles, the designer so shapes his linear and nonlinear gain characteristics in order

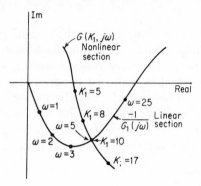

Fig. 11.19 Plots of $G(K_1, j\omega)$ and $-1/G_1(j\omega)$ loci indicating a limit cycle having the form 10 cos 5t.

to avoid intersections. This can be accomplished by adding new linear or nonlinear blocks into the control system.

11.15 Summary

The phase-space and describing function techniques are used to best advantage when employed in such a fashion as to complement each other. The transient behavior of the system for various classes of inputs is best displayed by the phase-space approach. On the other hand, instabilities of the limit cycle kind are most easily determined and avoided using the describing-function technique. The two methods should correspond to the right and left hands of the designer with each hand aware of what the other hand is doing. After all, it is well recognized that nonlinear analysis and synthesis is one of the most difficult branches of engineering, and therefore every possible tool should be employed to its utmost utility.

REFERENCES

1. Courant, R.: "Differential and Integral Calculus," vol. 2, p. 451, Nordeman Publishing Company, New York, 1936.
2. Bendixson, I.: Sur les courbes définies par des équations différentielles (Curves Defined by Differential Equations), *Acta Mathematica*, vol. 24, Stockholm, Sweden, 1901.
3. Hopkin, A. M.: A Phase Plane Approach to the Compensation of Saturating Servomechanisms, *Trans. AIEE*, vol. 70, part I, pp. 631–39, 1951.
4. Bogner, I., and L. F. Kazda: An Investigation of the Switching Criteria for Higher Order Contactor Servomechanisms, *Trans. AIEE*, vol. 73, part 2, pp. 118–27, 1954.
5. Kuba, R., and L. F. Kazda: A Phase Space Method for the Synthesis of Nonlinear Servomechanisms, *Trans. AIEE*, vol. 75, part 2, pp. 282–290, 1956.

ADDITIONAL REFERENCES

Phase-space Techniques

1. van der Pol, B.: On Relaxation Oscillations, *Phil. Mag.*, ser. 7, vol. 2, pp. 978–992, 1926.
2. Kryloff, N., and N. Bogoliuboff: "Introduction to Non-linear Mechanics," translated from the Russian by S. Lefschetz, Princeton University Press, Princeton, N.J., 1943, 1947, 1952.
3. Minorsky, N.: "Introduction to Non-linear Mechanics," J. W. Edwards Publisher, Inc., Ann Arbor, Mich., 1947.
4. Andronow, A., and S. Chaikin: "Theory of Oscillations," Moscow, 1937, translated from the Russian by S. Lefschetz, Princeton University Press, Princeton, N.J., 1949.
5. McLachlan, N. W.: "Ordinary Nonlinear Differential Equations," 2d ed., Oxford University Press, New York, 1956.
6. Stoker, J. J.: "Nonlinear Vibrations," Interscience Publishers, Inc., New York, 1950.
7. McDonald, D. C.: Non-linear Techniques for Improving Servo Performance, *Proc. Natl. Electronics Conf.*, Chicago, vol. 6, pp. 400–421, 1950.
8. Lewis, J. B.: The Use of Nonlinear Feedback to Improve the Transient Response of a Servomechanism, *Trans. AIEE*, vol. 71, part II, pp. 449–453, 1952.
9. McDonald, D. C.: Multiple-mode Operation of Servomechanisms, *Rev. Sci. Instr.*, vol. 23, pp. 22–30, 1952. (*Bull.* no. S-3, Cook Laboratories, Chicago, 1951.)
10. Hayashi, C.: "Forced Oscillations in Non-linear Systems," Nippon Printing and Publishing Co., Ltd., Tokyo, 1953.
11. Flügge-Lotz, I.: "Discontinuous Automatic Control," Princeton University Press, Princeton, N.J., 1953.
12. Bellman, R.: "Stability Theory of Differential Equations," McGraw-Hill Book Company, Inc., New York, 1953.
13. Ku, Y. H.: Nonlinear Analysis of Electromechanical Problems, *J. Franklin Inst.*, vol. 255, pp. 9–31, 1953.
14. Ku, Y. H.: A Method of Solving Third and Higher Order Nonlinear Differential Equations, *J. Franklin Inst.*, vol. 256, pp. 229–244, 1953.
15. Caldwell, R. R., and V. C. Rideout: A Differential-Analyzer Study of Certain Nonlinearly Damped Servomechanisms, *Trans. AIEE*, vol. 72, part II, pp. 165–170, 1953.
16. Neiswander, R. S., and R. H. MacNeal: Optimization of Nonlinear Control Systems by Means of Nonlinear Feedbacks, *Trans. AIEE*, vol. 72, part II, pp. 262–272, 1953.
17. Kazda, L. F.: Errors in Relay Servo Systems, *Trans. AIEE*, vol. 72, part II, pp. 323–328, 1953.
18. Kalman, R. E.: Phase-plane Analysis of Automatic Control Systems with Non-linear Gain Elements, *Trans. AIEE*, vol. 73, part I, pp. 383–390, 1954.
19. Ku, Y. H.: Analysis of Nonlinear Systems with More than One Degree of Freedom by Means of Space Trajectories, *J. Franklin Inst.*, vol. 259, pp. 115–131, 1955.
20. Rauch, L. L., and R. M. Howe: A Servo with Linear Operation in a Region About the Optimum Discontinuous Switching Curve, *Proc. Symposium on Nonlinear Circuit Analysis*, Polytechnic Institute of Brooklyn, Brooklyn, N.Y., pp. 215–223, 1956.
21. Ku, Y. H.: The Phase-space Method for Analysis of Nonlinear Control Systems, *Trans. ASME, Paper* 56-A-103, vol. 79, pp. 1897–1903, 1957.
22. Doll, H. G., and T. M. Stout: Design and Analog-computer Analysis of an Optimum Third-order Nonlinear Servomechanism, *Trans. ASME*, vol. 79, pp. 513–525, 1957.

23. Kuba, R. E., and L. F. Kazda: The Design and Performance of a Model, Second Order, Nonlinear Servomechanism, *IRE Trans. Profess. Group on Automatic Control*, vol. PGAC-5, pp. 43–48, July, 1958.
24. Cosgriff, R. L.: "Nonlinear Control Systems," McGraw-Hill Book Company, Inc., New York, 1958.
25. Ku, Y. H.: "Analysis and Control of Nonlinear Systems," The Ronald Press Company, New York, 1958.

Describing Function Techniques

26. Kochenburger, R. J.: A Frequency Response Method for Analyzing and Synthesizing Contactor Servomechanisms, *Trans. AIEE*, vol. 69, part I, pp. 270–284, 1950.
27. Johnson, E. C.: Sinusoidal Analysis of Feedback-control Systems Containing Nonlinear Elements, *Trans. AIEE*, vol. 71, part II, pp. 169–181, 1952.
28. Kochenburger, R. J.: Limiting in Feedback Control Systems, *Trans. AIEE*, vol. 72, part II, pp. 180–194, 1953.
29. Truxal, J. G.: "Automatic Feedback Control System Synthesis," McGraw-Hill Book Company, Inc., New York, 1955.
30. Vallese, L. M.: Analysis of Backlash in Feedback Control Systems with One Degree of Freedom, *Trans. AIEE*, vol. 74, part II, pp. 1–4, 1955.
31. Chao, S. K.: Design of a Contactor Servo Using Describing Function Theory, *Trans. AIEE*, vol. 75, part II, pp. 223–233, 1956.
32. Satyendra, K. N.: Describing Functions Representing the Effect of Inertia, Backlash, and Coulomb Friction on the Stability of an Automatic Control System—I, *Trans. AIEE*, vol. 75, part II, pp. 243–249, 1956.
33. Klotter, K.: A Practical Method of Producing Describing Functions for Nonlinear Circuits, *Proc., Symposium on Nonlinear Circuit Analysis*, Polytechnic Institute of Brooklyn, Brooklyn, N.Y., pp. 151–162, 1956.
34. Klotter, K.: How to Obtain Describing Functions for Nonlinear Feedback Systems, *Trans. ASME*, vol. 79, pp. 509–512, 1957.

Other Techniques

35. Desoer, C. A.: The Bang Bang Servo Problem Treated By Variational Techniques, *Inform. and Control*, vol. 2, no. 4, pp. 333–348, 1959 (see references listed in this paper).
36. Bellman, R., I. Glicksberg, and O. Gross: On The Bang-Bang Control Problem, *Quart. Appl. Math.*, vol. 14, no. 1, pp. 11–18, April, 1956.
37. Steeg, C. W.: Techniques of Time Domain Synthesis for Control Systems, *Rept.* 100, Dynamic Analysis and Control Laboratory, MIT, April, 1957.
38. Krasovskii, N.: The Theory Of Optimal Regulation, *Matematika I. Mekhanika*, vol. 23, 1959.
39. Bellman, R.: "Dynamic Programming," Princeton University Press, Princeton, N.J., 1957.
40. Bellman, R.: "Adaptive Control Processes: A Guided Tour," Princeton University Press, Princeton, N.J., 1961.
41. Rozenoer, L. I.: L. S. Pontryagin Maximum Principle in the Theory of Optimum Systems, *Avtomatika I Telemekhanika*, vol. 20, no. 10, pp. 1288–1302, October; no. 11, pp. 1405–1421, November; no. 12, pp. 1517–1532, December, 1959.
42. Kalman, R. E. and J. E. Bertram: Control System Analysis and Design via the Second Method of Lyapunov, part I, Continuous Systems, part II, Sampled Data Systems, *Trans. ASME*, vol. 82, 1960.

12

Sampled-data Theory

JOHN M. SALZER

DIRECTOR, INTELLECTRONICS LABORATORIES
RAMO-WOOLDRIDGE DIVISION
THOMPSON RAMO WOOLDRIDGE CANOGA PARK, CALIF. INC.

12.1 Introduction

When driving a car on a highway we do not observe *constantly* all the factors that should control our driving. We have other preoccupations, such as listening to the radio, blowing our nose, or admonishing the children in the back. In between these activities we take notice of such details as the curvature of the road or the stop sign that we have just passed through. Thus, although we drive continuously, we make the required observations *intermittently*. Our system operates on sampled data.

Most conventional control systems operate on continuous data, and techniques have been developed to deal with the analysis of such systems. In the linear case a set of differential equations describes the operation of the system, and the solution of these equations constitutes an analysis yielding the time response. Transformation techniques have provided an alternate and powerful method of analysis, which is now conventional. For the class of sampled-data systems to be discussed, linear-difference equations serve to describe the system. Transformation methods are similarly applicable to sampled-data systems and will be used throughout this chapter.

The transform calculus for sampled-data systems is based on sampled or impulsed functions, the use of which lead to a new auxiliary variable, the definition of transfer functions, the derivation of theorems, and the construction of tables of transforms. The treatment is analogous to the Laplace-transform methods used with continuous-data systems. Furthermore, the complex frequency variable is related to the auxiliary variable of sampled-data analysis to provide a firm basis for the investigation of mixed systems, wherein data appear in both continuous and sampled form at various points in the systems.

Actually, a control system usually contains elements operating in a continuous fashion, for the controlled unit itself is often a physical mechanism. If at some point the data are sampled, portions of the system will operate on continuous data, other portions on sampled data. Figure 12.1 shows the essential elements of such a sampled-data system.

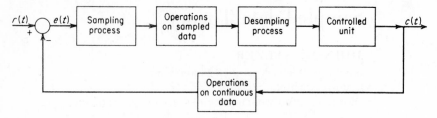

Fig. 12.1   Block diagram of a sampled-data system.

Since the continuous-data parts of the system can be handled by conventional methods, it remains to describe the following:

1. The sampling process, which converts continuous data to discontinuous form
2. The operations that may be performed on data in sampled form
3. The desampling process, which converts discontinuous data to continuous form

A large variety of sampled-data control systems is already in existence, and indeed, the use of such systems is rapidly being multiplied as digital and pulse techniques become increasingly applied in control and simulation. In addition, the methods developed for dealing with sampled-data systems will further be useful in other areas of systems analysis. They constitute a useful approach to problems in numerical analysis, the design of discrete filters, and the study of pure-delay networks. Even more importantly, sampled-data theory can be extended directly to the treatment of conventional continuous-data control systems, providing thereby another effective tool for the use of the servo engineer. Moreover, it turns out that these methods provide certain advantages also in the study of numerous time-variant and nonlinear systems. The reader can, therefore, look forward to gaining a deeper background of systems analysis and acquiring a set of additional tools for dealing with a host of diverse problems in the broadest reaches of control and computer engineering.

The problem is how and what to present on this vast topic in one easy chapter. In view of three up-to-date books[1] already published, it seems

---

[1] John R. Ragazzini and Gene F. Franklin, "Sampled-data Control Systems," McGraw-Hill Book Company, Inc., New York, 1958; Eliahu I. Jury, "Sampled-data Control Systems," John Wiley & Sons, Inc., New York, 1958; Julius T. Tou, "Digital

best to sacrifice completeness and detail for the sake of generating a useful insight into the workings of sampled-data systems, providing an understanding of the basic tools of dealing with them, and surveying the applications of these techniques and the accomplishments of the field.

12.2 Examples of Sampled-data Systems

We already noted that in sampled-data systems the transfer of information at one or more points is intermittent rather than continuous. It is as though a switch were opened and closed at predetermined instants of time.   This may sound like a so-called contactor servomechanism, but two very essential differences can be pointed out.   First, the contactor-type servo operates when the *magnitude* of a particular quantity reaches predetermined values, rather than at *specific times;* thus, a contactor servo is by necessity nonlinear.   Second, the points of the contactor usually switch a *fixed* supply or level, rather than being in line with the flow of a *variable signal.*

For the development of an effective transform calculus the following additional restrictions are imposed on the class of sampled-data systems handled:

1. The time variation is *periodic;* i.e., the time interval between consecutive operations of the switch is constant and called the sampling time T.

2. The time during which the signal is allowed to pass, called the switching time, is negligibly *short* compared to the sampling time T.

3. The system is *linear.*   Note that if the rest of the system is linear, the time-dependent switching does not destroy this linearity.

In general, all the above conditions will be assumed to exist when referring to sampled-data systems unless otherwise stated.

One reason for sampling may be the *time sharing* of a communication link or equipment.   The possible efficiency resulting from the use of one piece of equipment for more than one purpose needs no emphasis.   Time-multiplexed transmission of data permits the sequential transfer of samples of several quantities over a single carrier.   One track-while-scan radar yields information on targets at every azimuth in sequence.   A television picture is composed of consecutive samples of spot brightness transmitted over a single channel.   Most digital computers contain one arithmetic element which is used to perform one operation after the other in sequence to generate an output sample (numerical result) from one or more input samples (numerically expressed measurements).   One of the most interesting pieces of time-shared equipment is the human, often part of a control system.   Not only does his great versatility enable him

---

and Sampled-data Control Systems," McGraw-Hill Book Company, Inc., New York, 1959.

to be time-shared among several tasks, but by his very nature he is unable to pay literally undivided attention to any one item.

Another reason for sampling information may be that it takes a *discrete length of time* to perform an individual measurement. An example of this is the pulsed tracking radar, which cannot take a new range reading before the echo of the last transmitted pulse returns. Actually, the sampling rate of such radars turns out to be so high that the measurement seems practically continuous. This is not the case with movies, each frame of which takes a fixed length of time to photograph. For a rapid-motion event, such as a rotating spoked wheel, the sampling rate is noticeably inadequate to create the illusion of continuity. The measurement of charge by means of a galvanometer and most null-type indications are discrete, as they require time to obtain individual samples of the measured quantity.

Often there are other advantages or reasons for sampling. The chopper bar regulator, for instance, amplifies a *low-power* measurement by a large factor, while it samples it. Often a quantity varies so slowly that its periodic determination is adequate and can further be performed very *precisely* in this manner. An example of this is the introduction of periodic fixes into a navigation system. In other cases the information may be available in *numerical* form, in which case it is usually convenient to apply it to the system in suitable sampled form, as is done for numerically controlled machine tools. Often it is convenient from an operational point of view to effect controls *periodically* rather than continually. Quality control, inventory control, and certain process control systems fall into this category.

These are then a few examples and reasons of control systems operating with data in sampled form. In some cases, as pulsed tracking radar, this intermittency is of no appreciable consequence; however, in other cases, as in track-while-scan radar, this intermittency can seriously affect the dynamic performance and stability of the system. Indeed, whenever the sampling time T is comparable to the essential time constants of the controlled elements, the sampled nature of the data in the system cannot be disregarded, and the application of sampled-data theory becomes imperative.

12.3   Representation of Sampled-data Components

The process of sampling replaces a continuous function by a sequence of its values at particular values of the independent variable. The process of desampling replaces such a sequence by a continuous function which usually agrees with the sequence wherever the latter is defined.

When copying the graph of a continuous function, we often go through the processes of sampling and desampling: first, we transfer a few points or samples of the curve; then, we connect these points by a smooth curve.

ι this procedure we perform no operations with the data in sampled
rm.

Suppose now that our task is to graph the *derivative* of the function $i(t)$.
he steps we may go through are illustrated in Fig. 12.2. First we may
)tain samples of $i(t)$ at time intervals spaced, for instance, uniformly
$= 0.5$ sec apart; this is the process of sampling. Second, using the
,mples of $i(t)$ we estimate the slope
the function at each sampling
,stant. For this illustration a simple
ιd rather inaccurate method is used:
ιe derivative $o(t)$ at each sampling
stant is assumed to equal the slope
the line connecting that input sam-
,e with the previous one. Stated
athematically

$$o(nT) = \frac{i(nT) - i[(n-1)T]}{T} \qquad (12.1)$$

hich in the limit, when T goes to
·ro, actually defines the derivative.
hird, the new set of samples are con-
ιcted or desampled to produce $o(t)$,
hich is the approximate derivative
$i(t)$.

This description of sampling, oper-
ions with sampled data, and desam-
,ing is straightforward. However,
ι make these processes more amena-
e to treatment by transform meth-
ls, it is convenient to introduce the
llowing equivalent representation:[1]
he equivalent representation of a
ιmple of value a will be an impulse
` area a.

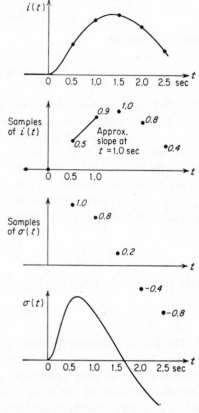

Fig. 12.2 Graphical differentiation
of a continuous function.

In terms of our previous example (Fig. 12.2) the samples of the second
ιd third graphs would be replaced by corresponding impulses, but the
·st and last curves would be the same to make the over-all procedure
juivalent.

The use of this equivalent representation opens the way to transform
ethods. The Laplace transform of the unit sample function—a func-
on which is zero everywhere except at $t = 0$ where it is unity—is

[1] William K. Linvill and John M. Salzer, Analysis of Control Systems Involving
igital Computers, *Proc. IRE*, vol. 41, no. 7, pp. 901–908, 1953.

zero and does not lend itself to rigorous transformation, although som kind of operational calculus could be applied. No such compromise however, is required to deal with the unit impulse function, which i defined by the following set of equations:

$$u_0(t - t_1) = \begin{cases} 0 & \text{when } t - t_1 \neq 0 \\ \infty, & \text{when } t - t_1 = 0 \end{cases} \qquad (12.2$$

$$\int_{-\infty}^{\infty} u_o(t - t_1) \, dt = 1 \qquad (12.3$$

and collaterally

$$\int_{a}^{b} u_o(t - t_1) f(t) \, dt = f(t_1) \qquad \text{when } a \leq t_1 < b \qquad (12.4$$

The last equation means that the integral of a function multiplied by th unit impulse equals the value of the function at the point at which th impulse occurs, provided the limits of integration include that point We adopted the arbitrary convention that the impulse occurring at th lower limit is considered completely inside, while that occurring at th upper limit is considered completely outside the limits of integration.

Now, Eq. (12.4) leads readily to the Laplace transform of a uni impulse occurring at $t = t_1$, where $t_1 \geq 0$; namely,

$$\mathcal{L}[u_o(t - t_1)] = \int_{0}^{\infty} u_o(t - t_1) e^{-st} \, dt = e^{-t_1 s} \qquad (12.5$$

and particularly, when the impulse occurs at $t = 0$,

$$U_o(s) = \mathcal{L}[u_o(t)] = 1 \qquad (12.6$$

The use of impulses has the further advantage that the action of th desampling filter can be directly interpreted, if its transfer function i known. The inverse transform of this transfer function is the uni impulse response of the filter, which is a most useful description of i when its input consists of nothing else but impulses.

In summary, we replaced the sampling unit by an impulse modulato and the desampling unit by a smoothing filter. Similarly, operations o data in sampled form were replaced by completely analogous operation on data in impulsed form. The two analogous procedures are equivalen from continuous input to continuous output. Indeed, our choice o equivalent representation could have been so arbitrary as to replac samples by apples of proportional weight and appropriately define de-appling" unit. But then, apples have no Laplace transforms!

Henceforth, we will always think of impulse modulation, impulses and ripple filtering even when we use the words sampling, samples, an desampling. Actually, once impulses have been chosen in our model c sampled-data systems, the validity of this choice has to be reestablished for the particular case being analyzed. A good example is the sampling-clamping device, which converts a smooth continuous function to one of equally spaced steps, as shown in Fig. 12.3, by clamping each sample of $i(t)$ over the ensuing sampling interval. The physical device accomplishing this action may be housed in a single black box, but for the purpose of analysis we may use a two-box model: one box would produce impulses which have areas equal to $i(nT)$, and a second box

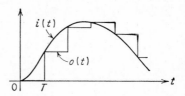

Fig. 12.3 Action of the sampling-clamping device.

would be a filter which responds to a unit impulse with a pulse of unit height and duration T, as will be seen in Sec. 12.6.

12.4 Operations on Sampled Data

In the example of Fig. 12.2 an approximate differentiation was performed on the data in sampled form. This operation was described by the difference equation of (12.1) which relates the output samples $o(nT)$ of the approximate derivative operation to the samples $i(nT)$ of the input function. The device that performs such operations is often referred to by such names as a discrete filter or a sampled-data processer.

A sampled-data filter accepts a series of samples as its input and produces a series of samples as its output. The difference equation is a description of the filter in the time domain. The equivalent representation of the input and output as a series of impulses permits the description of the discrete filter also by a transfer function in the frequency domain, as will be fully demonstrated in later sections.

Based on previous chapters dealing with the organization and programming of digital computers, it is not difficult to visualize that a digital computer can act as a discrete filter if it is programmed to solve the appropriate difference equation. For the particular example of Eq. (12.1) the new output sample $o(nT)$ is obtained by subtracting from the presently received input sample the input sample which was observed T sec ago and then multiplying this difference by $1/T$. This is the computational part of the program.

The manipulative part of the program prepares the computer for the next sampling instant at which time the same operations must again be performed. For this purpose, it is necessary to rearrange the computer storage such that the present sample $i(nT)$ is transferred to the storage location associated with the old sample $i(nT - T)$. In a more complicated case a number of such storage transfers are required.

One profoundly important feature of a computer used in an actual control situation is the accurate measure of time. Even for the simple differentiation illustrated, the *real* time interval between computation must be T sec, and any error in the measure of this time may affect, no only the accuracy, but also the over-all performance of the closed-loo system. The precise measure c time is important only in trul real-time systems, in which th next input sample is not know before it is actually observed, as would be in a navigation systen In contrast a numerically controlle machine tool is not truly a rea time system, since all the inpu samples had been recorded prior t the controlled operation of the too

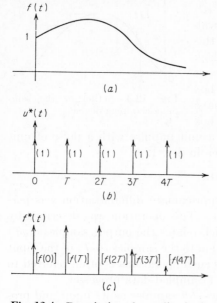

Fig. 12.4 Description of sampling in the time domain. (*a*) Continuous function. (*b*) Unit impulse train. (*c*) Sampled function.

12.5 Sampling and Impuls Modulation

In the equivalent representatio of the sampling process, the con tinuous function $f(t)$ is replaced b $f^*(t)$, which is a function consistin of a series of impulses spaced sec apart and having areas $f(nT)$ The same result is obtained if series of unit impulses are modu lated or multiplied by $f(t)$ a illustrated in Fig. 12.4.

The carrier of this modulation process is the unit impulse series $u^*(t)$ which can be described as

$$u^*(t) = \sum_{n=0}^{\infty} u_o(t - nT) \tag{12.7}$$

whose Laplace transform is readily obtained with the aid of Eqs. (12.5 and (12.6) as

$$U^*(s) = \sum_{n=0}^{\infty} e^{-nTs} = \frac{1}{1 - e^{-Ts}} \qquad \sigma > 0 \tag{12.8}$$

where σ is the real part of the complex frequency s. The condition $\sigma > ($ defines the abscissa of absolute convergence[1] for this transform as 0 anc arises from the region of convergence of the series (12.8) being $|e^{-Ts}| < 1$

[1] M. F. Gardner and J. L. Barnes, "Transient in Linear Systems," vol. 1, pp. 10: and 122, John Wiley & Sons, Inc., New York, 1942.

The function $u^*(t)$ itself can be thought of as the sampled (impulsed) form of the unit step function $u(t)$. It is interesting to note that the integrals of $u(t)$ and $u^*(t)$ are equal if $T = 1$ sec, for then a unit area is accumulated each second in the integral of $u^*(t)$ thus making it proportional to t, which is the integral of $u(t)$. Should the sampling time be halved, i.e., $T = 0.5$ sec, a unit area would be accumulated each *half* second to make the integral of $u^*(t)$ proportional to $2t$. In general, the integral of $u^*(t)$ is proportional to t/T.

The significance of this comparison is much deeper than a multiplying constant could suggest. There is actually a dimensional difference between $u(t)$ and $u^*(t)$ because the latter is only describable by areas or integrals under the impulses. It is very often mentioned in the literature that as the sampling time T approaches zero a sampled function or a sampled-data system becomes the corresponding continuous system. When we use the equivalent impulsed representation of sampled function, the factor T must be remembered and this limiting process stated as

$$\lim_{T\to 0} Tu^*(t) = u(t) \qquad (12.9)$$

for the step function, and in general it is true that

$$\lim_{T\to 0} Tf^*(t) = f(t) \qquad (12.10)$$

The proof of the last statement is a useful exercise. By the definition of impulse modulation

$$f^*(t) = f(t)u^*(t) = \sum_{n=0}^{\infty} f(nT)u_o(t - nT) \qquad (12.11)$$

Now

$$\lim_{T\to 0} Tf^*(t) = \lim_{T\to 0} \sum_{n=0}^{\infty} Tf(nT)u_o(t - nT) \qquad (12.11a)$$

But in the limit T goes to $d\tau$, n becomes correspondingly very large such that nT goes to τ, and the summation becomes an integration. Thus,

$$\lim_{T\to 0} Tf^*(t) = \int_0^{\infty} f(\tau)u_o(t - \tau)\, d\tau = f(t) \qquad (12.11b)$$

where the last step follows from the definition of the unit impulse, Eq. (12.4).

This derivation is likely to remind one of the derivation of the superposition integral in continuous-filter theory and shows that continuous-data theory was approached through sampled-data concepts in the first place. In a sense we have to retrograde our thinking from the hard-earned concept of *continuous* to the simpler concept of *discrete*.

One form of the transform of $f^*(t)$ can be obtained directly from Eq. (12.11):

$$\mathcal{L}[f^*(t)] = F^*(s) = \sum_{n=0}^{\infty} f(nT)e^{-nTs} \tag{12.12}$$

In the case of $u^*(t)$ we were able to reduce the series to a closed form as seen in Eq. (12.8). This will also be done for some specific functions $f^*(t)$, but further reduction of Eq. (12.12) is not possible without defining $f(t)$.

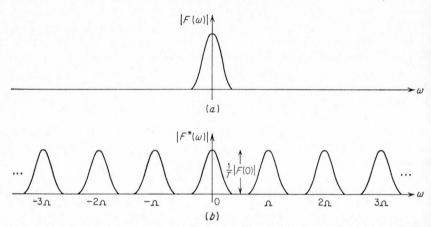

Fig. 12.5 Interpretation of sampling in the frequency domain. (a) Amplitude spectrum of continuous function. (b) Amplitude spectrum of sampled function.

Another definition of $F^*(s)$ is useful and relates it to $F(s)$, the transform of the continuous function. Stated without proof

$$F^*(s) = \frac{1}{T} \sum_{k=-\infty}^{\infty} F(s + jk\Omega) \tag{12.13}$$

where $\Omega = 2\pi/T$ is the sampling frequency in radians per second.[1]

Equation (12.13) demonstrates that a sampled function is periodic in the frequency domain. For example, as far as the amplitude characteristic is concerned, Fig. 12.5 shows how the amplitude spectrum of the continuous function is multiplied by $1/T$ and repeated at every Ω. These sidebands or complementary spectra are introduced by the modulation process.

---

[1] The two definitions of $F^*(s)$ in Eqs. (12.12) and (12.13) are equal when there are no discontinuities in $f(t)$ at the sampling instants. If there are discontinuities, the new values of $f(t)$ are generally assumed to be sampled, and $F^*(s)$ of (12.13) must be augmented by the transforms of impulses occurring at the jumps and having areas equal to half the jumps.

12.6 Desampling

It is clear from the illustration of Fig. 12.5 that—at least in principle—the original continuous function can be recovered from its samples if its frequency band was limited to no more than $\Omega/2$. Indeed, this is essentially a statement of the sampling theorem.[1] Assuming that this condition exists, the filter to perform the ideal desampling process must be a low-pass filter, having infinite attenuation above $\Omega/2$, a gain of T, and zero phase shift below $\Omega/2$. Such ideal characteristics are unrealizable.

Actually, fairly good approximations to the gain characteristic of the ideal desampling filter can be obtained if the phase characteristic is compromised. Such is often the case in nonreal time systems and open-loop systems. For example, the numerical interpolation of tabular data is a nonreal time desampling process because samples are available both ahead of and behind the point of operation. In such cases so-called central interpolation formulas are used, as opposed to extrapolation formulas, which correspond to real-time desampling. Similarly, a communication link is essentially an open-loop system where the delayed arrival of information (voice) is permissible. A delay of, say, 0.1 sec constitutes a phase lag of 36,000° for a 1,000-cps tone, but it would still not interfere with a satisfactory telephone conversation.

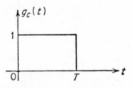

In the design of a closed-loop system such delays are so catastrophic that they are meaningless. Design refinements are often aimed at saving another 5 or 10° phase lag in the loop. Indeed, the compromise in desampling is reversed to trying to save the phase at the expense of the gain characteristic. In other words, it is better to be inaccurate but stable, than accurate but unstable.

Fig. 12.6 Unit impulse response of clamping filter.

One of the most commonly used desampling filters is the so-called clamping unit, which clamps the value of the sample until the next sample occurs. The effect of sampling and clamping a function $i(t)$ was already illustrated in Fig. 12.3. The clamping filter itself can be described by its unit impulse response, $g_c(t)$, shown in Fig. 12.6. If we call the unit step function $u(t)$,

$$g_c(t) = u(t) - u(t - T) \qquad (12.14)$$

By Laplace transformation, the transfer function of the clamper is

$$G_c(s) = \frac{1}{s} - \frac{e^{-Ts}}{s} = \frac{1 - e^{-Ts}}{s} \qquad (12.15)$$

[1] C. E. Shannon, Communication in the Presence of Noise, *Proc. IRE*, vol. 37, no. 1, pp. 11–12, January, 1949.

Letting $s = j\omega$ in the above equation results in the following amplitude and phase characteristics:

$$|G_c(j\omega)| = T \left| \frac{\sin T\omega/2}{T\omega/2} \right| \tag{12.15a}$$

$$\underline{/G_c(j\omega)} = -\frac{T\omega}{2} + \left(180° \text{ change whenever } \frac{T\omega}{2} = n\pi \right) \tag{12.15b}$$

where n are all nonzero integers.   Both these characteristics are sketched in Fig. 12.7.

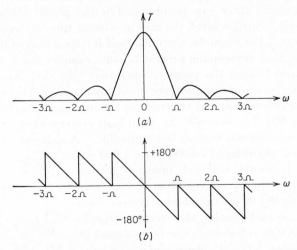

(a)

(b)

Fig. 12.7 Frequency characteristics of clamping filter. (a) Amplitude. (b) Phase.

The phase lag introduced by the clamper is linear in the range of interest and corresponds to a time delay of $T/2$ sec.   It is clear from Fig. 12.7 that on the average $o(t)$ is, indeed, a half of T late in equaling $i(t)$. At half the sampling frequency $\Omega/2$, the phase lag is

$$\left(\frac{T}{2} \right) \left(\frac{\Omega}{2} \right) = \frac{\pi}{2} \text{ rad} = 90°$$

but the gain is 63.6 per cent of that at zero frequency.   Although the attenuation beyond $\Omega/2$ is not as great as might be desired, at Ω and multiples of Ω the clamper does a perfect job of attenuation.   If $i(t)$ is a constant, it contains only zero frequency, and its sampled form will have only the frequencies 0, Ω, 2Ω, etc.   The clamper passes the zero frequency and removes all frequencies $n\Omega$; consequently, it recovers the original constant function.   That this is so, can be easily visualized from a sketch similar to Fig. 12.3 but drawn for a constant $i(t)$.

It is interesting to note that the gain of the clamping filter approaches T as the sampling time T approaches zero.   This is so because

$$\lim_{T\to 0} G_c(s) = \lim_{T\to 0} \frac{1 - (1 - Ts + T^2s^2/2 - \cdots)}{s} = T \qquad (12.15c)$$

and means that the sampler-clamper combination approaches a unity gain continuous amplifier as T goes to zero.   The clamper supplies the multiplier T demanded by Eq. (12.10).   Similar comments hold for the clamper at zero frequency, as $G_c(0)$ also equals T.

A praiseworthy characteristic of the clamping filter is that although its output $o(t)$ is noticeably different from the original continuous function $i(t)$, the two manage to agree at least at the sampling instants; thus if the samples $o(t)$ are taken just past the sampling instants, then

$$o(nT) = i(nT) \qquad \text{or} \qquad o^*(t) = i^*(t) \qquad (12.16)$$

In spite of its shortcomings the clamping filter is a reasonably satisfactory desampling device; moreover, it is practical to build.   The essential features of mechanizing a sampling-clamping device are indicated by the network of Fig. 12.8.   The voltage $e_i(t)$ is sampled by the closure of the switch S for a period very short compared to the sampling time T; the resistance R_i is low to allow C to charge to $e_i(t)$ during the brief closed-switch time; R_o is much greater than R_i so that the time constant CR_o

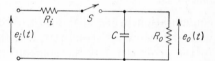

Fig. 12.8   Basic network realizing the sampling-clamping action.

is substantially greater than T; the output voltage $e_o(t)$ stays nearly constant between switch closures and is therefore the clamped value of the samples of $e_i(t)$.   In an actual piece of equipment an active circuit would probably have to be used to achieve the tremendous R_o/R_i ratio called for.   At any rate, the design will be a compromise between accuracy of clamping and simplicity of the circuit.   For a particular accuracy the maximum allowable T can be defined, but the nice thing about it is that the same circuit will operate as a clamper also with a shorter T. In most other desamplers some of the circuit parameters are directly related to T, and the design must be made for the specific sampling time chosen.

Other desamplers are possible, but not often used.   One class of such desamplers extrapolates the function in the intersample period by fitting a polynomial of degree n over the $n + 1$ last samples.   Such a desampler is often called an n-order hold, and indeed the clamping filter is the simplest member of this class, the zero-order hold.   The first-order hold generates straight lines in the sampling interval but also jumps at the sampling instant to the new sample value.   In general, n integrators are needed to realize an n-order hold and this becomes expensive. It is further not always desirable to use higher-order desamplers. It is best to handle the desampling problem as part of the over-all system compensation problem, rather than as an exercise in how best to recover a continuous signal. In feedback control systems the objective is a satisfactory over-all performance which may or may not require the reconstruction of a specific signal within the system.

12.7 Heuristic Analysis of Simple System

A new topic, like sampled-data analysis, may generate both the allure and the anxiety of the unknown. At the risk of dulling the former, but abating the latter, let us try to work our way through a simple example utilizing methods which are available from continuous-data analysis.

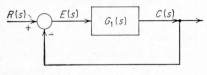

The example chosen will recur in later sections to form a familiar common denominator in comparing various methods of analysis and design.

Fig. 12.9 A simple closed-loop continuous-data system.

Figure 12.9 shows an elementary continuous-data closed-loop system configuration, wherein the controlled quantity $c(t)$ is directly compared with the reference signal $r(t)$, and the controlling action is proportional to the error $e(t)$. If the controlled member is an idealized d-c motor controlled by its shunt-field current, its transfer function $G_1(s)$ may be

$$G_1(s) = \frac{5}{s(s + 2)} = \frac{2.5}{s} - \frac{2.5}{s + 2} \tag{12.17}$$

in a particular case.

It is further known from feedback-system analysis that

$$C(s) = \frac{G_1(s)}{1 + G_1(s)} R(s) \tag{12.18}$$

which for a step function input reduces to

$$C(s) = \frac{5}{s(s^2 + 2s + 5)} = \frac{1}{s} - \frac{s + 2}{(s + 1)^2 + (2)^2} \tag{12.19}$$

The use of suitable tables leads to the time response for $t > 0$,

$$c(t) = 1 - 1.118e^{-t} \sin (2t + 63°26') \tag{12.20}$$

How meaningful is the expression (12.20)? Actually, as it stands, it does not tell us very much beyond the general nature of $c(t)$. Even the fact that $c(0) = 0$ is not at all obvious; neither is it clear where and what the overshoot is. To plot this function, one would calculate $c(t)$ for specific values of t, plot these samples and connect them by a continuous line. This straightforward computational process is quite tedious and can actually be simplified by sampled-data techniques, as will be indicated later. The point being made is that sampled-data methods can be utilized in the analysis of continuous-data systems.

Let us first do the opposite and analyze the sampled-data system of Fig. 12.10 by continuous-data techniques. The switch shown represents an impulse modulator, and in order to pass the same amount of charge (integral of current) into the motor field as in the continuous system just discussed, it is necessary to insert an amplifier of gain T, as was discussed in Sec. 12.5. If T is chosen to be 0.5 sec, then the gain is one-half; but this is evened out by the fact that two samples are taken in each second. The result is that the performance of this system can be compared with the continuous system on an equivalent basis. The choice of $T = 0.5$ sec makes the two systems noticeably, but not drastically, different from each other.

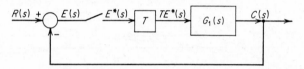

Fig. 12.10   A simple closed-loop sampled-data system.

To analyze the response of the sampled system, we note that the loop is closed only at the sampling instants and is open in the intervening interval. If a unit step function $r(t) = u(t)$ is applied to the system at rest at $t = 0$, and the sampling switch is operated just after the appearance of the step or at $t = 0^+$, the error at this time will be $e(0) = 1$ and an impulse of area $Te(0) = 0.5$ will appear at the motor input. This is quite a jolt for the motor to receive, but we assume that it agreed to be nice and linear about it all. Moreover, it will not be bothered again for T sec, because the loop is now open until the next sampling instant.

Now, we can complete the analysis since we know that the unit impulse response of the motor is the inverse Laplace transform of the motor transfer function $G_1(s)$. Thus, with the aid of Eq. (12.17)

$$g_1(t) = \mathcal{L}^{-1}[G_1(s)] = 2.5(1 - e^{-2t}) \qquad (12.21)$$

is readily found. Since the impulse applied to the motor at $t = 0$ has an area 0.5, the response will be

$$c(t) = 0.5g_1(t) = 1.25(1 - e^{-2t}) \qquad (12.22)$$

during the first sampling interval.

At the end of the first sampling interval an error impulse will again be allowed to pass and initiate another impulse response *in addition* to the one already in progress. Linearity of the motor permits the addition or superposition of the two responses, which describe the total response of the system in the second sampling interval. The development of this step-by-step process of solution is illustrated in Fig. 12.11, which shows both the error samples and the individual responses to them: $c_n(t)$ being the response to the impulse $Te(nT)u_0(t - nT)$.

Although we solved our first sampled-data problem, we are keenly aware that our method was rather clumsy. It does not lead readily to such criteria as stability, damping, overshoot, final value, etc. Our purpose for using the method was mainly to provide a quick intuitive

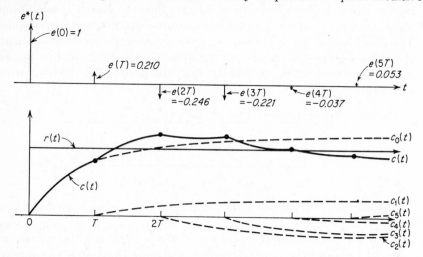

Fig. 12.11   Response of sampled-data system to a unit step $(T = 0.5 \text{ sec})$.

feeling for the workings of sampled-data systems and to reinvigorate our search for more elegant methods.

12.8 z Transforms of Sampled Function

In Eq. (12.8) we have derived a closed form of the Laplace transform of the sampled step function $u^*(t)$. This derivation was based on the use of the time delay operator e^{-Ts}, which arises naturally in dealing with a system having a constant sampling interval T. The introduction of a new complex variable[1]

$$z = e^{+Ts} \tag{12.23}$$

is justified at least for achieving some economy in printing. Actually, the use of this new variable will be made much more meaningful during our progress; for the moment, however, we can already exploit its definition as a time-advance operator.

[1] Defining z as exp $(+Ts)$ rather than exp $(-Ts)$ is in accordance with convention. Clearly even more economy in printing could be achieved with the negative-exponential definition.

To fix our ideas, let us repeat Eq. (12.8) showing the Laplace transform of $u^*(t)$:

$$U^*(s) = \sum_{n=0}^{\infty} e^{-nTs} = \frac{1}{1 - e^{-Ts}} \qquad \sigma > 0 \qquad (12.24)$$

If we now substitute the definition (12.23) in Eq. (12.24), we obtain what is called the z transform[1] of the step function $u(t)$:

$$U(z) = \sum_{n=0}^{\infty} z^{-n} = \frac{1}{1 - z^{-1}} \qquad |z| > 0 \qquad (12.25)$$

The above definition of this z transform underlines the close relationship, if not the identity of the Laplace and z transformations. Indeed, we have our first entry in our table of z transforms, which could read as:

Name of function	t Domain	s Domain	z Domain
Unit step	$u(t)$	$1/s$	$1/(1 - z^{-1})$

Let us further develop this table.

The exponential is the next more complicated function to handle. The z transform of the unit exponential e^{-at} can be readily written as an infinite series of samples properly shifted in time

$$\mathcal{Z}[e^{-at}] = 1 + e^{-aT}z^{-1} + e^{-2aT}z^{-2} + \cdots + e^{-naT}z^{-n} + \cdots$$

It is implicit in unilateral transformation that the function transformed is zero for $t < 0$; hence the absence of positive powers of z. Furthermore at $t = 0$, it is assumed that the full unity value of the exponential is sampled. The general term in the series for $F(z)$ is

$$e^{-naT}z^{-n} = (e^{-aT}z^{-1})^n$$

so that the series can be readily summed into the closed form

$$F(z) = \frac{1}{1 - e^{-aT}z^{-1}} \qquad \text{if } |e^{-aT}z^{-1}| < 1 \qquad (12.26)$$

The convergence condition is again identical to the condition $\sigma > -a$, where $-a$ is also the abscissa of absolute convergence for the Laplace transform of the exponential

$$\mathcal{L}[e^{-at}] = \frac{1}{s + a}$$

At any rate, a new entry to our table has been obtained.

[1] The notation $U^*(z)$ is also used, but the asterisk is redundant as long as z transfroms of only sampled functions are being investigated.

Having the z transform of an exponential we can obtain the z transform of other functions which can be expressed as a combination of exponentials. For example, since

$$\cos bt = 0.5(e^{+jbt} + e^{-jbt})$$

and since in the derivation of the exponential z transform a need not be restricted to real numbers, we can immediately write

$$\begin{aligned} \mathrm{Z}[\cos bt] &= \frac{0.5}{1 - e^{jbT}z^{-1}} + \frac{0.5}{1 - e^{-jbT}z^{-1}} \\ &= \frac{1 - (\cos bT)z^{-1}}{1 - 2(\cos bT)z^{-1} + z^{-2}} \end{aligned} \tag{12.27}$$

A damped cosine function can also be written in terms of exponentials as

$$e^{-at} \cos bt = 0.5e^{(-a+jb)t} + 0.5e^{(-a-jb)t}$$

and its z transform can thus be directly obtained. The z transforms of the sine and damped-sine functions are also derivable by the above method. Finally, sinusoids with phase angles can always be written as the sum of cosine and sine functions. Thus, a large class of transforms are generated in this manner.

Another class of functions has integer powers of t involved as a multiplier, an example of which is the t-multiplied exponential te^{-at}. The derivation of this z transform is based on the theorem of Laplace transformation which states that the sequence of taking the derivative of a function and taking its transform is inconsequential as long as the variable with respect to which the derivative is taken is independent of the variable of transformation. Stated mathematically,

$$\mathfrak{L}\left[\frac{\partial}{\partial a} f(t,a)\right] = \frac{\partial}{\partial a} \mathfrak{L}[f(t,a)] \tag{12.28}$$

and if $f(t,a)$ is allowed to be e^{-at}, then the application of this theorem yields the Laplace transform of te^{-at}, because

$$\begin{aligned} \mathfrak{L}\left[\frac{\partial}{\partial a} e^{-at}\right] &= \mathfrak{L}[-te^{-at}] = \frac{\partial}{\partial a} \mathfrak{L}[e^{-at}] \\ &= \frac{\partial}{\partial a}\left(\frac{1}{s+a}\right) = -\frac{1}{(s+a)^2} \end{aligned} \tag{12.29}$$

It turns out that the theorem equally applies to z transformation, which is not surprising in view of z transforms being just a special form of Laplace transforms. Stated without proof this theorem is

$$\mathrm{Z}\left[\frac{\partial}{\partial a} f(t,a)\right] = \frac{\partial}{\partial a} \mathrm{Z}[f(t,a)] \tag{12.30}$$

and applying it to our example it is seen that

$$\mathcal{Z}[te^{-at}] = \mathcal{Z}\left[-\frac{\partial}{\partial a} e^{-at}\right] = -\frac{\partial}{\partial a} \frac{1}{1 - e^{-at}z^{-1}}$$

$$= \frac{Te^{-aT}z^{-1}}{(1 - e^{-aT}z^{-1})^2} \qquad (12.31)$$

which becomes another entry in our table. In general, n successive differentiations would yield the z transform of $t^n e^{-at}$.

The z transforms of ramp function, t or $tu(t)$, can be obtained from that of te^{-at} by letting a go zero in Eq. (12.31):

$$\mathcal{Z}[t] = t^* = \lim_{a \to 0} \frac{Te^{-aT}z^{-1}}{(1 - e^{-aT}z^{-1})^2} = \frac{Tz^{-1}}{(1 - z^{-1})^2} \qquad (12.32)$$

Similarly, $\mathcal{Z}[t^n]$ can be obtained from $\mathcal{Z}[t^n e^{-at}]$. All entries of Table 12.1 can be prepared on the basis of the rules discussed.

Table 12.1 Basic z Transforms

No.	Name of function	t Domain	s Domain	z Domain
1	Any	$f(t)$	$F(s)$	$F(z)$
2	Step	$u(t)$	$\dfrac{1}{s}$	$\dfrac{1}{1 - z^{-1}}$
3	Ramp	$t \cdot u(t) = t$	$\dfrac{1}{s^2}$	$\dfrac{Tz^{-1}}{(1 - z^{-1})^2}$
4	Parabola	$t^2 \cdot u(t) = t^2$	$\dfrac{2}{s^3}$	$\dfrac{T^2 z^{-1}(1 + z^{-1})}{(1 - z^{-1})^3}$
5	Exponential	e^{-at}	$\dfrac{1}{s + a}$	$\dfrac{1}{1 - e^{-Ta}z^{-1}}$
6		$t \cdot e^{-at}$	$\dfrac{1}{(s + a)^2}$	$\dfrac{Te^{-Ta}z^{-1}}{(1 - e^{-Ta}z^{-1})^2}$
7	Sine	$\sin bt$	$\dfrac{b}{s^2 + b^2}$	$\dfrac{(\sin bT)z^{-1}}{1 - 2(\cos bT)z^{-1} + z^{-2}}$
8	Cosine	$\cos bt$	$\dfrac{s}{s^2 + b^2}$	$\dfrac{1 - (\cos bT)z^{-1}}{1 - 2(\cos bT)z^{-1} + z^{-2}}$
9	Damped sine	$e^{-at} \sin bt$	$\dfrac{b}{(s + a)^2 + b^2}$	$\dfrac{e^{-Ta}(\sin bT)z^{-1}}{1 - 2e^{-Ta}(\cos bT)z^{-1} + e^{-2Ta}z^{-2}}$
10	Damped cosine	$e^{-at} \cos bt$	$\dfrac{s + a}{(s + a)^2 + b^2}$	$\dfrac{1 - e^{-Ta}(\cos bT)z^{-1}}{1 - 2e^{-Ta}(\cos bT)z^{-1} + e^{-2Ta}z^{-2}}$

Just so that we do not quite lose the meaning of these z transforms, let us convince ourselves that Eq. (12.32) does indeed produce the sequence of samples of a ramp function. If we perform the long division indicated by the fraction in Eq. (12.32) we obtain the infinite series

$$\frac{Tz^{-1}}{1 - 2z^{-1} + z^{-2}} = Tz^{-1} + 2Tz^{-2} + 3Tz^{-3} + \cdots$$

$$= \sum_{n=0}^{\infty} nTz^{-n} \tag{12.33}$$

The term-by-term inverse transform of (12.33) yields the impulsed time series

$$t^* = \sum_{n=0}^{\infty} nTu_0(t - nT) \tag{12.34}$$

The value of the impulse at $t = nT$ is nT as it should be for the ramp function.

12.9   Filter Transfer Functions

Knowing the z transforms of sampled function is the halfway mark to the z-transform analysis of sampled systems. It remains to discuss filters, their effects on sampled data, and their representation by transfer functions.

It is customary to designate the transfer function of a continuous-data filter by $G(s)$ and that of a sampled-data filter by $D^*(s)$ or $D(z)$. A continuous-data filter has an output

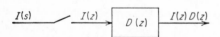

Fig. 12.12   Sampled-data filter.

which is continuous in time, or at least it is not zero everywhere between sampling instants. A discrete filter has a sampled output. While $G(s)$ can accept at its input either continuous or sampled data, $D(z)$ can only accept sampled data.

The effect of a discrete filter $D(z)$ on signals is quite straightforward and is illustrated in Fig. 12.12. A discrete filter can accept only sampled inputs and it produces a sampled function as an output. If the input and the output are rational functions of z, so is $D(z)$. It is noted that $D(z)$ is not followed by a sampler, because the output of $D(z)$ is already sampled. In fact, as long as the sampler has been defined as an impulse modulator, a redundant sampler following $D(z)$ is meaningless, for mathematics does not teach about the product of impulses.

Figure 12.13 characterizes the various possible outputs which can be obtained with $G(s)$ and various combinations of samplers. In part (a) a unit impulse input is shown to produce the continuous output $g(t)$, whose transform is $G(s)$. The sampled output $g^*(t)$ can be obtained by the addition of a sampler, as done in part (b) of the same figure. The transform of this output is $G^*(s)$, a function of e^{Ts}, or $G(z)$, the same function of z. Any sampled function can be thought of as being generated in this manner, and here is then a useful connection between sampled functions, about which we have already studied, and filters, about which we are learning.   It seems that $G(s)$ followed by a sampler is equivalent to a sampled-data filter $D(z)$: it is a function of z and its unit impulse response is a sampled function.   Actually the sampled-data transfer function $G(z)$ is a completely valid concept *as long as the input to $G(s)$ is sampled*, as the unit impulse is, indeed.

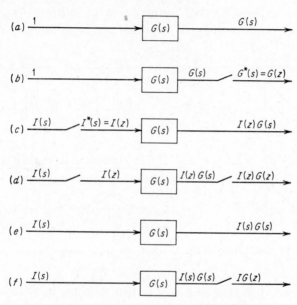

Fig. 12.13   Continuous-data filter and sampling.

Parts (c) and (d) of Fig. 12.13 generalize the concept of sampled transfer function.   In (c) the sampled function $i^*(t)$ is fed to $G(s)$ whose output transform is a mixed function of s and z.   This corresponds to a continuous function consisting of a linear combination of $g(t - nT)$, each of which being due to an impulse in $i^*(t)$.   By the sampling of this continuous function in part (d), the sampled function $I(z)G(z)$ is obtained. This shows that $G(z)$ acts like a cascade filter transfer function on $I(z)$. The proof of this very important result will follow later.

The filtering of the continuous input $I(s)$ is demonstrated in (e) and (f) of Fig. 12.13.   The continuous output of $G(s)$ in Fig. 12.13e is $O(s) = I(s)G(s)$.   The sampled output in (f) is $O^*(s)$ or $O(z)$, which is equal to

$$[I(s)G(s)]^* = IG^*(s) = \mathrm{Z}[I(s)G(s)] = IG(z)$$

all being different notations for the same thing.   It is particularly emphasized that in the case of (f) the combination of $G(s)$ followed by the sampler does not act as a transfer function $G(z)$ because the input $I(s)$ is continuous. If $G(z)$ were a transfer function, the output in (f) would be $I(s)G(z)$, which is a continuous function.

It is furthermore very important to remember that the outputs in (d) and (f) are different; i.e.,

$$I(z)G(z) \neq IG(z) \tag{12.35}$$

The specific example of Fig. 12.14 serves to illustrate this difference: $i(t)$ is a unit ramp lasting $2.5T$ sec, and $g(t)$ is an exponential having a

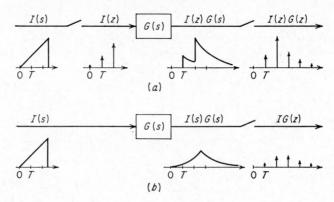

Fig. 12.14 Time-domain illustration of specific sampled signals.   (a) $I(z)G(z)$ (b) $IG(z)$.

time constant such that it decays to half its value in T sec.   The input transform therefore is

$$I(s) = \frac{1 - e^{-2.5Ts}}{s^2} - \frac{2.5}{s}$$

and the filter transfer function is

$$G(s) = \frac{1}{1 + \tau s}$$

where τ is defined so as to make $e^{-T/\tau} = 0.5$; that is, $\tau = T/\ln 2 = 1.44T$.

For the formal proof (12.35) we may use the definition

$$I^*(s) = \frac{1}{T} \sum_{k=-\infty}^{\infty} I(s + jk\Omega)$$

Although this definition of $I^*(s)$ is only valid if $i(t)$ has no discontinuities at the sampling instants, the proof of nonequality in this special case will certainly ensure nonequality for the general case.   We further recall that due to the periodic property of sampled-data transforms

$$I^*(s) = I^*(s + jm\Omega)$$

where m is an integer.   The left-hand side of (12.35) can now be derived as

$$[I^*(s)G(s)]^* = \frac{1}{T} \sum_{k=-\infty}^{\infty} I^*(s + jk\Omega)G(s + jk\Omega)$$

$$= I^*(s) \frac{1}{T} \sum_{k=-\infty}^{\infty} G(s + jk\Omega) = I^*(s)G^*(s) = I(z)G(z)$$

$$(12.36)$$

But for the right-hand side of the same nonequation no similar simplification is possible; thus

$$[I(s)G(s)]^* = \frac{1}{T} \sum_{k=-\infty}^{\infty} I(s + jk\Omega)G(s + jk\Omega) = IG^*(s)$$

$$= IG(z) \qquad (12.37)$$

12.10 z-Transform Analysis of Simple System

In Sec. 12.7 we made a transient analysis of the sampled-data system of Fig. 12.10.   We found that the conventional techniques proved rather clumsy, and now we can use z transformation to re-solve our problem.

The controlled quantity $c(t)$ is a continuous function, but it is often adequately described by its samples.   The use of z-transform techniques results in the solution for $C(z)$ and $c^*(t)$, and if the intersample behavior of $c(t)$ is also of interest, additional analysis or a different approach can be applied.   We will discuss these other methods later; for the moment we assume that the sampled output is an adequate result.

In the analysis of sampled systems one crucial step is the reduction of closed loops.   In general, if the loop transfer function is $L(s)$, the feedback loop reduces to a cascade element having the transfer function $1/[1 - L(s)]$.   How can we get a loop transfer function when there is a sampler in the loop?   Although the sampler itself does not have a transfer function, it is still possible to obtain the transfer function of the sampled loop, if our journey around the loop starts and ends at a point where the signal is sampled.   For then the input as well as the output of the loop path is sampled, and two sampled functions can be related to each other by a sampled loop transfer function $L(z)$.

The recognition of the sampled loop transfer function is the only cardinal rule that must be observed in reducing sampled-data systems. It means that the first step must always be to solve for the sampled function in the loop, even if that signal is of no specific interest in our problem. In our example we will first solve for the sampled error $E(z)$. Since

$$E(s) = R(s) - C(s) = R(s) - E(z)TG_1(s)$$

$E(z)$ can be obtained by termwise sampling of the above equation

$$E(z) = R(z) - TE(z)G_1(z) \tag{12.38}$$

where use was made of Eq. (12.36) in deriving the rightmost term. Solving for $E(z)$ in Eq. (12.38) gives

$$E(z) = \frac{R(z)}{1 + TG_1(z)} \tag{12.39}$$

It is now straightforward to write

$$C(s) = E(z)TG_1(s) = \frac{R(z)}{1 + TG_1(z)} \, TG_1(s) \tag{12.40}$$

Although Eq. (12.40) constitutes a formal solution in the frequency domain, it is not very useful. $C(s)$ is expressed as a product of rational functions of z and s, and no appropriate methods or tables are available to get a suitable expression for $c(t)$. Although some exploration in the frequency domain is possible, the usual methods of Nyquist, Bode, Nichols, or Evans are not applicable directly. The difficulty lies in that the numerator transfer function $TG_1(s)$ is unsampled, while in the denominator the sampled form appears. Some approximate investigations are possible but also potentially erroneous.

However, if the sampled output is an adequate answer, we can immediately write

$$C(z) = E(z)TG_1(z) = R(z) \frac{TG_1(z)}{1 + TG_1(z)} \tag{12.41}$$

which is a rational function in z only. Furthermore, now the numerator and denominator functions are the same, and some of the conventional methods are directly applicable. The Nyquist and Nichols plots for $TG_1(z)$ provide the usual introspection as far as M circles, phase margin, stability conditions, etc., are concerned. Bode's method is also applicable but it becomes clumsy, for the usual straight-line asymptotes do not apply. The root-locus method in the z plane can be used with simple modifications.

For the moment let us find the specific solution for $C(z)$ and show how the transient response can be readily determined. Using Table 12.1, we note that

$$R(z) = \frac{1}{1 - z^{-1}} \tag{12.42}$$

since $r(t)$ is a unit step. The sampling time $T = 0.5$ sec and $G_1(z)$ is found after appropriate partial fraction expansion of

$$G_1(s) = \frac{5}{s(s+2)} = \frac{2.5}{s} - \frac{2.5}{s+2}$$

With the aid of Table 12.1

$$G_1(z) = \frac{2.5}{1 - z^{-1}} - \frac{2.5}{1 - e^{-2T}z^{-1}} = \frac{2.5(1 - 0.632)z^{-1}}{1 - 1.368z^{-1} + 0.368z^{-2}} \quad (12.43)$$

Substitution of Eqs. (12.42), (12.43), and $T = 0.5$ into Eq. (12.41) yields

$$C(z) = \frac{1}{1 - z^{-1}} \frac{0.790z^{-1}}{1 - 0.578z^{-1} + 0.368z^{-2}} \quad (12.44)$$

Equation (12.44) is the z transform of the controlled output and allows us to proceed in three different ways. It is possible to disentangle Eq. (12.44) into *fractional components*, which can be identified with entries 2, 9, and 10 of Table 12.1. Thus

$$C(z) = \frac{1}{1 - z^{-1}} - \frac{1 - 0.289z^{-1}}{1 - 0.578z^{-1} + 0.368z^{-2}} - \frac{0.079z^{-1}}{1 - 0.578z^{-1} + 0.368z^{-2}}$$

corresponding to a step, a damped cosine, and a damped sine. By proper identifications with the tabular expressions it is possible to write a continuous function $c_{eq}(t)$ whose samples are the same as those of $c(t)$, but which is not necessarily equal to $c(t)$. This equivalent continuous output is

$$c_{eq}(t) = 1 - 1.01e^{-t} \sin (2.14t + 81.6°) \quad (12.45)$$

and makes an interesting comparison with $c(t)$ of Eq. (12.20), which was the output of the system before the sampler was inserted. Outside of this comparison, Eq. (12.45) is not very useful, but it provides a formal time-domain expression for the output, such that

$$c_{eq}^*(t) = c^*(t)$$

A more direct way of obtaining the actual samples of $c(t)$ is by the straightforward *long division* of the fraction of (12.44). After multiplying together the denominator factors and performing the long division indicated, we get

$$C(z) = 0.790z^{-1} + 1.246z^{-2} + 1.220z^{-3} + 1.037z^{-4}$$
$$+ 0.938z^{-5} + 0.949z^{-6} + 0.997z^{-7} + 1.018z^{-8} + \cdots \quad (12.46)$$

The third method is essentially similar to the second one, but it is considered computationally simpler. This *difference-equation* method permits the use of convenient tabular form of calculation in the time domain. If $R(z)$ is resubstituted into Eq. (12.44), we obtain

$$\frac{C(z)}{R(z)} = \frac{0.790z^{-1}}{1 - 0.578z^{-1} + 0.368z^{-2}}$$

Cross multiplication of the above yields

$$C(z) - 0.578z^{-1}C(z) + 0.368z^{-2}C(z) = 0.790z^{-1}R(z)$$

whose inverse transform can be rearranged into the difference equation

$$c^*(t) = 0.790r^*(t - T) - 0.368c^*(t - 2T) + 0.578c^*(t - T)$$

The latter can further be written in terms of the samples, rather than the complete impulsed functions. Thus

$$c(nT) = 0.790r(nT - T) - 0.368c(nT - 2T) + 0.578c(nT - T)$$

but it is even more convenient to use the subscript notation of numerical analysis, which results in

$$0.790r_{n-1} - 0.368c_{n-2} + 0.578c_{n-1} = c_n \tag{12.47}$$

The terms are already arranged in the last equation to make the tabulation and calculation as simple as possible.

Table 12.2 Calculation of Sample Values

Table 12.2a

n	$t = nT$	r_n	$0.790r_{n-1}$	$-0.368c_{n-2}$	$0.578c_{n-1}$	c_n
0	0	1	0	0	0	0
1	0.5	1	0.790	0	0	0.790
2	1.0		0.790	0	0.456	
3	1.5			−0.291		

Table 12.2b

n	$t = nT$	r_n	$0.790r_{n-1}$	$-0.368c_{n-2}$	$0.578c_{n-1}$	c_n
0	0	1	. . . . .	0	0	0
1	0.5	1	0.790	0	0	0.790
2	1.0	1	0.790	0	0.456	1.246
3	1.5	1	0.790	−0.291	0.720	1.219
4	2.0	1	0.790	−0.458	0.705	1.037
5	2.5	1	0.790	−0.448	0.599	0.941
6	3.0	1	0.790	−0.381	0.544	0.953
7	3.5	1	0.790	−0.346	0.551	0.995
8	4.0	1	0.790	−0.351	0.575	1.014

Table 12.2a illustrates the calculation of the first two samples, c_0 and c_1. The first row of this table is obtained as follows: n and $t = 0$; the input sample $r_0 = 1$ because $r(t)$ is a unit step; for this same reason $r_{-1} = 0$; similarly c_{-2} and c_{-1} are 0 because the system was said to be at rest to start with; c_0 is calculated on basis of (12.47) as the sum of the numbers in that row between the vertical lines.   In this case the sum of the three zeros yields the zero in the c_n column.   The arrows indicate how additional tabular values are obtained by appropriate "aging" of the data and their multiplication by the appropriate constants.   It is clear that $c_1 = 0.790$ is derived as the sum of 0.790, 0, and 0.   The new tabular values 0.456 and -0.291 are derived from c_1 as indicated by the arrows.   The reader can obtain the next value in the c_n as the sum of 0.790, 0, and 0.456, which is $c_2 = 1.246$.   The calculation is completed to $n = 8$ or $t = 4$ sec in Table 12.2b for illustration.   The c_n column shows values equal within computational accuracy to those of Eq. (12.46).

12.11   Effect of the Clamper

In going from the simple continuous-data system of Fig. 12.9 to the simple sampled-data system of Fig. 12.10, we have not changed the system response in a drastic manner.   At least, for the sampling time chosen, the overshoot, the response time, and other similar criteria were affected only moderately.   However, we made two very unrealistic assumptions: first, that the sampler produces impulses at its output, and second, that the motor can accept these impulses and react to them according to its analytical, linear impulse response.

A practical sampler produces pulses rather than impulses, and the areas under these pulses should be proportional to the areas of the impulses in the analytical model.   In some devices the height of each pulse would vary with the function being sampled, but samplers can be constructed which clamp the sampled value of the function for the duration of each pulse.   In the latter case, if the pulses are of short duration compared to T, the impulse modulator followed by a suitable amplifier is a good representation of the actual system.   On the other hand, if the pulses are comparatively wide, an impulse modulator followed by an appropriate clamper is an accurate representation.

In order to pass the same amount of power to the motor, narrower pulses must have greater heights for the same sampling rate.   To avoid the saturation problem in the motor, it is clearly desirable to stretch the pulse to the full width T, in which case the analytical model is an impulse modulator followed by the clamper described in Sec. 12.6.   The most striking disadvantage of this configuration is the phase lag introduced by the clamper.

The block diagram (Fig. 12.15) of the system incorporating a sampler-clamper combination shows that the amplifier of gain T (see Fig. 12.10) has been eliminated, since the clamper $G_c(s)$ provides this gain by its very nature, as was noted in Sec. 12.6. The output transform can be obtained by a method identical with that of the preceding section as

$$C(s) = \frac{R^*(s)}{1 + G_c G_1^*(s)} G_c(s)G_1(s) = \frac{R^*(s)}{1 + G^*(s)} G(s) \qquad (12.48)$$

from which the z transform becomes

$$C(z) = R(z) \frac{G(z)}{1 + G(z)} \qquad (12.49)$$

In order to solve for $C(z)$ the only new item to evaluate is $G(z)$. Now

$$G(s) = G_c(s)G_1(s) = \frac{1 - e^{-Ts}}{s} \frac{5}{s(s + 2)}$$

$$= (1 - e^{-Ts}) \frac{5}{s^2(s + 2)} \qquad (12.50)$$

In the last step above we separated that portion of $G(s)$ which is a rational

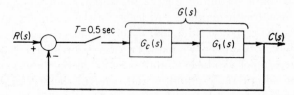

Fig. 12.15 A simple closed-loop system containing a sampler and a clamper.

function of $z = e^{Ts}$ from the portion which is rational in s. Let us call these portions $A(z)$ and $B(s)$ respectively, where

$$A^*(s) = 1 - e^{-Ts} \quad \text{or} \quad A(z) = 1 - z^{-1}$$

and

$$B(s) = \frac{5}{s^2(s + 2)} \qquad (12.51)$$

From Sec. 12.9, however, we know that

$$G(z) = \mathrm{Z}[A(z)B(s)] = A(z)B(z)$$

and so we are left with the task of finding $B(z)$.

Expanding (12.51) into partial fractions yields

$$B(s) = \frac{2.5}{s^2} - \frac{1.25}{s} + \frac{1.25}{s + 2} \qquad (12.52)$$

The use of Table 12.1 provides the corresponding terms of $B(z)$:

$$B(z) = \frac{2.5Tz^{-1}}{(1 - z^{-1})^2} - \frac{1.25}{1 - z^{-1}} + \frac{1.25}{1 - e^{-2T}z^{-1}} \qquad (12.53)$$

Recalling that $T = 0.5$ sec and combining the terms of (12.53), we derive

$$B(z) = \frac{0.460z^{-1} + 0.330z^{-2}}{(1 - z^{-1})^2(1 - 0.368z^{-1})} \qquad (12.54)$$

It follows in rapid succession that

$$G(z) = A(z)B(z) = \frac{0.460z^{-1} + 0.330z^{-2}}{(1 - z^{-1})(1 - 0.368z^{-1})} \qquad (12.55)$$

Finally, by one of the methods discussed in the preceding section the series of output samples becomes

$$C(z) = 0.460z^{-1} + 1.208z^{-2} + 1.566z^{-3} + 1.368z^{-4}$$
$$0.939z^{-5} + 0.689z^{-6} + 0.759z^{-7} + 1.009z^{-8} + \cdots$$

Let us now take a look at the three transient responses in Fig. 12.16: (a) is $c(t)$ for the continuous system; (b) is $c(t)$ for the sampled unclamped

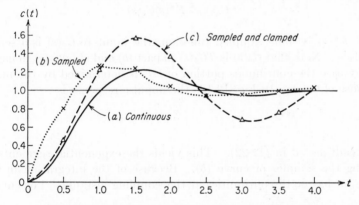

Fig. 12.16   Step responses of simple feedback systems.

system; and (c) is $c(t)$ for the sampled and clamped system. How the intersample behavior of $c(t)$ was determined in responses (b) and (c) will be discussed below. For the moment, let us compare these curves.

Going from curve (a) to (b) seems to suggest that sampling improved the system step response because the overshoot increased only slightly, but the response time decreased considerably. This is a fallacy resulting from the optimistic assumption that the sampler operates just a moment *after* the appearance of the input step. In the most pessimistic case the sampler would operate just *before* the occurrence of the step, and curve (b) would be delayed almost T sec. On the average, the delay is $T/2$, and a realistic comparison should show both curves (b) and (c) moved to the right by this amount. If this were done, the responses (a) and (b) would not be materially different.

On the other hand, the introduction of the clamper in (c), caused a drastic deterioration of the system. The overshoot changed from the generally acceptable 21 per cent of (a) and 25 per cent of (b) to the usually unacceptable 57 per cent of (c).   Moreover, in spite of this overshoot, even the response time in (c) is inferior to that in (b).

The above example demonstrates that the system performance generally deteriorates as a result of sampling, especially if the sampler is followed by a clamper in a realistic fashion.   It is clear that the use of sampled data must have other justifications, some of which were noted in Sec. 12.2.   In many cases sampling is an inherent system feature that must be accepted and lived with.   It is further true that compensation techniques can restore, or even improve upon, the original system performance as will be demonstrated in succeeding sections.

The intersample behavior of $c(t)$ in parts (b) and (c) of Fig. 12.16 was derived by simple heuristic reasoning.   Since by (12.48) the form of the continuous output transform is

$$C(s) = F^*(s)G_0(s)$$

where $F^*(s)$ is some sampled function, the input to $G_0(s)$ is a series of impulses.   Note that $G_0(s)$ is $TG_1(s)$ in part (b) and $(1/s)G_1(s)$ in part (c). In any case the continuous portion of $c(t)$ is determined by the impulse response of $G_0(s)$.   In Fig. 12.16b the impulse response is

$$Tg_1(t) = 1.25(1 - e^{-2t})$$

as already noted in (12.22).   This yields the exponential segments connecting the samples of curve (b).   Because of the integration in $G_1(s)$, curve (b) has no discontinuities at the sampling instants.   For curve (c)

$$G_0(s) = \frac{5}{s^2(s + 2)}$$

on basis of (12.50), so that

$$g_0(t) = 2.5t - 1.25 + 1.25e^{-2t}$$

In this case the superposition of $g_0(t)$ responses to the various impulses is not readily done.   The general nature of the curve, however, can be deduced from the double integration in $G_0(s)$ which implies that no discontinuities occur even in the derivative of $c(t)$.

12.12   More about z Transformation

The complex variable z was introduced in Sec. 12.8, where its role as a time advance operator was explained and used to obtain the z transforms of several functions.   It is time now to review other basic aspects of the variable z and the associated transform theory.

Conformal mapping between the s and z planes throws considerable light on the properties of the variable z and of sampled functions.   Since

$$s = \sigma + j\omega$$

it follows by the definition of z given in (12.23) that

$$z = e^{Ts} = e^{T\sigma+j\omega} = e^{T\sigma}e^{jT\omega} \tag{12.56}$$

The latter shows that

$$|z| = e^{T\sigma} \quad \text{and} \quad \underline{/z} = T\omega \tag{12.57}$$

Thus, the magnitude of z depends only on the real part of s, while the angle of z is a function of only the imaginary part of s.

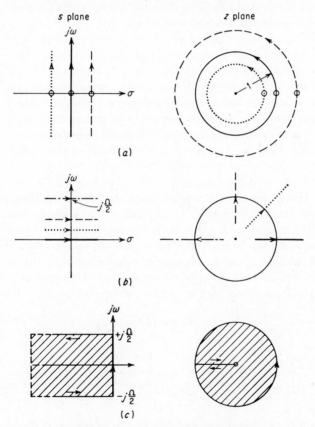

Fig. 12.17   Conformal contours.

The illustrative conformal contours in Fig. 12.17 are based on (12.57). Part (a) of the figure shows that vertical lines (constant σ) in the s plane map into circles (constant-magnitude lines) in the z plane.   Note particularly that the imaginary axis $j\omega$ corresponds to the unit circle.   Any of the circles is traversed in the counterclockwise direction with increasing ω, and this traversing repeats each time $T\omega$ changes $360°$ or 2π rad, or for changes in ω equal to $2\pi/T = \Omega$ rad, which is the radian sampling frequency. This again (see also Sec. 12.5) illustrates the periodic nature of z and z transforms in the s domain, according to which if $F(z)$ is a z transform and m an integer, then

$$F^*(s + jm\Omega) = F^*(s) \qquad (12.58)$$

In part (b) of Fig. 12.17 horizontal lines (constant ω) of the s plane are seen to map into radial (constant-angle) lines in the z plane. The angles of the radial lines are proportional to ω. As σ goes from $-\infty$ to 0, the radial lines go from the origin to the unit circle, while for positive σ the radial lines continue to increase toward infinity.

Note that just as the vertical and horizontal lines in the s plane cross at right angles, so do the circular and radial lines in the z plane, which is a well-known rule of conformal mapping. Note further that the point at infinity in the s plane has no uniquely corresponding point in the z plane; if $s = \infty$ is approached along a horizontal line, $z = 0$ or ∞ results; however, if $s = \infty$ is approached along a vertical line, the corresponding z is completely undetermined, except for being somewhere on the conformal circle. Thus, $s = \infty$ maps into any point of the z plane and the variable z has an *essential singularity* at infinity.

An exercise in conformal mapping shown in Fig. 12.17(c) is useful in examining the stability of sampled functions. For stability the poles of a function must fall within the left half of the s plane, or be on the imaginary axis and simple. However, in case of a sampled function it is sufficient to explore a horizontal strip of the left half-plane which has a width of $j\Omega$ radians, because periodicity assures us that the rest of the left half-plane will contain only repetitions of the same pole pattern. The conformal mapping of Fig. 12.17c is summarized in Table 12.3.

Table 12.3

s Plane		z Plane	
Vertical	$-j\Omega/2$ to $j\Omega/2$	Unit circle	-1 to -1
Horizontal	$j\Omega/2 \rightarrow -\infty$	Radial	$-1 \rightarrow 0$
Vertical	down near ∞	Infinitesimal circle around origin	
Horizontal	$-\infty$ to $-j\Omega/2$	Radial	0 to -1

Thus, the finite portion of the left half of the s plane is conformal to the inside of the unit circle excluding the origin itself in the z plane. However, a pole at the origin of the z plane produces a term in the partial fraction expansion proportional to z^{-1}, our well-known time-delay operator, which is both realizable and stable. As a result we can state that a *sampled function is stable or bounded, if the poles of its z transform fall anywhere within the unit circle or if they are located on the unit circle and are simple;* otherwise it is unstable.

Periodicity in the s plane is such an important property of a sampled function that we return to it for further elaboration. Figure 12.18a shows a possible pole configuration of the transform $F(s)$ of a continuous

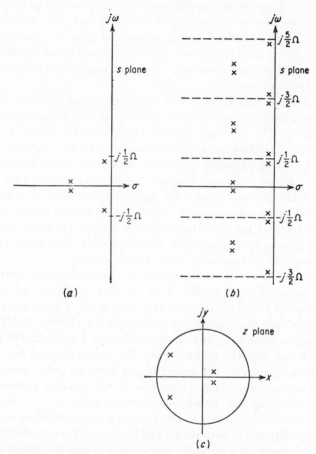

Fig. 12.18 Pole configurations in the s and z planes. (a) Continuous function. (b) Sampled function. (c) Sampled function.

function $f(t)$. After sampling this *same* pole pattern repeats as seen in part (b). That this is so follows from (12.13) according to which

$$F^*(s) = \frac{1}{T}[F(s) + F(s + j\Omega) + F(s - j\Omega) + F(s + j2\Omega) + \cdots] \quad (12.59)$$

The first term on the right proves that the poles of $F(s)$ are, indeed, included among the poles of $F^*(s)$ and the rest of the terms prove that all the other poles of $F^*(s)$ are just periodic repetitions. Note, however,

that the same cannot be concluded about the zeros of $F^*(s)$.   Although
it is true that the zeros of $F^*(s)$ repeat with a periodicity of $j\Omega$ in the
s plane, the zeros of $F(s)$ are generally not among the zeros of $F^*(s)$.

Part (c) of Fig. 12.18 illustrates the utility of the variable z in that
only a single set of poles exist in the z plane for $F(z)$.   If we conceive of
traveling up along the imaginary axis of the s plane in part (b), we find
that the pole scenery repeats after every Ω rad (like telephone poles
along the railroad track).   In the z plane of part (c), however, only a
single pole group need be erected, since after each Ω rad we circle around
the same track or, more properly stated, around an identical track on a
different Riemann surface.

An important property of both continuous and sampled-data transforms of real functions is *conjugate symmetry* or *conjugacy*, illustrated also
in Fig. 12.18.   The real axes of parts (a), (b), and (c) act as a mirror, so
to say, and the complex poles come in conjugate pairs.   Similar symmetry
is required in the arrangement of zeros, in Nyquist plots, in root loci, etc.

For continuous functions conjugate symmetry means that once the
nature of a transform is known for positive frequencies, it is also known
for negative frequencies and vice versa.   As a matter of fact, the use of
both negative and positive frequencies is merely an analytical convenience.   It follows from conjugacy that amplitude and phase are respectively even and odd functions of the real frequency.

For sampled functions the property of conjugacy combined with the
property of periodicity results in a peculiar *restriction on bandwidth*.
If the nature of $F^*(s)$ is known in the strip of the s plane between the 0
and $j\Omega/2$ (or indeed between any strip $jm\Omega/2$ to $j(m + 1)\Omega/2$ where m
is an integer), then it is known everywhere.   Figure 12.18b illustrates
this well: if not only the real axis, but also the horizontal line at $j\Omega/2$ is
thought of as a mirror, the reflections of the two poles located in this
strip will account for every other pole in the infinite pattern.   Thus,
sampling decreased the bandwidth horizon from $\omega = \infty$ to $\omega = \Omega/2$,
which in essence is the basis of the sampling theorem noted in Sec. 12.6.
It is the consequence of periodicity and conjugacy for sampled transforms
that the amplitude is a periodic and even, whereas the phase a periodic
and odd, function of frequency.

In addition to the comments made so far a large body of theorems and
principles of z transformation have been established, but we will note
here only two very useful theorems: the initial-value and the final-value
theorems.   Other formulas, theorems, and relations will be derived in
various sections as the need for their use arises.

Recall that a sampled-time function is defined by

$$f^*(t) = \sum_{n=0}^{\infty} f(nT)u_o(t - nT) \qquad (12.60)$$

where $f(nT)$ are samples or values of a continuous function $f(t)$, which produces $f^*(t)$ if it is sampled. The *initial-value theorem* defines $f(0)$ when $F(z)$ is known as follows:

$$f(0) = \lim_{n \to 0} f(nT) = \lim_{z \to \infty} F(z) \qquad (12.61)$$

The proof of (12.61) is rather straightforward if $F(z)$ is written as an infinite series:

$$F(z) = f(0) + f(T)z^{-1} + f(2T)z^{-2} + f(3T)z^{-3} + \cdots \qquad (12.62)$$

If in this expression $z \to \infty$ or $z^{-1} \to 0$, the only nonzero term remaining will be $f(0)$, and the theorem (12.61) is immediately established.

The *final-value theorem* states that

$$\lim_{n \to \infty} f(nT) = \lim_{z \to 1} (1 - z^{-1})F(z) \qquad (12.63)$$

The proof of (12.63) will not be given here, but can be found in standard texts.[1] Rather it will be compared with the final-value theorem of continuous transforms

$$\lim_{t \to \infty} f(t) = \lim_{s \to 0} sF(s) \qquad (12.64)$$

The limits on the right sides of (12.63) and (12.64) are conformal, since the s-plane origin maps into the point $z = 1$. Furthermore, multiplication of $F(s)$ by s corresponds to differentiation in the time domain, while the factor $1 - z^{-1}$ in (12.63) represents a differencing operation, which is a discrete differentiation.

Indeed, it can be shown that (12.64) derives from (12.63) as T approaches 0; thus

$$\lim_{T \to 0} (1 - z^{-1})F(z) = \lim_{T \to 0} \frac{1 - z^{-1}}{T} TF(z)$$

$$= \lim_{T \to 0} \frac{1 - z^{-1}}{T} \lim_{T \to 0} TF(z) \qquad (12.65)$$

It is rather instructive to derive these two limits. The first limit reduces as follows:

$$\lim_{T \to 0} \frac{1 - z^{-1}}{T} = \lim_{T \to 0} \frac{1 - e^{-Ts}}{T}$$

$$= \lim_{T \to 0} \frac{1 - (1 - Ts + T^2s^2/2 - \cdots)}{T} = s \qquad (12.66)$$

and corresponds actually to the definition of differentiation. The reduction of the second limit constitutes something like a theorem in itself. It defines the continuous function as the limit of the sampled

[1] Ragazzini and Franklin, *op. cit.*, pp. 62–63; Jury, *op. cit.*, pp. 30–31.

function as the sampling time decreases to zero.[1] Thus,

$$\lim_{T \to 0} TF^*(s) = \lim_{T \to 0} T \frac{1}{T} \sum_{k=-\infty}^{\infty} F\left(s + \frac{jk2\pi}{T}\right) = F(s) \qquad (12.67)$$

since $F(x)$ vanishes for $x = \infty$. Another derivation of the same relationship is based on the time series expression for $F^*(s)$

$$\lim_{T \to 0} TF^*(s) = \lim_{T \to 0} T \sum_{n=0}^{\infty} f(nT)e^{-nTs}$$
$$= \int_0^{\infty} f(t)e^{-ts}\, dt = F(s) \qquad (12.68)$$

Using (12.66) and (12.67) in (12.65) clearly demonstrates that

$$\lim_{T \to 0} (1 - z^{-1})F(z) = sF(s)$$

which in turn establishes the relation between the two final-value theorems.

12.13   Types of System Compensation

After this short detour through the s and z planes, let us return to our popular sampled-data system of Sec. 12.11. We recall that the introduction of the clamper had raised havoc with our system response. Since in many sampled systems something like a clamping filter used in combination with the sampler is a practical requirement, the resort to sampled data needs justification other than just raising havoc. Many of the reasons for sampling were discussed in Sec. 12.2, and if these reasons are overpowering—as they often are—the starting point in our design may, indeed, be a system already containing the sampler and clamper along with the plant as the fixed and unavoidable elements. With this as a starting point we can now examine various approaches to compensation.

Apart from eliminating the sampling device altogether, which would improve the response of this particular system, we may consider shortening the sampling time T without any other change in the system. Halving T to 0.25 sec, for example, can be shown to decrease the overshoot from 57 to about 37 per cent, and it is clear that further reduction of T will rapidly bring the response within manageable limits. It is not impossible that such system redesign may turn out to be less effort than the incorporation of compensating filters; however, this approach is not always a remedy. In many cases the corresponding continuous system itself has an unsatisfactory performance, while in other cases the sam-

---

[1] It is particularly important to realize that $\lim_{T \to 0} F^*(s)$ is not $F(s)$; indeed, the limit does not even exist. Review of Sec. 12.5 may prove useful at this point.

pling is already so short that its further reduction gives no important improvement.

Cascade compensation in the forward loop may be achieved either by a continuous-data filter $G_2(s)$ or by a sampled-data filter $D^*(s)$ or $D(z)$, as indicated in the two parts of Fig. 12.19. Let us explore the two alternatives using simple lead compensation.

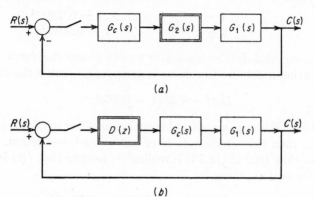

(a)

(b)

Fig. 12.19 Methods of cascade compensation in sampled-data system. (a) Continuous-data compensation. (b) Sampled-data compensation.

A suitable continuous-data lead compensation is

$$G_2(s) = 5\frac{s + 2}{s + 10} \qquad (12.69)$$

which moves the pole of the loop transfer function further out on the negative axis and introduces no change in the loop gain because $G_2(0) = 1$. The new loop transfer function is

$$G(s) = G_c(s)G_2(s)G_1(s) = (1 - e^{-Ts})\frac{25}{s^2(s + 10)} \qquad (12.70)$$

and the corresponding

$$G(z) = G_cG_2G_1(z) = \frac{1.002z^{-1} + 0.240z^{-2}}{(1 - z^{-1})(1 - 0.00674z^{-1})} \qquad (12.71)$$

which are similar in form to $G(s)$ and $G(z)$ of (12.50) and (12.55) respectively. As it turns out this compensation is very effective, as comparisons will confirm. It is important to note, however, that the method is not easy to apply, because the new $G(z)$ cannot be obtained from the old one by a simple multiplication of transfer functions. Thus,

$$G_{\text{new}}(z) \neq G_2(z)G_{\text{old}}(z)$$

so that it is impossible to apply the usual synthesis methods for cascade compensation.

In the case of the discrete compensator, on the other hand, direct multiplication applies so that $G(z)$ in this case becomes

$$G_{\text{new}}(z) = D(z)G_{\text{old}}(z) = D(z)G_cG_1(z)$$

A discrete lead filter which achieves the same shift of the pole without a change in gain is

$$D(z) = k\frac{1 - e^{-2T}z^{-1}}{1 - e^{-10T}z^{-1}} = 1.57\frac{1 - 0.368z^{-1}}{1 - 0.00674z^{-1}} \qquad (12.72)$$

But with a sampled-data compensator we can go one step further: instead of just shifting a pole we can make it disappear, because the filter

$$D(z) = 1.58(1 - 0.368z^{-1}) \qquad (12.73)$$

is realizable.   Whereas a realizable continuous filter must not have more finite zeros than poles, a discrete filter has no such restriction.

To show that $D(z)$ of (12.73) is realizable, assume that $I(z)$ is its input and $O(z)$ its output; then,

$$O(z) = D(z)I(z) = 1.58I(z) - 0.58z^{-1}I(z)$$

After inverse transformation we have the difference equation

$$o^*(t) = 1.58i^*(t) - 0.58i^*(t - T)$$

which shows that the present output sample is the linear combination of the present and the previous input samples.   This calculation can be realized (performed in real time) since no information as yet unavailable is required by the formula.

We may digress here and generalize the *realizability condition* of sampled-data filters.   The most general linear difference equation of finite number of terms can be written as

$$o^*(t) = \sum_{n=0}^{N} a_n i^*(t - nT) - \sum_{n=1}^{M} b_n o^*(T - nT) \qquad (12.74)$$

in which no future values of either the input or the output are used to obtain the present output. Transformation and rearrangement of (12.74) yields

$$D(z) = \frac{O(z)}{I(z)} = \frac{\displaystyle\sum_{n=0}^{N} a_n z^{-n}}{1 + \displaystyle\sum_{n=1}^{M} b_n z^{-n}} \qquad (12.75)$$

on the basis of which the realizability condition can be stated as: $D(z)$ is realizable if it can be written as a rational function of z^{-1} such that when the denominator polynomial has a constant term and only negative powers of z, the numerator polynomial has no positive powers of z.[1]

Returning now to our discrete compensator (12.73) we note that the resulting open-loop transfer function is easily found to be

$$G(z) = D(z)G_cG_1(z) = \frac{0.726z^{-1} + 0.521z^{-2}}{1 - z^{-1}} \qquad (12.76)$$

where $G_cG_1(z)$ was defined in (12.55). Using (12.76) $C(z)$ can be readily calculated; unfortunately, however, the resulting response is not sufficiently improved. The 57 per cent overshoot was brought down to only about 45 per cent.

This does not mean that digital compensation is less effective than continuous type; it means only that $D(z)$ of (12.73) achieves poorer compensation than $G_2(s)$ of (12.69). As a matter of fact, a $D(z)$ can be found to give exactly the same output samples as $G_2(s)$ by the following method. Since for the digitally compensated system the over-all loop transfer function is

$$G(z) = D(z)G_cG_1(z)$$

$D(z)$ can be explicitly defined as

$$D(z) = \frac{G(z)}{G_cG_1(z)} \qquad (12.77)$$

If now the desired $G(z)$ of (12.71) and $C_cG_1(z)$ of (12.55) are substituted into (12.77), $D(z)$ turns out to be

$$D(z) = \frac{(1.002 + 0.240z^{-1})(1 - 0.368z^{-1})}{(1 - 0.00674z^{-1})(0.460 + 0.330z^{-1})} \qquad (12.78)$$

Realizing that the denominator factor $(1 - 0.00674z^{-1})$ has negligible influence, essentially the same effect can be achieved by

$$D(z) = \frac{(1 + 0.250z^{-1})(1 - 0.368z^{-1})}{0.460 + 0.330z^{-1}}$$
$$= \frac{2.178 - 0.256z^{-1} - 0.200z^{-2}}{1 + 0.718z^{-1}} \qquad (12.79)$$

where the numerator factor was adjusted to keep $D(1) = 1$.

Table 12.4 compares the performance of the various systems, including the original and compensated systems. Both the continuous and sampled lead compensations are seen to have corrected the effect of the clamper; furthermore, they provide a faster rise time.

---

[1] It can be readily seen that positive powers z in the numerator would call for the use of future (nonreal time) samples of $i^*(t)$ and vitiate realizability.

Table 12.4   Comparison of Performance of the Various Systems

System	Reference	Velocity constant*	Damping ratio†	Overshoot, %
Continuous system; no compensation	Fig. 12.9	2.5	0.447	21
Sampled system; no clamping; no compensation	Fig. 12.10	2.5	0.413	25
Sampled system; clamping; no compensation	Fig. 12.15	2.5	0.177	57
Sampled system; clamping; continuous compensation	Fig. 12.19a Eq. (12.69)	2.5	0.406	25
Sampled system; clamping; sampled compensation	Fig. 12.19b Eq. (12.79)	2.5	0.404	25

* Calculated as $K_v = \lim\limits_{z \to 1} \dfrac{1 - z^{-1}}{T} G(z)$

† Calculated by finding the poles of the system transfer function $C(z)/R(z)$, then calculating the corresponding s-plane poles by the relation $z = \exp(Ts)$, and finally calculating the damping ratio based on the pair of complex poles closest to the real axis.

12.14   Compensations for Finite Settling Time

The previous section gave some indication of the potential ways of compensating a sampled-data system. Unfortunately, it is not possible here to delve into this problem deeper and discuss such matters as compensating the transient response to other inputs, using frequency-domain techniques and root-locus methods, or examining other system configurations. Only one other topic of compensation will be covered, one that underlines the simplicity with which a digital filter can be synthesized once the desired response is suitably defined.

In the previous section we derived a digital filter which resulted in a specified over-all loop transfer function $G(z)$. The difficult part of this design procedure was to define the desired $G(z)$ which will give a suitable system response and still not require an unrealizable compensating filter. Once $G(z)$ was determined, the necessary discrete filter $D(z)$ could be obtained by direct algebraic manipulation, as indicated in Eqs. (12.77) and (12.78). Similar direct synthesis will be used to obtain suitable compensation for finite settling time.

It is often desired that the controlled output, $c(t)$, of a positional servo system agree with the reference input, $r(t)$, exactly after a certain length of time. This finite settling time behavior contrasts with the damped oscillatory or the gradual monotonic approach to the error-free steady-state response. It can be shown[1] that it is possible to compensate our system containing the sampler, the clamper, and the motor so that the sampled output will agree with the sampled step input from T sec on. Thus, since the samples of the input are

$$[1, 1, 1, 1, \ . \ . \ .]$$

the samples of the output will be

$$[0, 1, 1, 1, \ . \ . \ .]$$

Stated formally

$$c^*(t) = r^*(t - T)$$

or in the z domain

$$C(z) = z^{-1}R(z) \tag{12.80}$$

We should really prove first that it is possible to compensate the system so as to satisfy (12.80)—and this is done in the reference cited; however, we can just go ahead and assume so. Should our assumption be incorrect, the resulting discrete filter $D(z)$ will turn out to be unrealizable and we can then sit back and ponder. Substituting for $C(z)$ in (12.80) the appropriate expression gives

$$R(z) \frac{D(z)G_cG_1(z)}{1 + D(z)G_cG_1(z)} = R(z)z^{-1} \tag{12.81}$$

where

$$G_cG_1(z) = \frac{0.460z^{-1} + 0.330z^{-2}}{(1 - z^{-1})(1 - 0.368z^{-1})} \tag{12.82}$$

as was derived in (12.55). Eliminating $R(z)$ in (12.81), solving for $D(z)$, and substituting the expression for $G_cG_1(z)$ immediately yields the desired compensating filter

$$D(z) = \frac{1 - 0.368z^{-1}}{0.460 + 0.330z^{-1}} \tag{12.83}$$

This sampled-data filter is realizable, since it satisfies the conditions stated in Sec. 12.13.

Although the above compensation ensures an exact match of the samples of $r(t)$ and $c(t)$ after T sec, it leaves the behavior of $c(t)$ between the sampling instants completely open. Indeed, we will illustrate that $c(t)$ is not at all constant between samples; that is, $c(t)$ contains a ripple. It is possible to design a ripple-free response using z-transform techniques,[2] but the settling time becomes generally longer. In our example, $c(t)$ can be made to match $r(t)$ exactly at and between samples after

---

[1] A. R. Bergen and J. R. Ragazzini, Sampled-data Processing Techniques for Feedback Control Systems, *Trans. AIEE*, vol. 73, 1954.

[2] Ragazzini and Franklin, *op. cit.*, pp. 169–173.

$2T$ sec, if $r(t)$ is a step.   The relationship between input and output can be made to be

$$C(z) = (0.582z^{-1} + 0.418z^{-2})R(z) \qquad (12.84)$$

which corresponds to the sequences

$$[1, \quad 1, 1, 1, 1, \ldots] \qquad \text{for samples of input } r(t)$$
$$\text{and} \quad [0, 0.582, 1, 1, 1, \ldots] \qquad \text{for samples of output } c(t)$$

The synthesis of the desired compensation $D(z)$ can proceed exactly as before and leads to

$$D(z) = \frac{1 - 0.368z^{-1}}{0.790 + 0.330z^{-1}} \qquad (12.85)$$

which is no more complicated than the compensating filter $D(z)$ in (12.83).

The responses of the two compensated systems are shown in Fig. 12.20. Curve (a) is the result of using the compensating filter $D(z)$ of (12.83),

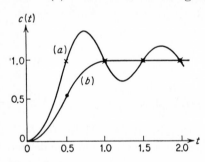

Fig. 12.20 Finite settling time responses.

and curve (b) corresponds to $D(z)$ of (12.85).   Note that curve (a) has unity samples starting at $T = 0.5$ sec, but it has a strong ripple and exhibits an overshoot of about 36 per cent.   Although this response is much better than that without compensation (see Fig. 12.16c which shows 57 per cent overshoot and much longer rise time), it is not sufficiently damped.   Curve (b) of Fig. 12.20 reaches unity value only at $2T$, but stays at that value thereafter at all times without an overshoot or a ripple.

These compensations serve to illustrate the power of discrete filter synthesis techniques for system compensation.   They also illustrate that z-transform techniques, powerful as they may be, in many cases reveal a blind spot as far as giving information about the nature of functions between samples.   We will now direct our attention toward just this blind spot.

In the next two sections we will discuss multirate sampling and modified z transforms, respectively.   Both methods are useful in determining the variations between samples of the continuous output $c(t)$ of our system. We will emphasize the use of these methods for the solution of our example, but we will also comment on the broader implications of these methods.

12.15 Multirate Sampling

We can explore the output function $c(t)$ by sampling it not only at multiples of T sec but several times in between. This will give us several values of $c(t)$ between the sampling points and thus provide an indication of its behavior at all times. Note that in doing so we do not change the sampled-data system in any manner whatsoever. What we are doing is purely an analytical examination of the output function at specific times. Since $c(t)$ is a continuous function, it has values at all times and for analytical convenience we have been examining its values only at intervals T. We will now do the same but make the examinations at intervals $T_n = T/n$.

If we are to use z-transform calculus for this multirate sampling, we must introduce a new variable z_n defined by

$$z_n = e^{T_n s} = e^{Ts/n} = \left(e^{Ts}\right)^{1/n}$$

It is clear then that z_n is related to z by

$$z = z_n{}^n \tag{12.86}$$

In terms of this new variable, the transform of the continuous output can be simply written as

$$C(s) = \frac{R(z_n{}^n)}{1 + G(z_n{}^n)} G(s) \tag{12.87}$$

To shed light on this notation it is worthwhile to examine the meaning of the expression $R(z_n{}^n)$ and compare it with the meaning of $R(z)$, the two having been stated to be equivalent. Considering $r(t)$ to be a step function, its z transform $R(z)$ is

$$R(z) = \frac{1}{1 - z^{-1}} = 1 + z^{-1} + z^{-2} + z^{-3} + \cdots \tag{12.88}$$

and the meaning of this expression in the time domain is illustrated in Fig. 12.21a. If now z is replaced by $z_n{}^n$, then in terms of the z_n transform

$$R(z) = R(z_n{}^n) = \frac{1}{1 - z_n{}^n} = 1 + z_n{}^{-n} + z_n{}^{-2n} + z_n{}^{-3n} + \cdots \tag{12.89}$$

This shows that although the sampling rate is n times what it was, only every nth sample is nonzero. The resulting time series is illustrated in 12.21b with $n = 2$, and is seen to be the same as part (a) as expected. This is contrasted in part (c) with the time series that would have resulted if the step function had been sampled every T_n sec. This $R(z_2)$ would have occurred in our system solution had we changed the sampling time inside the loop from T to $T_2 = T/2$ sec.

To continue the solution for the system output $c(t)$ we refer back to the transform $C(s)$ in (12.87).   Taking the z_n transform of this expression will yield the output at every T_n sec:

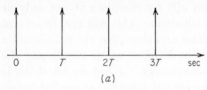

(a)

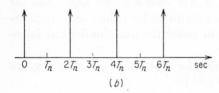

(b)

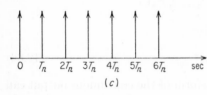

(c)

Fig. 12.21   The step function $r(t) = u(t)$ sampled at different rates.   (a) $R(z) = \dfrac{1}{1 - z^{-1}}$.   (b) $R(z_2{}^2) = \dfrac{1}{1 - z_2{}^{-2}}$ for $n = 2$.   (c) $R(z_2) = \dfrac{1}{1 - z_2{}^{-1}}$.

$$C(z_n) = \frac{R(z_n{}^n)}{1 + G(z_n{}^n)}\, G(z_n) \quad (12.90)$$

In view of our discussion of Fig. 12.21, it is clear that the transforms which are in terms of $z_n{}^n$ will yield samples at each T sec, while those which are in terms of z_n itself may produce samples at each T/n sec. Thus, the intersample behavior of the output is a function of only the forward loop $G(z_n)$.

As an example for the multirate sampling technique, let us use double-rate sampling ($n = 2$) and see if we can verify curve (a) of Fig. 12.20.   This is the curve which we had synthesized for the finite settling of its samples.   For this example $n = 2$ and $R(z_n{}^n)$ of (12.89) becomes

$$R(z_2{}^2) = \frac{1}{1 - z_2{}^{-2}}\,; \quad (12.91)$$

Similarly, $G(z_2{}^2)$ is readily obtained by recalling from (12.82) and (12.83) that

$$G(z) = D(z)G_cG_1(z) = \frac{z^{-1}}{1 - z^{-1}}$$

Therefore,

$$G(z_2{}^2) = \frac{z_2{}^{-2}}{1 - z_2{}^{-2}} \quad (12.92)$$

At this point it is worth our while to stop and evaluate part of the expression (12.90); namely, on basis of (12.91) and (12.92)

$$\frac{R(z_2{}^2)}{1 + G(z_2{}^2)} = 1$$

This means that for this specific example $C(z_2) = G(z_2)$, the evaluation of which is straightforward but somewhat lengthy.

Recall that

$$G(s) = D^*(s)G_c(s)G_1(s)$$

$$= \frac{1 - 0.368e^{-Ts}}{0.460 + 0.330e^{-Ts}} \frac{1 - e^{-Ts}}{s} \frac{5}{s(s+2)}$$

$$= D_0^*(s)G_0(s) = D_0(z)G_0(s) \tag{12.93}$$

In the above $D_0(z)$ contains all terms of z, and $G_0(s)$ all terms of s: the numerator of the clamper is part of $D_0(z)$, its denominator part of $G_0(s)$. If we now take the z_2 transform of $G(s)$, we have

$$G(z_2) = D_0(z_2^2)G_0(z_2) \tag{12.94}$$

From (12.83) we know that

$$D_0(z_2^2) = \frac{(1 - 0.368z_2^{-2})(1 - z_2^{-2})}{0.460 + 0.330z_2^{-2}} \tag{12.95}$$

where the second factor in the numerator comes from the numerator of the clamper. For future reference it is handy to factor (12.95) into

$$D_0(z_2^2) = \frac{(1 - 0.607z_2^{-1})(1 + 0.607z_2^{-1})(1 - z_2^{-1})(1 + z_2^{-1})}{0.460 + 0.330z_2^{-2}} \tag{12.96}$$

We now turn to the evaluation of $G_0(z_2)$. Since in terms of its partial fractions $G_0(s)$ is

$$G_0(s) = \frac{5}{s^2(s+2)} = \frac{2.5}{s^2} - \frac{1.25}{s} + \frac{1.25}{s+2} \tag{12.97}$$

its z_2 transform is readily obtained from Table 12.1 by using z_2 in place of z and remembering that $T_2 = 0.25$ sec. Then

$$G_0(z_2) = \frac{0.625z_2^{-1}}{(1 - z_2^{-1})^2} - \frac{1.25}{1 - z_2^{-1}} + \frac{1.25}{1 - 0.607z^{-1}}$$

$$= \frac{0.133z_2^{-1} + 0.113z_2^{-2}}{(1 - z_2^{-1})^2(1 - 0.607z^{-1})} \tag{12.98}$$

Finally $C(z_2) = G(z_2)$ is the product of (12.96) and (12.98):

$$C(z_2) = G(z_2) = \frac{(1 + 0.607z_2^{-1})(1 + z_2^{-1})(0.133 + 0.113z_2^{-1})z_2^{-1}}{(0.460 + 0.330z_2^{-2})(1 - z_2^{-1})} \tag{12.99}$$

Before the formal evaluation of this output sequence, we can examine the poles of $C(z_2)$: (1) the pole $z_2 = 1$ corresponds to the step function portion of the response; (2) the poles $z_2 = \pm j0.847$ are responsible for the oscillations in the response illustrated in Fig. 12.20a. These poles are on the imaginary axis of the z_2 plane or one-quarter way around the circle. Since a full circle corresponds to the frequency $\Omega_2 = 2\pi/T_2$, the imaginary poles cause an oscillation at a frequency $\Omega_2/4$. This gives one cycle per four sample times of $T_2 = 0.25$ sec each, as observed in Fig. 12.20a. The magnitude 0.847 of these poles determines the damping and can be shown to correspond to the very low damping ratio of 0.105.

The above discussion indicates the shortcomings of the output response $c(t)$, but a formal result is also readily obtained from (12.99). Either the long-division or difference-equation method can be used to yield the series

$$C(z_2) = 0.29z_2^{-1} + z_2^{-2} + 1.36z_2^{-3} + z_2^{-4} + 0.74z_2^{-5} + z_2^{-6}$$
$$+ 1.18z_2^{-7} + z_2^{-8} + 0.87z_2^{-9} + z_2^{-10} + 1.10z_2^{-11} + \cdots \quad (12.100)$$

The samples at odd multiples of T_2 as defined by the coefficients of odd powers of z_2^{-1} in (12.100) are the additional points on the $c(t)$ curve obtained through double-rate sampling. It is clear that triple-rate, quadruple-rate, and higher multirate sampling of $c(t)$ could provide additional detail, but never all detail and the labor could become prohibitive. In many cases, however—as in the present example—double-rate sampling is sufficient to answer the most important questions.

The method illustrated in this section can be used to analyze and synthesize systems containing two or more samplers operating at different rates.[1] Such multirate sampled-data systems often arise in practice, particularly, where a digital computer is used in a complex control system. The computer may perform different calculations at different rates to match the dynamic character of the different loops of the system. A very simple practical example of multirate system is where the digital controller is used to help in desampling. Although the input or the error may be sampled every T sec, the computer may recalculate a new output every T/n sec using some extrapolation which yields improved response over what sheer clamping would.

12.16 Modified z Transforms

A complete and powerful method for examining the total behavior of continuous functions in sampled-data systems is the so-called modified z-transform[2] method. In applying this method to our problem we leave the system solution again unchanged, and furthermore, we use the same sampling time T for the analytical sampling of the output as used in the actual sampling within the system. However, we delay the output function before we sample it, so that we obtain the samples $c(nT - \Delta T)$ where ΔT is the delay. By varying Δ from 0 to 1, all of $c(t)$ can be explored.

[1] G. M. Kranc, Compensation of an Error Sampled System by a Multirate Controller, *Trans. AIEE*, vol. 56, part 2, July, 1957.

[2] R. H. Baker, The Pulse Transfer Function and Its Application to Sampling Servo Systems, *Proc. IEE*, vol. 99, part IV, pp. 302–317, 1952; Elihu I. Jury, Synthesis and Critical Study of Sampled-data Control Systems, *Trans. AIEE*, vol. 75, part II, pp. 141–151, 1956.

The power of this method will become apparent after applying it to our example.   It turns out to be convenient to replace Δ by $1 - m$; thus

$$\Delta = 1 - m$$

and the samples to be examined are $c(nT - T + mT)$.   The z transform of the output will be a function of both z and m, and it is called the modified z transform $C(z,m)$. Based on the fact that the Laplace transform $C(s)$ of the continuous function $c(t)$ is given by (12.87), the expression for $C(z,m)$ is

$$C(z,m) = \frac{R(z)}{1 + G(z)} G(z,m) \quad (12.101)$$

We already know $R(z)$ and $G(z)$, but we need to determine $G(z,m)$. Given $g(t)$ or $G(s)$, it is possible to derive $G(z,m)$ uniquely, and indeed

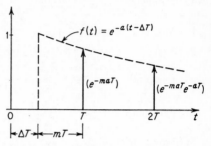

Fig. 12.22   Derivation of a modified z transform.

a table of modified z transforms can be built up for use in a variety of problems.

For illustration consider the exponential

$$f(t) = \begin{cases} e^{-at} & \text{for } t \geq 0 \\ 0 & \text{for } t < 0 \end{cases}$$

The delayed function shown by dashed lines in Fig. 12.22 is

$$f(t - \Delta T) = f(t - T + mT) = \begin{cases} e^{-a(t-T+mT)} & \text{for } t \geq \Delta T \\ 0 & \text{for } t < \Delta T \end{cases}$$

and has the samples

$$f[(l - 1 + m)T] = \begin{cases} e^{-a(lT-T+mT)} & \text{for } l \geq 1 \\ 0 & \text{for } l \leq 0 \end{cases}$$

Thus, the transform is

$$F(z,m) = \sum_{l=1}^{\infty} e^{-a(l-1)T} e^{-amT} z^{-l}$$

$$= e^{-amT} \sum_{n=0}^{\infty} e^{-anT} z^{-n-1}$$

$$= e^{-amT} z^{-1} \sum_{n=0}^{\infty} (e^{-aT} z^{-1})^n = \frac{e^{-amT} z^{-1}}{1 - e^{-aT} z^{-1}} \quad (12.102)$$

By similar methods the modified z transforms of other functions can be derived and the entries in Table 12.5 obtained. This table lists the modified z transforms of all functions whose z transforms appear in Table 12.1. Note that the parameter m appears only in the numerator

Table 12.5   Basic Modified z Transforms

No.	Function	s Domain	z Domain
1	Any	$F(s)e^{-(1-m)Ts}$	$F(z,m)$
2	Step	$\dfrac{1}{s}e^{-(1-m)Ts}$	$\dfrac{z^{-1}}{1-z^{-1}}$
3	Ramp	$\dfrac{1}{s^2}e^{-(1-m)Ts}$	$\dfrac{Tz^{-2}}{(1-z^{-1})^2}+\dfrac{mTz^{-1}}{1-z^{-1}}$
4	Parabola	$\dfrac{2}{s^3}e^{-(1-m)Ts}$	$T^2\left[\dfrac{z^{-2}+z^{-3}}{(1-z^{-1})^3}+\dfrac{2mz^{-2}}{(1-z^{-1})^2}+\dfrac{m^2z^{-1}}{1-z^{-1}}\right]$
5	Exponential	$\dfrac{e^{-(1-m)Ts}}{s+a}$	$\dfrac{e^{-amT}z^{-1}}{1-e^{-aT}z^{-1}}$
6	Time multiplied exponential	$\dfrac{e^{-(1-m)Ts}}{(s+a)^2}$	$Te^{-amT}\left[\dfrac{e^{-aT}z^{-2}}{(1-e^{-aT}z^{-1})^2}+\dfrac{mz^{-1}}{1-e^{-aT}z^{-1}}\right]$
7	Sine	$\dfrac{be^{-(1-m)Ts}}{s^2+b^2}$	$\dfrac{(\sin mbT)z^{-1}+[\sin(1-m)bT]z^{-2}}{1-2(\cos bT)z^{-1}+z^{-2}}$
8	Cosine	$\dfrac{se^{-(1-m)Ts}}{s^2+b^2}$	$\dfrac{(\cos mbT)z^{-1}-[\cos(1-m)bT]z^{-2}}{1-2(\cos bT)z^{-1}+z^{-2}}$
9	Damped sine	$\dfrac{be^{-(1-m)Ts}}{(s+a)^2+b^2}$	$e^{-amT}\dfrac{(\sin mbT)z^{-1}+e^{-aT}[\sin(1-m)bT]z^{-2}}{1-2e^{-aT}(\cos bT)z^{-1}+e^{-2aT}z^{-2}}$
10	Damped cosine	$\dfrac{(s+a)e^{-(1-m)Ts}}{(s+a)^2+b^2}$	$e^{-amT}\dfrac{(\cos mbT)z^{-1}-e^{-aT}[\cos(1-m)bT]z^{-2}}{1-2e^{-aT}(\cos bT)z^{-1}+e^{-2aT}z^{-2}}$

of these transforms and that the denominators are the same as for the corresponding z transforms. This is so because the poles determine the nature of these functions, and this is not dependent on the times at which the samples are taken.[1] Note also that the z transforms can be obtained from the modified z transforms through the relationship

$$C(z) = \lim_{m \to 0} zC(z,m) \qquad (12.103)$$

Another important relationship gives us the inverse transform of the modified z transform

$$f(nT,m) = \frac{1}{2\pi j}\int_{\Gamma} F(z,m)z^{n-1}\,dz \qquad (12.104)$$

---

[1] The only exception to this is when after sampling some of the basic character of the continuous function is lost, for example, when a sinusoid is sampled at the zero crossover points. In this case the z transform might not show a pole that appears in the modified z transform and the continuous s transform.

The value of the function $f(t)$ in the interval $(n-1)T \leq t < nt$ can be explored by use of Eq. (12.104) when m is allowed to vary from 0 to 1.

In view of Eq. (12.101), we can obtain the modified z transform of the system output in our example by evaluating $G(z,m)$. To do this, we recall Eq. (12.93) in which $G(s)$ was separated into rational functions of z and s. The portion of $G(s)$ which is only a function of z is

$$D_0(z) = \frac{(1 - 0.368z^{-1})(1 - z^{-1})}{0.460 + 0.330z^{-1}} \tag{12.105}$$

and will remain unchanged in evaluating $G(z,m)$. The portion of $G(s)$ which is a rational function of only s is

$$G_0(s) = \frac{5}{s^2(s+2)} = \frac{2.5}{s^2} - \frac{1.25}{s} + \frac{1.25}{s+2} \tag{12.106}$$

and we can now embark upon the evaluation of $G_0(z,m)$.

Using the appropriate entry of Table 12.5 we find the modified z transform for each of the partial fractions in (12.106), so that

$$G_0(z,m) = \frac{1.25z^{-2}}{(1 - z^{-1})^2} + \frac{1.25mz^{-1}}{1 - z^{-1}} - \frac{1.25z^{-1}}{1 - z^{-1}} + \frac{1.25e^{-m}z^{-1}}{1 - 0.368z^{-1}} \tag{12.107}$$

Substituting (12.107) and (12.105) into (12.101) gives $C(z,m)$ as

$$C(z,m) = \frac{1.25}{(0.460 + 0.330z^{-1})(1 - z^{-1})} [(-1 + m + e^{-m})z^{-1}$$
$$+ (2.368 - 1.368m - 2e^{-m})z^{-2} + (-0.736 + 0.368m + e^{-m})z^{-3}] \tag{12.108}$$

The expression for $C(z,m)$ can be evaluated to give a sequence of values of $c(t)$ by using long division or other similar methods. If so, this sequence of values will be a function of m, and for any particular m, a different sequence can be obtained. If Eq. (12.108) is multiplied by z and m is made equal to zero, it will reduce to the z transform $C(z)$ of the controlled output

$$C(z) = \frac{z^{-1}}{1 - z^{-1}} \tag{12.109}$$

As another example, if m is made equal to one-half in (12.108) and the long division is then carried out, the odd-power samples of the multirate output function $C(z_2)$ of Eq. (12.100) can be obtained.

It is possible to derive a total expression for the output time series as a function of m, but it is of more interest to this problem to determine the overshoot in the transient response. The power of the modified z-transform method is demonstrated by deriving analytically the maximum value of the function $c(t)$. We already know that this maximum occurs between T and $2T$ so that we want to explore the time-domain behavior of $c(t)$ between these two sampling instants. Referring to (12.104), we let $n = 2$ and keep m as a parameter. The resulting integral

$$c(2T,m) = \frac{1}{2\pi j} \int_\Gamma C(z,m)z \, dz \qquad (12.110)$$

can be evaluated by substituting (12.108) into the integrand and using the method of residues. Doing so yields

$$c(2T,m) = 5.67 - 2.95m - 4.67e^{-m} \qquad (12.111)$$

which is the behavior of the output function between T and $2T$ in terms of the variable m.

Taking the partial derivative of (12.111) and equating it to 0 gives $m = 0.460$ as the value at which the function has a maximum or minimum, but we know from previous considerations that it is a maximum. This maximum occurs at

$$t = (n - 1 + m)T = (2 - 1 + 0.460)T = 1.460T$$

and is

$$c(t)_{max} = c(1.460T) = 1.36$$

which further confirms the fact that this is a maximum and not a minimum. It is seen then that the overshoot is 36 per cent within the accuracy of this computation. This exercise also shows that the double-rate sampling effort of the preceding section was quite adequate in defining the outstanding characteristics of the output.

The above discussion gives us some indication of the manner in which the method of modified z transforms can be utilized in system analysis and design. The synthesis for specified overshoots at specific times or in specific sampling intervals can be made part of the specifications, and compensation can be derived to achieve specified performance.[1] The price for this added analytical insight into sampled-data design problems is, of course, the use of more complex transforms, and it is up to the designer to determine whether such effort is justified. It is noted that very often pure unmodified z transformation gives adequate description of system behavior.

Irrespective of the extent to which a sampled behavior is to be examined, the table of modified z transforms can be useful where actual pure delays are part of the system. In this case the use of delayed transforms are part of the analysis and evaluation of the system. In such cases the modified z-transform table can be used with m being a specific value such that $1 - m = \Delta$ corresponds to the delay in question.

12.17 Solution of Generalized Sampled-data System

In all of our discussions so far we concentrated on simple single-loop systems containing a single sampler within the loop. It seems that we

---

[1] F. W. Semelka, Time Domain Synthesis of Sampled-data Control System, *Univ. Calif. (Berkeley) Electronic Research Lab. Rept.*, ser. 60, issue 175, Jan. 18, 1957.

should also touch on the more complex problem of solving sampled-data systems having several loops or several samplers.   In this it is found convenient to use signal-flow diagrams in place of block diagrams.   Both types of diagrams are topological representations of the same system, but signal-flow diagrams offer several advantages: (1) they can be drawn with fewer lines and present a clearer picture of the interrelationship of the system variables, and (2) they make directly available a body of theory and techniques developed in the past.[1]

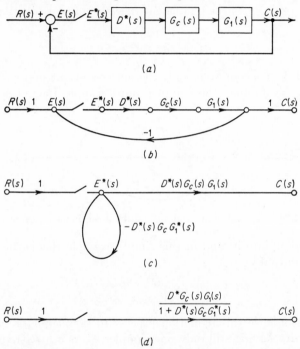

Fig. 12.23 Solution of digitally compensated single-loop sampled-data system. (*a*) System block diagram. (*b*) System signal-flow diagram. (*c*) Three-node signal-flow diagram.   (*d*) Two-node signal-flow diagram.

To start with an example, we show the block diagram of our digitally compensated system in Fig. 12.23*a* and compare this with the corresponding signal-flow diagram in part (*b*).   The signal-flow diagram consists of nodes and branches.   The nodes represent the variables of the system; the branches the transfer relationships connecting these variables.   A variable at the node is the sum of the inputs to that node.   The variable at a node is the input to each branch leaving that node.

The difficulty in reducing this signal-flow diagram is that the sampler cannot be represented by a transfer function.   In particular, to reduce the loop which contains the sampler, it is necessary to first obtain a loop transfer function. From Sec. 12.9 we know that it is possible to obtain a sampled-data transfer function if both the input and the output of the loop are sampled. For this reason the point in the loop at which the data are sampled must be pinpointed as is done in Fig. 12.23c. The three nodes of this diagram are: the source node $R(s)$, the sink node $C(s)$, and the sampled-data node $E^*(s)$. The feedback loop from the sampled node back onto itself has the transfer function $-D^*(s)G_cG_1^*(s)$ or $-D(z)G_cG_1(z)$ and the loop reduces to the equivalent cascade transfer function

$$\frac{1}{1 + D(z)G_cG_1(z)}$$

The reduced system containing only the source and sink nodes is shown in Fig. 12.23d. Note that the sampler must sample the total quantity

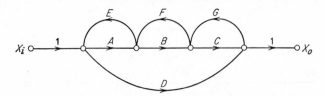

Fig. 12.24 Signal-flow diagram of multiloop continuous-data system.

which is feeding into it, and in this simple example this is the quantity $R(s)$. The output is

$$C(s) = R^*(s) \frac{D^*(s)G_c(s)G_1(s)}{1 + D^*(s)G_cG_1^*(s)} \qquad (12.112)$$

We can generalize this reduction process to sampled-data systems of any complexity having still only one sampler.[1] As a first step we want to illustrate without proof Mason's method of reducing any complex linear unsampled flow diagram by inspection. Figure 12.24 shows a reasonably complex multiloop system whose gain or transfer relationship we obtain by inspection as

$$X_o = X_iG_{io} = X_i \frac{ABC + D(1 - BF)}{1 - AE - BF - CG - DGFE + AECG} \qquad (12.113)$$

where A, B, etc., are transfer functions of the corresponding branches and the functional notation $A(s)$, $B(s)$, etc., has been compromised for clarity. Note that the denominator is obtained by substracting from unity each of the individual loop transfer functions. These terms are

[1] S. J. Mason, Feedback Theory: Further Properties of Signal Flow Graphs, *Proc. IRE*, vol. 44, pp. 920–926, July, 1956; J. M. Salzer, Signal Flow Reductions in Sampled-data System, 1957 *IRE Wescon Conv. Record*, part 4, pp. 166–170.

followed by adding the product $AECG$ of the two loops which do not touch each other. If there were other pairs of nontouching loops, their products would also be added. If there were three nontouching loops their products would be subtracted, etc.

The numerator terms are made up of forward paths ABC and D connecting from source to sink. Each of these is multiplied by an expression consisting of unity minus the loop transfer functions which do not touch that forward path, plus products of loop transfer functions in pairs which do not touch that forward path, etc. In this particular example, BF is the loop transfer function which does not touch the forward path D.

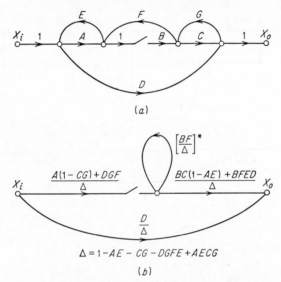

Fig. 12.25 Reduction of multiloop sampled-data system. (*a*) System signal-flow diagram. (*b*) Three-node signal-flow diagram.

The above rules, then, provide a method of relating one node variable to another node variable by inspection regardless of the complexity of the intervening structure. If there is a sampler anywhere in the system, the point at which the data is sampled must be made an intermediate node and the transfer relationships among the three nodes can be written down by inspection according to the above rules. Once this is done, the last step of system reduction is readily carried out in a manner similar to going from part (*c*) to part (*d*) of Fig. 12.23.

For an example, consider the complex system just discussed and assume that a sampler is inserted in branch B, as indicated in Fig. 12.25*a*. The next step in the reduction process is shown in part (*b*) of the same figure. Three nodes are kept and the transfer relationships among them are derived according to the rules discussed. The last step of the reduction process eliminates the sampled-data loop and leads immediately to the input-output relationship

$$X_o = X_i \frac{D}{\Delta} + \frac{\{X_i[A(1 - CG) + DGF]/\Delta\}^*}{1 - (BF/\Delta)^*} \frac{BC(1 - AE) + BFED}{\Delta}$$

$$\text{(12.114)}$$

where $\Delta = 1 - AE - CG - DGFE + AECG$

As complicated as the expression (12.114) is, it was derived in a straightforward fashion with much less effort than would have been

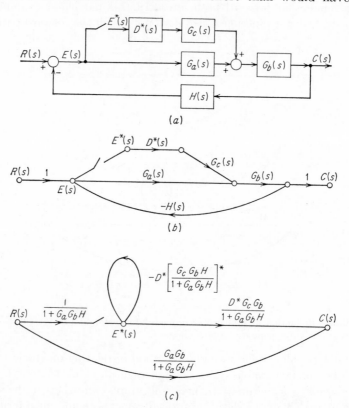

(a)

(b)

(c)

Fig. 12.26 Solution of digital-assist system.   (a) Block diagram.   (b) Signal-flow diagram.   (c) Three-node signal-flow diagram.

expended had we used the usual analytical means.   In the analytical method we would put down a set of equations relating the various variables (nodes) to each other and then solve this system of equations for $X_o(s)$ in terms of $X_i(s)$ and the branch transfer functions.   Because of the mixture of sampled and continuous data in these equations, it is not always readily seen how the variables can best be eliminated.   The analyst may often find himself going around in circles without getting any closer to a solution.

Another example of signal-flow reductions is shown in Fig. 12.26. In Fig. 12.26a we have a conventional continuous-data system composed of $G_a(s)$, $G_b(s)$, and $H(s)$. The performance of the system is improved by a parallel digital forward loop consisting of a discrete filter and a clamping unit. The delays caused by this sampled-data branch do not affect the stability of the system because the loop is closed on itself in a continuous fashion, but the accuracy of the system can be enhanced by suitable periodic corrections applied through the sampled path. An analog dead-reckoning navigation system utilizing corrections by periodic fixes would have some of the characteristics of the illustrated system.

In Fig. 12.26b we have the signal-flow diagram of this same system, while in part (c) this diagram is reduced to the canonic three-node form, from which the expression for the output is directly obtained as

$$C(s) = \frac{R(s)G_a(s)G_b(s)}{1 + G_a(s)G_b(s)H(s)}$$
$$+ \frac{\left[\dfrac{R(s)}{1 + G_a(s)G_b(s)H(s)}\right]^*}{1 + D^*(s)\left[\dfrac{G_c(s)G_b(s)H(s)}{1 + G_a(s)G_b(s)H(s)}\right]^*} \frac{D^*(s)G_c(s)G_b(s)}{1 + G_a(s)G_b(s)H(s)} \quad (12.115)$$

The solution of multiloop systems containing more than one sampler can become a rather complicated procedure, but the methods discussed for the case of a single sampler can be directly extended. For example, a most general two-sampler system can be reduced in one step to the four-node configuration shown in Fig. 12.27. Each of the path transfer functions A through K^* may be a complicated expression in terms of the original system transfer functions but each has been obtained in a straightforward fashion using Mason's method which was discussed

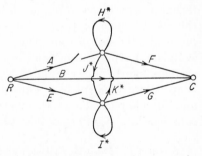

Fig. 12.27 Reduction of two-sampler complex system.

above. The important point to note in this signal-flow diagram is that all feedback loops can be described by transfer functions, since the samplers appearing in branches A and E are not part of a feedback loop.

It is now possible to apply Mason's technique for continuous-data systems directly to the signal-flow graph of Fig. 12.27. Note that the loops are: H^*, I^*, and J^*K^*. The two nontouching loops are H^* and I^*. The forward paths are A-F, A-J^*G, B, E-G, E-K^*F where the hyphens indicate the position of samplers. The output expression is obtained directly as

$$C = RB$$
$$+ \frac{(RA)^*(1 - I^*)F + (RA)^*J^*G + (RE)^*(1 - H^*)G + (RE)^*K^*F}{1 - H^* - K^* - J^*K^* + H^*K^*}$$

$$(12.116)$$

We will not pursue and extend this method to the general case of n samplers, but it is clear that such can be done in a straightforward fashion. Although the expressions may become complicated, their derivation by signal-flow techniques are straightforward. It is further true that most practical systems do not have paths connecting all of the sampled-data variables with each other and, therefore, their signal-flow diagrams are considerably simpler than the general case.

12.18   Summary

With these fleeting comments about discouraging complexities of the general case versus the encouraging simplicity of practical cases, we come to the end of the chapter on sampled-data theory. Our mixed feelings about this subject are compounded by our knowledge of having covered only a very limited amount of material. We said not a word about random processes in sampled-data systems;[1] the numerical solution of linear and nonlinear differential equations by the use of z transforms;[2] the treatment of digital-computer operations, both for full-value mathematics and incremental mathematics; the utilization of z-transform techniques to solve continuous-data systems consisting of delay elements;[3] the use of some of these techniques in dealing with the quantization problem;[4] the use of root-locus methods in the z plane;[5] the analysis of samplers having finite pulse widths;[5] multipole sampled-data control systems synthesis techniques[6] and a host of other related topics. In contrast we hope to have gained an insight into sampled-data systems and an appreciation of the methodology used in their solutions—for sampled-data systems are here to stay.

[1] See Sec. 13.7; also H. C. Hsieh and C. T. Leondes, The Optimum Synthesis Of Multipole Sampled Data Control Systems with Random and Non Random Inputs, *IRE Natl. Conv. Record*, March, 1960.

[2] R. Boxer and S. Thaler, A Simplified Method of Solving Linear and Non Linear Systems, *Proc. IRE*, vol. 44, pp. 89–101, January, 1956.

[3] J. G. Truxal, "Automatic Feedback Control System Synthesis," pp. 546–558, McGraw-Hill Book Company, Inc., New York, 1955.

[4] J. Bertram, Effect of Quantization Sampled-feedback Systems, *Trans. AIEE*, part II, no. 38, pp. 177–181, September, 1958.

[5] Jury, *op. cit.;* Ragazzini and Franklin, *op. cit.;* and Tou, *op. cit.*

[6] See Sec. 13.7; also Hsieh and Leondes, *op. cit.;* also E. B. Stear and C. T. Leondes, Extended Synthesis Techniques for Multipole Sampled Data Control Systems, *Proc. Natl. Electronics Conf.*, vol. 15, pp. 299–309, 1959.

13

Random Processes in Automatic Control

ASSISTANT PROFESSOR OF ENGINEERING

UNIVERSITY OF CALIFORNIA, LOS ANGELES

13.1 Introduction

Very broadly, the modern approach of applying the mathematical theory of random processes to the design of control systems began with a military problem. For the purposes of the following discussion, it will be useful to begin with this problem, which will be presented here somewhat in its historical setting.

Just prior to the entry of the United States into World War II, the nature of the aerial warfare threat was in transition. Specifically, the bomber threat was growing because of newly developed high-altitude, high-speed aircraft. This brought a need for improved antiaircraft guns and fire-control systems, and, in fact, required pushing the system designs to the level of the inherent accuracy of the type of target trackers used. This in turn led to the design of the fire-control system based on statistical concepts.

13.2 Fire-control System

Even the most rudimentary antiaircraft fire-control system has all the elements of a feedback control system including a computer. Although primitive by modern standards, a 1940-vintage system will suffice as a practical model for study and has the advantage of not introducing the irrelevant complications of a more sophisticated system. Let us now consider such a system (see Fig. 13.1).

The target tracker is supposed to provide instantaneous measurements of the target coordinates: azimuth and elevation angles to the target, and slant range (i.e., distance to the target along the line of sight). Each angle is tracked individually by aligning, by hand, a telescopic sight with the target.   The slant range is measured by using a hand-adjusted optical range finder.   The settings of the optical sights and the range finder are used as input data by an analog computer.   The computer determines from these settings the proper lead angle and the proper fuze setting for the shell to burst at the point of closest approach.   The lead angle in turn, is transferred to the gun drive, that is, an electromechanical system designed to align the gun barrel with the computed direction.

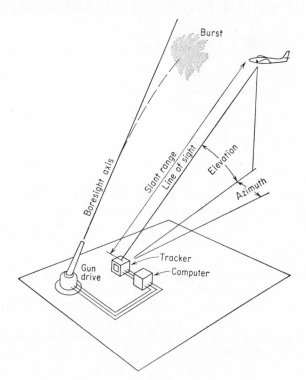

Fig. 13.1 Geometry of fire control problem.

The fuze setting requires, in principle, an extrapolation in time of the measured slant range, extrapolated to the time of the shell burst.   Likewise, the lead angle requires an extrapolation of the measured angular coordinates.   But the actual measured coordinate values have a sort of random error which varies with time.   This error is caused by the insensitivity of the optical instruments and the operators' attempts to adjust, as best they can, to the moving target.   In addition, it has to be assumed that the target may fly a pattern of evasive maneuvers, giving the actual target coordinates a randomly irregular pattern.   Thus, both the lead angle and the fuze setting require an extrapolation forward in time to be computed from measured values of target coordinates, when the latter are known to have irregular and apparently random variations and errors.

One should expect that in a properly designed and properly operated tracker, the mean tracking error would be zero, since any consistent bias can be compensated for. Granting that this is so, a partial solution to the problem of the random error consists in taking the measured coordinates, and individually averaging them over some finite time interval. Or, in other terms, one might transmit the data by means of a low-pass filter, thus attenuating the short term or higher frequency variations in the measured coordinate values. However, such a solution introduces a time delay in the data which are presented to the lead-angle and fuse-setting computer, since the time average is not available until the receipt of the last value averaged. But this is contrary to the ultimate goal of prediction of future values. Thus one can only hope for a compromise, where one trades some time delay for the desired smoothing of the data.

This trade-off, and its optimization for purposes of prediction, was one of the principal problems facing the fire-control system designers in 1940. And this is one of the problems included by N. Wiener in his now famous monograph. This monograph was first published in February, 1942, when it was classified as military security information with restricted distribution; later it was published in book form.[14] In Wiener's approach to the problem, he introduced a new element which was novel to communication engineering at the time. His innovation was to conceive of the fluctuating input data as random variables, and then to bring mathematical probability theory to bear on the problem. In applying this approach to the fire-control problem, one considers the true target coordinates as continuous time series of random values which have been perturbed by the addition of continuous time series of random errors. The object is to specify the transfer function of the over-all chain of tracking system to computer to gun and its drive in such a way that the predicted gun lead and fuse setting are, on the average, the best possible. The next few sections present Wiener's solution to the problem.

13.3   Random Processes

The following material is presented elsewhere* in much greater detail than is possible here. Therefore, in this and the following sections, the concepts will be reviewed somewhat briefly, with emphasis more on their

---

* In addition to the monograph by Wiener already cited,[14] there are many other literature sources. Material on prediction (without smoothing) is presented from a mathematical point of view in the book by Doob.[6] The broader problem (with smoothing) is presented from more of an engineering point of view in the books by Davenport and Root[5] and Laning and Battin.[10] Some elementary, and virtually all advanced textbooks on control system synthesis have some material on the subject.

broad aspects than on the difficult theoretical or computational aspects. Some of the latter are collected together in the appendix to this chapter.

Let us turn first to the concept of the random process. Suppose $x(t)$ is the value, at time t, of some sort of physical variable, such as the measured slant range to a moving target. Then, abstractly, the symbol $x(t)$ can be regarded as a random variable. If t_1 and t_2 are arbitrary epochs, then $x(t_1)$ and $x(t_2)$ are both random variables, where, of course, there is no a priori reason to suppose that they are either identical or independent of each other. Extending this observation to all values of t leads to the mathematical concept of the random process. One then says that $x(t)$ constitutes a family of random variables related through the t parameter, or more simply, one says that the *random process* $x(t)$ constitutes a one-parameter family of random variables.

At any selected value of t, the *mathematical expectation* or *mean* of $x(t)$ may exist, but in general its expected value depends upon t. Similarly, at any two epochs t_1, t_2, the pair of random variables $x(t_1)$, $x(t_2)$ has a *covariance* defined by

$$\gamma = E[x(t_1) - m_1][x(t_2) - m_2] \tag{13.1}$$

where Ez is used to denote the mathematical expectation of the generic random variable z, and $m_i = Ex(t_i)$. The covariance of these two random variables, which depend upon t_1 and t_2, naturally depends upon t_1 and t_2; and so generally it can be thought of as some function of t_1 and t_2. This function plays a central role in the Wiener theory, and therefore a few observations pertaining to it shall later have to be set down. But first let us restrict our attention to a special subclass of random processes.

Consider now those random processes for which the joint probability distribution of any finite set of variables, say $x(t_1)$, . . . , $x(t_n)$ is the same as that for those obtained by a common translation in time, $x(t_1 + \alpha)$, . . . , $x(t_n + \alpha)$, irrespective of n and α. Processes which fall into this category are called *strictly stationary* processes. The restriction to this class of processes is quite often justifiable in applications, since it requires only that the data represented by the stationary process be generated in a way which is independent of the particular epoch chosen as the origin of the time scale.

If the expected value and covariance exist for a particular strictly stationary process, then they enjoy the following properties: (1) The mean is constant with time, and (2) the covariance function depends on a single variable, namely the magnitude of the time difference, $|t_1 - t_2|$. If the converse is true for a not necessarily strictly stationary process, that is, if

$$Ex(t) = m = \text{constant} \tag{13.2}$$
$$E[x(t_1)x(t_2)] - m^2 = \gamma(t_1 - t_2) \tag{13.3}$$

then the process is called stationary in the *wide sense*. From this point on, attention shall be aimed primarily at processes which are stationary in the wide sense.

Another concept which is useful in the Wiener development is that of the *power spectrum* of a random process. For processes which are stationary in the wide sense, it can be defined as the Fourier transform of the covariance function. That is, if

$$\gamma(\tau) = E[x(t + \tau)x(t)] - m^2$$

as before, then the power spectrum of the random process $x(t)$ can be defined, when it exists, to be equal to

$$\hat{\gamma}(\omega) = \frac{1}{2\pi} \int_{-\infty}^{\infty} \gamma(\tau)e^{-i\omega\tau} \, d\tau \qquad (13.4)$$

The adjective "power" comes from the following physical interpretation. Suppose that the process is sufficiently restricted so that the generalized law of large numbers* applies not only to $x(t)$, but to $[x(t)]^2$ as well. Suppose also that $Ex(t) = 0$. Then, the time average of $[x(t)]^2$, namely,

$$\mathcal{Q}[x(t)]^2 = \lim_{T_1, T_2 \to \infty} (T_2 + T_1)^{-1} \int_{-T_1}^{T_2} [x(t)]^2 \, dt \qquad (13.5)$$

is equal to its mean value, namely

$$[Ex(t)]^2 = \gamma(0) = \frac{1}{2\pi} \int_{-\infty}^{\infty} \hat{\gamma}(\omega) \, d\omega \qquad (13.6)$$

If $x(t)$ were the value of a voltage or current, its square would equal the power dissipated if the current or voltage were applied to a unit resistance. Thus, the time average of the power which would be dissipated in a unit resistance is the integral, over-all frequencies of the so-called power spectrum.

The important concept which will be applied is the consideration of the input to a physical system as being a random process. In general, if the input is so considered, then also the output may be so considered. If the system is linear and time invariable, then the system transfer function relates the power spectrum of the output to that of the input.

---

* The law of large numbers has several forms asserting, as generalized to continuous time series, that the time average

$$\mathcal{Q}x(t) = (T_2 + T_1)^{-1} \int_{-T_1}^{T_2} x(t) \, dt$$

approaches the mean, $Ex(t)$ as $T_1, T_2 \to \infty$. In order to apply to $x(t)$, it is necessary and sufficient that $\gamma(t)$ be continuous at $t = 0$, and that $T^{-1} \int_0^T \gamma(\tau) \, d\tau \to 0$ as $T \to \infty$.

In particular, if the system transfer function is $h(s)$, and if the input $x_1(t)$ has a power spectrum $\hat{\gamma}_1(\omega)$, then the output $x_2(t)$ has power spectrum

$$\hat{\gamma}_2(\omega) = \hat{\gamma}_1(\omega)|h(i\omega)|^2 \tag{13.7}$$

[This equation provides a corollary to the paragraph above to the effect that $2\hat{\gamma}(\omega)$ is actually the density per cycle per second of the average power dissipated in a unit value resistance when the current or voltage applied is considered equal to $x(t)$.]

13.4 The Wiener Filter

With the definitions and concepts above, we can return to the problems of prediction, smoothing, etc. In terms of the fire-control problem discussed earlier, let us consider each of the three target coordinates individually. Let us follow Wiener and suppose that the available signal (a target coordinate) can be considered to be the sum of two components. That is, what we have to work with is $r(t) = s(t) + n(t)$, where the desired signal is $s(t)$, and $n(t)$ is the random perturbation (noise). Let us suppose that $s(t)$ and $n(t)$, and consequently $r(t)$, are random processes which are stationary in the wide sense. Further, let us suppose $s(t)$, $n(t)$, and $r(t)$ have (without loss of generality) zero-valued means and have covariance functions σ, ν, and ρ, respectively. Finally, it will be convenient to suppose that $s(t)$ and $n(t)$ are uncorrelated; that is, that $En(t_1)s(t_2) \equiv 0$. Although the more general case presents no greater difficulty, the results appear simpler and consequently slightly more revealing, in this case.

Let us first look at the problem of prediction in the presence of noise. In the present terms, the problem will be to specify the transfer function of that linear time-invariant system, which, when $r(t)$ is applied as input, produces an output $s^*(t)$ which differs from $s(t + \alpha)$ as little as possible. If $\alpha > 0$, the system predicts with lead time α; if $\alpha = 0$, the system merely smooths the signal; if α is allowed to be negative then the signal is smoothed with time lag $(-\alpha)$.

Denote by $\epsilon(t)$ the error committed in supposing $s^*(t)$ is the desired $s(t + \alpha)$

$$\epsilon(t) = s^*(t) - s(t + \alpha) \tag{13.8}$$

One measure of the acceptability of using $s^*(t)$ in place of $s(t + \alpha)$ is the mean-squared value of $\epsilon(t)$. Using this measure, then, we seek either the system's transfer function $h(s)$, or equivalently, its inverse Laplace transform or weighting function $k(t)$, such that the system's output makes

$$P = E[\epsilon(t)]^2 \tag{13.9}$$

the least possible.

From the quadratic dependence of P on the weighting function $k(t)$, it is necessary that the weighting function which minimizes P satisfy the following Wiener-Hopf integral equation:

$$\sigma(t + \alpha) = \int_0^\infty \rho(t - \tau)k(\tau) \, d\tau \qquad t \geqq 0 \qquad (13.10)$$

(For $t < 0$, the equality need not hold.)   Under fairly general conditions on the supposed known functions σ and ρ, the unknown function k can be analytically represented in terms of σ and ρ (see appendix).   At any rate, if a solution $k(\tau)$ to Eq. (13.10) exists, then it must be unique.

If $k_0(\tau)$ is the solution to Eq. (13.10), then the corresponding value of the mean-squared error is given by

$$P_0 = \sigma(0) - 2 \int_0^\infty \sigma(\tau + \alpha)k_0(\tau) \, d\tau + \int_0^\infty \int_0^\infty \rho(t - \tau)k_0(t)k_0(\tau) \, dt \, d\tau$$

$$(13.11)$$

This, the minimum mean-squared error, can also be written in various alternate forms, each of which has its own advantage.   For example, using Eq. (13.10), we can get

$$P_0 = \sigma(0) - \int_0^\infty \sigma(\tau + \alpha)k_0(\tau) \, d\tau \qquad (13.12)$$

and $\qquad P_0 = \sigma(0) - \int_0^\infty \int_0^\infty \rho(t - \tau)k_0(t)k_0(\tau) \, dt \, d\tau \qquad (13.13)$

and $\qquad P_0 = \int_0^\infty \nu(\tau + \alpha)k_0(\tau) \, d\tau \qquad \text{if } \alpha \leqq 0 \qquad (13.14)$

Using power spectra and the corresponding system transfer function $h_0(s)$, these equations can be written

$$P_0 = \frac{1}{2\pi} \int_{-\infty}^\infty [\hat{\sigma}(\omega) - 2\hat{\sigma}(\omega)h_0(i\omega)e^{-i\omega\alpha} + |h_0(i\omega)|^2\hat{\rho}(\omega)] \, d\omega \quad (13.15)$$

$$P_0 = \frac{1}{2\pi} \int_{-\infty}^\infty \hat{\sigma}(\omega)[1 - h_0(i\omega)e^{-i\omega\alpha}] \, d\omega \qquad (13.16)$$

$$P_0 = \frac{1}{2\pi} \int_{-\infty}^\infty [\hat{\sigma}(\omega) - |h_0(i\omega)|^2\hat{\rho}(\omega)] \, d\omega \qquad (13.17)$$

and lastly

$$P_0 = \frac{1}{2\pi} \int_{-\infty}^\infty \hat{\nu}(\omega)h_0(i\omega)e^{-i\omega\alpha} \, d\omega \qquad \text{if } \alpha \leqq 0 \qquad (13.18)$$

These various representations are useful because a knowledge of P_0 has considerable practical value irrespective of whether or not one can actually produce a system having h_0 as its transfer function.   Its value lies in the fact that it shows the inherent limit to which a linear system can perform.

Even if h_0 were not known analytically, bounds on the possible value of P_0 would serve to show, somewhat, the ultimate performance capability of linear systems. This is always useful information for the designer of practical systems. One can easily obtain, for example, the following bounds

$$\frac{1}{2\pi} \int_{-\infty}^{\infty} \frac{\hat{\sigma}(u)\hat{\nu}(u)}{\hat{\sigma}(u) + \hat{\nu}(u)} \, d\omega \leq P_0 \leq \sigma(0) \tag{13.19}$$

These bounds are not as sharp as one would occasionally like. This lack of sharpness occurs because of their generality, applying as they do for all values of α; being, in fact, the best possible in those circumstances. That is, if Eq. (13.10) has a solution for all values of α, then as $\alpha \to +\infty$, P_0 approaches the upper bound, while if $\alpha \to -\infty$, P_0 approaches the lower bound.

It frequently occurs in practice, that $\hat{\sigma}(\omega)$ and $\hat{\nu}(u)$ are not very accurately known. It also frequently occurs, even if $\hat{\sigma}(u)$ and $\hat{\nu}(\omega)$ were known precisely, that for practical reasons, systems with transfer functions only approximating the true minimizing $h_0(s)$ can be constructed. In either case, one must rely on approximations. In such cases one would like some estimate of the loss in performance suffered when an approximation is used in place of h_0, or better still some way of estimating the sensitivity of the mean-squared error P to small errors in the approximation. If $h(s)$ is any transfer function, then the mean-squared error resulting when h is used in place of h_0 is given by

$$P = P_0 + \frac{1}{2\pi} \int_{-\infty}^{\infty} \hat{\rho}(\omega) |h(i\omega) - h_0(i\omega)|^2 \, d\omega \tag{13.20}$$

Observe that the contribution due to the approximation can be written

$$\rho(0) \frac{1}{2\pi} \int_{-\infty}^{\infty} \frac{\hat{\rho}(\omega)}{\rho(0)} |h(i\omega) - h_0(i\omega)|^2 \, d\omega$$

or, in words, it is equal to the product of the mean-squared fluctuation of $r(t)$ multiplied by the mean-squared approximation error, weighted on the frequency axis by the relative distribution of power in $r(t)$, that is, by $\hat{\rho}(\omega)/\rho(0)$. Clearly, the approximation should be good at those frequencies where $\hat{\rho}(\omega)$ is large, but the approximation can be less good, in fact it could be bad, where $\hat{\rho}(\omega)$ drops in value.

In cases where, for example, $\hat{\sigma}$ and $\hat{\nu}$ are known rational functions of ω, then, at least in principle, the determination from these spectra, of the transfer function h_0 for prediction or smoothing is straightforward. In fact, it only requires the application of the formula given in the appendix. The result (for $\alpha \geq 0$) is always a rational function. Thus, on the face of it, it would appear that in such cases, the theory represents a complete solution. But the practical problem of calculating h_0 and P_0

can be quite formidable even in relatively innocuous appearing examples. Only the simplest examples can be easily handled; the complications mount rapidly as the order of the rational functions becomes greater. Thus, in some cases of actual system designs, the transfer function needed has been arrived at by guessing at h_0 directly. This guessing game has often been successful, and the result of the above paragraph shows why it can be. But its success logically depends upon a good understanding of the theory, and the insight gained from exact calculations in some of the simpler cases. Below are two illustrative calculations. The reader is referred to Wiener,[14] for example, for more of such illustrative examples.

EXAMPLE 1. Suppose $\hat{\sigma}(\omega) = S/(1 + \omega^2)^2$, $\hat{\nu}(u) = N\omega^2/(1 + \omega^2)^2$. Then $\hat{\rho}(\omega) = N(A^2 + \omega^2)/(1 + \omega^2)^2$ where $A^2 = S/N$. If $\alpha \geqq 0$ (smoothing without time lag, or with prediction) then

$$h_0(s) = \frac{(A^2 e^{-\alpha})}{(1 + A)^2} \frac{2 + A + \alpha(1 + A) + s[1 + \alpha(1 + A)]}{A + s} \qquad (13.21)$$

Using Eq. (13.16), we can get, for $\alpha = 0$,

$$P_0 = \frac{S}{4} \frac{1 + 4A + A^2}{(1 + A)^4} \qquad (13.22)$$

It is interesting to compare this with the bounds given by Inequality (13.19). The lower bound is

$$\frac{1}{2\pi} \int_{-\infty}^{\infty} \frac{\hat{\sigma}(\omega)\hat{\nu}(\omega)}{\hat{\sigma}(\omega) + \hat{\nu}(\omega)} \, d\omega = \frac{S}{4(1 + A^2)} \qquad (13.23)$$

while the upper bound is $\sigma(0) = S/4$.

EXAMPLE 2. Let $\hat{\sigma}(\omega) = S/(1 + \omega^2)$ and $\hat{\nu}(\omega) = S\omega^8/(1 + \omega^8)$, and consider the problem of smoothing ($\alpha = 0$). Now, $S\omega^8/(1 + \omega^8)$ is not the power spectrum of a second-order process, that is, not of a process with finite mean-squared value. But formally applied, the formulas yield a physically significant result. It is, as one would expect, the limiting form of the result one obtains by truncating $\hat{\nu}(\omega)$ at some large frequency and then letting this frequency increase. That is, the limit as one considers, in place of $\hat{\nu}$,

$$\hat{\nu}_W(\omega) = \begin{cases} \hat{\nu}(u) & |\omega| \leqq W \\ 0 & |\omega| > W \end{cases} \qquad (13.24)$$

with $W \to \infty$.

The resulting transfer function for smoothing is

$$h_0(s) = \frac{2 + 3as + 2a^2 s^2 + as^3}{4(1 + 2as + 2a^2 s^2 + 2as^3 + s^4)} \qquad (13.25)$$

where $a = \sin(\pi/8) + \cos(\pi/8) = \frac{1}{2}(2 + \sqrt{2})^{\frac{1}{2}} + \frac{1}{2}(2 - \sqrt{2})^{\frac{1}{2}}$. In this example, $P_0 = 9a\mathcal{S}/64$, while the lower and upper bounds given by Inequality (13.19) are respectively $a\mathcal{S}/32$ and $a\mathcal{S}/4$.

13.5 Prediction and Smoothing of Related Signals

Sometimes, one is interested not in the signal itself, but, for example, in its time derivative, or perhaps a function which is related through some other linear operation on the signal. Even then, one can proceed in the same general way as before, and determine that system which minimizes the mean-squared difference between the actual system output and the desired output. Specifically, suppose $\mathbf{L}$ is a linear time-invariable operator such as, e.g.,

$$\mathbf{L} = a_0 + a_1 \frac{d}{dt} + a_2 \frac{d^2}{dt^2} + \cdots + a_n \frac{d^n}{dt^n}$$

or perhaps such that

$$\mathbf{L}f(t) = \int_{-\infty}^{\infty} g(t - \tau)f(\tau)\,d\tau$$

In any case, the essential property required is that if $F(t) = \mathbf{L}f(t)$, then $\mathbf{L}$ is linear and $\mathbf{L}f(t + T) = F(t + T)$ for constant T. Suppose one desires $p(t + \alpha)$, where $p(t) = \mathbf{L}s(t)$. Now the integral equation which must be satisfied if the mean-squared error is minimized is

$$\psi(t + \alpha) = \int_0^{\infty} \rho(t - \tau)k(\tau)\,d\tau \qquad (13.26)$$

where $\psi(t) = \mathbf{L}\sigma(t)$. The same technique of solution applies as before since the only change is in the form of the function on the left-hand side.

If the solution to the more elementary signal prediction problem is known for all values of α in the neighborhood of the prediction (or lag) time of interest, then this solution can be used to obtain the solution to Eq. (13.26). Proceeding formally, let $k_0(t,\alpha)$ be the solution to Eq. (13.10). Let the subscript on the operator, viz., in $\mathbf{L}_t$ or $\mathbf{L}_\alpha$, indicate the argument of the function upon which $\mathbf{L}$ operates. Then

$$\psi(t + \alpha) \equiv \mathbf{L}_t\sigma(t + \alpha) = \mathbf{L}_\alpha\sigma(t + \alpha)$$
$$= \mathbf{L}_\alpha \int_0^{\infty} \rho(t - \tau)k_0(\tau,\alpha)\,d\tau$$
$$= \int_0^{\infty} \rho(t - \tau)\mathbf{L}_\alpha k_0(\tau,\alpha)\,d\tau \qquad (13.27)$$

Thus, formally, $\mathbf{L}_\alpha k_0(\tau,\alpha)$ is the solution to Eq. (13.26).* For example, returning to Example 1 above, if we wanted to predict ($\alpha \geqq 0$) the value of the signal derivative, ds/dt, then $\mathbf{L}_t = d/dt$, and the desired weighting

---

* Cf. Zakai.[19]

function $k_1(\tau)$ would be

$$k_1(\tau) = \frac{dk_0(\tau,\alpha)}{d\alpha}$$
$$= \frac{A^2 e^{-\alpha}\{-1 - \alpha(1 + A) + s[1 - \alpha(1 + A)]\}}{(1 + A)^2(1 + As)} \tag{13.28}$$

13.6 Multiple Time Series

For purposes of simplicity, the above presentation was restricted to the consideration of a single perturbed random process. But returning to the fire-control system with which we began, we can see that the three series of input data—measured target azimuth and elevation angles and slant range—need not be uncorrelated. In fact there will be correlation if for no other reason than that physical limitations constrain the permissible target maneuvers. For example, the target velocity component in one plane is restricted by that in the other planes. Therefore, one should expect that all three measurements, used simultaneously, should provide more information about any one target coordinate than only one of the measurements would. Therefore, one should reexamine the earlier analysis to allow predictions or calculations from multiple data sources.

The first, and for our immediate purposes, the greatest difficulty in the analysis of multiple time series is solved by the use of appropriate notation. Let there be I signals, not necessarily uncorrelated, denoted by $s_i(t)$, $i = 1, 2, \ldots, I$. (The fire-control system only requires $I = 3$, but generalization to an arbitrary I involves no greater difficulty.) These signals are perturbed by noise components $n_i(t)$, $i = 1, 2, \ldots, I$. The available data consist of the set of I processes $r_i(t) = s_i(t) + n_i(t)$. As before, let us suppose the expected values of s_i and n_i vanish identically. Let

$$\sigma_{ij}(\tau) = E[s_i(t + \tau)s_j(t)] \tag{13.29}$$
and
$$\nu_{ij}(\tau) = E[n_i(t + \tau)n_j(t)] \tag{13.30}$$

Again, for the same reason of simplicity used before, let the s_i and n_j be uncorrelated time series. That is, the various noise components are mutually correlated and the various signal components are mutually correlated, but no signal component is correlated with any noise component.

If we were to need a prediction of each of the signal components, i.e., $s_i(t + \alpha)$, then our system would have to produce I outputs, which we may denote by $s_i^*(t)$. Each output would be in error by an amount

$$\epsilon_i(t) = s_i^*(t) - s_i(t + \alpha) \tag{13.31}$$

and this error would have a mean-squared value

$$P_i = E[\epsilon_i(t)]^2 \tag{13.32}$$

As before, we shall only consider linear time-invariable systems, that is, the computation of $s_i^*(t)$ will be representable in the form

$$s_i^*(t) = \int_0^\infty \sum_{j=1}^I k_{ij}(\tau) r_j(t - \tau)\, d\tau \qquad (13.33)$$

Then the I mean-squared errors will be minimized simultaneously if the I^2 weighting functions $k_{ij}(\tau)$ satisfy the I^2 integral equations.

$$\sigma_{ij}(t + \alpha) = \int_0^\infty \sum_{l=1}^I k_{il}(\tau) \rho_{lj}(t - \tau)\, d\tau \qquad t \geqq 0 \qquad (13.34)$$

Equation (13.34) can be written more succinctly using matrix notation. Let $\mathbf{\sigma}(t)$ be the matrix of signal covariances, that is,

$$\mathbf{\sigma}(t) = [\sigma_{ij}(t)]$$

Similarly, let $\mathbf{\varrho}(t) = [\rho_{ij}(t)]$, and let $\mathbf{k}(t) = [k_{ij}(t)]$. Then Eq. (13.34) can be written

$$\mathbf{\sigma}(t + \alpha) = \int_0^\infty \mathbf{k}(\tau) \mathbf{\varrho}(t - \tau)\, d\tau \qquad t \geqq 0 \qquad (13.35)$$

where one defines the integral of the matrix product as the matrix whose elements are the integrals of the functional elements of the matrix integrand.

The minimum mean-squared errors $P_i{}^0$ are given, for example, by

$$P_i{}^0 = \sigma_{ii}(0) - \int_0^\infty \sum_{j=1}^I k_{ij}(\tau) \sigma_{ji}(\tau + \alpha)\, d\tau \qquad (13.36)$$

The covariance matrix of the errors $[\epsilon_i(t)]$, namely, $\mathbf{P}_0 \equiv [E\epsilon_i\epsilon_j]$, is given by

$$\mathbf{P}_0 = \mathbf{\sigma}(0) - \int_0^\infty \mathbf{k}(\tau) \mathbf{\sigma}(\tau + \alpha)\, d\tau$$

$$= \mathbf{\sigma}(0) - \int_0^\infty \int_0^\infty \mathbf{k}(t) \mathbf{\varrho}(t - \tau) \mathbf{k}^*(\tau)\, d\tau \qquad (13.37)$$

where $\mathbf{k}^*(\tau)$ is the transposed of $\mathbf{k}(\tau)$. In passing it is interesting to note the formal identity of Eqs. (13.35) and (13.37) to the corresponding equations as developed for the single-input–single-output case. This similarity is a reflection of the fact that, conceptually, the problem is not made more complicated by the multiplicity of time series. However, essentially the noncommutivity of the factors of matrix products makes the solution to Eq. (13.35) more difficult than that of Eq. (13.10) (see appendix to this chapter for form of solution).

The generalization to the prediction or smoothing of signals related to the $s_i(t)$ by linear operations, $p_i(t) = \Sigma L_{ij} s_j(t)$, follows the same pattern set in the single-signal case, and therefore will not be pursued here.

13.7 Discrete Time Series

If our self-imposed restriction to the 1940-model fire-control system is removed, we are likely to find modern radar trackers providing the input data to a digital computer. This requires operations to be performed on samples of the data. If all the computations were performed only on the sampled data, then the problems of prediction and filtering are reduced to problems involving discrete time series.

In point of fact, discrete time series are, in many ways, simpler to analyze than are continuous time series. Although the paragraph above might lead one to believe that the concept of discrete time series should be based on the continuous parameter series, and although this can be done, this approach has little justification. It is simpler, and more natural, to consider discrete time series as the more elementary variety, and to derive the appropriate problem formulations and their solutions directly.

If a continuous (wide sense) stationary process is sampled periodically, then the sampled data constitute a (wide sense) stationary process. For example, let the sampling period be δ, and let $x_p = x(p\delta)$, $p = \cdots$, $-1, 0, 1, 2, \ldots$. If $\gamma^c(t)$ were the covariance function of the wide sense stationary continuous $x(t)$, then the *covariance sequence* of the samples x_p, which is defined by

$$\gamma_p \equiv E(x_{p+q} x_q) - (E x_q)^2 \tag{13.38}$$

would be related to γ^c by

$$\gamma_p = \gamma^c(p\delta) \tag{13.39}$$

The discrete process has a "power spectrum" defined as

$$\hat{\gamma}(\omega) = \sum_{-\infty}^{\infty} \gamma_p e^{-ip\omega} \qquad -\pi \leq \omega < \pi \tag{13.40}$$

provided the series converges. As with the continuous case, the power spectrum is a nonnegative even function. When defined by the above series, it is related to the continuous series spectrum $\gamma^c(\omega)$ by

$$\hat{\gamma}(\omega) = \sum_{p=\infty}^{\infty} \gamma^c \left(\omega + \frac{2\pi p}{\delta} \right) \tag{13.41}$$

If the system behavior between sampling points is immaterial, then one need only consider the transformation from the discrete-input time series to the discrete-output series. If the discrete time series x_p, is transformed by a realizable linear and (discrete) time-invariable system, then the output y_p can be represented formally by

$$y_p = \sum_{q=0} k_q x_{p-q} \tag{13.42}$$

where k_q is the weighting function, or more properly, the discrete weighting sequence.

We may now return to the filtering problem. Let $r_p = s_p + n_p$. Again, if the sampling is done periodically on wide sense stationary processes $s(t)$, $n(t)$, and $r(t) = s(t) + n(t)$, then the sampled processes s_p, n_p, and r_p are (discrete) wide sense stationary. As before, let us suppose, for simplicity, that $Es_p = En_p = 0$ and s_p and n_p are mutually uncorrelated. Let

$$\sigma_p = Es_{p+q}s_q \tag{13.43}$$
$$\nu_p = En_{p+q}n_q \tag{13.44}$$

If we seek that system weighting sequence k_p which minimizes the mean-squared prediction or smoothing error, then it must necessarily satisfy

$$\sigma_{p+d} = \sum_0^\infty k_q \rho_{p-q} \qquad p \geqq 0 \tag{13.45}$$

where $|d|$ is the prediction or smoothing time. This is the analog of Eq. (13.10), and essentially the same sort of analytical technique can be used to solve both equations (see the appendix).

The minimum mean-squared error is given by, for example,

$$P_0 = \sigma_0 - \sum_0^\infty \sigma_{p+d}k_p{}^0 \tag{13.46}$$

where $k_p{}^0$ is the sequence which satisfies Eq. (13.45).

The solution to the discrete-time-series prediction and smoothing problems can be extended in the very same way the continuous-time-series problem was extended to include the prediction and smoothing of signals which are related to $s(t)$ through a linear operation on $s(t)$. For example, if Δ is the "difference" operator so that $p_p = \Delta s_p \equiv s_p - s_{p-1}$, and if $h_p{}^0$ is the solution to Eq. (13.45), then p_p is predicted or smoothed with minimum mean-squared error if the weighing sequence is

$$k'_{p,d} = \Delta k^0_{p,d} = k^0_{p,d} - k^0_{p-1,d} \tag{13.47}$$

Also, in an identically similar way to that described above for continuous series, the discrete-time-series analysis can be extended to include multiple discrete time series. By the introduction of the covariance matrices, etc., the necessary condition, Eq. (13.45), remains formally unchanged except, as was the case for multiple continuous time series, the symbols σ_{p+d}, k_p, and ρ_{p-q} are replaced by their matrix equivalents.

13.8   Variants of the Wiener Problem

The results of Wiener were directly applicable to the sort of illustrative system presented above in its historical setting.   They could have and may actually have been responsible for some early improvements in system design.   But his analysis was really epoch-making in another way.   More important than the design formulas which he obtained, his work represented the first definitive analysis in which the system inputs were represented as stochastic processes and the system output evaluated statistically.   This marked a major innovation, setting a new pattern of analysis and hence of design.   This new pattern subsequently blossomed into a many-faceted theoretical approach by relaxing or varying several of the hypotheses used.

In general, the aspects of the problem which can be varied can be summarized as being of three types.   It was supposed that:

1. The signals and perturbations are wide sense stationary random processes.

2. The operations performed on the input data are linear.

3. The goal is to minimize the mean-squared error.

These suppositions can and have been relaxed in a variety of ways. For example, consider the following relaxation of supposition 1 above.

Returning to our classical fire-control system, we might regard the noise as it was described before, but now we might prefer to think of the signal component as having a nonrandom component.   For example, if the target were to fly a straight-line course at constant velocity V, then the slant range to the target varies with time as $s_2(t) = \sqrt{R^2 + V^2 t^2}$, where t is the time to go to the point of closest approach.   The complete description of a maneuvering target might then consist of the superposition of a randomly fluctuating component on such a nonrandom variation, or on some approximation thereto.   Thus, we would write

$$s(t) = s_1(t) + s_2(t) \qquad (13.48)$$

where $s_1(t)$ might be the random process considered earlier, but $s_2(t)$ would be some nonrandom function.

Now one has a variety of natural ways to pose the problem.   One can weigh the importance of the error in response to the random part differently from that of the nonrandom part.   For example, the following was done by Phillips and Weiss[11] and later generalized by Zadeh and Ragazzini.[18]   One considers an error in the nonrandom part $s_2(t)$ as intolerable.   Then, the mean-squared error is minimized after imposing the constraint that, in the absence of the random part $s_1(t) + n(t)$, the response has absolutely no error.   Thus, as an example, if $s_2(t)$ were representable (or approximated) by a linear combination of linearly independent functions of known form, i.e.,

$$s_1(t) = \sum_1^M a_i \phi_i(t) \tag{13.49}$$

then the constraints imposed on the weighting function $k(t)$ would be of the form

$$\phi_i(t + \alpha) = \int_0^\infty k(\tau)\phi_i(t - \tau)\, d\tau \qquad -\infty \leqq t \leqq \infty \tag{13.50}$$

If $\phi_i(t)$ were of the form $t^{q_i}e^{p_i t}$ with $q_i \geqq 0$, and p_i an arbitrary constant, real or complex, then Eq. (13.50) would be satisfied for all t if only

$$\phi_i(\alpha) = \int_0^\infty k(\tau)\phi_i(-\tau)\, d\tau \tag{13.51}$$

Formally, without regard to the existence of solutions, if the ϕ_i were of the form just considered, the minimization of the mean-squared error would require the system weighting function to be such that

$$\sigma(t + \alpha) + \sum_1^m \lambda_i\phi_i(-t) = \int_0^\infty \rho(t - \tau)k(\tau)\, d\tau \qquad t \geqq 0 \tag{13.52}$$

(where the λ_i are Lagrange multipliers determined by the constraints).

Although Eq. (13.52) is a *necessary* condition to be satisfied when a minimum mean-squared error exists, its satisfaction by some $k(\tau)$ is by no means sufficient to establish the existence of a bona fide minimum. In fact, the solution to Eq. (13.52) does not minimize the mean-squared error unless some further modification of the problem is made. (This does not mean that the problem as stated cannot be used to suggest a practical solution, but it does make the problem mathematically less definite.) In the papers of the authors cited above, the modification which leads to a bona fide minimum is the restriction of the system memory to a finite time. That is, it is supposed that for some finite T, $k(\tau) \equiv 0$ if $\tau \geqq T$. Then the integral equation which must be satisfied is

$$\sigma(t + \alpha) + \sum_1^m \lambda_i\phi_i(-t) = \int_0^T \rho(t - \tau)k(\tau)\, d\tau \qquad 0 \leqq t \leqq T \tag{13.53}$$

where the two sides need not be equal if $t < 0$ or $t > T$. The reader is referred to the paper by Zadeh and Ragazzini[18] where the computational details of determining specific weighting functions are outlined for $\phi_i(t) = t^i$, i.e., for $s_2(t)$ components which are polynomials.

The above variant, one of many possible,† involves the relaxation of hypothesis (1) to allow for a form of nonstationary signal. One can go

† Cf., e.g., Ule.[13]

still further in this direction by supposing that the random components $s_1(t)$ and $n(t)$ are also nonstationary. This broadened hypothesis leads to the same sort of minimization problem already discussed, except that in place of the simpler functions of a single variable, the covariance functions, and consequently also the optimum weighting function, become functions of two variables. For example, suppose $s_1(t)$ and $n(t)$ have zero mean values but are not necessarily stationary in the wide sense, while $s_2(t) = \Sigma \phi_i(t)$ as before. The covariances are then functions of two variables, namely

$$\sigma_1(t,\tau) = Es_1(t)s_1(\tau) \tag{13.54}$$
$$\nu(t,\tau) = En(t)n(\tau) \tag{13.55}$$

The output $s^*(t)$ of the most general linear system can be represented by

$$s^*(t) = \int_0^\infty k(t,\tau)r(t - \tau) \, d\tau \tag{13.56}$$

If the response to $s_2(t)$ is required to be distortionless, then the system with finite memory (i.e., for which $k(t,\tau) \neq 0$ only if $0 \leqq \tau \leqq T$), and which minimizes the remaining mean-squared error, must satisfy

$$\sigma_1(t + \alpha, \tau) + \Sigma\lambda_i\phi_i(t - \tau) = \int_0^T k(t,\theta)\rho(t - \theta, \tau) \, d\theta$$
$$t - T \leqq \tau \leqq t \quad (13.57)$$

(The reader is referred to Booton's paper[3] for a discussion of the case $s_2 \equiv 0$, $T \to \infty$. Also, see the excellent paper by Koschmann.[9])

13.9   Mean-squared Error Criterion

In general, it is easier to solve the problem of specifying the linear system which minimizes the mean-squared error than it is the system which minimizes any other scalar error criterion. The integral equation (13.10) which determines the Wiener filter weighting function is a *linear* equation because of the particular analytic character of this measure of the error. If another criterion were used, we would generally lose this simplicity. For example, if we sought to minimize the mean ($2n$th) power of the error, the linear system weighting function would generally be determined by a nonlinear (if $n > 1$) integral equation.

However, there is one very important circumstance where the analysis is not so intractable using other criteria. This is the case of Gaussian processes, and the following measure of the error. An error weighting function ϕ is chosen such that $\phi(\epsilon) = \phi(-\epsilon)$, and $0 \leqq \phi(\epsilon_1) \leqq \phi(\epsilon_2)$ if $\epsilon_1 \leqq \epsilon_2$. Now we look for the filter which minimizes the mean-weighted error. That is, where the error is $\epsilon(t) = s^*(t) - s(t + \alpha)$, we look to minimize $Q = E\phi[\epsilon(t)]$. This includes the Wiener criterion, $\phi(\epsilon) = \epsilon^2$, as well as the more interesting criterion for fire-control systems obtained by letting

$$\phi(\epsilon) = \begin{cases} 0 & \text{if } \epsilon < A \\ 1 & \text{if } \epsilon \geq A \end{cases} \qquad (13.58)$$

The mean value of such a weighted error is just the probability that $|\epsilon| \geq A$. Thus, if one chose the value of A so that the system just barely missed the target when $|\epsilon| = A$, minimizing the mean of this weighted error would provide the system which has the least probability of a miss.

The facts in this case are these. Because of a special property of Gaussian processes, even if restriction 2 above is entirely removed, the mean-squared error is still minimized by a linear system. In other words, for Gaussian processes $s(t)$ and $n(t)$ (having zero means), condition 2 is a corollary rather than a necessary hypothesis. Finally, for such processes, that system which minimizes the mean-squared error, also minimizes the mean weighted error Q (at least for ϕ as described above, and which do not grow faster than $\exp(a\epsilon^2)$ for any $a > 0$ as $\epsilon \to \infty$). This fact was pointed out recently by S. Sherman[12] for pure prediction (i.e., in the absence of noise), but essentially the same argument used by Sherman carries over for smoothing or prediction in the presence of noise. It also holds where, not $s(t)$, but the linearly related $p(t) = \mathbf{L}s(t)$ is to be predicted or smoothed; and further it even holds where the processes $s(t)$ and $n(t)$ are nonstationary.

The restriction to Gaussian processes may appear somewhat artificial, but in a great many applications, it is not unnatural. In a rough way, the central limit theorem[4,5,6] suggests that whenever a wideband random signal is transmitted by a linear, narrow-bandwidth system, the output is nearly Gaussian, irrespective of the distributions of the original input. Since a good many of the random processes occurring as input data to control systems are wideband in origin and are narrowed in bandwidth by the signal processing, it follows that the above result is of more than academic interest. Thus, for example, if applied to the fire-control problem, where the observation about the central limit theorem is generally applicable, we have the implication that, for all practical purposes, *the design which minimizes the mean-squared miss distance simultaneously minimizes the probability that a miss will exceed any fixed, preassigned limit.*

In the case of non-Gaussian processes, not only must one expect, as noted, that different criteria may yield different optimizing systems, but also, one must expect the restriction to linear systems, supposition 2 above, to be possibly severe. That is, for general processes, among the most general systems, that one which minimizes the mean-squared error generally will be nonlinear. If this is the case, the analysis may become most intractable, and the best hope for analysis appears to be restricted to small perturbations from the Gaussian processes (thus leading to small perturbations from system linearity), or else to nonlinearities with no memory.[2,7]

13.10 Tracking Loss Rates

The whole of the discussion thus far has been concerned with the problem of determining system specifications for the most effective signal prediction or smoothing, that is, it has been with the system synthesis problem. To reiterate, this was, historically, the first significant problem. It is still one of the most common settings for the application of the theory of random processes. However, it by no means exhausts the field of applications. There are many problems which are related to the analysis and evaluation of systems designed on the basis of possibly other factors. One such problem is the determination of the probability of failure due to overdrive, when the system has a limited dynamic range. For example, consider again our fire-control system; but now suppose our subsystem tracking the angular coordinates of the target is updated and replaced by an automatic radar tracker. There is still a noise component due to the radar receiver noise and the target echo fluctuation (scintillation). Irrespective of the particular implementation of the tracker, it usually has a small instantaneous field of view. That is, the radar receiver detects a target echo only if the target lies within a small angle from the direction in which the radar antenna points. Roughly, if the random fluctuation causes the tracker pointing error to exceed half the field of view, the tracker receives no target echo, and so cannot continue to track.

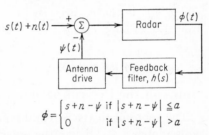

$$\phi = \begin{cases} s+n-\psi & \text{if } |s+n-\psi| \leq a \\ 0 & \text{if } |s+n-\psi| > a \end{cases}$$

Fig. 13.2 Radar loop for tracking loss rate problem (one dimension).

Consider the system shown schematically in Fig. 13.2, and for simplicity consider only one angular coordinate of the target. Basically, the tracking error has two components: the response of the closed loop (with transfer function $[1 + h(s)]^{-1}$) to $n(t)$, and the response of a system with function $h(s)[1 + h(s)]^{-1}$ to $s(t)$, where, in both cases, $h(s)$ is the open-loop transfer function.

Let $s(t)$ and $n(t)$ be uncorrelated Gaussian processes with zero mean values and power spectra $\hat{\sigma}(\omega)$ and $\hat{\nu}(\omega)$. Then, if the system is tracking, the tracking error is also a Gaussian process with zero mean value and with a power spectrum

$$\hat{\eta}(\omega) = \frac{\hat{\sigma}(\omega)|h(i\omega)|^2}{|1 + h(i\omega)|^2} + \frac{\hat{\nu}(\omega)}{|1 + h(i\omega)|^2} \tag{13.59}$$

The problem is to determine the probability that the tracking system will develop in excess of the maximum permissible tracking error a.

Let us consider the performance of another system, equivalent except for the absence of a limited field of view. We may transfer our attention to this conceptual system and now ask for the probability that its tracking error exceed a, since both systems are supposed identical, if tracking. If the frequency of occurrence of tracking errors in excess of a is very low compared to the bandwidth of the closed-loop system, then the number of such occurrences in a given time interval will be very nearly a Poisson variable.[8] But if it is Poisson, then the probability of the loss of the target from the field of view, in a time interval T, is equal to $1 - \exp(-\lambda T)$, where λ is the mean frequency with which the tracking error increases beyond a in the conceptually modified version. The mean time interval required before a loss occurs is λ^{-1}. The value of λ, called the *loss rate*, can be calculated for Gaussian processes. It is, in fact, given by*

$$\lambda = \frac{1}{\pi} \left[\frac{-\eta''(0)}{\eta(0)} \right]^{\frac{1}{2}} \exp \frac{-a^2}{2\eta(0)}$$

where $\eta(t)$ is the covariance function of the tracking error, obtainable from Eq. (13.59), and $\eta''(t) = d^2\eta/dt^2$.

APPENDIX

Notes on the Determination of $k_0(t)$

The solution to the integral equation (13.10) and its various analogs is presented first. From the outset, let us suppose that the power spectrum $\hat{\rho}(\omega)$ exists, and has a finite integral (thus implying that $\rho(0) < \infty$). There are two distinct cases to consider:

Case 1:

(a) $\hat{\rho}(\omega) > 0$ except on, at most, an ω set of zero Lebesgue measure

(b) $\displaystyle\int_0^\infty \frac{\log \hat{\rho}(\omega)}{1 + \omega^2} \, d\omega > -\infty$

Case 2:

Either (a) or (b) is violated.

If and only if condition 1 is satisfied, then there will exist an analytic function ψ of the complex variable $s = \chi + i\omega$, such that: (1) neither ψ nor its reciprocal $1/\psi$ has any zeros in the right half of the s plane (Re $s \geq 0$), and (2) $|\psi(i\omega)|^2 = \hat{\rho}(\omega)$. This function is, in fact, given by

$$\psi(s) = \exp\left[\frac{1}{2\pi} \int_{-\infty}^\infty \frac{\log \hat{\rho}(\omega)}{s - i\omega} \, d\omega \right] \quad \text{if Re } s > 0 \qquad (A.1)$$

*See Bartlett,[1] pp. 187–188.

If $\hat{\rho}(\omega)$ is a rational function, then it must be expressible in the form

$$\hat{\rho}(\omega) = \frac{\Pi_1{}^n(\omega^2 + z_k{}^2)}{\Pi_1{}^m(\omega^2 + p_k{}^2)} \tag{A.2}$$

where it can be assumed that the real parts of z_k and p_k are all positive. In this case, clearly,

$$\psi(s) = \frac{\Pi_1{}^n(s + z_k)}{\Pi_1{}^m(s + p_k)} \tag{A.3}$$

Wiener's solution to Eq. (13.10) is given in terms of its Laplace transform $h_0(s)$. It is

$$h_0(s) = \frac{g(s)}{\psi(s)} \tag{A.4}$$

where

$$g(s) = \int_0^\infty e^{-st}G(t + \alpha)\, dt \tag{A.5}$$

and where

$$G(t) = \frac{1}{2\pi}\int_{-\infty}^\infty \frac{\hat{\sigma}(\omega)\psi(i\omega)}{\hat{\rho}(\omega)} e^{i\omega t}\, d\omega$$

$$= \frac{1}{2\pi}\int_{-\infty}^\infty \frac{\hat{\sigma}(\omega)}{\psi(-i\omega)} e^{i\omega t}\, d\omega \tag{A.6}$$

The function $\hat{\sigma}(\omega)$ is, as in the text, the power spectrum of the signal being predicted or smoothed, and $\infty < \alpha < \infty$.

If condition 1 is violated, then in linear prediction theory the $r(t)$ process is called singular, or deterministic.* The terminology follows from the fact that the future of such a process is perfectly predicted by a linear operation on the remote past only of the process. As an illustration of such a process, suppose that the random process $r(t)$ had a power spectrum $\hat{\rho}(\omega) = \exp(-\omega^2)$. Then the derivatives of $r(t)$ of all orders exist (as limits in mean square), and, in terms of these, $r(t)$ can be predicted by a Taylor series expansion, e.g.,

$$r(t + \alpha) = \sum_0^\infty \frac{(\alpha)^p}{p!} s^{[p]}(t) \tag{A.7}$$

or more generally, for any $\tilde{\iota}$

$$r(t + \alpha) = \sum_0^\infty \frac{(t + \alpha - \tilde{\iota})^p}{p!} s^{[p]}(t - \tilde{\iota}) \tag{A.8}$$

Since the violation of condition 1 by $\hat{\rho}(\omega)$ implies also that $\hat{\sigma}(\omega)$ and $\hat{v}(\omega)$ individually violate the same condition, it follows in this case that prediction or smoothing problems can be reduced to operations on the (infinitely) remote past.

* Cf. Doob,[6] chap. 12.

For a single discrete time series, it is Eq. (13.45) to which we must return. Here, the condition of case 1 is modified as follows. We first define the power spectrum of r_p as the function

$$\hat{\rho}(\omega) = \sum_{p=-\infty}^{\infty} \rho_p e^{-i\omega p} \qquad -\pi \leqq \omega < \pi \qquad (A.9)$$

Case 1:

(a) $\hat{\rho}(\omega) > 0$, except on, at most, an ω set of zero Lebesgue measure

(b) $\int_0^{\pi} \log \hat{\rho}(\omega) \, d\omega > -\infty$

Case 2:

Again the negation of case 1.

In case 1, but only in this case, there exists an analytic function ψ of the complex variable z, such that: (1) $\psi(z)$ is analytic with neither ψ nor its reciprocal vanishing in $|z| < 1$, and (2) $|\psi(e^{-i\omega})|^2 = \hat{\rho}(\omega)$. It can be represented by

$$\psi(z) = \exp\left(\tfrac{1}{2}a_0 + \sum_{1}^{\infty} a_p z^p\right) \qquad (A.10)$$

where

$$a_p = \frac{1}{\pi} \int_0^{\pi} \log \hat{\rho}(\omega) \cos (\omega p) \, d\omega \qquad (A.11)$$

The solution to Eq. (13.45) can now be written in terms of the Fourier transform of the weighting sequence. That is, in terms of

$$h_0(\omega) = \sum_{0}^{\infty} k_p{}^0 e^{-i\omega p} \qquad -\pi \leqq \omega < \pi \qquad (A.12)$$

It is

$$h_0(\omega) = \frac{g(\omega)}{\psi(e^{-i\omega})} \qquad (A.13)$$

where

$$g(\omega) = \sum_{0}^{\infty} G_{p+d} e^{-i\omega p} \qquad (A.14)$$

where

$$G_p = \frac{1}{2\pi} \int_{-\pi}^{\pi} \frac{\hat{\sigma}(\omega)\psi(e^{-i\omega})}{\hat{\rho}(\omega)} e^{i\omega p} \, d\omega \qquad (A.15)$$

[The power spectrum of s_p, $\hat{\sigma}(\omega)$, is defined similarly to $\hat{\rho}(\omega)$ above, Eq. (A.9), $-\infty < d < \infty$.]

Equations (A.11), (A.12), and (A.13) appear somewhat formidable, but in practice they are more manageable than those for the continuous time series. This is particularly true for periodically sampled continuous processes when the latter have rational power spectra. As an illustration, consider the following: $\sigma_p = \sigma_0 a^{-|p|}$ (s_p is obtained by periodically sampling $s(t)$, which has for its covariance function $\sigma(t) = \sigma_0 e^{-|t|}$, $a = e^{\delta}$, δ = sampling period), $\nu_p = 0$ if $p \neq 0$ (n_p are mutually uncorrelated).

Then the discrete process power spectra concerned are

$$\hat{\sigma}(\omega) = \sigma_0 \frac{a^2 - 1}{1 + a^2 - 2a \cos \omega} \qquad (A.16)$$

$$\hat{\nu}(\omega) = \nu_0 \qquad (A.17)$$

$$\hat{\rho}(\omega) = \frac{\nu_0 a}{b} \frac{1 + b^2 - 2b \cos \omega}{1 + a^2 - 2a \cos \omega} \qquad (A.18)$$

where $b = c + \sqrt{c^2 - 1}$, and $c = \cosh \delta + (\sigma_0/\nu_0) \sinh \delta$. The appropriate factor of $\hat{\rho}(\omega)$ is

$$\psi(z) = \left(\frac{\nu_0 a}{b}\right)^{\frac{1}{2}} \frac{(z - b)}{(z - a)} \qquad (A.19)$$

Hence,

$$
\begin{aligned}
\frac{\hat{\sigma}(\omega)}{\hat{\rho}(\omega)} \psi(e^{-i\omega}) &= \frac{\sigma_0(a^2 - 1)(b/a\nu_0)^{\frac{1}{2}}}{(e^{i\omega} - b)(e^{-i\omega} - a)} \\
&= \frac{\sigma_0(a^2 - 1)(b/a\nu_0)^{\frac{1}{2}}}{ab - 1} \left\{ \frac{e^{-i\omega}}{a - e^{-i\omega}} + \frac{b}{b - e^{i\omega}} \right\} \\
&= \frac{\sigma_0(a^2 - 1)(b/a\nu_0)^{\frac{1}{2}}}{ab - 1} \left\{ \sum_{1}^{\infty} a^{-p}e^{-i\omega p} + \sum_{0}^{\infty} b^{-p}e^{i\omega p} \right\} \quad (A.20)
\end{aligned}
$$

Hence

$$
G_p =
\begin{cases}
\sigma_0(a^2 - 1) \left(\dfrac{b}{a\nu_0}\right)^{\frac{1}{2}} \Big/ (ab - 1)(a^p) & \text{if } p > 0 \\[2ex]
\sigma_0(a^2 - 1) \left(\dfrac{b}{a\nu_0}\right)^{\frac{1}{2}} \Big/ (ab - 1)(b^{-p}) & \text{if } p \leqq 0
\end{cases}
\qquad (A.21)
$$

If we restrict d to nonnegative values (prediction or smoothing without time lag), then

$$g(\omega) = \frac{\sigma_0(a^2 - 1)(ab/\nu_0)^{\frac{1}{2}} a^{-d}}{(ab - 1)(a - e^{-i\omega})} \qquad (A.22)$$

Finally,

$$h_0(\omega) = \frac{\sigma_0(a^2 - 1)}{\nu_0(ab - 1)} \frac{ba^{-d}}{(b - e^{-i\omega})} \qquad (A.23)$$

or equivalently,

$$k_p{}^0 = \frac{\sigma_0(a^2 - 1)a^{-d}}{\nu_0(ab - 1)} b^{-p} \qquad p = 0, 1, \ldots \qquad (A.24)$$

is the desired optimum linear predictor of s_p, d steps ahead.

The solution to the matrix integral equation in the case of multiple time series is complicated by the fact that the above factorization step now requires the factorization of a matrix of functions. The main points of this mathematical problem were presented by N. Wiener,[15] and the principal theorem later proven rigorously by Wiener and Masani.[16]

Below is an extension of the theorem of Wiener and Masani to continuous time series matrix spectra; we begin by introducing appropriate notation.

Suppose $s_i(t)$, $n_i(t)$, $1 \leq i \leq I$, are I-ple random processes, which are stationary in the wide sense. As in the text, denote by $\mathbf{\sigma}(t)$, $\mathbf{v}(t)$, and $\mathbf{\varrho}(t)$ respectively, the covariance matrices of $s_i(t)$, $n_i(t)$, and $r_i(t)$. For simplicity, suppose that the s_i are uncorrelated with the n_i, so that we can write $\mathbf{\varrho} = \mathbf{\sigma} + \mathbf{v}$. Let $\hat{\mathbf{\sigma}}$, $\hat{\mathbf{v}}$, and $\hat{\mathbf{\varrho}}$ be the matrix power spectra, i.e., the matrices, the elements of which are the Fourier transforms of those of $\mathbf{\sigma}(t)$, etc. Let $\Delta[\hat{\mathbf{\varrho}}(\omega)]$ denote the determinant of the matrix $\hat{\mathbf{\varrho}}(\omega)$. Finally, suppose that $\mathbf{\varrho}(0)$ has only finite, i.e., noninfinite elements, that $\Delta[\hat{\mathbf{\varrho}}(\omega)]$ vanishes on, at most, an ω set of zero Lebesgue measure, and that

$$\int_0^\infty \frac{\log \Delta[\hat{\mathbf{\varrho}}(\omega)]}{1 + \omega^2}\, d\omega > -\infty \qquad (A.25)$$

Then there exists a matrix $\mathbf{\psi}$ of analytic functions of the complex variable s with the following properties: (1) Neither the determinant of $\mathbf{\psi}$ nor its reciprocal vanish if $\mathrm{Re}\, s \geq 0$, and (2) denoting the complex conjugate transposed of $\mathbf{\psi}$ by $\mathbf{\psi}^*$, we have $\mathbf{\psi}(i\omega)\mathbf{\psi}^*(i\omega) = \hat{\mathbf{\varrho}}(\omega)$. The calculation of the matrix is the essential and only really formidable step in the solution of Eq. (13.35). Wiener and Masani[17] have been able to outline a specific limiting procedure which leads to a determination of the matrix $\mathbf{\psi}$.

In terms of the matrices $\hat{\mathbf{\sigma}}$, $\hat{\mathbf{\varrho}}$, and $\mathbf{\psi}$, the remaining steps are direct, and they follow the pattern already set. The $I \times I$ matrix of functions $\mathbf{h}(s)$ which gives the input-output relation of the desired linear system is given by the following matrix equations:

$$\mathbf{h}(s) \equiv \int_0^\infty e^{-st}\mathbf{k}(t)\, dt \qquad (A.26)$$

$$\mathbf{h}(s) = \mathbf{g}(s)[\mathbf{\psi}(s)]^{-1} \qquad (A.27)$$

$$\mathbf{g}(s) = \int_0^\infty e^{-st}\mathbf{G}(t + \alpha)\, dt \qquad (A.28)$$

$$\mathbf{G}(t) = \frac{1}{2\pi}\int_{-\infty}^\infty \hat{\mathbf{\sigma}}(\omega)[\hat{\mathbf{\varrho}}(\omega)]^{-1}\mathbf{\psi}(i\omega)e^{i\omega t}\, d\omega$$

$$= \frac{1}{2\pi}\int_{-\infty}^\infty \hat{\mathbf{\sigma}}(\omega)[\mathbf{\psi}^*(i\omega)]^{-1}e^{i\omega t}\, d\omega \qquad (A.29)$$

where $-\infty < \alpha < \infty$.

Finally, a remark is made on the practical reduction of the mean-squared error when the signal has a polynomial component and infinite memory is allowed. The constraint of permitting no error in the polynomial component $s_2(t) = a_0 + a_1 t + \cdots + a_m t^m$ amounts to requiring

$$\int_0^\infty k(t)t^i\, dt = (-\alpha)^i \qquad 0 \leq i \leq m \qquad (A.30)$$

This is a relatively weak condition on the system transfer function $h(s)$, and in terms of the latter it requires only

$$\frac{d^i h(s)}{ds^i}\bigg|_{s=0} = (-\alpha)^i \qquad 0 \leq i \leq m \qquad (A.31)$$

Now suppose $h_0(s)$ is the system function which results from the Wiener problem obtained by suppressing s_2, that is, by setting $s(t) = s_1(t)$. Let $h_1(s)$ be any physically realizable transfer function such that

$$\frac{d^i h_1(s)}{ds^i}\bigg|_{s=0} = (-\alpha)^i - \frac{d^i h_0(s)}{ds^i}\bigg|_{s=0} \qquad 0 \leq i \leq m \qquad (A.32)$$

but also such that $|h_1(i\omega)|$ assumes negligible values for $\omega \geq \omega_0 > 0$ with ω_0 very small. Then if the sum $h(s) = h_0(s) + h_1(s)$ were specified as the system transfer function, there would be no error in the response to s_2 as required, and the mean-squared error would be

$$P = P_0 + \frac{1}{2\pi} \int_{-\infty}^{\infty} |h_1(i\omega)|^2 \hat{\rho}(\omega)\, d\omega \qquad (A.33)$$

where P_0 is the mean-squared error in the unconstrained case. [Compare with Eq. (13.20) of text.] Thus it follows that h_1 can be so constructed that $h = h_0 + h_1$ satisfies the constraints, and the mean-square error differs as little as we please from that of the unconstrained problem P_0. Notice, however, that the limit of such h_1's as make $P \to P_0$ is *not* a function with the required property, Eq. ($A.32$). In other words, we can make the mean-squared error approach P_0 as closely as desired, even though there is no transfer function which satisfies the constraints and yields the limit mean-squared error P_0.

REFERENCES

1. Bartlett, M. S.: "Introduction to Stochastic Processes," Cambridge University Press, Cambridge, Mass., 1955.
2. Balakrishnan, A. V., and R. Drenick: On Optimum Nonlinear Extraction and Coding Filters, *Trans. IRE Profess. Group on Inform. Theory*, vol. PGIT 2–3, pp. 166–172, September, 1956.
3. Booton, R. C., Jr.: An Optimization Theory for Time-varying Linear Systems with Nonstationary Statistical Inputs, *Proc. IRE*, vol. 402, pp. 977–981, 1952.
4. Cramer, H.: "Mathematical Methods of Statistics," Princeton University Press, Princeton, N.J., 1946.
5. Davenport, W. B., and W. L. Root: "Random Signals and Noise," McGraw-Hill Book Company, Inc., New York, 1958.
6. Doob, J. L.: "Stochastic Processes," John Wiley & Sons, Inc., New York, 1953.
7. Drenick, R.: A Non-linear Prediction Theory, *Trans. IRE Profess. Group on Inform. Theory*, vol. PGIT 4, pp. 146–162, September, 1954.
8. Feller, W.: "Probability Theory and its Applications," John Wiley & Sons, Inc., New York, 1950.

9. Koschmann, A. H.: "On the Filtering of Nonstationary Time Series," *Purdue Univ. Eng. Bull., Research Ser., No.* 135.

10. Laning, J. H., Jr., and R. H. Battin: "Random Processes in Automatic Control," McGraw-Hill Book Company, Inc., New York, 1956.

11. Phillips, R. S., and R. P. Weiss: Theoretical Calculation on Best Smoothing of Position Data for Gunnery Prediction, *Mass. Insti. Technol. Radiation Lab. Rept.* 532.

12. Sherman, S.: Non-mean-square Error Criteria, *Trans. IRE Profess. Group on Inform. Theory,* vol. PGIT 4-3, pp. 125–126, September, 1958.

13. Ule, L.: A Theory of Weighted Smoothing, *Trans. IRE Profess. Group on Inform. Theory,* vol. PGIT 3-2, pp. 131–135, June, 1957.

14. Wiener, N.: "Extrapolation, Interpolation, and Smoothing of Stationary Time Series," John Wiley & Sons, Inc., New York, 1949.

15. Wiener, N.: On the Factorization of Matrices, *Comment. Math. Helv.,* vol. 29, pp. 97–111, 1955.

16. Wiener, N., and P. Masani: The Prediction Theory of Multivariate Stochastic Processes, part I, *Acta Math.,* vol. 98, pp. 111–150, 1957.

17. Wiener, N., and P. Masani: On the Prediction Theory of Multivariate Stochastic Processes, part II, *Acta Math.,* vol. 99, pp. 93–137, 1958.

18. Zadeh, L. A., and J. R. Ragazzini: An Extension of Wiener's Theory of Prediction, *J. Appl. Phys.,* vol. 21, pp. 645–655, 1950.

19. Zakai, M.: On a Property of Wiener Filters, *Trans. IRE Profess. Group on Inform. Theory,* vol. PGIT 5-1, pp. 15–16, March, 1959.

14

Optimal Control Problems in Discrete-time Systems

LOTFI A. ZADEH

PROFESSOR OF ELECTRICAL ENGINEERING
UNIVERSITY OF CALIFORNIA, BERKELEY

14.1 Introduction

Like many other branches of technology, the field of automatic control underwent visible changes in recent years as a result of the increasing availability of both analog and digital computers. Just a decade or so ago, theory of control systems was concerned primarily with problems which are amenable to purely analytical treatment—problems centering for the most part on the analysis and synthesis of linear time-invariant systems. Essential nonlinearities were disregarded or, at best, linearized, as were nonlinear constraints on power, torque, and other variables.

Current trends in control system theory reflect our ability to use analog and, especially, digital computers to obtain numerical solutions to complex problems which do not admit of treatment in general terms. Furthermore, they reflect the possibility of employing special-purpose digital computers—as control system components—to process large amounts of data and/or implement complex control laws. The use of digital computers in these capacities is particularly natural in the case of systems which are discrete in nature, e.g., (1) sampled-data systems, in which the time varies discretely but the control signals range over continua, and (2) sequential systems, in which both control signals and time are discrete. The common characteristic of sampled-data and sequential systems is the discreteness of time. For this reason, they will be referred to as *discrete-time* systems.

The availability of digital computers and controllers makes it feasible, particularly in the case of discrete-time systems, to take into consideration not only the constraints on control signals, but also quantitative measures of system performance expressed in terms of criterion functions.

389

This in turn makes it practicable to formulate many problems pertaining to the design of control systems in much more realistic terms than was possible in the past. Among such problems is the basic problem of finding an input, subject to some specified constraints, which on application to a given system in a prescribed initial state would produce an output which is "best" in some specified sense. During the past few years problems of this type have been receiving increasing attention in the literature of control systems and are commonly referred to as *optimal control* problems.

The present chapter is given over to a compact exposition of several basic kinds of optimal control problems and methods by which they can be solved. For the most part, the problems are formulated in terms of sequential systems, since such systems present least conceptual difficulties and require but very rudimentary mathematical tools for their analysis. Essentially, they are patterned on the conventional optimal control problems for continuous-time systems and, more particularly, on the problems formulated by Bellman, Glicksberg, and Gross,[1] Bellman and Kalaba,[2] Pontryagin,[3] Hopkin,[4] Feldbaum,[5,6] Lerner,[7] Kalman and Bertram,[8] and many others. In the case of sequential systems, the problems in question can be solved by a very straightforward and elementary method which is, in effect, a simplified and somewhat disguised form of dynamic programming.

As a preliminary to our analysis, it will be helpful to review some of the basic notions relating to discrete-time systems and, in particular, discuss their characterization in terms of input-output relationships. A brief treatment of these notions is given in the following section.

14.2   Characterization of Discrete-time Systems

To simplify exposition, we shall restrict our discussion to two poles, that is, systems with one input and one output. This restriction does not entail any significant loss in generality.

Consider a discrete-time system in which the input x and the output y have the form of sequences

$$x = \cdots, x_{t-1}, x_t, x_{t+1}, x_{t+2}, \cdots \tag{14.1}$$

$$y = \cdots, y_{t-1}, y_t, y_{t+1}, y_{t+2}, \cdots \tag{14.2}$$

in which x_t and y_t denote, respectively, the values of the input and output at time t, with t ranging over the integers $\ldots, -1, 0, 1, 2, \ldots$. In the sequel, we shall be concerned with two types of discrete-time systems: (1) sequential systems, in which x_t and y_t for each t range over a finite set, and (2) sampled-data systems, in which x_t and y_t range over real numbers.

In both these cases and, particularly, in the case of sequential systems, it is expedient to represent the input-output relationship of the system in a form which places in evidence the *state variable* s_t at time t. This form—which seems to have originated essentially in the work of Turing[9] and was effectively employed by Shannon[10] in his classical work on communication theory—is now standard in the theory of sequential systems;[11] it reads

$$s_{t+1} = f(s_t, x_t) \tag{14.3}$$
$$y_t = g(s_t, x_t) \tag{14.4}$$

where the first equation defines the state at time $t + 1$ in terms of the state and input at time t, while the second equation gives the output at time t in terms of s_t and x_t. The range of the state variable constitutes the *state space* of the system, and a sequence of s_t's constitutes a *trajectory* in state space. In the case of finite-state sequential systems, the state space is a finite set whose elements, i.e., the states of the system, will be denoted by ①, ②, ③, . . . , ⓝ, or, where this notation is inconvenient, by $q_1, q_2, q_3, \ldots , q_n$. In the case of lumped-parameter linear sampled-data systems, as well as modular circuits, (14.3) and (14.4) reduce to matrix equations

$$s_{t+1} = A s_t + B x_t \tag{14.5}$$
$$y_t = C s_t + D x_t \tag{14.6}$$

where s_t is a vector with real-valued components and A, B, C, and D are matrices. Such matrix representations of input-output relationships have been effectively employed by Kalman and Bertram,[8] and Friedland[12] in the analysis and synthesis of sampled-data and modular systems.

In the case of stochastic (probabilistic, nondeterministic) systems, f and g in (14.3) and (14.4) are random functions, and the input-output relationship is defined by the conditional probability functions $p(s_{t+1}|s_t, x_t)$ and $p(y_t|s_t, x_t)$. Incidentally, in terms of these conditional probability functions, the state variable s_t may be conveniently defined by the relations

$$p(s_{t+1}|s_t, x_t) = p(s_{t+1}|s_t, s_{t-1}, s_{t-2}, \ldots , x_t, x_{t-1}, x_{t-2}, \ldots) \tag{14.7}$$
$$p(y_t|s_t, x_t) = p(y_t|s_t, s_{t-1}, s_{t-2}, \ldots , x_t, x_{t-1}, x_{t-2}, \ldots) \tag{14.8}$$

which mean that s_t is a state variable if and only if the conditional probability of s_{t+1} given s_t and x_t is the same as the conditional probability of s_{t+1} given all the previous s_t's and x_t's, and likewise for y_t.

The input-output relationships (14.3) and (14.4) are usually represented in a tabular form or, equivalently, in the form of a state diagram, of which an example is shown in Fig. (14.1). Here s_t ranges over four states ①, ②, ③, ④; x_t ranges over 0, 1; and y_t ranges over the symbols A, B. A transition from, say, ③ to ② is labeled $0/A$, which means that if $s_t =$ ③ and $x_t = 0$, then $s_{t+1} =$ ② and $y_t = A$. Thus, if the system is initially (at $t = 0$) in state ④ and the sequence $x = 01101$ is applied, the corresponding output sequence will be $y = BBABB$, and the trajectory will be ④ ① ④ ④ ① ④, in which the first term represents the initial state.

Essentially, the mode of characterization of discrete-time systems expressed by Eqs. (14.3) and (14.4) is all we need to formulate and solve some of the basic problems of optimal control in the case of sequential

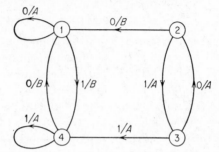

Fig. 14.1   State diagram of a sequential system.

and sampled-data systems.   In the following section, these problems and their variants are stated in general terms, while their methods of solution are discussed in Secs. 14.4 and 14.5.

14.3   Optimal Control Problems for Sequential Systems

A common characteristic of all the problems stated in the sequel is that the entity to be determined is an optimal input sequence rather than an optimal system   Thus, in all these problems one is given a system in a specified initial state, a criterion function (or a cost function) which serves as a measure of performance, and one or more constraints on input sequences.   The object, then, is to find an allowable input sequence which maximizes the criterion function (or minimizes the cost function).

PROBLEM 1.   A sequential system has n states ①, ②, . . . , ⓝ.   The input x_t ranges over p symbols $l_1, l_2, . . . , l_p.$ *Given:* (a) The function f

$$s_{t+1} = f(s_t, x_t) \qquad (14.9)$$

in a tabular or state-diagram form.   (b) An initial state $s_0 = i$.   (c) The duration of input sequence N (N being a positive integer).   (d) A criterion function $\varphi(s_N)$ defined on the states at time $t = N$.   *Find:* An input sequence $x = x_0 \, x_1 \, x_2 \, \cdots \, x_{N-1}$ which maximizes $\varphi(s_N)$.

This type of problem arises in connection with terminal control processes in which the performance of a system is measurable in terms of its state at some prescribed time $t = N$ and is independent of previous states as well as previous inputs and outputs.   For example, s_t might represent the position and velocity of a guided object at time t, x_t be the force applied to the object, and $\varphi(s_N)$ be a measure of closeness of the object at time N to a specified point in space.

There are several variants of Problem 1 which can be solved by essentially the same techniques as Problem 1. Of these, the following two variants will be considered in Sec. 14.4.

PROBLEM 1a. The given sequential system is a stochastic system (i.e., f is a random function) characterized by the conditional probability function $p(s_{t+1}|s_t,x_t)$. The object is to find an input sequence $x = x_0 x_1 \cdots x_{N-1}$ which maximizes the expected value of $\varphi(s_N)$, $E\{\varphi(s_N)\}$, rather than $\varphi(s_N)$ itself (as in Problem 1).

PROBLEM 1b. In this case, the time N is determined by a subsidiary condition rather than being given in advance. More specifically, let a subset, say $\Gamma = \{①, ②, \ldots, ⓥ\}$, of the set of states $①, ②, \ldots, ⓝ$ be designated as the class of "admissible" states, with its complement $\Gamma' = \{ \nu+1, \ldots, ⓝ\}$ constituting the class of inadmissible states. Let the criterion function $\varphi(s_N)$ be defined on the class of admissible states, and N be the t at which s_t becomes an admissible state (i.e., a member of Γ) for *the first time* (or, more generally, kth time). The object, as in Problem 1, is to maximize $\varphi(s_N)$. However, N is determined by the condition $s_N \epsilon \Gamma$ and $s_t \epsilon \Gamma'$ for $t < N$, and is not known in advance. This problem is a slightly generalized version of a problem formulated by Bellman, in which the object is to minimize the velocity of a rocket at the first time it reaches a specified point in space. Problems of this type are referred to by Bellman as implicit variational problems.

PROBLEM 1c. In this variant, the performance is measured by a cost function $\varphi(x_0, x_1, \ldots, x_{N-1}, s_N)$ which involves not only s_N but also the input sequence $x_0, x_1 \cdots x_{N-1}$. The object is to find an input sequence which minimizes $\varphi(x_0, x_1, \ldots, x_{N-1}, s_N)$.

In all of the foregoing problems, the choice of input sequences is assumed to be unrestricted. In most practical situations, however, there are some constraints on x. Three representative problems of this type are the following:

PROBLEM 2. The statement of this problem is identical with that of Problem 1, except that the input sequences are assumed to be constrained by an inequality of the form

$$g(x_0, x_1, \ldots, x_{N-1}) \leqslant L \qquad (14.10)$$

where g is a specified real-valued function and L is a given constant. The object is to find an allowable input sequence $x_0 x_1 \cdots x_{N-1}$ [i.e., an x satisfying (14.10)] which maximizes $\varphi(s_N)$.

PROBLEM 3.   *Given:* (a), (b), (c) as in Problem 1; (d) A specified state at time N, say $s_N = \text{Ⓙ}$; (e) a cost function $\varphi(x_0, x_1, \ldots, x_{N-1})$.   Find an input sequence $x = x_0 x_1 \cdots x_{N-1}$ which would take the system from the state $s_0 = \text{Ⓘ}$ to the state $s_N = \text{Ⓙ}$ at minimum cost.   In other words, the object is to find an x which minimizes $\varphi(x_0, x_1, \ldots, x_{N-1})$ subject to the constraint $s_N = \text{Ⓙ}$.

PROBLEM 4.   *Given:* (a), (b) as in Problem 1; (c) a specified state Ⓙ; (d) a constraint on input sequences of the form

$$g(x_0, x_1, \ldots, x_{N-1}) \leqslant L \tag{14.11}$$

where g is a real-valued function and L is a specified constant.   Find an allowable sequence $x_0 x_1 \cdots x_{N-1}$ of minimum length which would take the system from $s_0 = \text{Ⓘ}$ to $s_t = \text{Ⓙ}$.   To put it differently, the object is to find an input sequence which minimizes, subject to Eq. (14.11), the time needed to take the system from state Ⓘ to state Ⓙ.

The last problem is one of the basic problems of optimal control.   In the case of ON-OFF systems, various special cases of it have been studied by Hopkin,[4] Feldbaum,[5,6] Lerner,[7] Bass,[13] Bellman,[1] Bushaw,[14] Rose,[15] and others, while the sampled-data case has been investigated by Kalman and Bertram,[8] and Krasovskii.[17]   A very general method employing the so-called "maximum" principle has recently been described in a series of papers by Pontryagin[3,18] and his students, Boltyanskii,[19] and Gamkrelidze.[20]

14.4   Solution of Optimal Control Problems

The problems formulated in the preceding section are not, in general, amenable to purely analytical treatment.   Thus, one must be content with "solutions" which amount essentially to reductions of the original problem to one which can be handled, at least in principle, by a machine computer.   Such is the nature of solutions discussed in the sequel.

In the case of Problems 1 to 3, the method described in the sequel suggests itself in a natural way.   In effect, it is merely a somewhat disguised form of dynamic programming.   For Problem 4, we shall employ a method developed by Krasovskii, which in turn makes use of some earlier results of Krein.

We begin with Problem 1 and its variants.   For convenience (at the cost of some redundancy) the statement of each problem—in some cases with slight modifications—will be repeated in this section.

PROBLEM 1.   A sequential system has n states $q_1, q_2, \ldots, q_n$.   The input x ranges over two symbols, 0 and 1.   (This is an inessential simplifying assumption.)   *Given:* (a) the function f

$$s_{t+1} = f(s_t, x_t)$$

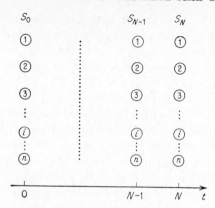

Fig. 14.2 State-time diagram.

(b) an initial state $s_0 = q_i$; (c) the duration N of input sequence $x = x_0 \; x_1 \cdot \cdot \cdot x_{N-1}$; ($d$) a criterion function $\varphi(s_N)$. *Find:* An input sequence $x_0 \; x_1 \ldots x_{N-1}$ which minimizes $\varphi(s_N)$.

METHOD OF SOLUTION. For convenience in visualization, the states ①, ②, . . . , ⓝ are arranged in columns (Fig. 14.2), each column corresponding to a particular instant of time. Starting with the last column (corresponding to s_N, the terminal state of the process), associate with each state ⓘ (or q_i) the value assumed by $\varphi(s_N)$ for $s_N = q_i$ (Fig. 14.3). As a specific illustration, consider the simple system shown in Fig. 14.1 and assume that $N = 2$, $\varphi(q_1) = -1$, $\varphi(q_2) = 3$, $\varphi(q_3) = -2$, and $\varphi(q_4) = 2$, as shown in Fig. 14.4. Returning to Fig. 14.3, consider the

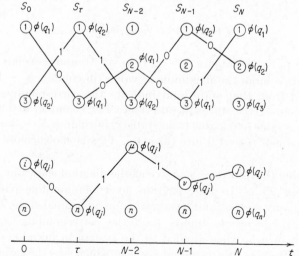

Fig. 14.3 φ-Value diagram.

set of states at $t = N - 1$ and associate with each state in column $N - 1$ the maximum value of $\varphi(s_N)$ that can be attained from that state by a transition from $N - 1$ to N. For example, referring to the state diagram of Fig. 14.1, we see that state ① in column $N - 1$ is taken by input 0 to ① at N, and by input 1 to ④ at N. The corresponding values of $\varphi(s_N)$ are -1 and 2. Thus, with ① at $N - 1$ we associate the φ value 2, and join ① to ④ with a line labeled 1, meaning that if the system is in state ① at time $N - 1$, then by application of input 1 we can take it into state ④ at $t = N$ and thereby obtain the value 2 for the criterion function $\varphi(s_N)$. The same process yields the φ values -1, 3, and 2 for the states ②, ③, ④ at $N - 1$, with the corresponding inputs indicated in Fig. 14.4. In short, the φ-value associated with a state is the maximum value of the criterion function which can be attained from that state.

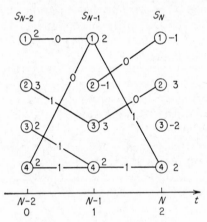

Fig. 14.4 φ-Value diagram.

Next we move to column $N - 2$ (Fig. 14.3), and associate with each state in this column the maximum φ value (in column $N - 1$) that can be attained from that state, and indicate the corresponding transition by a line joining the states in question. For example, in Fig. 14.3 the maximum φ value attainable from state ② in column $N - 2$ is $\varphi(q_0)$, and the input which takes ② into ③ is 0. This is shown more concretely in Fig. 14.4.

Continuing this process, we arrive at the diagram shown in a simplified form in Fig. 14.3. In this diagram, every broken-line path from an initial state, say $s_0 = q_i$, and terminating on a terminal state, say $s_N = q_j$, identifies a sequence of inputs (and the corresponding trajectory in state space) which, when applied to the system in initial state q_i, takes the system from q_i to a terminal state q_j which has the largest φ value among the states which can be reached at $t = N$ from $s_0 = q_i$. This

φ value is the value of the criterion function associated with each state in the chain.   Thus, given any initial state $s_0 = q_i$, one can obtain by inspection the optimal sequence of inputs $x_0 \, x_1 \, \cdots \, x_{N-1}$, the corresponding trajectory $s_0 \, s_1 \, \cdots \, s_N$, and the maximal value of $\varphi(s_N)$.   For example, in Fig. 14.4, if the initial state is ③, then the maximum attainable value of $\varphi(s_N)$ is 2, and the input sequence which attains it is $x = 11$.

In principle, the procedure outlined above is quite simple and straightforward.   In practice, it may be unworkable if the number of states and/or N are large.   Unfortunately, for such cases there are no alternative methods of solution which are exact.

The straightforward approach used for the solution of Problem 1 can readily be extended to stochastic systems.   For such systems, the statement of Problem 1a reads:

PROBLEM 1a.   A stochastic sequential system is characterized by the probability function $p(s_{t+1}|s_t,x_t)$.   Given an initial state $s_o = $ ⓘ and a criterion function $\varphi(s_N)$.   Find an input sequence $x = x_0 \, x_1 \, \cdots \, x_{N-1}$ which maximizes the expected value of $\varphi(s_N)$.

It should be noted that, as it stands, the statement of the problem does not make it clear whether the desired input sequence is to be determined

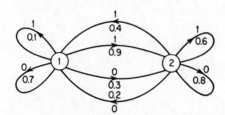

Fig. 14.5   State diagram of a stochastic system.

as a function of the initial state (as in Problem 1) or as a function of successively observed states, i.e., in the form $x_t = v_t(s_t)$, $t = 0, 1, 2, \ldots,$ $N - 1$, where v_t is a function defining the dependence of tth input, x_t, on the observed state at time t.   The procedure outlined below is applicable in the latter case only.

METHOD OF SOLUTION.   As in Problem 1, we associate with each state ⓘ $(i = 1, 2, \ldots, n)$ in column N the values $\varphi(g_i)$ and call these the φ values for column N.   Next we consider each state in column $N - 1$ and by the use of $p(s_{t+1}|s_t,x_t)$ compute the expected value of $\varphi(s_N)$ for each state and every possible input; in other words, we compute the conditional expectations $E[\varphi(s_N)|s_{N-1}, x_{N-1}]$ for all values of s_{N-1} and x_{N-1}.

To illustrate this step, consider the simple two-state system shown in Fig. 14.5. Here a transition from, say, ① to ② with the label $\xrightarrow[0.9]{1}$ means that the conditional probability of transition from ① to ② when input 1 is applied is equal to 0.9. The outputs are not indicated since they do not enter into the problem.

The φ value associated with $s_N =$ ① is 3 and that associated with $s_N =$ ② is -1. The conditional expectations in question are easily computed to be

$$E[\varphi(s_N)|s_{N-1} = ①, x_{N-1} = 0] = 1.8$$

$$E[\varphi(s_N)|s_{N-1} = 1, x_{N-1} = 1] = -0.6$$

$$E[\varphi(s_N)|s_{N-1} = ②, x_{N-1} = 0] = -0.2$$

$$E[\varphi(s_N)|s_{N-1} = ②, x_{N-1} = 1] = -0.6$$

Now for each state ⓘ in column $N - 1$ we fiind the input which maximizes the conditional expectation and associates with ⓘ the maximum value of the conditional expectation. For example, for state ① in Fig. 14.5 the input $x_{N-1} = 0$ yields the maximum value 1.8 for the conditional expectation. Similarly, for state ② $x_{N-1} = 1$ yields the maximum value 1.8 for the conditional expectation. Similarly, for state ② $x_{N-1} = 1$ yields the maximum value 0.6. Thus, the φ values associated with the states ① and ② in column $N - 1$ are 1.8 and 0.6, respectively (see Fig. 14.6).

Next, the states in column $N - 2$ are treated in exactly the same way, using the φ values computed previously for the states in column $N - 1$

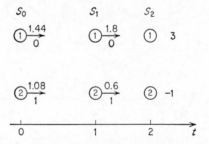

Fig. 14.6 φ-Value diagram for a stochastic system.

to compute the φ values for the states in column $N - 2$. The process is repeated until the φ values of the states in column $N = 0$ are obtained. For $N = 2$ and the system shown in Fig. 14.5, the results are indicated in Fig. 14.6. Their meaning is this: If the initial state is, say, $s_0 =$ ①, apply the input 0. With this initial state and choice of input, the conditional expectation of $\varphi(s_N)$ is 1.44. Now if on applying $x_0 = 0$ the next state (s_1) turns out to be, say, ②, apply $x_1 = 1$. With this choice of input, the conditional expectation of $\varphi(s_N)$ is 0.6. On the other hand, if $s_1 =$ ①, then $x_1 = 0$ and the conditional expectation is 1.8. In this way, the optimal input sequence is defined by a relation of the form

$x_t = v_t(s_t)(t = 0, \; 1)$, where the function v_t is given by $v_0(q_1) = 0,$ $v_0(q_2) = 1, v_1(q_1) = 0, v_1(q_2) = 1.$

PROBLEM 1b. For concreteness, it will be convenient to reformulate this problem in terms of a particular system such as shown in Fig. 14.7. Here the outputs are omitted since they are irrelevant. The class of admissible states Γ comprises ① and ③. The remaining states are inadmissible. The φ values for admissible states are assumed to be $\varphi(q_1) = -1$ and $\varphi(q_3) = 6.$

The problem is as follows. *Given:* An initial state, say $s_0 =$ ④. *Find:* An input sequence which would maximize $\varphi(s_K)$, where K is the first time at which the state of the system becomes one of admissible states, i.e., either ① or ③. Note that K is not known a priori.

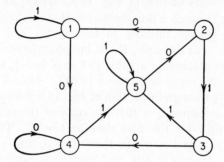

. **Fig. 14.7** State diagram of a system.

METHOD OF SOLUTION. To solve this problem, it is sufficient to modify in minor ways the solution of Problem 1. Specifically, the inadmissible states at $t = K$ are crosshatched (Fig. 14.8), while the

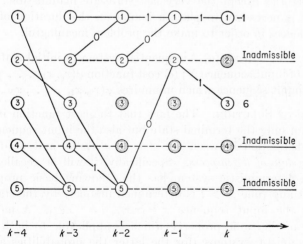

Fig. 14.8 Transition diagram for a process with inadmissible states.

admissible states are associated with their φ values. Proceeding to column $K - 1$, each state (i) in this column is associated with a φ value which is the largest φ value among the φ values of the admissible states in column K which can be reached from (i). If no admissible state in column K can be reached from the state in question, then it is cross-hatched. For example, the φ value of (1) in column $K - 1$ is -1, since the only admissible state in column K which can be reached from (1) in column $K - 1$ is (1), whose φ value is -1. Similarly, the φ value of (2) in column $K - 1$ is 6 and the corresponding input is 1. States (3), (4), and (5) are crosshatched since no admissible states in column K can be reached from them.

This procedure is repeated for the states in columns $K - 2$, $K - 3$, . . . , with the results shown in Fig. 14.8. Here, as in Problem 1, a trajectory passing through a noncrosshatched state defines the successive inputs (with the system initially in that state) which maximize the φ value at $t = K$. For example, if the initial state at $t = K - 3$ is (2), then the maximum attainable φ value at $t = K$ is -1, and it is attained by application of the input sequence $x = 011$. Now if the initial state at $t = K - 3$ is (4), then an inspection of Fig. 14.8 shows that on application of the input sequence $x = 101$, the state of the system becomes an admissible state ((3)) for the first time at $t = K$. Thus, if $K - 3$ is identified with $t = 0$ and $s_0 = $ (4), then $K = 3$, and a solution to the problem is the sequence $x = 101$, yielding the φ value 6. It should be noted, however, that in general there might be still other trajectories passing through (4) in columns to the left of $K - 3$, which possibly (though not in the particular problem under discussion) may be associated with larger φ values and have the property that all the states in such trajectories except the very last state are inadmissible. Thus, in general, it is necessary to place a bound on the duration of allowable input sequences in order to make the problem meaningful.

PROBLEM 1c. *Given:* (a) A sequential system in initial state $s_0 = $ (i); (b) length of input sequence N; (c) cost function $\varphi(x_0, x_1, \ldots, x_{N-1}, s_N)$. *Find:* An input sequence which minimizes $\varphi(x_0, x_1, \ldots, x_{N-1}, s_N)$.

METHOD OF SOLUTION. The fact that the cost function in this case involves not only the terminal state but also the input sequence raises a need for distinction between the *state of a system* and what might be called the *state of the process*. Specifically, it will be recalled that the state of a deterministic system has the following basic property: The state s_N at any time $N > t$ is determined uniquely by the state at time t, s_t, and the input sequence $x = x_t x_{t+1} \cdots x_{N-1}$. A more general statement of the same property which is applicable to both stochastic and deterministic systems (for the latter the probabilities are 0 or 1) is expressible in terms of conditional probabilities thus:

$$p(s_N|s_t, x_t, x_{t+1}, \ldots, x_{N-1}) = p(s_N|s_t, s_{t-1}, s_{t-2}, \ldots, x_0, x_1, \ldots,$$
$$x_t, \ldots, x_{N-1}) \qquad t = 0, 1, \ldots, N-1 \quad (14.12)$$

which means that if s_t and the input sequence $x_t x_{t+1} \cdot \cdot \cdot x_{N-1}$ are given, the conditional probability of s_t is not changed by giving also the states and inputs previous to s_t and x_t.

Now in the case of optimal control problems in which the criterion function involves only the terminal state, i.e., is of the form $\varphi(s_N)$, (14.12) implies

$$p(\varphi(s_N)|s_t, x_t, x_{t+1}, \ldots, x_{N-1}) = p(\varphi(s_N)|s_t, s_{t-1}, \ldots, s_0, x_0,$$
$$x_1, \ldots, x_t, \ldots, x_{N-1}) \qquad t = 0, 1, \ldots, N-1 \quad (14.13)$$

which in the case of a deterministic system means that $\varphi(s_N)$ is uniquely determined by s_t and the input sequence $x_t x_{t+1} \cdot \cdot \cdot x_{N-1}$, that is, $\varphi(s_N)$ can be expressed as a function $\varphi = \varphi(s_t, x_t, x_{t+1}, \ldots, x_{N-1})$. It is essentially this property of the criterion function which validates the methods of solution of Problems 1, 1a, and 1b described previously.

Clearly, (14.13) does not hold when the criterion function is not of the simple form $\varphi(s_N)$. However, it is possible to define what might be called a *process state variable* π_t in terms of which a relation similar to (14.13) can be written. Specifically, we shall say that π_t is a *process state variable* (as distinguished from a *system state variable* s_t) if for the given system and criterion function we can write

$$p(\varphi|\pi_t, x_t, \ldots, x_{N-1}) = p(\varphi|\pi_t, \pi_{t-1}, \ldots, \pi_0, x_0, x_1, \ldots, x_t, \ldots,$$
$$x_{N-1}), t = 0, 1, \ldots, N-1 \quad (14.14)$$

which in the case of a deterministic system means that φ is uniquely determined by π_t and the input sequence $x_t x_{t+1} \cdot \cdot \cdot x_{N-1}$. The usefulness of π_t is due to the fact that its employment makes possible the extension of methods of solution of Problems 1, 1a, and 1b to a broader class of problems of which Problems 1c and 2 are typical examples.

To illustrate, consider the φ function $\varphi(x_0, x_1, \ldots, x_{N-1}, s_N)$. Clearly, π_t can be identified with the $(t+1)$tuple

$$\pi_t = (s_t, x_0, x_1, \ldots, x_{t-1}) \qquad (14.15)$$

since with this definition of π_t we can write (for a deterministic system)

$$\varphi = \varphi(\pi_t, x_t, x_{t+1}, \ldots, x_{N-1}) \qquad (14.16)$$

Unfortunately, π_t thus defined ranges in general over such a large set that it is impracticable to apply the method of Problem 1 to Problem 1c except in cases where the dependence of the cost function on the x_t is of a simple form. For example, if φ is of the form

$$\varphi = \varphi(x_0 + x_1 + \cdot \cdot \cdot + x_{N-1}, s_N) \qquad (14.17)$$

then π_t can be defined as the two-tuple

$$\pi_t = (s_t,\ x_0 + x_1 + \cdots + x_{t-1}) \tag{14.18}$$

which is much simpler than the $(t + 1)$tuple appearing in (14.15). As a more concrete illustration, consider the system shown in Fig. 14.1 and assume that

$$
\begin{aligned}
\varphi(x_0 + x_1 + \cdots + x_{t-1}, q_1) &= -1 &&\text{if } x_0 + x_1 + \cdots + x_{t-1} \text{ is even}\\
&= 1 &&\text{if } x_0 + x_1 + \cdots + x_{t-1} \text{ is odd}
\end{aligned}
\tag{14.19}
$$

$$
\begin{aligned}
\varphi(x_0 + x_1 + \cdots + x_{t-1}, q_2) &= 3 &&\text{if } x_0 + x_1 + \cdots + x_{t-1} \text{ is even}\\
&= -3 &&\text{if } x_0 + x_1 + \cdots + x_{t-1} \text{ is odd}
\end{aligned}
\tag{14.20}
$$

$$
\begin{aligned}
\varphi(x_0 + x_1 + \cdots + x_{t-1}, q_3) &= -2 &&\text{if } x_0 + x_1 + \cdots + x_{t-1} \text{ is even}\\
&= 2 &&\text{if } x_0 + x_1 + \cdots + x_{t-1} \text{ is odd}
\end{aligned}
\tag{14.21}
$$

$$
\begin{aligned}
\varphi(x_0 + x_1 + \cdots + x_{t-1}, q_4) &= 2 &&\text{if } x_0 + x_1 + \cdots + x_{t-1} \text{ is even}\\
&= -2 &&\text{if } x_0 + x_1 + \cdots + x_{t-1} \text{ is odd}
\end{aligned}
\tag{14.22}
$$

and that the problem is to find an input sequence of length N which would maximize φ, with the system initially in, say, state ③.

The process states, then, are two-tuples of the form $\pi_t = (s_t, \sigma_t)$, where σ_t is a binary variable ranging over, say, 0 and 1, meaning that $x_0 + x_1 + \cdots + x_{t-1}$ is even if $\sigma_t = 0$ and $x_0 + x_1 + \cdots + x_{t-1}$ is odd if $\sigma_t = 1$. Analogous to the diagram of Fig. 14.3, we have the diagram shown in Fig. 14.9, in which π_t's play the same role as s_t's in Fig. 14.3, and each process state is associated with a φ value in exactly the same way as in Problem 1. For example, in Nth column the two-tuple consisting of $s_N = $ ③ and $\sigma_N = 0$ is denoted by (③,0) and the corresponding φ value is found from (14.19) to be -2.

Proceeding as in Problem 1, we associate each process state in column $N - 1$ with a φ value which is the largest φ value in column N attainable from that state. Thus, the state (①,0) in column $N - 1$ is taken by the inputs $x_{N-1} = 0$ and $x_{N-1} = 1$ respectively into (①,0) and (④,1) in column N. The corresponding φ values in column N are -1 for (①,0) and -2 for (①,1). Hence the maximizing input is 0 and the φ value associated with (①,0) is -1.

Again, proceeding as in Problem 1, we find the φ values associated with the process states in columns $N - 2$, $N - 3$, $\ldots$, 0. The lines joining the states define the optimal trajectories and the inputs yielding them, each trajectory being associated with a φ value which is the largest φ value at time N attainable from any state in the trajectory. For

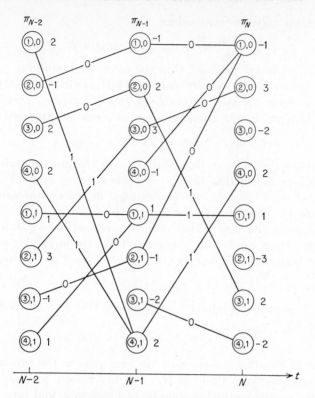

Fig. 14.9   Transition diagram for process states.

example, referring to Fig. 14.9 we see that if $N = 2$ and the initial state is ③, then the maximizing input sequence is $x = 01$ and the corresponding φ value is 2.

The method of solution outlined above is applicable to a broad class of problems of which Problem 2, restated below, is another typical example.

PROBLEM 2.   *Given:* (a) A sequential system in initial state $s_0 = ⓘ$; (b) length of input sequence N; (c) criterion function $\varphi(s_N)$; (d) an inequality of the form

$$g(x_0, x_1, \ldots, x_{N-1}) \leqslant L \tag{14.23}$$

which defines the class of allowable input sequences. *Find:* An input sequence $x = x_0 x_1 \cdots x_{N-1}$ which maximizes $\varphi\ (S_N)$ subject to the constraint (14.23).

METHOD OF SOLUTION.   We proceed as in Problem 1c. Specifically, consider the $(t + 1)$tuple $\pi_t = (s_t, x_0, x_1, \ldots, x_{t-1})$. In terms of π_t, the constraint may be expressed as

$$g(\pi_t, x_t, x_{t+1}, \ldots, x_{N-1}) \leqslant L \tag{14.24}$$

Thus, if π_t is known at time t, then the succeeding inputs x_t, x_{t+1}, $\ldots$, x_{N-1} are known to be constrained by (14.24). Given (14.24), one can find the φ value for any allowable sequence $x_t x_{t+1} \ldots x_{N-1}$ starting at t. Consequently, the criterion function φ can be expressed as

$$\varphi(s_N) = \varphi(\pi_t, x_t, x_{t+1}, \ldots, x_{N-1}) \tag{14.25}$$

which implies that π_t may be identified with the process state variable.

Having established that the $(t + 1)$tuple $\pi_t = (s_t, x_0, x_1, \ldots, x_{N-1})$ is a process state variable, one can proceed in exactly the same way as in Problem 1c. The difficulties, too, are of a similar nature. Here, as there, the main difficulty is that in most practical cases π_t ranges over a set having a large number of elements. Thus, the method is unworkable except for relatively simple types of g functions, e.g., of the form

$$g(x_0, x_1, \ldots, x_{N-1}) = h(x_0) + h(x_1) + \cdots + h(x_{N-1}) \tag{14.26}$$

where h is some real-valued function. In this case, π_t reduces to a two-tuple

$$\pi_t = [s_t, h(x_0) + \cdots + h(x_{t-1})] \tag{14.27}$$

which can be handled in essentially the same way as the two-tuple of the illustrative example in Problem 1c. For this reason, we shall not dwell any further on the method of solution of Problem 2, and turn our attention to Problems 3 and 4.

Although Problems 3 and 4 were stated earlier as separate problems, the method of solution of Problem 4 described in the sequel reduces Problem 4 to Problem 3. Thus, it will be convenient to start with a statement of Problem 4.

PROBLEM 4. *Given:* (a) A discrete-time, not necessarily sequential, system in a specified initial state $s_0 = \alpha$; (b) a prescribed terminal state $s_N = \beta$, with N not specified in advance; (c) a constraint on input sequences:

$$g(x_0, x_1, \ldots, x_{N-1}) \leqslant L \tag{14.28}$$

where g is a real-valued function and L is a given constant. *Find:* Among all allowable sequences a sequence which takes the system from $s_0 = \alpha$ to $s_N = \beta$ in the shortest possible time. In other words, the problem is to minimize N subject to the constraint that the system be in a prescribed state β at $t = N$.

Since constraints having the form of inequalities are, in general, more difficult to deal with than those having the form of equalities, it would be advantageous to reduce the given problem to one in which the constraints are of the latter form.   The way in which this can be done for systems of very general type has been shown by Krasovskii.[16,17]   Basically, the idea is a simple one.   Consider the class Ω of all sequences of length T which take the system form $s_0 = \alpha$ to $s_T = \beta$, and let a generic sequence in Ω be denoted by ω_T.   Now let $Q(T)$ be the minimum value of $g(x_0, x_1, \ldots , x_{T-1})$ over this class, i.e.,

$$Q(T) = \min_{x\epsilon\Omega} g(x_1, x_2, \ldots , x_{T-1}) \qquad (14.29)$$

Clearly, in order to satisfy the constraint

$$g(x_0, x_1, \ldots , x_{T-1}) \leqslant L \qquad (14.30)$$

it is necessary and sufficient that $Q(T) \leqslant L$.   Now let N be the smallest value of T satisfying the inequality $Q(T) \leqslant L$, and let ω_N be an input sequence of length N for which this inequality is satisfied.   Then ω_N is a solution to the problem, i.e., ω_N is an input sequence which takes the system from $s_0 = \alpha$ to $s_N = \beta$ in the shortest possible time N.   In general ω_N is not unique.

To sum up, the problem of minimizing T subject to the constraint (14.30) has been reduced to (1) minimizing $g(x_0, x_1, \ldots , x_{T-1})$ subject to the constraint $s_T = \beta$, and (2) finding the smallest value of T satisfying $Q(T) \leqslant L$.   The reduced problem (1) is, in effect, Problem 3.   Thus, by using the method sketched above, Problem 4 can be reduced essentially to Problem 3.

Krasovskii's method can be applied to a wide variety of systems, although the results are frequently too complex to be of practical interest. In particular, it was shown by Krasovskii that in the case of a linear sampled-data system the problem of optimal control reduces to the so-called L problem which was formulated and solved by Krein in 1938.* In what follows, we shall discuss some of Krasovskii's results together with the main theorems of Krein's work.

14.5   Method of Solution for Linear Sampled-data Systems

Consider a linear sampled-data system in which [(see 14.5)]

$$\mathbf{s}_{t+1} = A\mathbf{s}_t + Bx_t, \qquad (14.31)$$

where $\mathbf{s}_t$ is a state vector having, say, r components,

$$\mathbf{s}_t = (s_t^{\,1}, s_t^{\,2}, \ldots , s_t^{\,r})$$

A is an $r \times r$ matrix, B is an $r \times 1$ matrix, and x_t is a scalar representing the amplitude of the input at time t.   The constraint imposed on the

---

* The author is indebted to Professor Ya. Tsypkin for loaning him a copy of the book by N. Akhiezer and M. Krein, "Some Questions in the Theory of Moments," GONTI, Kharkov, 1938, in which Krein's results are presented.

input sequences is assumed to be of the form

$$|x_t| \leqslant L \qquad \text{for } t \geqslant 0 \tag{14.32}$$

where L is a specified constant. If $g(x_0, x_1, \ldots, x_{T-1})$ is defined as

$$g(x_0, x_1, \ldots, x_{T-1}) = \max_{0 \leqslant t \leqslant T-1} |x_t| \tag{14.33}$$

this constraint may be put into the standard form (14.28)

$$g(x_0, x_1, \ldots, x_{T-1}) \leqslant L \tag{14.34}$$

Now let α and β denote, respectively, the specified initial and final state vectors, and let Ω be the class of all input sequences which take the system [disregarding the constraint (14.33)] from the state $s_0 = \alpha$ to the state $s_T = \beta$ at some fixed time T. Following the method outlined previously, our object is to find the minimum of $g(x_0, x_1, \ldots, x_{T-1})$ over Ω. Since $g(x_0, x_1, \ldots, x_{T-1})$ is given by (14.33), this means that we have to determine

$$Q(T) = \min_x \max_{0 \leqslant t \leqslant T-1} |x_t| \tag{14.35}$$

subject to the side condition $s_T = \beta$. To put this side condition into a more explicit form, let the vector $\mathbf{h}_t$ denote the *state impulsive response* of the system, i.e., the solution of the set of equations

$$s_{t+1} = As_t + B\delta_t \qquad t = 0, 1, 2, \ldots \tag{14.36}$$

($\delta_t = 1$ for $t = 0$, $\delta_t = 0$ for all other values of t) for $s_0 = 0$. It can readily be shown that the z transform of $\mathbf{h}_t$ is given by the vector

$$\mathbf{H}(z) = (zI - A)^{-1}B \tag{14.37}$$

where I is the identity matrix and $(zI - A)^{-1}$ is the inverse of $(zI - A)$. In terms of $\mathbf{h}_t$, the state vector at $t = T$ is given by

$$s_T = A\alpha + \sum_{t=1}^{T} \mathbf{h}_t x_{T-t} \tag{14.38}$$

where α is the initial state vector. Consequently, in order that the state at time T be β, it is necessary and sufficient that the input sequence satisfy the condition:

$$\sum_{t=1}^{T} \mathbf{h}_t x_{T-t} = \beta - A\alpha \tag{14.39}$$

At this point, then, we are faced with the following variational problem. Find

$$Q(T) = \min_x \max_{0 \leqslant t \leqslant T-1} |x_t| \tag{14.40}$$

subject to the side condition

$$\sum_{t=1}^{T} \mathbf{h}_t x_{T-t} = \beta - A\alpha \tag{14.41}$$

where $\mathbf{h}_t$ is the state impulsive response [given by the inverse z transform of (14.37)], A is the matrix appearing in (14.36), α is the initial state vector, and β is the terminal state vector.

As was recognized by Krasovskii, this variational problem is a special case of the so-called L problem studied by Krein.[21] In order to understand how the problem in hand can be solved, it will be necessary for us to make a digression and sketch some of the pertinent results of Krein's work.

14.6   Digression

Consider an m-dimensional vector space E in which the norm of a vector $u = (u^1, u^2, \ldots, u^m)$ is defined by

$$\|u\| = \sum_{1}^{m} |u^j| \tag{14.42}$$

A linear functional f, defined on E, may be expressed as

$$f(u) = \sum_{1}^{m} f^j u^j \tag{14.43}$$

where the f^j denote the components of f. The norm of f is given by

$$\|f\| = \max_{x} \frac{|f(u)|}{\|u\|} = \max_{j} |f^j| \tag{14.44}$$

Let $u_1, u_2, \ldots, u_n$ be n linearly independent vectors in E, let $c_1, c_2, \ldots, c_n$ be n constants, not all zero, and let L be a positive constant. Form a linear combination of the u_i with the ξ_i as coefficients

$$u = \xi_1 u_1 + \xi_2 u_2 + \cdots + \xi_n u_n \tag{14.45}$$

and define $\lambda = \lambda(c_1, c_2, \ldots, c_n)$ by the following relation:

$$\frac{1}{\lambda(c_1, c_2, \ldots, c_n)} = \min_{u} \|\xi_1 u_1 + \xi_2 u_2 + \cdots + \xi_n u_n\| \tag{14.46}$$

with the ξ_i subject to the constraint $\sum_{1}^{n} c_i \xi_i = 1$. (By min in (14.46) is meant $\min_{\xi_i}$, since varying u varies the ξ_i and vice versa. In the sequel, $\min_{u}$ and $\min_{\xi_i}$ are used interchangeably.) Equivalently,

$$\lambda(c_1, c_2, \ldots, c_n) = \max_{\xi_i} \frac{\displaystyle\sum_{1}^{n} c_i \xi_i}{\| \xi_1 u_1 + \xi_2 u_2 + \cdots + \xi_n u_n \|} \quad (14.47)$$

and
$$\lambda(c_1, c_2, \ldots, c_n) = \max_{\xi_i} \sum_{1}^{n} c_i \xi_i \quad (14.48)$$

subject to the constraint $\| \xi_1 u_1 + \xi_2 u_2 + \cdots + \xi_n u_n \| = 1$.

A basic result which is of direct relevance to the problem of optimal control is the following:

Theorem. A necessary and sufficient condition for the existence of a functional f satisfying the conditions

$$\| f \| \leqslant L \qquad f(u_i) = c_i \qquad i = 1, 2, \ldots, n \quad (14.49)$$

is $L \geqslant \lambda(c_1, c_2, \ldots, c_n)$, where λ is defined by (14.46) [or (14.47), (14.48)].

We shall confine ourselves to giving a proof of the necessity of this condition. From $f(u_i) = c_i (i = 1, 2, \ldots, n)$ and the linearity of f it follows that

$$\left| \sum_{1}^{n} c_i \xi_i \right| = \left| \sum_{1}^{n} \xi_i f(u_i) \right| = \left| f \left(\sum_{1}^{n} \xi_i u_i \right) \right| \quad (14.50)$$

Now by the definition of $\| f \|$, we have

$$\frac{|f(u)|}{\|u\|} \leqslant \max_{u} \frac{|f(u)|}{\|u\|} = \| f \| \quad (14.51)$$

and therefore

$$\sum_{1}^{n} c_i \xi_i = \left| f \left(\sum_{1}^{n} \xi_i u_i \right) \right| \leqslant \| f \| \left\| \sum_{1}^{n} \xi_i u_i \right\| \quad (14.52)$$

Since $\| f \| \leqslant L$

$$\sum_{1}^{n} c_i \xi_i \leqslant L \left\| \sum_{1}^{n} \xi_i u_i \right\| \quad (14.53)$$

for all real values of the ξ_i. Consequently

$$L \geqslant \max_{\xi_i} \frac{\displaystyle\sum_{1}^{n} c_i \xi_i}{\left\| \displaystyle\sum_{1}^{n} \xi_i u_i \right\|} = \lambda(c_1, c_2, \ldots, c_n) \quad (14.54)$$

which establishes the necessity of the condition.

An immediate consequence of the theorem is the following. Assume that we wish to minimize $\| f \|$ over all f's satisfying the constraints $f(u_i) = c_i (i = 1, 2, \ldots, n)$. By the theorem, the minimum value of

$\|f\|$ is $\lambda(c_1, c_2, \ldots, c_n)$. Thus, we can assert that

$$\min_{f(u_i) = c_i(i = 1, 2, \ldots, n)} \|f\| = \frac{1}{\min_{\xi_i} \|\xi_1 u_1 + \cdots + \xi_n u_n\|} \quad (14.55)$$

$$\sum_1^n c_i \xi_i = 1$$

or more explicitly

$$\min_{f} \max_{i} |f^i| = \frac{1}{\min_{\xi_i} \sum_1^m |\xi_1 u_1^j + \cdots + \xi_n u_n^j|}$$

subject to $\sum_1^m f^j u_i^j = c_i \quad i = 1, \ldots, n$

$$\text{subject to } \sum_1^n c_i \xi_i = 1$$

$$(14.56)$$

This result establishes an equivalence between two variational problems, namely, that of finding $\min_{\xi_i} \sum_1^m |\xi_1 u_1^j + \cdots + \xi_n u_n^j|$ subject to the constraint $\sum_1^n c_i \xi_i = 1$, and that of finding $\min_{f} \max_{i} |f^i|$ subject to the constraints $\sum_1^m f^j u_i^j = c_i \ (i = 1, \ldots, n)$. It will be noted that the latter is of the same form as the problem of optimal control (14.40), (14.41).

There is still another relation between these two variational problems which is of relevance to the problem of optimal control. Specifically, let f_0 be an f which minimizes $\|f\|$ subject to the constraints

$$f(u_i) = c_i(i = 1, \ldots, n)$$

and let u_0 be a u, $u = \xi_1 u_1 + \cdots + \xi_n u_n$, which minimizes $\|u\|$, $\|u\| = \|\xi_1 u_1 + \cdots + \xi_n u_n\| = \sum_1^m |\xi_1 u_1^j + \cdots + \xi_n u_n^j|$, subject to the constraint $\sum_1^n c_i \xi_i = 1$. Then, we can assert that u_0 is an extremal vector for f_0, that is,

$$\|f_0\| = \frac{|f_0(u_0)|}{\|u_0\|} \quad (14.57)$$

To prove this, let $\xi_i^0(i = 1, \ldots, n)$ be the value of ξ_i for which $u = u_0$. Then

$$f_0(u_0) = f_0 \left(\sum_1^n \xi_i^0 u_i \right) = \sum_1^n \xi_i^0 f(u_i) = \sum_1^n \xi_i^0 c_i = 1 \quad (14.58)$$

by virtue of the constraint $\sum_1^n c_i \xi_i = 1$. Furthermore, since u_0 minimizes $\|u\|$, we have

$$\|u_0\| = \frac{1}{\lambda(c_1, c_2, \ldots, c_n)} \tag{14.59}$$

and since f_0 minimizes $\|f\|$,

$$\|f_0\| = \lambda(c_1, c_2, \ldots, c_n) \tag{14.60}$$

by virtue of (14.55). From (14.58), (14.59), and (14.60), the relation expressed by (14.57) follows immediately.

To put this relation into a more explicit form, we note that if a vector $u_0 = (u_0{}^1, u_0{}^2, \ldots, u_0{}^m)$ with norm $\|u_0\| = \sum_1^m |u_0{}^j|$ is an extremal vector for a functional $f_0 = (f_0{}^1, f_0{}^2, \ldots, f_0{}^m)$ with norm $\|f\| = \max_j |f_0{}^j|$, then (14.57) becomes

$$|f_0{}^1 u_0{}^1 + f_0{}^2 u_0{}^2 + \cdots + f_0{}^n u_0{}^n| = [|u_0{}^1| + |u_0{}^2| + \cdots + |u_0{}^n|] \\ \max_j |f_0{}^j| \quad (14.61)$$

which can readily be shown to hold if and only if

$$\begin{aligned} f_0{}^j &= C \operatorname{sign} u_j{}^0 && \text{if } u_j{}^0 \neq 0 \\ &= c && \text{if } u_j{}^0 = 0 \end{aligned} \tag{14.62}$$

where C is an arbitrary constant, c is any number of magnitude not exceeding C, and sign $u_0{}^j = \pm 1$ according as $u_0{}^j$ is positive or negative.

The results expressed by (14.50), (14.57), and (14.62) are summarized in the following statement:

Let $\qquad u_i = (u_i{}^1, u_i{}^2, \ldots, u_i{}^m) \qquad i = 1, 2, \ldots, n$

be n given linearly independent vectors, and let $c_i (i = 1, 2, \ldots, n)$ be n given constants, not all zero. Denote by $\xi_i{}^0$ $(i = 1, 2, \ldots, n)$ the values of ξ_i which minimize

$$\|u\| = \sum_{j=1}^m |\xi_1 u_1{}^j + \xi_2 u_2{}^j + \cdots + \xi_n u_n{}^j| \tag{14.63}$$

subject to the contraint $\sum_1^n c_i \xi_i = 1$. Denote by $f_0{}^j$ $(j = 1, 2, \ldots, m)$ the values of f^j which minimize

$$\|f\| = \max_j |f^j| \tag{14.64}$$

subject to the constraints

$$\sum_{j=1}^{m} f^{j}u_{i}^{j} = c_{i} \qquad i = 1, 2, \ldots, n \tag{14.65}$$

Then

$$\min_{f} \max_{j} |f^{j}| \qquad = \frac{1}{\|u_0\|} = \frac{1}{\sum_{1}^{m} |\xi_1{}^{0}u_1{}^{j} + \cdots + \xi_n{}^{0}u_n{}^{j}|}$$

$$\text{Subject to} \sum_{1}^{m} f^{j}u_{i}^{j} = c_{i} \qquad i = 1, \ldots, n$$

$$\tag{14.66}$$

and

$$f_0{}^{j} = \frac{1}{\sum_{1}^{m} |\xi_1{}^{0}u_1{}^{j} + \cdots + \xi_n{}^{0}u_n{}^{j}|}$$

$$\text{sign} (\xi_1{}^{0}u_1{}^{j} + \cdots + \xi_n{}^{0}u_n{}^{j}) \qquad j = 1, \ldots, m \tag{14.67}$$

if
$$\xi_1{}^{0}u_1{}^{j} + \cdots + \xi_n{}^{0}u_n{}^{j} \neq 0$$

and
$$f_0{}^{j} = c \qquad \text{if } \xi_1{}^{0}u_1{}^{j} + \cdots + \xi_n{}^{0}u_n{}^{j} = 0 \tag{14.67a}$$

where c is any number of magnitude not exceeding

$$\left(\sum_{1}^{m} |\xi_1{}^{0}u_1{}^{j} + \cdots + \xi_n{}^{0}u_n{}^{j}|\right)^{-1}$$

As will be seen in the following section, this result makes it possible in many cases to reduce the variational problem (14.40), (14.41) to a somewhat more tractable problem. However, even the latter problem cannot be solved in explicit terms except in relatively simple special cases.

14.7 Application to Optimal Control Problem

It will be recalled that the problem of optimal control in the case of sampled-data systems reduces to the solution of the variational problem: Find

$$Q(T) = \min_{x} \max_{0 \leqslant t \leqslant T-1} |x_t| \tag{14.68}$$

subject to the side condition

$$\sum_{t=1}^{T} \mathbf{h}_t x_{T-t} = \mathbf{\beta} - A\mathbf{\alpha} \tag{14.69}$$

Now on identifying x_{j-1} with f^{j}, n with r, m with T, h_{T-j+1}^{i} with $u_i{}^{j}$ ($h_t{}^{j}$ denotes the jth component of the impulsive response vector $\mathbf{h}_t$), and c_i with the ith component of the vector $\mathbf{\beta} - A\mathbf{\alpha}$ [denoted by $(\mathbf{\beta} - A\mathbf{\alpha})_i$], we observe that this problem is identical with the problem expressed by (14.64), (14.65). Thus, let the $\xi_t{}^{0}$ denote the values of

ξ_t $(t = 1, 2, \ldots, r)$ which minimize

$$\|u\| = G(T, \xi_1, \ldots, \xi_r) = \sum_{t=1}^{T} |\xi_1 h_t{}^1 + \xi_2 h_t{}^2 + \cdots + \xi_r h_t{}^r| \quad (14.70)$$

subject to the side condition $\sum_{1}^{r} (\beta - A\alpha)_i \xi_i = 1$. Then $Q(T)$ is given by

$$Q(T) = \frac{1}{\sum_{t=1}^{T} |\xi_1{}^0 h_t{}^1 + \cdots + \xi_r{}^0 h_t{}^r|} \quad (14.71)$$

and the corresponding inputs are expressed by

$$x_t = Q(T) \operatorname{sign} (\xi_1{}^0 h_t{}^1 + \cdots + \xi_r{}^0 h_t{}^r) \quad (14.72)$$

if $\xi_1{}^0 h_t{}^1 + \cdots + \xi_r{}^0 h_t{}^r \neq 0$, and $x_t = c$, where c is an arbitrary number such that $|c| \leqslant Q(T)$, if $\xi_1{}^0 h_t{}^1 + \cdots + \xi_r{}^0 h_t{}^r = 0$.

As a simple illustration, consider a second-order sampled-data system characterized by the difference equation

$$y_t - 0.8 y_{t-1} + 0.15 y_{t-2} = x_t \quad (14.73)$$

For this system, it is convenient to define the two components of the state vector thus

$$\begin{aligned} s_t{}^1 &= y_{t-1} - 0.5 y_{t-2} \\ s_t{}^2 &= y_{t-1} - 0.3 y_{t-2} \end{aligned} \quad (14.74)$$

since with this choice the matrix A in (14.5) becomes a diagonal matrix. Specifically, we have

$$\mathbf{s}_t = A \mathbf{s}_t + B x_t \quad (14.75)$$

where $$A = \begin{pmatrix} 0.3 & 0 \\ 0 & 0.5 \end{pmatrix} \quad \text{and} \quad B = \begin{pmatrix} 1 \\ 1 \end{pmatrix}. \quad (14.76)$$

From (14.37), the z transform of the impulsive response is found to be

$$\mathbf{H}(z) = \begin{bmatrix} 1/z - 0.3 \\ 1/z - 0.5 \end{bmatrix} \quad (14.77)$$

and hence $$h_t = \begin{bmatrix} (0.3)^{t-1} \\ (0.5)^{t-1} \end{bmatrix} \quad (14.78)$$

Assume that the initial and terminal states are specified to be

$$\alpha = (10,2)$$

and $\beta = (0,0)$. Then

$$c_1 = (\beta - A\alpha)_1 = -3 \quad (14.79)$$
$$c_2 = (\beta - A\alpha)_2 = -1 \quad (14.80)$$

and the constraint $\xi_1 c_1 + \xi_2 c_2 = 1$ becomes $-3\xi_1 - \xi_2 = 1$. At this point, the problem reduces to minimizing the expression

$$G(T, \xi_1, \xi_2) = \sum_{t=1}^{T} |\xi_1(0.3)^{t-1} + \xi_2(0.5)^{t-1}| \qquad (14.81)$$

subject to $-3\xi_1 - \xi_2 = 1$, or, equivalently, to minimizing

$$G(T, \xi_1, -3\xi_1 - 1) = \sum_{t=1}^{T} |\xi_1(0.3)^{t-1} + (-3\xi_1 - 1)(0.5)^{t-1}| \qquad (14.82)$$

with no side conditions.

To minimize expressions of this form it is sufficient to note that minima of $G(T, \xi_1, -3\xi_1 - 1)$ cannot occur at points other than zeros of the summands of (14.82), i.e., at

$$\xi_1 = \frac{(0.5)^{t-1}}{(0.3)^{t-1} - 3(0.5)^{t-1}} \qquad t = 1, 2, \ldots, T \qquad (14.83)$$

Thus, ξ_1^0 can be determined by evaluating (14.82) at the values of ξ_1 given by (14.83) and finding that value (or values) of ξ_1 which minimizes $G(T, \xi_1, -3\xi_1 - 1)$. Once ξ_1^0 is determined, the minimal value N of T can readily be obtained from the constraint (14.34); that is, N is the smallest value of T satisfying the inequality

$$G(T, \xi_1^0, -3\xi_1^0 - 1) \leqslant L \qquad (14.84)$$

where L is a specified bound on the maximum amplitude of input sequences. Then, optimal input sequences are determined from (14.72), with T replaced by its minimal value N.

It is clear that the foregoing procedure loses much of its simplicity when the state vector has more than two components or, equivalently, the order of the system is in excess of 2. Nevertheless, there is in general some gain in reducing the optimal control problem to the minimization of an expression of the form $\|u\| = \sum_{j} |\sum_{i} \xi_i u_i^j|$, subject to the side condition $\sum_{1}^{n} c_i \xi_i = 1$.

REFERENCES

1. Bellman, R., I. Glicksberg, and O. Gross: "Some Aspects of the Mathematical Theory of Control Processes," *Rept. R*-313, The Rand Corp., Santa Monica, Calif., 1958.
2. Bellman, R., and R. Kalaba: "Dynamic Programming and Adaptive Processes," *Paper P*-1416, The Rand Corp., Santa Monica, Calif., 1958.

3. Pontryagin, L. S.: Some Mathematical Problems Arising in Connection with the Theory of Optimal Automatic Control Systems, *Proc. Conf. on Basic Problems in Automatic Control and Regulation*, Academy of Sciences, Moscow, 1957.

4. Hopkin, A. M.: "A Phase-plane Approach to the Compensation of Saturating Servomechanisms," *Trans. AIEE*, vol. 70, part I, pp. 631–639, 1951.

5. Feldbaum, A.: Optimal Processes in Automatic Control Systems, *Avtomat. i Telemekh.*, vol. 14, no. 6, pp. 712–728, 1953.

6. Feldbaum, A.: On the Synthesis of Optimal Systems with the Aid of Phase-space, *Avtomat. i Telemekh.*, vol. 16, no. 2, pp. 29–49, 1955.

7. Lerner, Ya: Improvement of the Dynamic Properties of Automatic Compensators by Means of Nonlinear Feedback, *Avtomat. i Telemekh.*, vol. 13, no. 2, pp. 134–144; no. 4, pp. 429–444, 1952.

8. Kalman, R., and J. Bertram: General Synthesis Procedure for Computer Control of Single and Multiloop Linear Systems, *Proc. Computers in Control Systems Conf., AIEE Spec. Publ. T*-101, 1958.

9. Turing, A. M.: On Computable Numbers, with an Application to the *Entscheidungsproblem*, *Proc. Lond. Math. Soc.*, vol. 42, ser. 2, pp. 230–265, 1936–1937.

10. Shannon, C. E., and W. Weaver: "A Mathematical Theory of Communication," University of Illinois Press, Urbana, Ill., 1949.

11. Mealy, G.: A Method for Synthesizing Sequential Circuits, *Bell System Tech. J.*, vol. 34, pp. 1045–1079, 1955.

12. Friedland, B.: Linear Modular Sequential Circuits, *IRE Trans. on Circuit Theory*, vol. CT-6, pp. 61–68, March, 1959.

13. Bass, R. W.: The Analysis and Synthesis of Relay Servomechanisms, *Final Rept. Contract DA* 36-034-ORD-1273 RD, Johns Hopkins University, Baltimore, Md., 1955.

14. Bushaw, D. W.: Differential Equations with a Discontinuous Forcing Term, *ETT Rept.* 469, Stevens Institute of Technology, Hoboken, N.J., 1953.

15. Rose, N. J.: Theoretical Aspects of Limit Control, *ETT Rept.* 459, Stevens Institute of Technology, Hoboken, N.J., 1953.

16. Krasovskii, N.: On the Theory of Optimal Regulation, *Avtomat. i Telemekh.*, vol. 18, no. 11, pp. 960–970, 1957.

17. Krasovskii, N.: On a Problem of Optimal Regulation, *Priklad. Mat. i Meh.*, vol. 21, no. 5, pp. 670–677, 1957.

18. Boltyanskii, V., R. Gamkrelidze, and L. S. Pontryagin: On the Theory of Optimal Processes, *Doklady Akad. Nauk SSSR*, vol. 110, no. 1, pp. 7–10, 1956.

19. Boltyanskii, V.: The "Maximum" Principle in the Theory of Optimal Processes, *Doklady Akad. Nauk SSSR*, vol. 119, no. 6, pp. 1070–1073, 1958.

20. Gamkrelidze, R.: On a General Theory of Optimal Processes, *Doklady Akad. Nauk SSSR*, vol. 123, no. 2, pp. 223–226, 1958.

21. Krein, M.: L-problem in Abstract Linear Normed Space, paper no. 4 in N. Akhiezer and M. Krein, "Some Questions in the Theory of Moments," Gonti, Kharkov, 1938.

22. Boltyanskii, V., R. Gamkrelidze, and L. S. Pontryagin: On the Theory of Optimal Processes, I, *Izvest. Akad. Nauk SSSR*, vol. 24, pp. 3–42, 1960.

PART III

Applications to
Complex Systems

15

Navigation, Guidance, and Control Problems for Aerospace Vehicles*

ROBERT O. FERNER AND **A. F. SCHMITT**

DESIGN SPECIALISTS

CONVAIR-ASTRONAUTICS DIVISION

GENERAL DYNAMICS CORPORATION, SAN DIEGO, CALIF.

15.1 Introduction

In Part I of this book, theory and technique in the operation of digital and analog computer facilities were discussed. Part II presented theory and techniques in the solution of feedback control problems. As a first example of the blending of these two major engineering fields in a practical application, this chapter will consider problems of synthesis and analysis of the guidance and control systems for missiles and space vehicles.

It will be seen that this task is of such complexity that many of the tools developed in Parts I and II will have to be applied in order to obtain satisfactory solutions of the problems. We will recognize that, during the early phases of orienting synthesis, there exists an economic and logical requirement to minimize the utilization of computers. During this phase of the investigation the over-all problem must be simplified in order to emphasize the main parameters and their interrelation for the system under study. To attempt all studies through the use of computers during this phase would not only be too costly but would also limit the inventiveness and creativity of the engineer for formulating novel concepts. Only after the main parameters and distinguishing features of the problem have been roughed out should the simplifications be removed and the complete system be established progressively by an iterative procedure between synthesis and analysis using computer techniques.

---

* Hans Friedrich was scheduled as the lecturer for this chapter in the series until his untimely death in December, 1958. His place was very ably filled by Messrs. R. O. Ferner and A. F. Schmitt. Dr. R. M. Leger delivered this lecture in Los Angeles.

It is appropriate at this time to define the three problem areas of the title and their interrelations. *Navigation*, as used herein, is the process of computing the vehicle's position in space—past, present, and future. *Guidance* is concerned with the problem of modifying the flight path by maneuvering the vehicle such that it navigates to intercept a given target. *Control* is the problem of providing the means by which the vehicle may be steered, since it is through changes in attitude that maneuvers (changes in the flight path) are achieved.

Navigation is essentially a high-ordered bookkeeping operation in which the accelerations in each of three coordinate directions are continuously integrated to produce an instantaneous reckoning of position. A faculty for navigation is, of course, an essential feature of the guidance system but will be understood primarily as a tool within that system. In the discussion herein we will therefore concern ourselves primarily

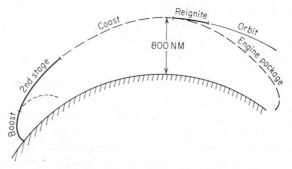

Fig. 15.1   The mission profile.

with treatments of the problems associated with synthesis and analysis of the guidance and control phases, these being the areas which can illustrate computer and controls technology.

The subjects of guidance and control of a missile or space vehicle are entirely too broad to be discussed fruitfully in generalizations. It becomes necessary therefore to direct our attention to a specific system. To this end, a vehicle of given characteristics has been chosen to exemplify these areas of investigation. Before setting forth the characteristics of the example vehicle it is desirable to explain briefly the way in which such data are obtained prior to the guidance and control synthesis and analysis.

In the evolution of the design of a large missile or space vehicle of the type to be studied, a considerable number of "feasibility studies" are conducted in the preliminary design phases to determine the payload capability and mode of operation of the vehicle for different missions. These studies may be of varying degrees of sophistication in the extent to which they consider propulsion characteristics, g-field perturbations, aerodynamic drag, etc. Almost invariably, however, they will employ the common approximation of studying the motion of a point mass under the combined actions of gravity and a thrust vector which can be steered perfectly to produce flight along the desired trajectories. These studies are sufficient to define quite closely the nominal trajectory and flight characteristics of the system.

These preliminary studies then, outline what is feasible for a properly controlled and guided vehicle to achieve. One might say that the task of the guidance and control system is to realize these capabilities.

The vehicle to be studied is a satellite supply vehicle whose mission is to deliver a 10,000-lb payload into an 800-nautical-mile orbit. Figure 15.1 shows the mission profile consisting of the following phases:

1. A boost phase through the atmosphere after which the boost vehicle is dropped
2. A second-stage firing
3. A coast period up to the 800-mile level, during which a portion of the engine package is jettisoned
4. A reignition of the remaining second stage engine to achieve circular velocity

The mission profile as given is not optimum from an energy standpoint, but is a compromise, chosen to achieve rendezvous with the satellite over an established ground station (among other problems). Table 15.1 and Fig. 15.1 give various flight data of interest.

Table 15.1   Flight Data for Satellite Supply Mission

ASSUMED DATA

$I_{sp \text{ av}}$ in boost $= 275$
Drag and g losses in boost $= 4,000$ fps
$I_{sp \text{ av}}$ in second stage $= 300$
g loss in second stage $= 1,300$ fps
$I_{sp \text{ av}}$ in final firing $= 300$
$V_{\text{orbit}}^{\text{inertial}}$ at 800 nm $= 23,300$ fps

CALCULATED DATA

Time	Weight, lb	Thrust, lb	Thrust/ weight ratio	V^{earth}, fps	Remarks
Launch	600,000	860,000	1.44	. . . . . .	Jettison 25,000-lb booster vehicle
Booster cutoff	130,800	1,100,000	8	10,000	
Second-stage start	155,800	235,000	1.5	10,000	Coast-jettison 2,000-lb engine pack
Second-stage end	26,200	237,000	9	22,000	
Reignite remaining engines	24,200	50,000	2.05	16,500	
Final cutoff	14,000*	50,000	3.6	21,800	$= 23,300$ inertial

* Breakdown: 4,000 engine, tankage plus 10,000 useful load.

A detailing of the preliminary studies which led to the above mission profile cannot be undertaken here. Instead, we will begin the study of the control and guidance problems by assuming that the preliminary studies have been conducted yielding nominal flight trajectories and nominal values for all pertinent flight parameters. Thus, such data as the time histories of vehicle inertial properties, accelerations, thrust, drag, Mach number, dynamic pressure, etc., are known rather closely. Subsequent modifications to the flight mode, which may have to be made as compromises to certain problem areas, should not produce changes great enough to invalidate studies based upon these data.

15.2 Introductory Remarks on the Design of the Attitude Control System

To enable guidance of the vehicle it must be possible to control its attitude. This section will consider some of the problems in the design of the attitude control system. These problems may be considered uncoupled from the guidance problems because of the wide separation in frequency spectra of the guidance and control systems. Thus, for guidance problems, use of a simple time lag to represent missile response will often suffice. For control studies, on the other hand, it may be assumed that the guidance steering commands have no frequency components in the control band.

As in any engineering design problem it is convenient to carry the work in two phases: (1) A preliminary analysis and system synthesis phase, in which appropriate simplifications are made in the equations to permit rapid study and tentative choice of gains; and (2) a detailed analysis phase during which effects of additional degrees of freedom, higher-order terms, nonlinearities, and time-varying effects can be considered to determine the suitability of the design under conditions closest to actual operation, disclose additional detailed problems, and make appropriate system modifications (additional compensation, other minor loops, gain adjustments, etc.).

To illustrate some of the approaches to vehicle attitude control system design, a review will be given in the following of some studies accomplished in each of the two phases just described for the booster phase of flight of the vehicle under discussion.

15.3 Booster System Specification

The governing characteristics and mode of operation of the vehicle must be understood before an attitude control system can be studied. This section will summarize these factors.

The booster vehicle is designed to lift the upper stages and payload through the earth's atmosphere, imparting to them a suitable velocity (magnitude and direction). To fulfill this mission, in an efficient manner, a mode of operation is devised which capitalizes on the presence of large propulsive forces and on the very low maneuver requirements. The flight plan is tailored so as to minimize aerodynamic loading inputs to permit a low structural weight in both booster and upper stages.

The vehicle is launched vertically to minimize launcher load inputs. An angled launch would require large lateral stabilizing loads on the vehicle and hence is undesirable. Shortly after lift-off, the missile is turned off the vertical into a zero lift (zero angle of attack) flight trajectory. Only during the brief transition turn off the vertical, made at low dynamic pressures, does the vehicle assume an intentional angle of attack. Thereafter attitude turning rate is made equal to flight-path turn rate to maintain a zero angle of attack in still air. Obviously atmospheric inputs of wind profiles and gusts will produce some unintended loadings which the control system must cope with.

Because the vehicle maneuver requirements are so modest (the transition turn off the vertical is probably the only "maneuver" worthy of the name) and because vehicle weight is completely sustained by propulsive thrust, no wings are required on the vehicle. As will be seen below, stability problems may usually be solved by thrust vector gimbaling alone, removing any necessity for tail surfaces. Thus, the vehicle presents a clean external configuration.

In summary, the mode of operation and the vehicle configuration are so chosen that lateral load inputs consist primarily of relatively low distributed airloads, there being no heavy concentrated loads from launcher or from aerodynamic surfaces. Structural weight of both booster and upper stages is kept correspondingly low.

15.4 Preliminary Analysis and System Synthesis— Equations and Block Diagram

For purposes of the primary study on an attitude control system it is satisfactory to consider the vehicle and its contents as being rigid. Such an assumption implies that the control frequencies will be kept sufficiently low that their separation from those of other major degrees of freedom (propellant sloshing and elastic modes) is reasonably great.

Figure 15.2 shows the parameters employed. The vehicle is assumed to be aerodynamically unstable [lift ahead of center of gravity (c.g.)] and to employ thrust vector control for attitude stabilization. (The adequacy of thrust vector control for stabilization at maximum dynamic pressure has yet to be demonstrated, but it will be assumed here nevertheless.) The attitude angles shown are perturbation angles from a reference trajectory. This reference trajectory is the zero lift path, having a turn rate so adjusted as to cancel the transverse gravitational acceleration. Consequently, in summing forces there will be no weight term acting normal to the reference path.

The equations of motion are (small angles assumed throughout)

$$\Sigma M_{\text{c.g.}} = I\ddot{\theta} = Tl_c\delta + F_\alpha \alpha l_a$$
$$\Sigma F_{\text{normal path}} = MV_p\dot{\gamma} = F_\alpha \alpha - T(\delta - \alpha) \tag{15.1}$$

Here F_α is the normal aerodynamic force per unit angle of attack. An additional geometric relation is needed to define the system $\theta = \gamma + \alpha$.

For stability studies the θ/δ transfer function is needed. Solving the equations yields

$$\frac{\theta}{\delta} = \mu_\delta \frac{s + T/MV + [F_\alpha/MV](l_c + l_a)/l_c}{s\{s^2 + [(F_\alpha + T)/MV]s - \mu_\alpha\}} \tag{15.2}$$

where $\mu_\delta \equiv Tl_c/I$ is the control effectiveness parameter, and $\mu_\alpha \equiv F_\alpha l_a/I$ is the measure of aerodynamic instability. These parameters have the units of (seconds)$^{-2}$ and give the angular acceleration per unit thrust

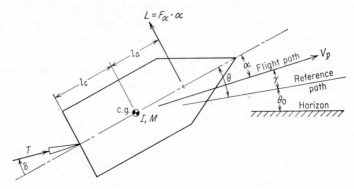

Fig. 15.2   Rigid vehicle control parameters.

vector deflection and per unit angle of attack, respectively. (For an aerodynamically *stable* aircraft μ_α is the square of the short period mode natural frequency.)

At launch, or out of the atmosphere, when the dynamic pressure is low $(F_\alpha \to 0)$ Eq. (15.2) simplifies to

$$\frac{\theta}{\delta} = \frac{\mu_\delta}{s^2} \tag{15.3}$$

At another extreme, when the velocity is very high, $(V \to \infty)$, one has

$$\frac{\theta}{\delta} = \frac{\mu_\delta}{s^2 - \mu_\alpha} \tag{15.4}$$

For a vehicle of the class being studied here, we find that Eq. (15.4) is a good approximation at any time that the aerodynamic instability is sufficiently great to necessitate its inclusion. The other terms of Eq. (15.2) which are omitted thereby only lead to a dipole of small residue (pole-zero grouped closely together), having little influence on this problem. Physically, the approximation is that $\theta \doteq \alpha$, a satisfactory assumption for a massive vehicle whose transverse forces are low by design intent.

Figure 15.3 shows a block diagram of the attitude control system for one axis of vehicle rotation. A gyro provides attitude reference, a deviation from which results in a thrust vector gimbaling command. To fix ideas, we will assume the thrust vector positioning is achieved by gimbaling the rocket engine thrust chambers—a popular solution. The response of the thrust chamber positioning mechanism is represented by a first-order lag. Sufficient lead will have to be provided in the control loop to stabilize the system. The necessary lead may be provided by either a lead compensation network or by insertion of a rate gyro, the latter solution being assumed herein.

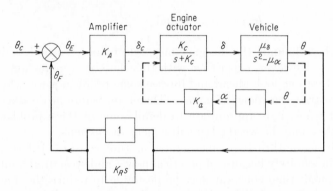

Fig. 15.3 Block diagram of one axis of attitude control system.

An aerodynamically stable vehicle is one which responds to an angle of attack by turning into the velocity vector so as to reduce the angle of attack. The aerodynamically unstable vehicle can be given a degree of synthetic aerodynamic stability by sensing angle of attack variations as they develop and commanding the engine to gimbal so as to turn the vehicle into the velocity vector. Thus, the inner feedback loop (shown dashed) with gain K_a induces such a stability.

Angle of attack feedback has the potential advantage of relieving aerodynamic loads on the vehicle since it moves the vehicle so as to reduce an angle of attack as it develops. Some of the disadvantages of this additional feedback loop lie in the increase in complexity (and attendant decrease in reliability) and in the introduction of additional higher-order degrees of freedom in the angle of attack sensor which can lead to further stability problems. An additional shortcoming of the system lies in the failure of this loop at low dynamic pressures (near launch or outside the atmosphere), possibly necessitating some compensation by gain changes in the outer position loop.

Pending further study into the problem of aerodynamic loads on the vehicle, it will be assumed that α feedback is not used in the system under study.

15.5   Preliminary Gain Choice

It is desired at this time to make a preliminary selection of system gains so as to provide working values for subsequent studies.   There are three gains at the designer's disposal: K_c, K_A, and K_R.   The characteristic equation for the system of Fig. 15.3 is

$$s^3 + K_c s^2 + (K_A K_c K_R \mu_\delta - \mu_\alpha)s + K_c(K_A \mu_\delta - \mu_\alpha) = 0 \qquad (15.5)$$

A brief study of this equation by use of Routh's criteria yields two simple inviolate criteria for stability, *viz.*,

$$K_A \mu_\delta > \mu_\alpha \qquad \text{and} \qquad \frac{1}{K_R} < K_c$$

Within these bounds the designer may select many suitable gain combinations.   However, experience with this class of systems and vehicles requires that one look ahead and foresee some problem areas which may further restrict the choice of gains.   Therefore, before proceeding with a choice of gains, it is appropriate to detail some of these problem areas so that they may be weighed in subsequent discussions.

1. The engine thrust chamber gimbaling time constant $1/K_c$ cannot be reduced indefinitely because of practical power and structural limitations. While a small time constant may be desirable to reduce the amount of lead necessary in stabilizing the system, the practical problems associated with providing high accelerations and velocities to a massive thrust chamber and of stabilizing the necessarily high-gain servo loop will result in a compromise upper limit to K_c.

2. Vehicle response to transients, particularly gust inputs, must be considered if system loads are to be limited to within the capability of a lightweight structure.   The control system without angle of attack feedback does not respond to a gust until a change in vehicle attitude has occurred.   This attitude change, in the case of the aerodynamically unstable vehicle, is always in a direction which increases the angle of attack, the gust thereby "overshooting" the imposed value.   The vehicle's gust response is strongly dependent upon the system's transient response.   A "tight" system, having a rapid response with good damping, leads to small gust overshoots.

3. Stability of the system when higher-order terms (other degrees of freedom) are included must be considered in selecting gains, these being particularly significant in limiting the upper values of the gains.   A number of these problems will be considered below in relation to additions to the basic system equations and modifications to the root-locus plots.

Briefly, some of these additions are: inclusion of propellant sloshing modes, addition of vehicle body bending modes, inclusion of higher-order terms in the engine thrust chamber servo loop transfer function and in the transfer functions of the reference gyros, and the insertion of additional shaping and filtering networks within the autopilot as required to stabilize these new terms.

To select some tentative gains we can assume the roots of the characteristic equation are of the form

$$(s + \rho)(s^2 + 2\zeta\omega s + \omega^2) = 0 \tag{15.6}$$

i.e., an oscillatory mode (a pair of complex poles) plus an exponential decay (real pole). If Eq. (15.6) is expanded and the results compared term by term with Eq. (15.5), one finds

$$K_c = 2\zeta\omega + \rho$$
$$K_A K_c K_R \mu_\delta - \mu_\alpha = \omega^2 + 2\zeta\omega\rho \tag{15.7}$$
$$K_c(K_A \mu_\delta - \mu_\alpha) = \rho\omega^2$$

Equations (15.7) permit a choice of the gains for a given μ_δ and μ_α, *provided* one can rationally select ρ, ω, and ζ. To make this selection one can be guided by considerations from the problem areas enumerated above.

Specifically:

1. A fast, well-damped transient response is desired.
2. K_c should be kept reasonably low.
3. The over-all gains should be kept low so as not to excite higher modes (body bending in particular).

These requirements are conflicting, of course. However, one can begin with an observation, based upon experience, that a separation of at least 4 to 1 between the rigid body mode and first body bending mode frequencies will relieve problem 3, above. This simple rule of thumb will often provide a basis for choice of ω, since the first body bending frequency will have been previously established by the configuration.

From a study of transients for systems with the pole configuration of Eq. (15.6), it is known that a good well-damped transient will result from choosing $\zeta = 0.3$ and $\rho = \omega$.

The value of K_c which results from the above calculations should be examined from two points of view. First, the value should be reasonable as it affects the thrust chamber servo system requirements (a separate study in itself). Second, K_c should not be too low inasmuch as the complete gust transient response contains a zero at K_c, too low a value of which will adversely affect the gust overshoot. As a general rule, if K_c exceeds twice the value of ρ, the influence of the zero on the gust transient will be slight.

The first approximation gains chosen in the above manner should form a satisfactory basis for more elaborate analysis. Before proceeding to a root-locus presentation and to the study of additional degrees of freedom, it is important to discuss one other prime factor. The properties of this vehicle—its inertial, aerodynamic, and propulsive parameters—vary over wide ranges through the boost phase. Moreover, many of the higher-order effects to be discussed below change in relative importance as the flight progresses. Consequently, it is understood that the tentative gain selection just described, when carried out for a specific time of flight, may require different adjustments for different flight times when analyzed further. Such a result may lead to the necessity for programmed gain changes. It is probably reasonable to carry out the preliminary gain selection for conditions at the time of maximum dynamic pressure (usually in the mid-portion of the boost phase) arguing that these are mean conditions of a sort and will lead to suitable working values for studies through the entire phase. It is quite possible that gains so chosen may prove satisfactory without time programming, thus leading to the simplest, most reliable system.

15.6   Root-locus Studies—Rigid Vehicle

To permit plotting root loci, numerical data will be introduced at this point. For convenience, all data are expressed here nondimensionally using the first body bending mode period $(1/\omega_1)$ as the unit of time.

At maximum dynamic pressure, data taken from the feasibility phase studies show that the vehicle studied has

$$\mu_\delta = 0.012\omega_1{}^2 \quad \text{and} \quad \mu_\alpha = 0.0067\omega_1{}^2$$

Following a rule of thumb given earlier, we let the control frequency be less than one-quarter of ω_1. Let $\omega = 0.2\omega_1$ and set this also equal to ρ. Let $\zeta = 0.3$. Equations 15.7 now yield

$$K_c = 0.32\omega_1$$
$$K_A = 2.65$$
$$K_R = \frac{7}{\omega_1}$$

With these data the root locus for the control system of Fig. 15.3 has been drawn in Fig. 15.4, showing the operating point for the above gains.

Considering also the problem of changing vehicle properties, we will check the operating point root locations for the gains chosen above at conditions near launch and near the time of booster staging. At both of these times dynamic pressure is low so that $\mu_\alpha \doteq 0$. Since engine thrust increases somewhat with altitude (as the back pressure from the atmosphere decreases) and vehicle moment of inertia decreases with flight, the control effectiveness parameter μ_δ varies over a modest range.

For the vehicle studied

$$\mu_{\delta \text{ launch}} = 0.0068\omega_1{}^2$$
$$\mu_{\delta \text{ staging}} = 0.020\omega_1{}^2$$

Assuming all autopilot gains are kept constant, Fig. 15.5 shows the root loci and operating points for the beginning and end of this boost phase.

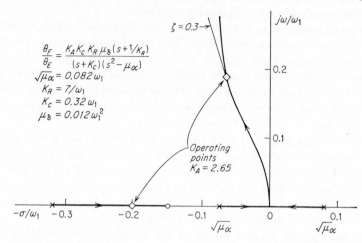

$$\frac{\theta_F}{\theta_E} = \frac{K_A K_C K_R \mu_\delta (s + 1/K_R)}{(s + K_C)(s^2 - \mu_\alpha)}$$

$\sqrt{\mu_\alpha} = 0.082\,\omega_1$
$K_R = 7/\omega_1$
$K_C = 0.32\,\omega_1$
$\mu_\delta = 0.012\,\omega_1{}^2$

Fig. 15.4 Root locus for system of Fig. 15.3 using preliminary gains.

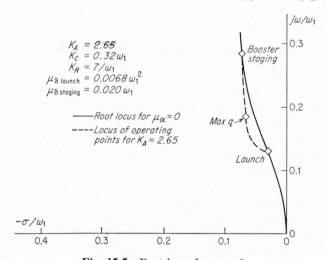

$K_A = 2.65$
$K_C = 0.32\omega_1$
$K_R = 7/\omega_1$
$\mu_{\delta \text{ launch}} = 0.0068\,\omega_1{}^2$
$\mu_{\delta \text{ staging}} = 0.020\,\omega_1$

———Root locus for $\mu_\alpha = 0$
- - - -Locus of operating points for $K_A = 2.65$

Fig. 15.5 Root locus for $\mu_\alpha = 0$.

Also shown (dashed) is a locus of the operating points as they vary over the boost phase due to changes in both μ_δ and μ_α.

By inspection of the loci of Fig. 15.5 it would be concluded that the preliminary gains chosen would be satisfactory for use throughout the boost phase, at least insofar as the rigid body stability is concerned.

Such a constant gain autopilot is highly desirable from a reliability standpoint.

It is appropriate to examine here the suitability of thrust vector control alone, assumed a priori earlier. While a complete justification must consider many factors aside from the control problem, some feeling for the problem may be had from a consideration of the engine chamber gimbaling requirements in balancing air loads.

The maximum ratio of μ_α to μ_δ for this vehicle is 0.56. Thus, to balance one degree of steady angle of attack (due to a wind) requires only 0.56° of thrust chamber deflection at maximum dynamic pressure. From trajectory studies run during the feasibility phase it is known that angles of attack developed by flying this vehicle through a wind profile are of the order of a few degrees. Hence steady engine balancing angle requirements are low.

Again, using a standard gust velocity it is found that gust angles of attack near maximum dynamic pressure are also of the order of a few degrees. Consequently the engine need only gimbal about half that amount to correct against a gust. Gust response may be assumed superposed on the steady wind-balancing deflection. It is clear, however, that the combined deflection required is small.

In summary, the control power of the thrust vector control is great enough in comparison with the aerodynamic instability of the vehicle so that the range of control motion required is quite reasonable for the planned mode of flight.

15.7   Root-locus Studies—Propellant Modes Included

One of the important stability problems in the attitude control of large liquid fueled vehicles is that of the control of sloshing modes of the internal propellants. An attitude sensing control system, such as that proposed here, couples together the rigid body and sloshing modes quite strongly under some circumstances often producing a divergent mode. Since the inherent damping in a tank of fluid varies inversely with tank diameter, these propellant modes are only very lightly damped in large vehicles. Thus, the energy imparted to the propellants by the vehicle motion is but slowly dissipated and sloshing-control system modes may build up to destructive amplitudes unless properly treated.

A number of authors[1,2,3] have shown that the problem of propellant sloshing in a cylindrical tank can be treated satisfactorily by the substitution of a mechanical analogy for the fluid. The analogy consists of a rigid mass plus a series of harmonic oscillators—spring masses or pendulums—one for each fluid mode. The mechanical system duplicates the fluids' response and the resultant forces and moments on the tank. In practical control problems only the first propellant mode of each tank is treated, the higher modes producing negligible contributions.

The vehicle considered has a multiplicity of tanks, there being two per stage. The transfer functions for such a system are too unwieldy to treat by algebraic solution and will therefore be deferred for later solution by machine computation. It is instructive however to begin with the more modest problem of a single tank to discover some features of the problems.

Figure 15.6 shows the basic vehicle with the addition of a simple pendulum representing the sloshing propellants of the first fluid mode. The "rigid" (non-sloshing) portion of the mechanical

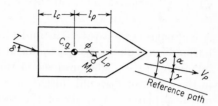

Fig. 15.6 Sloshing model.

analogy is lumped in with the vehicle structure in computing an effective center of gravity, mass, and moment of inertia. The appropriate parameters for the sloshing analogy, as a function of tank proportions, are given in the references cited.

The equations of motion become

$$\Sigma M_{\text{c.g.}} = I\ddot{\theta} = Tl_c\delta - M_p\alpha_T l_p\phi$$
$$\Sigma F_{\text{normal path}} = MV_p\dot{\gamma} = -T(\delta - \alpha) - M_p\alpha_T(\phi + \alpha) \qquad (15.8)$$
$$(s^2 + \omega_p{}^2)\phi = -\frac{1}{L_p}\left[\frac{\Sigma F_z}{M} - (l_p - L_p)\ddot{\theta}\right]$$

where $\alpha_T = T/M_{\text{total}}$ is the absolute longitudinal acceleration of the vehicle, this being the parameter affecting the tension in the pendulum rod. ($M_{\text{total}} = M + M_p$).

In writing Eqs. (15.8) we have omitted the aerodynamics. While the influence of the aerodynamic forces on sloshing is not necessarily small at all times of flight, it develops that the sloshing problem seldom becomes acute until the vehicle mass has burned down considerably, by which time the dynamic pressure will have fallen off to where these aerodynamic forces are small. The pendulum is shown as responding to the absolute transverse acceleration at the pendulum mass station, the force summation indicated being the summation of all *real* forces transverse to the missile's longitudinal axis (gravitational attractions do not displace the pendulum). Again we remark that all inertial properties (including lever arms) are the *effective* properties, computed with the sloshing propellant mass (M_p) excluded but including the "rigid" portion of the analogy.

Putting

$$\Sigma F_z = T\delta + M_p\alpha_T\phi$$

one sees that the first and last equations of Eq. 15.8 are uncoupled from the flight-path equation (the result of assuming no aerodynamics).

Hence one finds, by simple substitution, that

$$\frac{\theta}{\delta} = \frac{\mu_\delta}{s^2} \frac{s^2 + \omega_p'^2 + (M_p/M)(\alpha_t/L_p)(l_p/l_c)}{s^2 + \omega_p'^2 + (M_p/M)(\alpha_t/L_p)(l_p/l_c)[(l_p - L_p)l_c/r^2]} \qquad (15.9)$$

where $\omega_p'^2 = [\alpha_T/L_p](1 + M_p/M)$
$r^2 = I/M$

A comparison of Eqs. (15.9) and (15.3) reveals that the addition of the harmonic oscillator has introduced a pair of pole-zero dipoles on the imaginary axis. The presence of the very small fluid damping (omitted in the equations) would shift these points slightly into the left-hand half of the s plane. A study of the root loci for the closed-loop autopilot

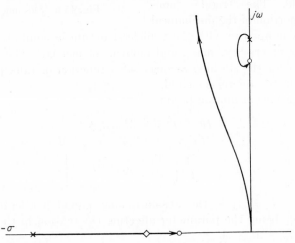

Fig. 15.7 Typical root loci for vehicle with single tank of sloshing propellants.

system may be made using this transfer function. Figure 15.7 shows a typical result for one of the main tanks of the booster vehicle.

A number of observations may be made concerning the effects of sloshing by interpretation of Eq. (15.9) relative to a root-locus plot:

1. If the dipole has a very small residue (pole-zero close together) its effect upon the rigid body mode is slight. Since the instantaneous center for vehicle motion is a distance r^2/l_c ahead of the center of gravity, it is apparent that, if the sloshing mass is located at or very near to the vehicle's instantaneous center, the pole-zero will cancel each other. Physically, the propellant is not excited into motion.

2.* If the pole is greater than the zero, the root locus yields a loop of stable roots as in Fig. 15.7. When the pole and zero are sufficiently separated, the locus will appear as in Fig. 15.8. For a tank so located

* The generalizations drawn in observations 2 and 3 apply principally to the simple lag-engine-plus-rate-gyro-lead autopilot of Fig. 15.3. Additional autopilot elements may modify the picture, as will be seen later.

that its pendulum hinge point is behind the vehicle center of gravity ($l_p < 0$) the pole will be greater than the zero. For a tank located far enough forward such that its sloshing mass is ahead of the instantaneous center ($l_p - L_p > r^2/l_c$) the pole will be greater than the zero.

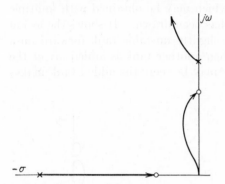

Fig. 15.8 System with stable sloshing roots when sloshing residue is large.

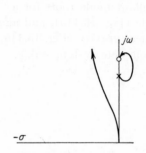

Fig. 15.9 System with unstable sloshing roots.

3. If the pole is less than the zero, the locus will yield unstable roots as in Fig. 15.9. From Eq. (15.9) it is readily seen that unstable roots will result for an oscillator whose pendulum hinge point is ahead of the vehicle center of gravity but whose pendulous mass is behind the vehicle's instantaneous center.

A tank having a locus such as that of Fig. 15.9 may be stabilized for a low range of gains by the addition of a sufficient amount of fluid damping. As shown in Fig. 15.10, fluid damping shifts the pole-zero pair into the left-half plane. Such damping is readily provided by the introduction of mechanical baffles into the tank.

While the elementary root-locus analysis above is useful in revealing certain stability characteristics of a propellant mode, a brief trial will show that such a procedure is very difficult

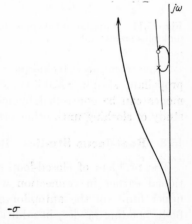

Fig. 15.10 Locus for mechanically damped propellant tank.

to follow for the general multitank configuration and that resort will have to be made to numerical or computer studies for these cases. A few of the complications encountered for the general case are:

1. The modes for the multitank vehicle couple together making it very difficult to obtain a simple analytic transfer function of the form of Eq. 15.9.

2. Propellant tank properties change very radically over the course of the flight, leading to extreme variations in the parameters associated with the various mechanical analogy oscillators and making generalizations directly from the equations quite difficult.

As an illustration of the effects which may be obtained with multiple tanks coupling together, Fig. 15.11 has been drawn.   It shows the loci of propellant mode roots for a single, slightly unstable tank forward on a vehicle (Fig. 15.11a), and again when another tank is added aft of the center of gravity (Fig. 15.11b).   As may be seen, the added tank makes the complete system stable.

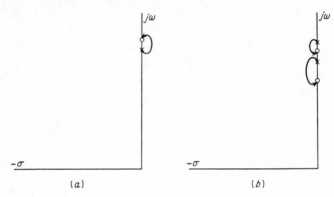

Fig. 15.11   Propellant mode roots (a) for a single forward tank and (b) for a forward tank plus an aft tank.

Some computer techniques for making more elaborate studies of propellant sloshing stability will be discussed later.   Since propellant modes can be controlled by mechanical damping we can defer further study of sloshing until other problem areas have been investigated.

15.8   Root-locus Studies—Body Bending Included

The problem of closed-loop stability of the flexible missile was mentioned earlier in connection with phenomena which will establish an upper limit on the autopilot gains.   The attitude gyros sense missile body bending modes, in addition to rigid body attitude changes; these modal contributions providing a gimbaling command to the thrust chambers.   Since the thrust vector movement in turn excites body bending modes, a closed loop is formed which can lead to a divergent oscillation at the bending frequency if excessive gains and incorrect phasing are employed.[4]

Figure 15.12 shows the parameters used in a simple one-mode analysis for moderate frequencies.*

* Frequencies at which thrust chamber lateral inertia forces are small relative to the gimbaling thrust vector's transverse component.

The equations of motion for rigid body attitude and the first bending mode are

$$Is^2\theta = Tl_c(\delta - q_b\sigma_b^e)$$

$$(s^2 + 2\zeta_b\omega_b s + \omega_b^2)q_b = -\frac{T\phi_b^e}{m_b}\delta$$

(15.10)

where σ_b^e and ϕ_b^e are the normalized modal slope and deflections, respectively, at the engine station (superscript e). q_b is the mode normal coordinate, and ζ_b, ω_b, and m_b are the mode damping, frequency, and generalized mass, respectively.

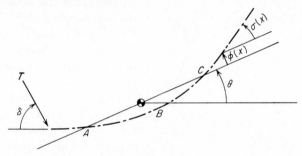

Fig. 15.12   Vehicle with one elastic mode—points A and C are nodes (zero deflection).   Point B is an antinode (zero slope from mode).

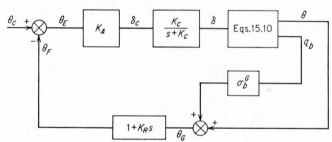

Fig. 15.13   Block diagram of attitude system including bending mode.

Because the gyro package senses the total attitude at the gyro station we write $\theta_G = \theta + q_b\sigma_b^G$.   Here σ_b^G is the normalized mode slope (positive nose up) at the gyro station.   Schematically, the block diagram could be drawn as in Fig. 15.13.

If these additional relations are incorporated, the open-loop transfer function becomes

$$\frac{\theta_F}{\theta_\epsilon} = K_A K_C K_R \mu_\delta \left(1 - \frac{T\phi_b^e\sigma_b^G}{m_b\mu_\delta}\right) \frac{s + (1/K_R)}{s^2(s + K_C)}$$

$$\frac{s^2 + 2\zeta_b\omega_b's + \left[\left(\omega_b^2 + \frac{\sigma_b^e T\phi_b^e}{m_b}\right) \middle/ \left(1 - \frac{T\phi_b^e\sigma_b^G}{m_b\mu_\delta}\right)\right]}{s^2 + 2\zeta_b\omega_b s + \omega_b^2}$$

(15.11)

where

$$\omega_b' = \omega_b \frac{1}{1 - (T\phi_b^e\sigma_b^G/m_b\mu_\delta)}$$

A comparison between Eq. (15.11) and the open-loop transfer function for Fig. 15.2 (*cf.* Fig. 15.5) reveals that the addition of the mode has affected the gain as well as introduced a pole-zero doublet. We recall from previous discussions in connection with the sloshing dipole that the

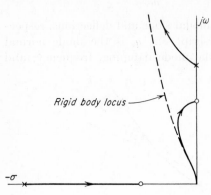

bending mode zero should be less than the pole to yield a locus of stable roots. Thus, an inspection of the equation reveals that it is desirable to locate the gyro on the *aft* portion of the vehicle, (behind the antinode) where $\sigma_b{}^G$ is *negative*. We hasten to add, however, that this simple conclusion applies only to modes of moderate frequency—probably only the fundamental—and that a more elaborate study will be required to provide a reasonable assurance of stable operation when higher frequency modes are considered.

Fig. 15.14 Root locus for system with one low-frequency body bending mode, gyros located aft on the vehicle.

Figure 15.14 shows a typical result for the gyro placed well aft on the vehicle. Note that the addition of this mode has had an undesirable effect on the rigid body mode.

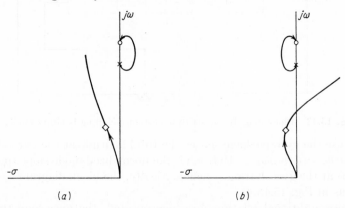

(a)   (b)

Fig. 15.15 Stabilizing an unstable bending mode (*a*) by addition of a simple lag filter (*b*).

Of additional interest is the result of using a forward placement of the gyro ($\sigma_b{}^G > 0$). This would normally be thought of as producing an unstable situation in the context discussed above. However, if enough additional phase-shifting elements (say, one or more lag filters) are inserted into the control loop, one can phase-stabilize the bending mode. Figure 15.15 illustrates these results. Figure 15.15*a* shows the unstable mode when no additional compensation is used. In Fig. 15.15b the additional lag element is represented by a pole at $\sigma = -0.8\omega_1$. The element may be thought of as having been inserted into the loop with the gain amplifier K_A. This lag element adds enough additional phase shift at the bending mode frequency to stabilize it. At the same time, it does add some phase to the rigid body mode and thereby decreases its damping somewhat. An allowance for this could be made by increasing K_R but such fine adjustments are best made in connection with a more complete system analysis.

15.9 Refined Analysis of Attitude Control System— Application of Computers

Introductory Remarks. In the foregoing sections we have discussed some of the thinking which might lead to a preliminary choice of gains during a system synthesis study. We have also outlined some of the problems associated with the other primary degrees of freedom (sloshing and body bending) in the form of an heuristic discussion.

In performing what might be referred to as a "refined analysis" of the system, it becomes necessary to rely heavily upon the use of computers for the solution of the complex equations. To provide every reasonable assurance that the system as designed is satisfactory for use in the vehicle, only the most complete studies, including all significant effects, will suffice. Here a word of caution is in order. While it is found that the system equations are seldom amenable to hand solution, it is well to remember that very often a little time spent trying to develop a simple analysis of a situation, before rushing to the computer, is time well invested. Even when a problem cannot be completely treated by hand, many of its basic features can be found by a preliminary study assisting greatly thereby in an interpretation of the computer results.

The following is a list of some of the effects which lead one to the use of machine computation in the analysis:

1. *Multiple propellant tanks.* The equations couple together here such that simple symbolic transfer functions cannot be found.

2. *Higher bending modes.* These modes all couple strongly through the rate gyro whose output is proportional to the frequency of mode vibration within the range of the gyro. At the higher frequencies inertial loads on the engine become significant. At these same higher frequencies it is found that the gimbaled thrust chamber responds to transverse accelerations of the gimbal mount as well as to autopilot commands. In addition, the engine transfer function itself cannot be taken as a simple lag—mount flexibilities and nonlinear effects being significant.

3. *Multiple nonlinearities.* The possibilities of entering into limit cycle oscillations upon response to strong disturbances, cannot be treated readily by hand.

4. *Time-varying parameters.* Since the system flies with changing parameters and flies for only a finite time, the effects of various inputs, and of very marginal stabilities (even instabilities) in some modes, can best be studied by computer simulations.

5. *Transient effects.* Since vehicle loads are of prime importance, the transient response of the system leading to many (if not most) of the critical loads must be computed. Analytic tools are available for doing transient studies on relatively simple equations, of course. However, the importance of the interaction of many degrees of freedom under transient conditions usually leads one to consider problems which are not amenable to hand calculations.

The variety of computer studies which may be made for the refined system analysis can be classified in several categories depending upon:

1. Whether the equations used have fixed or time-varying coefficients. Obviously the majority of all parameters of each problem change throughout flight and hence almost all problems have time-varying coefficients. It is however, most convenient to make studies at various conditions throughout the flight using as fixed coefficients the instantaneous parameter values. The assumption is, of course, that the parameters do not change rapidly enough to invalidate results so obtained.

2. The type of problem, whether a stability study or transient analysis.

3. The type of computer employed, whether analog or digital. In theory most problems can be done on either type of computer, hence there would be no distinction to make. In practice, however, some problems lend themselves more readily to one type than the other by the nature of the problem, information to be extracted and the extent to which the problem is defined. (In early study stages problems have a tendency to "grow" as experience is gained. An analog computer is more flexible in absorbing spur-of-the-moment adjustments in the problem.)

In the remainder of this section we describe the studies and results carried out for the vehicle under study. No exhaustive detail is given, the presentation being directed rather to give the reader a picture of the applications of the computers as a tool in performing a refined analysis of the control system of the boost vehicle.

15.10   Detailed Root-locus Studies

For purposes of studying more carefully the variations in roots of the significant modes (modes within the range of control frequencies), it is convenient to employ a digital computer, particularly when the equations become quite numerous and strongly coupled. The digital routine should be capable of extracting the roots directly from the equations when they are written as a set of simultaneous differential equations in all the variables. The homogeneous equations of motion (independent

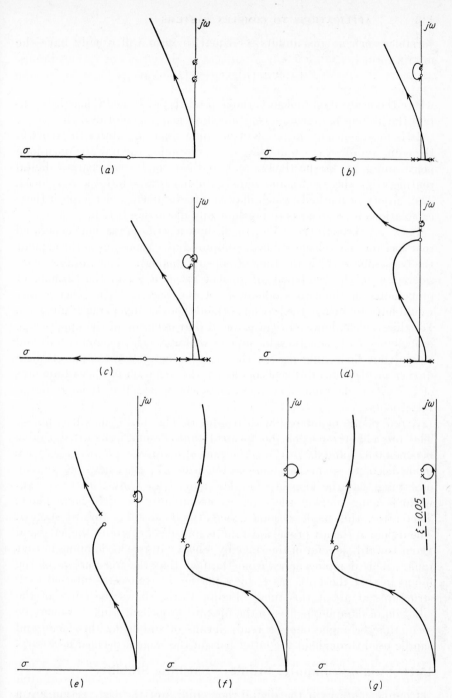

Fig. 15.16 (a) Root loci for boost stage two-propellant modes $t = 0$. (b) Root loci for boost stage two-propellant tanks $t = 0.30T_s$. (c) Root loci for boost stage two-propellant tanks $t = 0.50T_s$. (d) Root loci for boost stage two-propellant tanks $t = 0.70T_s$. (e) Root loci for boost phase two-propellant tanks $t = 0.9T_s$. (f) Root loci for boost phase two-propellant tanks $t = T_s$. (g) Root loci for boost phase two-propellant tanks $t = T_s$. Stabilization of forward tank unstable mode by baffling.

variables such as gust inputs set equal to zero) will usually have the matrix form

$$\{[A]s^2 + [B]s + [C]\}\{q_i\} = 0$$

where the q_i are the problem variables and the A, B, and C matrices contain the system parameters, constant for a given instant of flight.

It is most efficient, in terms of machine time, to extract the roots of the equation for $K_A = 0$ and $K_A \to \infty$, obtaining thereby the open-loop poles and zeros (respectively) and to then employ a separate digital routine using these poles and zeros as inputs to generate the root locus. The variety of methods which may be programmed to accomplish these calculations is so great as to preclude any discussion herein.

Parts (a) through (f) of Fig. 15.16 show a series of machine-generated root loci for the vehicle studied, computed at various times throughout the boost phase (T_s is the time of booster staging). The variables considered were the rigid body degree of freedom θ and the sloshing of propellants in the two main tanks of the booster. [In general, one would have to include the propellant modes of the upper stage tanks, too. For this vehicle, however, it was found that inclusion of the upper-stage propellants led to small residue dipoles well up on the imaginary axis and having but little influence on the main modes. While some of these dipoles yielded unstable root-loci loops, the inclusion of a small amount of propellant damping was found sufficient to stabilize them (refer to Fig. 15.10).]

A few points of interest with respect to Fig. 15.16 should be noted. The propellant mode of the forward tank becomes slightly unstable between $0.3 T_S$ and $0.5 T_S$ (T_S is the time of booster staging). This same mode becomes somewhat more *stable* near $0.7 T_S$, as may be seen by observing that the loop of roots has moved up away from the origin while keeping roughly the same excursion into the right-hand plane. Thereafter, this mode becomes increasingly unstable toward staging. The dipole of the aft propellant tank is pulled sharply into the left-hand plane toward the end of the stage by a heavy degree of damping in that tank. This damping arises from the fact that the free surface of the liquid in that the tank passes by a portion of transverse internal tank structures at about this time. Figure 15.16g shows the effect of the addition of damping baffles to the forward propellant tank. As may be seen, this technique offers a ready means of stabilizing this mode and can be used throughout the latter part of the stage if deemed necessary.

15.11 Analog-computer Studies—Sloshing Stability

Complementary to the digital-root studies of the last section are a series of fixed-coefficient analog stability studies made for various times of flight. An analog simulation of the vehicle equations, including all pertinent degrees of freedom and the autopilot, is set up for the conditions at a given time of flight.   The equations simulated are similar to Eqs. (15.8) but with the additional terms for the other propellant modes. There are also, of course, the equations representing the autopilot. These are linear equations with fixed coefficients (fixed since they are to be studied for selected flight time) and hence are readily patched for the computer.

To study the stability of the propellant sloshing modes the system is excited by introducing a transient such as a step attitude command. Following the transient disturbance the heavily damped rigid body modes will quickly damp out, leaving the propellant modes, whose rate of decay or growth can be measured.   By employing the above procedure for conditions at different flight times, the plot of Fig. 15.17 was obtained

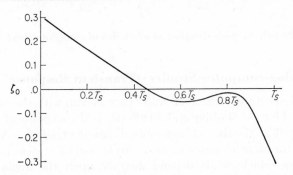

Fig. 15.17 Plot of propellant mode damping versus flight time in boost stage (nominal gains).

for this vehicle.   The correspondence between dampings of this propellant mode and the root-loci plots of Fig. 15.16 is immediately obvious.

If duplication of the digital results were the only output, the effort of setting up the analog study would not be warranted.   The major use of such a simulation for this problem is in making a parameter study. From the foregoing it is obvious that the most critical propellant sloshing problem occurs just prior to staging of the booster vehicle.   Hence, a study was run for conditions at that time of flight in which autopilot gains were varied in different combinations to obtain their effect upon sloshing stability.   The results are given in Fig. 15.18.

An examination of Fig. 15.18 shows that no reasonable gain change can effect a significant improvement in stability of the propellant mode. On the other hand, this same insensitivity of the mode to gain changes means that gain tolerances will not have to be too tightly held, insofar as this control problem is concerned.   It would also indicate that any gain changes made as a consequence of further analyses into other problem areas should have little influence on the design of a set of propellant baffles to control sloshing.

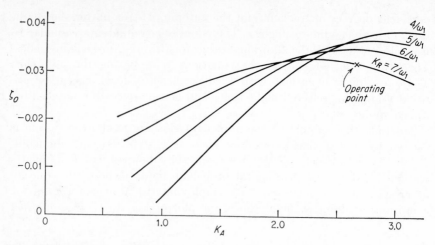

Fig. 15.18   Propellant mode damping as a function of autopilot gains $t = T_s$ (before staging).

15.12   Analog-computer Studies—Transient Response

Another important parameter study may be run with the same analog setup as used for the sloshing stability;* this is the response of the system to a gust input at the time of maximum dynamic pressure. As discussed earlier, the transient response of an attitude control system is important inasmuch as vehicle loads depend directly upon the angle of attack resulting from a gust input.

Figure 15.19 shows the variation in per cent overshoot to a step gust input with changes in autopilot gains. A separate loads study on the vehicle had shown that a 30 per cent overshoot in a 60-fps sharp-edged gust could be tolerated by the vehicle structure while flying through a standard wind profile. One of the important properties of the system shown by these data is that for low nominal loop gains K_A, the gust overshoot is very sensitive to a change in gain (steep slope of curves). Gains in this region would be undesirable (even if the structure could carry the higher loadings) because of the necessity for close tolerances. The chosen operating point is highly satisfactory since the overshoot is low and the gain sensitivity is also low.

It should be noted that, if one studies the variation in body bending moments due to the combination of aerodynamic, inertia, and control forces as a function of K_A, the trend follows that of Fig. 15.19 for the range of gains shown. For still higher loop gains, however, the bending moment will begin to increase with gain as the effects of the inertia and control forces begin to predominate over the aerodynamic loadings.

---

* One will, however, have to include the flight-path equation in this study, i.e., we can no longer use $\theta \doteq \alpha$.

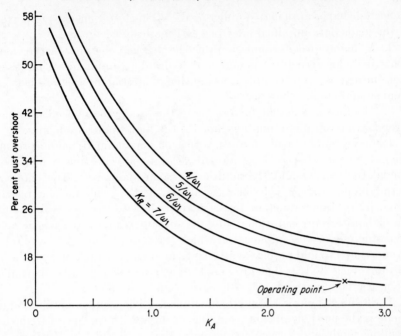

Fig. 15.19   Per cent gust overshoot at maximum dynamic pressure as a function of autopilot gains.

15.13   Analog-computer Studies—Flexible Vehicle

One of the most difficult problems encountered in the analysis of a high-performance vehicle control system is that of a closed-loop servoelastic instability in which vehicle body bending modes couple into the autopilot.[4]   Closely allied to the stability problem is the problem of loads and accelerations on the flexible vehicle, such loads sometimes exceeding those computed for a rigid body (Sec. 15.12).   Thus it is necessary to establish a computer simulation for the flexible vehicle plus autopilot, which simulation is sufficiently comprehensive that it can yield data for both problem areas.

The rudiments of the closed-loop stability problem were discussed in Sec. 15.8, wherein the importance of proper location of the attitude gyros on the vehicle was demonstrated.   In that analysis only a (relatively) low-frequency bending mode was considered and many higher-order effects were neglected.   For the more complete study simulated on the computer, most or all of the following additional effects must be included:

1.   Higher-frequency bending modes.   All modes within the bandpass of the rate gyro and/or the engine thrust chamber position servo must be included.   A further requirement is that the necessary number of natural modes be included to represent with sufficient accuracy the

deflected shapes anticipated under loads.   This latter check is important
if the loads data obtained are to be satisfactorily accurate.

2. A higher-order simulation of the engine chamber servo loop.
This includes structural mount and hydraulic compliances, important
non-linearities, and a complete accounting of inertial interactions between
vehicle and engine chamber.[5]

3. The higher-order characteristics of the rate gyro are needed to yield
proper gain and phase relationships for the high-frequency modes.

4. Aerodynamic loads near the time of maximum dynamic pressure
should be included.   These airloads lead to an effective reduction in
modal frequencies and the addition of some damping.   The choice of
aerodynamic theory will have to be made by weighing the relative
importance of aerodynamic forces against the effort required to provide
an elaborate representation.   For the present study a quasistatic aerodynamic model was employed in which the instantaneous lift was taken
proportional to and in phase with the local angle of attack at each station
of the vehicle body.   The local angle of attack was, of course, dependent
upon the bending modes as well as the rigid body motion.

5. Sloshing modes should be included.   The fundamental sloshing
mode is the most significant, coupling strongly with the lowest frequency
bending mode under some conditions.   It is doubtful whether inclusion
of higher sloshing modes is worthwhile inasmuch as experimental evidence shows that these modes are seldom successfully excited in test
tanks.   Further, they would have to be excited by the flexing walls of
the tanks responding to the higher bending modes (these being closer to
their natural frequencies), and the problem of fluid response to a flexing
wall is not readily treated.   For the fundamental bending mode however,
tank curvature is slight, and hence the interaction of this mode with the
fundamental sloshing mode is probably well represented.

In setting up this simulation, one is again patching a set of constant-
coefficient equations which are linear with the possible exception of some
nonlinearities in the engine chamber servo system such as hydraulic-
pressure–valve-flow relations, gimbal bearing, coulomb friction, servo
valve dead zone, etc.   There are two distinguishing characteristics of
this simulation: (1) A large amount of equipment is required in the
computer which leads to reliability problems, and (2) the high frequencies
of some important modes lead to large gains in certain computer loops,
in turn leading to problems with circuit noise.   The latter problem is
overcome by scaling the problem in time, all frequencies being reduced
by the scale factor.   The former problem is only overcome by diligence.

A detailed simulation was employed incorporating the effects discussed
above to check the suitability of autopilot gains and gyro package location for the vehicle studied.   For any given position of the gyros along
the body, a loop rate gain $K_A K_R$ may be found at which oscillations of a

body bending mode will be sustained at constant amplitude. If various positions along the vehicle are tested in this manner, a locus of gains for neutral stability is found for each mode as shown in Fig. 15.20. The locus for any one mode peaks at the antinode for that mode. The envelope of these loci (shown crosshatched) forms an upper boundary to the rate gains. From the discussion of Sec. 15.8, one would not expect to obtain a finite boundary for the first mode over the aft portion of the body. In the detailed simulation, however, various nonlinearities were incorporated in the engine gimbaling servo loop representation which led to a subharmonic mode (at roughly one-half the mode's natural frequency). This subharmonic provides the first mode locus over the rear half.

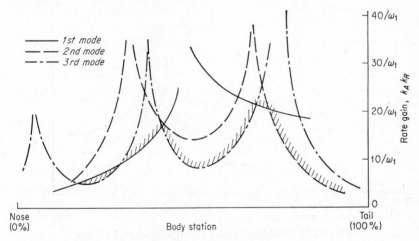

Fig. 15.20 Loci of neutrally stable gain points $t = T_{\text{launch}}(= 0)$.

The results shown in Fig. 15.20 are those obtained for only one time of flight. These were repeated at various other flight times to obtain the composite picture of Fig. 15.21. In Fig. 15.21, emphasis has been placed upon the boundaries in the 75 per cent station region since this offers the most promise for satisfactory gains. The boundaries tend to move upward with flight time (as the modal frequencies go up with the expenditure of propellants, the frequencies move out of the bandpass of the autopilot), but there is also some lateral shifting. Thus, the "clear" area of Fig. 15.20 has narrowed down somewhat in Fig. 15.21. The shaded area of Fig. 15.21 is the safe operating region.

It is now observed that the preliminary gain choice of

$$K_A K_R = 2.65 \times \frac{7}{\omega_1} = \frac{18.5}{\omega_1}$$

is exactly on the boundary if the gyro is placed at the 71 per cent station.

Such a situation is undesirable since it leaves no margin for tolerances on the gain or for inaccuracies in this analysis. Consequently, a new gain choice will be made at this time to provide an approximately 3.5-db gain margin. The revised operating point is shown at the 69 per cent station with

$$K_A K_R = \frac{12.5}{\omega_1}$$

It is necessary to backtrack over some of the previous parameter studies into the problem of propellant sloshing and transient response to see if such a gain reduction is permissible and to see in which way it is

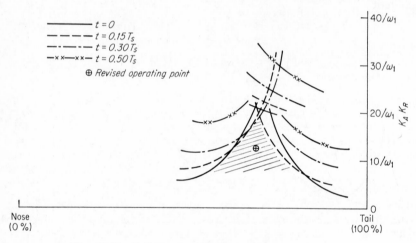

Fig. 15.21   Stability boundaries at various flight times.

best effected—a straight reduction in K_A, a reduction in K_R, or a combination of the two. A little study shows that it is probably best to reduce only K_A down to 1.8. This change results in a slight increase in gust overshoot (from 13 to 16.5 per cent as shown by Fig. 15.19) with a small beneficial effect on propellant sloshing (Fig. 15.18). Going still further back to the rigid vehicle root loci of Figs. 15.4 and 15.5, it is found that operating points throughout the flight are those of stable well-damped modes. Thus, the revised gains will be set at

$$K_A = 1.80$$
$$K_R = \frac{7}{\omega_1}$$

Having established a suitable gain and gyro location it is now possible to employ this flexible vehicle simulation for a variety of load studies under transient conditions. Some of the important transient inputs are gusts, wind profiles, launch transients when the vehicle is released and the autopilot is activated, and staging transients when the booster engines are shut down and/or other engines are ignited.

Some of the data gathered in these transient studies include:

1. Body bending moments at various stations. These are formed by an integration of the transverse aerodynamic and inertia loads on the beam. By using suitable preliminary numerical calculations these moments may be read directly from the computer as the simulation responds to a transient. These moments provide some of the design loads for the vehicle body.

2. Transverse accelerations may be determined at various points to obtain the loadings on specific equipment installations.

3. Engine gimbaling responses, which may provide data on the engine chamber servo requirements.

4. Local angles of attack can be read to check loadings on various body protuberances such as antennae, instrumentation booms, etc.

5. Propellant sloshing responses, since such data may be required to design internal tank structure and propellant damping baffles.

15.14 Time-varying Simulation

As a final check upon the suitability of the system for use throughout the boost phase, a complete simulation is set up having time-varying parameters. Depending upon the extent to which this simulation is to be used, the configuration and flight parameters (dynamic pressure, center of pressure, mass, center of gravity, engine thrust, etc.) may be either of two types:

1. The parameters are set functions of time, being those which a vehicle of nominal characteristics would experience in normal flight. The assumption made is, of course, that deviations from this nominal trajectory due to flight control system effects will be small enough to neglect. This simulation is probably the simplest but is also restricted to studying control system problems alone.

2. The parameters are self-generating, the input functions being properties of the atmosphere (functions of altitude) and the propulsion system.* The vehicle flies any trajectory it will; parameters such as dynamic pressure, Mach number, center of gravity, and mass moment of inertia are computed as the flight progresses. This is the most complete simulation (and the most complex). It may be used for studying such problems as the effects of variation in launching weight, propellant flow rates, variations in propulsive efficiency, etc., upon the flight and their possible effects upon flight control quality. It is also the more realistic problem for use in a combined guidance-control simulation.

For the greatest potential utilization of this simulation it is desirable that the problem run on a one-to-one scale with real time. It is not

---

* Thrust is a function of altitude; vehicle inertial properties are functions of propellant flow rates.

likely that body bending modes would be included in these simulations, but propellant sloshing would have to be.

With a time-varying simulation, a number of tests of performance quality may be made which were not possible in the previous fixed-coefficient studies. Primarily, these studies consist of a complete launch-to-staging simulation to observe the behavior of the vehicle and control system during the launch, forced turn off the vertical, and flight through various wind profiles and gusts. The implications of the instability in the forward propellant tank mode and the amount of damping which must be added to that tank may be examined. In the vehicle under study, for instance, it was found possible to allow the slight degree of propellant mode instability up to about $t = 0.7T_s$ without adding propellant damping baffles. After $t = 0.7T_s$ it was found necessary to add baffles. (A baffle is "added" after a certain time of flight by locating it in the propellant tank such that the free surface of the liquid arrives at the baffle station just shortly before the damping is needed. Baffle damping is only effective when the baffle is close to the liquid's free surface.)

Figures 15.22 through 15.24 show some traces taken from the time-varying simulation of the vehicle studied. Figure 15.22 shows traces for the vehicle flying through still air and without propellant baffles in the tanks. The angle of attack and engine deflection which develop shortly after launch are those occurring during the pitchover off the vertical. Propellant sloshing was started right from launch in these runs to simulate the effect of a strong launch disturbance. As may be seen, propellant motions themselves (ϕ_1 and ϕ_2) are quite moderate throughout the major portion of the flight, and their influence on vehicle motions and control deflections is negligible. It is not until the propellant instability becomes very great, together with the decrease in vehicle inertia toward the end of the stage, that propellant sloshing requires control by baffling. The run of Fig. 15.22 was cut off automatically by the computer short of the nominal staging time when the engine amplitudes reached those of full gimbal travel—an assumed system failure. Note that the engine deflections in the latter portion of the flight are biased off the zero position. This effect is due to the inclusion of thrust misalignments and center-of-gravity offsets in the simulation.

In the run of Fig. 15.23 the presence of damping baffles in the lower portion of the forward tank has been simulated. As may be seen, sloshing is now contained and resultant engine motions are considered acceptable.*

---

* Determination of "acceptable" amplitudes requires consideration of such factors as engine gimbaling servo hydraulic demand, vehicle body bending moments, etc. Note that sloshing amplitudes at launch appear larger on Figs. 15.23 and 15.24 than on Fig. 15.22 because of a change in recording scale.

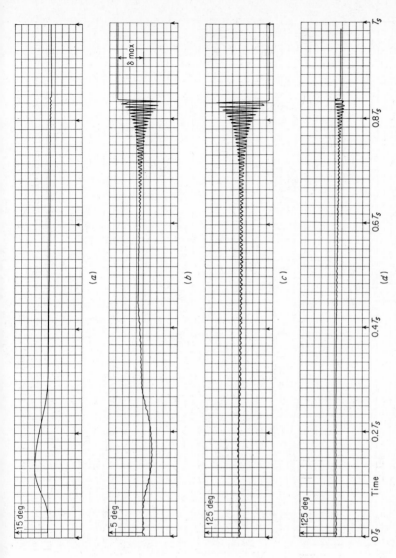

Fig. 15.22 Boost stage flight without propellant slosh compensation (still air flight condition). (*a*) Vehicle angle of attack α. (*b*) Engine gimbal angle δ. (*c*) Forward propellant tank slosh angle (ϕ_1). (*d*) Aft propellant tank slosh angle ϕ_2.

447

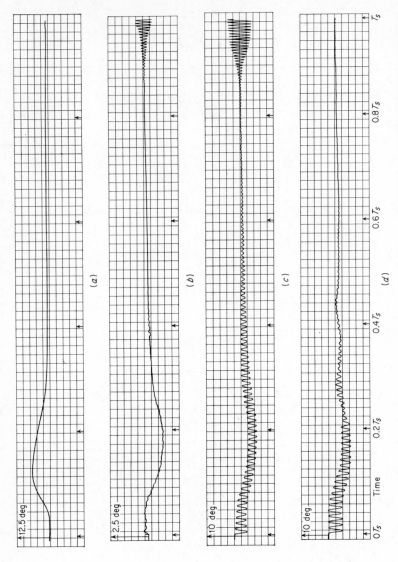

Fig. 15.23 Boost stage flight with forward propellant tank baffled (still-air flight condition). (a) Vehicle angle of attack α. (b) Engine gimbal angle δ. (c) Forward propellant tank slosh angle ϕ_1. (d) Aft propellant tank slosh angle ϕ_2.

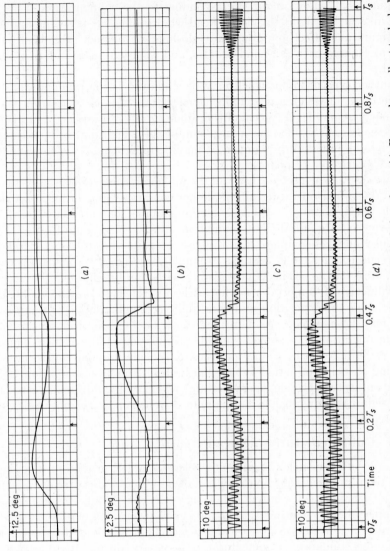

Fig. 15.24 (*a*) Vehicle angle of attack α. (*b*) Engine gimbal angle δ. (*c*) Forward propellant tank slosh angle ϕ_1. (*d*) Aft propellant tank slosh angle ϕ_2.

449

Figure 15.24 shows a run corresponding to the configuration of Fig. 15.23 in which a flight through a head-wind profile has been simulated. No significant effect on propellant sloshing developed. Similar runs were also made with tail-wind profiles, and with various standard gusts added.

Another type of input which may be employed is the random atmospheric input in which a gust input signal having a power spectrum and root-mean-square level typical of that found in the atmosphere[6] is added. Since the system studied has a large number of degrees of freedom, some of which are but slightly damped, it may be found that a random input provides excessive responses.

It was established by means of all the foregoing studies that the system is suitable when operating at the design conditions and in an approximately linear manner. While a certain number of parameter studies were run on the fixed-time simulations (Secs. 15.11 and 15.12), the influence on the complete flight phase of gain variations and other off-design conditions (variations in tankage weights, propellant flow rates, etc.) can be studied quite readily with this simulation. Further, the influence of important nonlinearities in the system (threshold of gyros; dead zone, position and rate limit, coulomb friction in engines; etc.) may be assayed. As a further check on the practical aspects of system operation, the analog-computer simulation of the vehicle equations of motion can be connected into a physical autopilot consisting of working elements of actual vehicle hardware. This last simulation will check out actual system operation and will permit additional tests of off-design conditions such as fluctuations of vehicle power-supply voltage and frequency.

15.15   Guidance—Introductory Remarks

In order for a vehicle to arrive at a selected target, provisions must be made to ensure that the vehicle will follow a preselected course or trajectory. Deviations of limited extent are allowable and are corrected during the flight. During a flight the vehicle is acted upon by a source of thrust, a gravitational field, and atmospheric lift and drag effects. Continuous guidance of some form is necessary during those periods when thrust is applied to the missile. During periods of free fall or coasting, passive guidance may be used continuously or intermittently to track the vehicle and to compute the corrections to be made when thrust is again applied.

Since the thrust is usually applied in the direction of the vehicle's longitudinal axis, the attitude determines the direction of thrust acceleration. If the assigned attitude is a constant or programmed by a preset function generating mechanism, the vehicle is said to be operating with open-loop guidance. When the assigned attitude is made a function of an error signal derived from a comparison of the vehicle's position and velocity with desired position and velocity values, the vehicle is said to be operating under closed-loop guidance. Depending on factors such as accuracy, stability, and fuel efficiency, a vehicle may be in either open-loop or closed-loop guidance during various portions of its powered flight.

15.16 Guidance System Elements

For other than a simple pursuit type of guidance, a necessary element in the closed-loop phase of flight is a computer. The function of the computer is twofold: it performs the navigation calculations giving past, present, and future positions (of both the vehicle and the target) and evaluates those "guidance equations" with which an error signal is generated to be applied as an appropriate command input to the auto-pilot. This command results in a change of attitude of the vehicle such that the guidance-error signal tends to approach zero. The computer

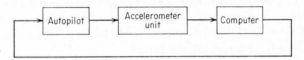

Fig. 15.25 Block diagram of self-contained guidance system.

may be either on board the vehicle or earth-based. Generally, for terrestrial flight, if the velocity and position determinations are made aboard the vehicle, the advantage lies with a vehicle-borne computer since this results in a self-contained system without the problem of two-way communications with the ground. If the velocity and position determinations are made from an earth-based tracker, the advantage clearly lies with a computer at the tracker from a weight-saving standpoint.

For a minimum number of elements, a self-contained vehicle system might consist of an autopilot, a set of three accelerometers aligned with the three axes of the vehicle, and a computer as shown in the block diagram of Fig. 15.25.

The autopilot maintains an attitude of the vehicle with respect to inertial space in accordance with the command received from the computer. The accelerometer unit computes the three components of acceleration along the vehicle's axes resulting from all forces acting on the vehicle except that due to the gravitational field. The computer must then perform the following operations:

1. It must transform the acceleration vector of the accelerometers from a vector in vehicle coordinates to a vector in inertial coordinates. The orientation of the inertial coordinate system with respect to the vehicle coordinate system is fixed at the time of launch, but thereafter

is continuously changing in accordance with the commands to the autopilot. The computer must then compute a continuously varying transformation matrix with which the acceleration vector is multiplied to obtain the acceleration vector in the inertial reference system. To this acceleration vector must be added the acceleration vector due to the gravitational field. The resultant vector is integrated twice to yield increments of position and velocity of the vehicle in the inertial reference system.

2. The computer must determine an error function based on the data of the vehicle's position and velocity and the position of the target.[7] The error function may be computed in several ways: (a) The computer may have a reference path stored with which the actual position and velocity can be compared in a continuous manner so that the difference will result in an error function. (b) The computer may calculate the target which would be reached if the powered phase were immediately terminated. The difference between this position vector and the position vector of the desired target is the basis of calculating an error function. (c) The computer may calculate as an error function the incremental velocity vector which would have to be added to the present velocity vector in order to hit the target.

The error function must fulfill two requirements. It must provide an adequate basis for generating angular rate commands to the autopilot so that the vehicle attitude is changed in such a manner that the velocity gained during powered flight is in the direction necessary for the vehicle to arrive at the target, and it must also determine the time at which the powered phase is terminated. Also when the calculations are made in an inertial reference system, the time of flight must be estimated, and the inertial position which the target will have at the end of the flight must be computed.

The major sources of error arising from this simplified system are the autopilot system and the accelerometer unit. Assume, for instance, that autopilot attitude reference is obtained from single-degree-of-freedom integrating gyros. Then an attitude change is accomplished by applying a torque to the proper gyro, creating thereby an error signal. This signal is reduced to zero as the vehicle responds. Errors arise from nonlinearities in the torquing system, drifts in the gyros, and a time lag in the response of the vehicle. These appear as errors in the transformation used to change the measured accelerations to an inertial reference. Any constant error in the inertial acceleration vector will accumulate in the integration processes to produce an increasing error in position and velocity with time. The accelerometer unit has inherent errors related to the sensitivity of the accelerometers, and also errors of misalignment.

With accuracies presently available in gyros and accelerometers, such a system would be satisfactory for terrestrial flights where the powered flight phase is of only a few minutes duration. For interplanetary flights the power requirements for continuous operation would be large, and the accumulated drifts would have to be corrected at intervals by means of astronomical observations or radio tracking.

The errors due to the autopilot may be improved but not entirely eliminated by the use of a stable platform. The stable platform is a device which remains fixed with respect to an inertial reference while the vehicle's attitude may be continually changing. The platform makes use of a gyro sensing and feedback unit which maintains its orientation with very low drift rates, and since no torques are applied, the torquing error is eliminated. The accelerometers are mounted on the three axes of the stable platform so that a coordinate transformation is no longer necessary for the acceleration vector.

Depending upon the length of the mission and accuracy required, the computer may be either a digital, analog, digital-differential analyzer, or a combination of types. For example, the integrations might be accomplished by analog units, while a coordinate transformation might be made digitally.

So far the case of a complete navigational unit on board the vehicle has been discussed. A second system is one in which the velocity and position determinations are made from an earth-based tracker. In this system the computer is at the tracker and the necessary elements in the ship are the autopilot, a command receiver for receiving autopilot and engine cutoff commands, and usually a transponder of some type which facilitates the determination of position and of velocity by the earth-based tracker. The command data may be superimposed on the tracker channel in the form of modulation, thus eliminating the requirement for a separate command receiver. The problems related to setting up a guidance system in this case are similar to those mentioned in the previous system. The sources of error however, are largely those of the tracker. The tracker may use a continuous-wave (c-w) system which utilizes the phase difference between a signal retransmitted from the vehicle and the original signal for range determination, or it may use pulsed radar, or combined pulsed and c-w systems for position and velocity measurements. The errors of measurement consist of tropospheric and ionospheric effects on the velocity of radio propagation, changes in baseline distance (the distance between two receivers), frequency instability, and radio noise from various sources. The block diagram of such a simplified system is shown in Fig. 15.26.

Limitations peculiar to this system result from the necessity of maintaining a direct line of sight from the tracker to the vehicle's antenna. The accuracy of the tracker decreases rapidly as the line of sight nears the horizon. Reception of the radio signals becomes erratic if the radio beam passes through the exhaust flame of the rocket engine, and finally with a directional antenna on the vehicle, the vehicle must follow such a trajectory as to maintain the angle between the radio beam and the vehicle antenna within the proper limits.

In order to decide what guidance system is to be used for a given vehicle and the specifications of the computer to be used in the closed-loop guidance, it is apparent that a very extensive analysis must be made, considering the factors of reliability, optimization of range or payload, and accuracy. For such an analysis, a simulation of the entire system on a digital computer is a necessity. This is not to imply that such a simulation is the first step in the analysis or that individual elements in the system cannot be analyzed in approximate fashion without com-

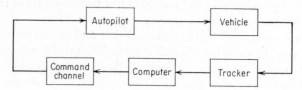

Fig. 15.26   Block diagram of command guidance system.

puter aid. In addition, as will be seen, the analog computer plays an essential role in preliminary analysis of the guidance loop.

For the vehicle studied (having the mission given in the introduction), considerations too numerous to mention here led to a choice of guidance system using a ground-based tracker and computer. This system will be used to illustrate the steps necessary for a complete guidance and performance analysis.

15.17   Analysis of a Guidance System

It is assumed that a preliminary analysis has determined the general specifications of the vehicle such as the weight, engine thrust, nominal performance, and over-all configuration. For a detailed examination of the performances of the vehicle under the influence of errors in velocity and position determinations, weight and thrust variations, and atmospheric variations in density and wind, a three-dimensional simulation on a large-scale computer is used. Thus, the procedure begins with gross effects and simplifying assumptions, proceeds to the examination of small and second-order effects, and goes on finally to a simulation of the entire flight of the vehicle in as great detail as possible.

In the following discussion we present first a picture of the techniques for computation in the general case, after which some of the simplified analyses, obtained by stripping away various secondary effects, will be considered.

Initially it must be decided what quantities and effects are to be included in the problem and in what coordinate systems they are to be expressed. Experience has shown that the simulation of a complex physical system is greatly expedited by:

1. The use of a coordinate system for each effect which is appropriate or natural for that effect. This generally requires the use of several coordinate systems and the use of transformations from one coordinate system to another. This technique permits one to use both simpler equations and to obtain intermediate numerical read-outs in the natural coordinates, thus aiding the engineer in the interpretation of the physical behavior of the system and the avoidance of conceptual errors.

2. The use of rectangular coordinates makes the use of vector subroutines in the computer feasible. Vector operations such as dot and cross products have a form which is independent of the coordinate system used, so that the computation of many needed quantities is facilitated by the use of vector equations which are independent of the coordinate system. The use of vector notation simplifies the mathematical expressions and facilitates the mathematical description of the system in the simplest manner.

In the system to be simulated there are three principle coordinate systems in which the quantities are expressed. In order to maintain the distinction between them a system of subscripts is used. For all vector quantities the first subscript refers to the object being measured. Thus m indicates a vector associated with the missile, e refers to the earth, l the point of launch, and t the tracker. The second subscript refers to the coordinate system. i refers to an earth-centered nonrotating inertial coordinate system, e refers to an earth-fixed system with its center at the center of the earth, and s refers to the coordinate system of the vehicle.

Lower-case letters used for vectors indicate quantities measured with respect to the inertial coordinates, and upper-case letters indicate quantities measured with respect to earth-fixed coordinates. As examples, V_{mi} is the vector velocity of the vehicle measured with respect to the earth but expressed in inertial coordinates, while v_{mi} is the vector velocity measured with respect to the inertial reference and expressed in inertial coordinates. In this case the two vectors are related by the equation: $V_{mi} = v_{mi} - \omega_{ei} \times R_{mi}$ where ω_{ei} is the angular velocity vector of the earth in inertial coordinates and R_{mi} is the position vector of the vehicle in inertial coordinates.

By using an inertial coordinate system for the vehicle's acceleration, velocity, and position, the computation of Coriolis and centrifugal forces is avoided. Tracker measurements are made in an earth-fixed coordinate system and similarly for wind velocity. Aerodynamic forces and thrust forces exerted on the vehicle are logically expressed in the vehicle coordinate system.

In order to transform a vector from one system to another it is multiplied by a nine-element matrix. To convert back again, the inverse of the matrix is used.   Since for rectangular systems, a unitary orthogonal matrix consisting of the components of the unit vectors of one system in terms of the other is used, the inverse of the matrix is easily obtained by interchanging the rows and columns of the matrix.   In the program, routines are used to compute the nine time-varying elements of the matrix which are stored and available to be used at any point in the program.   The matrix to transform earth to inertial coordinates is designated as M_R and its inverse as M_R^{-1}, while the matrix to transform vehicle to inertial coordinates is designated as M_S and its inverse as M_S^{-1}.

Figure 15.27 identifies the three coordinate systems at the time of launch.   Let the inertial axes be u, v, w; the earth-fixed axes be x, y, z;

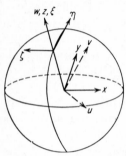

and the vehicle axes be ξ, η, ζ.   The w and z axes are coincident and pass through the launch point; the x axis is pointed east, while the u axis points in the initial direction of flight, and the y axis points north with the v axis perpendicular to the u and w axes.   The longitudinal axis of the vehicle, ξ, is pointed vertically upwards, the ζ axis which lies in the pitch plane during flight is in an opposite direction to the u axis, and the η axis, which lies in the yaw plane during flight,

Fig. 15.27 Coordinate systems at time of launch.

is pointed in the same direction as the v axis. The center of the vehicle system is at the launch point rather than the earth's center at the beginning of flight.

If the tracker is at a point other than the launcher, it is also desirable to use a coordinate system centered at the tracker to compute the quantities such as range, elevation, and azimuth angles measured by the tracker. In a similar manner as before, a matrix is used to convert to the desired coordinate system.   If in addition to transforming the coordinates of a given vector it is desired to change the reference of the vector, it is necessary to add or subtract a vector relating the two reference systems. For example, if the vector from the tracker to the vehicle in tracker coordinates is desired, it may be obtained by multiplying the vector from the center of the earth to the vehicle by the proper matrix and then subtracting the vector from the center of the earth to the tracker.

Figure 15.28 shows the sequential relation of the computations necessary in the full simulation of a flight.   The computations within each block utilize the results of the previous block.   An interval of time h is selected which represents the elapsed real time between each set of computations.   The actual time required for the complete set of computations may be less or greater than the real-time interval h depending on the speed of the computer.   Block 1, however, requires as an input the results of block 4 which is computed later than block 1, implying that one or more complete iterations may be necessary within one time

interval.   At the beginning of a computation interval, block 1 uses a
predicted value of $\mathbf{a}_{ci}$ available from the previous computation interval.
A test is made at the end of block 4 which compares the computed value
of $\mathbf{a}_{ci}$ with the value used as the input to block 1.   If the difference
exceeds a selected tolerance the entire set of computations is repeated
until the tolerance conditions are met.   Care must be taken to ensure
that such iteration loops are stable, i.e., that an error does not increase

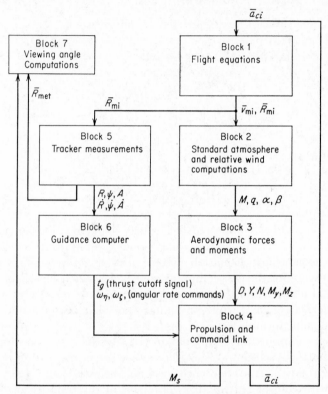

Fig. 15.28   Simplified block diagram of flight simulation.

with each iteration.   By properly choosing the points at which the
extrapolations and tests are made, computing time may be minimized.
In this case, since the output of block 4 is a single vector quantity, a
minimum of computation for extrapolation is required.

Within each block there may be additional required iteration loops.[8]
Again the problem is to minimize computing time and to maintain loop
stability.   Iteration loops may sometimes be avoided through the use of
recursion formulas, particularly in the case of the simulation of filters.
The parallel loop of blocks 5 and 6 presents no problem since blocks 5
and 6 may be computed either before or after blocks 2 and 3 without
affecting the input to block 4.

Figure 15.29 breaks down the blocks of Fig. 15.28 in more detail, showing the principle equations used. Since block 1 requires an iteration loop for the calculation of the gravitational acceleration, it is of interest to examine the digital form of the equations used. These are given in vector notation with each vector equation representing three scalar equations:

$$\mathbf{R}_{mi(p)} = \mathbf{R}_{mi(t-h)} + h\mathbf{v}_{mi(t-h)} + \frac{h^2}{2}\,\mathbf{a}_{mi(t-h)} \tag{15.12}$$

$$\mathbf{g}_{ei} = \frac{-\mu\mathbf{R}_{mi}}{|\mathbf{R}_{mi}|^3} \tag{15.13}$$

$$\mathbf{a}_{mi} = \mathbf{g}_{ei} + \mathbf{a}_{ci} \tag{15.14}$$

$$\mathbf{v}_{mi} = \mathbf{v}_{mi(t-h)} + \frac{h}{12}\left(5\mathbf{a}_{mi(t)} + 8\mathbf{a}_{mi(t-h)} - \mathbf{a}_{mi(t-2h)}\right) \tag{15.15}$$

$$\mathbf{R}_{mi} = \mathbf{R}_{mi(t-h)} + \frac{h}{2}\left(\mathbf{v}_{mi(t)} + \mathbf{v}_{mi(t-h)}\right) - \frac{h^2}{12}\left[\mathbf{a}_{mi(t)} - \mathbf{a}_{mi(t-h)}\right] \tag{15.16}$$

If $\qquad\qquad\qquad \mathbf{R}_{mi} - \mathbf{R}_{mi(p)} > K$

return to Eq. (15.13) and repeat computations.

If $\qquad\qquad\qquad \mathbf{R}_{mi} - \mathbf{R}_{mi(p)} \leqslant K$

proceed to block 2.

Equation (15.12) computes the present value $\mathbf{R}_{mi(p)}$ from values of $\mathbf{R}_{mi}$, $\mathbf{v}_{mi}$, and $\mathbf{a}_{mi}$ available from the previous computational cycle using a Taylor's expansion. Equation (15.15) uses a three-point integration formula except for the first computational cycle when a two-point formula is used. Equation (15.16) avoids the three-point formula by using the second derivative, $\mathbf{a}_{mi}$, while providing somewhat better accuracy than the three-point formula[9].

Block 2 computes the Mach number M, dynamic pressure q, and the angles of attack α and β. Since the earth's atmosphere is rotating with respect to the inertial reference system, the relative velocity of the vehicle with respect to the air is obtained by subtracting the velocity vector of the earth's rotation and the velocity of the wind in inertial coordinates. The wind velocity may be generated as a function of altitude and then converted to inertial coordinates by multiplication by the matrix M_R. The angles of attack α and β are determined by expressing the relative air velocity in terms of the vehicle's coordinate system. This is accomplished by the matrix M_S obtained from block 4. .

In block 3 the aerodynamic forces and moments are computed. The coefficients C_d, C_y, C_n are functions of Mach number and angles of attack, and are computed by polynomials in these variables. A significant simplification is obtained in the case of sharply varying functions by the use of rational fractions. A curve-fit using rational fractions is made easily with the aid of a digital computer. The moments computa-

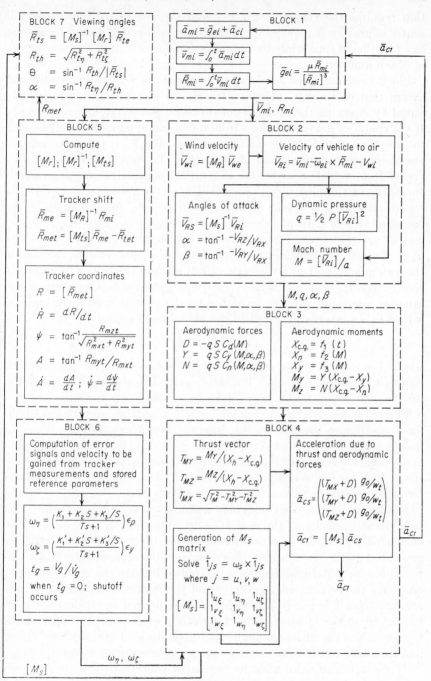

Fig. 15.29 Detailed calculations in flight simulation.

tion requires the center of gravity and the centers of pressure. The center of gravity X_{cg}, varies with fuel consumption and may be expressed as a function of time while the centers of pressures X_y and X_n are functions of Mach number.

Block 4 computes the acceleration vector of the vehicle due to all forces except that of gravity. The components of the thrust vector are computed by equating the moments of thrust to the aerodynamic moments. If the center of gravity is offset from longitudinal axis, the moments due to this effect would also be included. The value $\mathbf{a}_{ci}$ is then extrapolated ahead by one computational interval (h). To convert the acceleration vector from vehicle coordinates to inertial coordinates, an (M_S) matrix consisting of the nine direction cosines l_{ij} of the vehicle axis referred to the inertial axes is used. The direction cosines are functions of the angular rates of attitude change about the vehicle's axes, η, ζ. ω_ξ, ω_η, and ω_ζ are the commands sent to the vehicle's autopilot from block 6. ω_η is the rate of change of attitude in the pitch plane; ω_ζ is the rate in the yaw plane; and ω_ξ is the rate of roll of the vehicle. ω_ξ is generally zero except for a small value of gyro drift. Three sets of three simultaneous equations, each as indicated by the vector equation below, are solved by an integration to yield the nine direction cosines.

$$\dot{\mathbf{l}}_{js} = \boldsymbol{\omega}_s \times \mathbf{l}_{js}$$

where $j = u$, v, w. The components of the unit vectors $\mathbf{l}_{js}$ are then the required direction cosines. The M_S matrix has the value appropriate for the next computation interval.

Block 5 computes the M_r matrix which is used to convert the earth-fixed coordinate system to the inertial coordinate system. The M_{ts} matrix shifts the earth-fixed coordinate system to the tracker coordinate system since the tracker may be situated some distance from the launch site. The tracker coordinates are computed as shown with provision for adding simulated noise to each of the quantities.

Block 6 generates the commands which are sent to the vehicle. The position and velocity of the vehicle as determined by the tracker may be compared against a stored reference trajectory. An error signal is generated and is transformed into angular rate commands to be sent to the autopilot. A signal is also generated to initiate the transition from one stage to the next and finally cut off the engines completely. There are many possible methods of achieving the desired result depending on the nature of the mission. For the problem of placing a 10,000-lb payload in orbit, the altitude, angle, and magnitude of the velocity vector and the plane of the orbit must be properly determined at cutoff.

These last quantities may be compared continuously with reference values in such a manner as to result in ϵ_p and ϵ_y, errors to be corrected by changing the attitude in the pitch and yaw planes respectively, and

V_g which is the required increase in velocity magnitude. The guidance system then should ensure that these three quantities go to zero at the time of power cutoff. In order to accomplish this ϵ_p and ϵ_y are converted to angular rate commands ω_η and ω_ζ through the transfer functions as shown. V_g is used to compute the "time-to-go." When the time-to-go equals zero a signal is sent to the vehicle for power cutoff. A constant offset is used to account for the expected delay in executing the cutoff command. Depending on the requirements of the mission, considerable time and effort are necessary to ensure that the guidance block achieves the desired cutoff conditions in an optimum manner, that is, with a minimum error and fuel loss due to maneuvering of the vehicle. It must be also noted that block 6 alone represents the simulation of the computer used in the control loop of an actual flight.

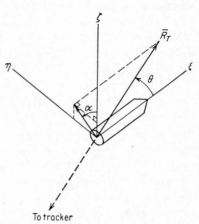

Fig. 15.30 Angles with which the vehicle is viewed from the tracker.

Block 7 computes the angles with which the vehicle is viewed from the tracker.[10]   These angles, shown in Fig. 15.30, are computed for the reference flight path in order to determine the antenna parameters such as placement and beam width.   In some instances it may be necessary to change the form of the reference path in order to produce more favorable viewing angles.   Vector notation again simplifies the form of these computations.   The vector from the tracker to vehicle $\mathbf{R}_{te}$ is obtained in vehicle coordinates $\mathbf{R}_{ts}$. R_{th} is the projection of $\mathbf{R}_{ts}$ in the ζ,η plane.   Then $\theta = \sin^{-1} R_{th}/|\mathbf{R}_{ts}|$ and $\alpha = \sin^{-1} R_{th}/R_{ts}$.

The computation of the reference trajectory may be done before the contents of block 6 has been completely determined, since with no errors assumed, the flight of the vehicle is simulated with open-loop guidance. It is assumed in the present example that preliminary analysis has provided a roughed-out reference trajectory which optimizes the payload. The analysis determined that the stages of flight are as follows:

First Stage.   This encompasses the powered flight from the launch platform where the vehicle starts to rise vertically, shortly after which the attitude is turned toward the horizontal by means of a programmed angular rate command.   The stage ends at a point where the vehicle is well out of the sensible atmosphere.

Second Stage.   This stage commences after dropping off the booster vehicle.   The stage continues until the main vehicle has sufficient velocity to carry it through the coasting stage to the perigee altitude of the desired orbit.

Third Stage. The engines are shut off with the vehicle coasting in free flight to the desired altitude. During this stage additional engines and structure are dropped off.

Fourth Stage. The engines of the final stage are ignited and the thrust continued until the vehicle attains sufficient velocity to maintain it in the desired orbit.

By the use of the switching sequences in the computer program the simulation shown in Fig. 15.29 suffices for all three stages. During the first boost stage all blocks shown are used with the exception of block 6, since guidance is "open loop." (A programmed angular rate ω_η is fed in during this phase.) At the end of the first stage block 3 is bypassed since the vehicle is essentially out of the atmosphere. Corrections are made to the thrust and weight to allow for the dropping of the booster and (later) the other engines. If a closed-loop flight is being simulated, block 6 is used in second stage for guidance. At the beginning of the third stage, the thrust is reduced to zero, and t_g (time-to-go) is made a function of altitude with $\omega_\eta = \omega_\zeta = 0$. At the beginning of the fourth stage the thrust and weight are given the proper value with the guidance equations in block 6 again activated using a different set of constants.

For an open-loop "reference trajectory flight" block 6 is continually bypassed (no guidance). Thus $\omega_\eta = \omega_\zeta = 0$, or some programmed value.

15.18 Guidance Loop Analysis

At this point a more detailed discussion of block 6 will be made. Block 6 results in two types of commands. The first is the angular rate commands ω_η and ω_ζ, which, by properly governing the attitude of the missile, ensure that the velocity vector of the vehicle at power cutoff has the proper direction. The second is the power cutoff command which ensures that the velocity vector has the proper magnitude.

The second type of command is discussed first. It is generally the less complex, particularly if the mission is the achievement of a circular orbit. In this case the required velocity magnitude is a constant or a simple function of altitude. A velocity magnitude to be gained, V_g, may be set up as equal to the required magnitude minus the measured velocity of the vehicle. When $V_g = 0$, the power is cut off. Since the measurements of the vehicle's velocity contain some amount of random noise due to radio noise and fluctuation in the refractive index of the atmosphere, some filtering is desirable. While the filtering process reduces the random noise, it introduces dynamic lag error—unless the filter is designed to handle the time variations of the velocity data. The problem then is to use an optimum filter such that the combination of noise and lag error is a minimum. Several avenues of approach may be used.   One is to use a higher-order filter which decreases the lag but also decreases the reduction in noise.   Another method is to generate a synthetic V_g function which is equal to the actual V_g for the reference trajectory.   The synthetic value is subtracted from the actual V_g, and the difference filtered.   The filtered difference is then added to the synthetic value to give the final smoothed value.   If an accelerometer is mounted on the missile so as to measure the acceleration along the longitudinal axis, its data may be combined with the radio velocity data from the ground in such a way that the accelerometer's drift errors are corrected by the radio data without introducing either substantial noise or drift errors.   A final method is to transform the velocity function into a form that is nearly linear and filter with a second-order filter.   All of these methods have been studied, and here the digital simulation proves a valuable aid in their analysis.   Not only must the results of a given type of filter be evaluated for a reference trajectory but also for all types of variations from the reference which are likely to be encountered.

In order to simplify the analysis of the angular rate commands, two-dimensional guidance is considered in the pitch plane.   Three types of control are discussed: attitude control, velocity control, and position control.   In the first type the attitude of the vehicle is compared with that attitude necessary to achieve the proper direction of the velocity vector at cutoff.   The difference is an error signal which the control system reduces to zero.   In the second type the magnitude of the velocity component normal to the direction of a reference velocity vector is the error which is reduced to zero by the control system.   In the third type, the difference between a position component such as the altitude is compared with a reference value to yield an error signal which goes to zero.   If the position error becomes zero this also implies that the velocity component in the direction of the position component must also go to zero.

It will be assumed for the present that there exists a means of computing a reference function for each case that establishes a value of attitude, velocity, or position such that if the vehicle has such a value it would normally proceed to cutoff without need of further correction in a constant attitude course.   Figure 15.31 shows the feedback loops for each of the three types of controls.   For simplification the autopilot is assumed to have a θ/ω_n transfer function equal to unity, i.e., no lag assumed in the vehicle's response to a rate steering command.   Zero gravity is assumed, and the vehicle's reference attitude is in the same direction as the required velocity.

In all three systems θ represents a deviation in attitude from a reference attitude.   When θ is multiplied by the acceleration a and integrated, the incremental velocity error normal to the reference velocity is obtained.

The incremental velocity tends to reduce any existing normal component ΔV to zero.

In method (a) of Fig. 15.31 $\Delta V / V_g$ represents the angle ϕ which is that change from the reference attitude which would ensure that ΔV goes to zero by the time that V_g goes to zero as shown in the vector diagram of Fig. 15.32. The effect of gravity is ignored in the diagram but may be taken into account by properly adjusting the required velocity V_R.

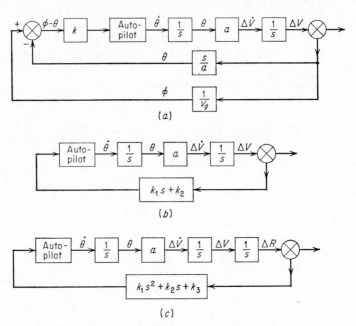

Fig. 15.31   Feedback loops for each of the three types of control.

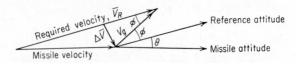

Fig. 15.32   Vector diagram for velocity to be gained.

If $\theta = \phi$ the increment in missile velocity would be along the V_g vector and the required velocity would be eventually attained. In method (a) θ is computed by dividing the rate of change of ΔV by the acceleration. The error $\phi - \theta$ is multiplied by a suitable constant and the attitude of the vehicle forced to change until $\phi = \theta$. This method of guidance results in a minimum of maneuvering since the control tends to maintain the vehicle in a constant attitude in the direction of V_g. As V_g approaches zero the gain goes to infinity so that the control must be shut off a short time before. The high gain near cutoff indicates that the noise present in the measurement and calculation of ΔV is amplified and presents an undesirably noisy signal to the autopilot.

In method (b) of Fig. 15.31, which is a velocity control type, the gain is held constant, thus reducing the noise problem.   There is a greater maneuvering of the vehicle with consequent fuel loss since the vehicle is turned until the missile velocity vector is in the same direction as the V_R.   The $K_1 s$ term is necessary as a damping term.   The values K_1 and K_2 determine the speed with which the correction is made and the stability of the system.

In method (c) the error in position ΔR is fed to the autopilot.   The terms $K_1 s^2 + K_2 s$ are necessary to provide stability for the system. This system requires more maneuvering than either methods (a) or (b). A variation of (c) would be to use ΔV as the error signal with a feedback transfer function of $K_1 s + K_2 + K_3/s$.   The difference is that any position error existing at the beginning of guidance would be maintained without change at cutoff.   Because of the tracker noise, it may be necessary to insert a filter of the form $1/(Ts + 1)$ just before the autopilot. If the time constant T is small with respect to the time constant of the over-all system, the performance of the loop is only slightly changed; as T is increased it becomes increasingly difficult to maintain the stability of the system.

The analog computer is ideally suited to the preliminary analysis and comparison of these systems.   The runs are made quickly, and the desired quantities are plotted graphically so that a partial evaluation can be made immediately after each run.   The gain constants are varied until optimum results are achieved for each system.   Evaluation of gyro drifts, effects of noise, maneuvering, and stability may be made. The best combinations are selected and used in the digital simulation for a final evaluation.   The analog study yields transfer functions of the form

$$\frac{w_n}{\epsilon_p} = \frac{K_1 + K_2 s + K_3/s}{Ts + 1}$$

In block 6 of Fig. 15.29 this is the form of the equation shown.

15.19 Study for the Example System

It is of interest to consider the selection of a set of guidance equations to satisfy a specific mission such as the example cited.   It is assumed that a reference trajectory has been calculated which results in the payload's being placed in a circular orbit 800 n.m. above the surface of the earth whose plane has a specified orientation with respect to inertial space.   To achieve this result closed-loop guidance is to be used in the second and fourth stages.   The reference trajectory is set up so that the missile is to be launched at a specified time with a programmed turning rate during the first stage. The attitude is held constant during the second stage and also during the fourth stage after a fixed change has been made in the attitude during the coast period. It is assumed that the allowable tolerances are a maximum of 1 millirad in the angle of inclination of the actual orbit to that of the reference orbit and the apogee and perigee of the actual orbit must be within 800 ± 10 n.m.

In considering position control for the guidance equations there is the disadvantage of the extra fuel consumption required for the additional maneuvering necessary to guide to a reference position. Also experience has shown that to use position control with this type of vehicle, a power stage duration of over 125 sec is desirable from a standpoint of stability and minimization of the final error. This requirement is satisfied for the second stage but not for the fourth stage. Since velocity control has the advantages of simplicity, a relatively small amount of maneuvering required, and less time required for the correction of initial errors, it will be considered here. With velocity control it is also possible to allow considerable deviation positionwise during the second stage and still arrive at a reference position at the beginning of the fourth stage. The position error accumulated during the fourth stage should then be well within the tolerances set forth.

Let the reference position for the beginning of the fourth stage be regarded as a point through which the vehicle must pass. One requirement then is that the velocity vector at the end of the second stage lie in the plane formed by the position vector of the vehicle and the fourth-stage reference position vector, both position vectors having their origin at the center of the earth. A velocity error function for guidance in the yaw plane may then be expressed by

$$\epsilon_y = \frac{\mathbf{v}_{mi} \cdot (\mathbf{R}_{mi} \times \mathbf{R}_{Ti})}{|\mathbf{R}_{mi} \times \mathbf{R}_{Ti}|}$$

where $\mathbf{v}_{mi}$ and $\mathbf{R}_{mi}$ are the velocity and position vectors of the vehicle in inertial coordinates and $\mathbf{R}_{Ti}$ is the target position vector. ϵ_y then represents the velocity component perpendicular to the desired plane. The transfer function to convert ϵ_y to ω_{ζ}, the turning rate command sent to the vehicle, is of the form

$$\frac{K_1 s + K_2}{T s + 1}$$

From Fig. 15.31b the closed-loop transfer function is obtained

$$\Delta V = \frac{s^2 (T s + 1) \epsilon_y}{T s^3 + s^2 + a K_1 s + a K_2}$$

Since this is a time-varying system, the values of the coefficients K_1 and K_2 can best be determined by an analog simulation. By assuming a constant acceleration of 50 ft/sec at the beginning, an analysis of the transient response indicates a value of K_2 of about 0.00007 to yield an undamped frequency of $w_0 = 0.06$ rad/sec.[11] This should yield a crossing of the zero axis at between 25 and 50 sec which would be appropriate for a length of 100 sec or more for the correction to take place. Figure 15.33 shows the transient response to a step input for two sets of values for K_1 and K_2 from an analog simulation. The first set shown would be preferred since the residual error is zero by 100 sec. It requires however, a somewhat larger change in attitude and therefore uses a little more fuel than the lower gain set of values.

If the direction of the trajectory is other than east or west, the rotation of the earth requires the vehicle to fly a nonplanar course due to the

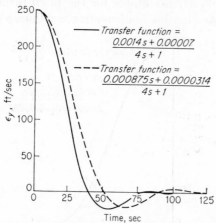

Fig. 15.33 Step input transient response for two sets of values for K_1 and K_2.

velocity acquired from the rotating earth for a constant yaw attitude reference trajectory. The guidance equations above would correct to a planar trajectory so that for the reference trajectory there would be a substantial value of ϵ_y at the beginning of the stage. Rather than allow the extra maneuvering and consequent fuel loss required for the correction to a planar flight, two alternatives are possible:

1. A function is set up that is equal to ϵ_y at all times during the flight for the reference case. This preferably should be a function of the velocity to be gained such that the value of the function would be zero at cutoff. This function is then subtracted from ϵ_y to give a new error signal to be used for yaw guidance.

2. The gain coefficient K_2 is set up as a function of time such that its value is low at the beginning and high near the end of the stage. This would tend to lessen the maneuvering for the reference case. Figure 15.34 shows the response for such a time-varying gain, where

$$K_2 = A + Bt$$

Guidance in the pitch plane may be handled in a similar manner. The radial velocity component directed toward the center of the earth may be expressed as

$$\dot{r} = \frac{\mathbf{v}_{mi} \cdot \mathbf{R}_{mi}}{|\mathbf{R}_{mi}|}$$

and the error ϵ_p given by

$$\epsilon_p = \dot{r} - \sum_{i=0}^{4} K_i V_g{}^i$$

where the polynomial $\sum_{i=0}^{4} K_i V_g{}^i$ is fit to the curve of $\dot{r}$ versus V_g for the reference trajectory. The transfer function, whose transient response is shown in Fig. 15.34, is suitable for the pitch turning rate command since as for yaw steering the maneuvering is minimized.

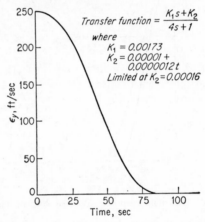

Fig. 15.34   Response with a time-varying gain.

Finally the equation for determining the power cutoff signal is set up. The guidance equations in pitch and yaw may be depended upon to ensure that the velocity vector has the proper direction at cutoff within the limits set by the accuracy of the tracking system. Since velocity control is used however, the position vector at cutoff may be expected to deviate somewhat from the reference position.

The required velocity magnitude for a free-fall trajectory to intersect a specified target in the plane, defined by the position and velocity vectors of the vehicle, is a function of cutoff position and radial velocity. This function may be represented by a polynomial expression using up to and including second-order terms.

$$|V_r| = f(\mathbf{R}_{mi}, \dot{r})$$
$$V_g = |V_r| - |V_{mi}|$$

Engine cutoff occurs when V_g becomes zero.

For guidance in the last stage the guidance equations are modified as follows:

$$\epsilon_\gamma = \mathbf{A}_i \cdot \mathbf{v}_{mi}$$

where $\mathbf{A}$ is a unit vector normal to the desired orbit.

$$\epsilon_p = \dot{r} - \sum_{i=0}^{4} K_i V_g{}^i$$

where the K_i are a new set of constants.

$$V_R = V_C + \alpha \frac{V_C}{R} \Delta R$$

ΔR is then the difference in altitude between the actual altitude and the reference altitude. V_C is the circular velocity corresponding to the reference altitude.

$$V_g = V_R - V_{mi}$$

For these equations the position, being uncontrolled, may be expected to deviate from the reference position by as much as 2 n.m. at cutoff. The apogee of the resultant orbit is given by[13]

$$r_a = r_0 + 0.36 \left(\Delta V + \sqrt{\Delta V^2 + \frac{\dot{r}^2}{4}} \right)$$

and perigee by

$$r_p = r_0 + 0.36 \left(\Delta V - \sqrt{\Delta V^2 + \frac{\dot{r}^2}{4}} \right)$$

where r_0 = distance from center of earth at cutoff, n.m.

ΔV = deviation in magnitude from that required for circular orbit

$\dot{r}$ = radial velocity, ft/sec

If the magnitude and $\dot{r}$ deviate by $+10$ ft/sec and r_0 is 2 n.m. more than the reference value, the resultant apogee is 9.5 n.m. above the reference, and the perigee 1.74 n.m. below the reference. The angle of inclination i between the actual orbit and this desired orbit is given by

$$\cos i = \frac{(\mathbf{R}_{mi} \times \mathbf{v}_{mi}) \cdot \mathbf{A}}{|\mathbf{R}_{mi}| \times |\mathbf{v}_{mi}|}$$

where $\mathbf{A}$ is the unit vector perpendicular to the desired orbit. From the errors assumed above the value of i is computed to be less than 1 millirad. The value of a complete simulation is that these estimates of cutoff error may be calculated more accurately by making a number of dispersion runs with closed-loop guidance and with simulated noise added to the tracker measurements.

15.20   Complete System Guidance—Control Simulation

Having studied the vehicle control systems and guidance systems separately, a combined simulation may be prepared if desired. Such a simulation may be looked upon as an extension of the previous ones in either of two ways:

1. The detailed flight control simulation is to be extended to include the guidance equations.

2. The guidance simulation is to be elaborated upon in the area which represents the vehicle transfer function.

Both approaches have their merits since the point of view is shaded differently in each case. Thus, in the first approach the analyst may use a somewhat simplified set of guidance equations coupled to an elaborate control simulation. His main attention may be directed toward such questions as "How does the ripple on the guidance signal effect vehicle elastic modes?" and "What are the effects of the guidance signals on propellant sloshing?", etc. In the second case the analyst will use a very complete guidance simulation with a somewhat simplified control system representation. His interest is directed at questions such as "What are the effects of higher-order terms in the vehicle response upon the guidance system's behavior?"

Obviously, the degree of detail required in each simulation (or even the necessity for setting one up at all) must be subject to engineering judgment. No advice can be given in this respect.

A combined analog-digital simulation may be prepared for this type of study if an analog-to-digital conversion link is available. Such a simulation has the advantage that those portions of the simulation requiring high accuracy—such as the navigation and guidance equations—may be handled digitally while the higher frequency modes in the flight control system simulation are handled on the analog computer. By use of an analog link in the problem further realism may be obtained by the insertion of actual hardware components from either (or both) the flight control or guidance system as desired.[8]

REFERENCES

1. Graham, E. W.: "The Forces Produced by Fuel Oscillation in a Rectangular Tank," *Rept. SM*-13748, Douglas Aircraft Company, Apr. 13, 1950.
2. Lorell, Jack: "Forces Produced by Fuel Oscillations," *Rept.* 20-149, Jet Propulsion Laboratory, Pasadena, Calif., Oct. 16, 1951.
3. Kachigan, K.: "Forced Oscillations of a Fluid in a Cylindrical Tank," *Rept.* Zu-7-046, Convair-Astronautics, Oct. 4, 1955.
4. Beharrell, J., and H. R. Friedrich: The Transfer Function of a Rocket-type Guided Missile with Consideration of its Structural Elasticity, *J. Aeronaut. Sci.,* vol. 21, 1954.

5. Friedrich, H. R.: A Method for Investigating the Influence of Flexibility of the Mounting Structure of Hydraulic Servo Systems on the Dynamic Stability Quality of Control Systems, *J. Aeronaut. Sci.*, vol. 22, February, 1955.

6. Press, Harry: "Atmospheric Turbulence Environment with Special Reference to Continuous Turbulence," NACA paper presented to AGARD, April, 1957.

7. Locke, A. S.: "Guidance," chap. 16, D. Van Nostrand Company, Inc., Princeton, N.J., 1955.

8. Leger, R. M., and J. L. Greenstein: Simulate Digitally or by Combining Analog and Digital Computing Facilities, "Control Engineering Manual," pp. 48–56, McGraw-Hill Book Company, Inc., New York, 1957.

9. Salzer, H. E.: Numerical Integration of $y'' = \phi(x, y, z)$ Using Osculatory Interpolation, *J. Franklin Inst.*, vol. 263, no. 5, May, 1957.

10. Locke, A. S.: *op. cit.*, chap. 16.

11. Truxal, J. G.: "Automatic Feedback Control System Synthesis," chap. 9, McGraw-Hill Book Company, Inc., New York, 1955.

12. Russell, William T.: Inertial Guidance for Rocket-propelled Missiles, *Jet Propulsion*, vol. 28, no. 1, January, 1958.

13. Ehricke, K. A., Error Analysis of Keplerian Flight Involving a Single Central Force Field and Transfer between Two Central Force Fields, *Navigation*, vol. 6, no. 1, Spring, 1958.

16

Air-traffic Control*

HANS GIESECKE

FEDERAL AVIATION AGENCY
BUREAU OF RESEARCH AND DEVELOPMENT
ATLANTIC CITY, N.J.

16.1 Introduction

The growth of aviation in the United States has no comparable parallel. The most progressive elements of the nation have relentlessly pushed forward against all technical, economical, and social difficulties. Within half a century air transportation has taken the lead over all other common carriers in intercity traffic. Long-distance air travel over the oceans has become big business. Three times more passengers prefer air travel to ship journeys. Military aviation has twice successfully defended the country and continues to advance with speed and unyielding vigor. Now, the business aviator and private flyer show intentions of competing with the private automobile, at least for longer distances of travel. However, we have permitted the development of a serious obstacle to continued rapid progress. The lack of success in finding means of affording equitable access to the air space for all of the competitive users has created severe inconveniences of a nature which could retard the previous enormous rate of expansion. This is not only economically undesirable for one of the largest and youngest economic segments of the country but also endangers the nation's military survival strength. In addition to air-defense interception, air transportation has become a vital necessity in military defense operations.

It is quite certain that automation and the use of computers will be among the major tools to overcome this dilemma. However, the fact that computers have not yet been introduced into operational use may indicate that the obstacles to significant system improvements are considerable. Some reasons for this will be explored.

* The statements made in this chapter do not represent the official views of the Federal Aviation Agency. All statements, opinions, and facts presented are those solely of the author.

16.2   Air-traffic Problems

Air traffic is a three-headed giant.   It constitutes a vital government-operated defense system, a fully developed commercial transportation system of high safety, both internationally involved, and a progressive social air-transportation system for individual airplane owners.   For later consideration it is worthwhile to note that this highly competitive triple system encompasses more than physical equipment such as airplanes, mechanized control centers, communication networks, navigation aids, landing systems and radars.   A large number of nonphysical parameters determine, equally decisively, the performance of the air-traffic system.   Some of these are such intangibles as different grades of proficiency status for more than 100,000 military, commercial, and private pilots, the operating habits of thousands of controllers, the established travel desires of passengers and private business aviators, the military training requirements, international considerations, and certainly many more.   Another category of parameters is exemplified by the billions of dollars invested in airports and in the many business corporations involved in aviation and geared to the present way of operations.   These factors tend to suggest caution in the introduction of revolutionary major changes since these carry the potential of producing discomforting transients in the economy or the true defense strength of the country.   The next paragraph indicates that, nevertheless, immediate improvements must be obtained.

Scientific forecasts indicate that air traffic would nearly double within the next decade if the control system could move such traffic loads.   This represents an expansion which is faster than the estimates for the growth of the population or the growth of the gross national product.   It is predicted that by 1975 there will be more than 120,000 aircraft in the United States.   About three-quarters of these will be rather conventional airplanes of moderate speed and performance.   At any one instant about half of the airplanes in the air space over the United States will be piloted without the assistance of copilots.

The air-traffic dilemma may be expressed as follows: the quantitative growth of air traffic, the increasing variance of vehicle performance, the continuing spread of pilot abilities, and the requirements for common usage of air space have produced a situation where the existing traffic system can no longer meet the needs and competitive desires of the three major categories of air-space users.   This has the potential of a threatening crisis because it endangers the progress in military operational readiness by denying training capabilities, and it represents a serious obstacle to the economic expansion of aviation.   Hence, immediate effective action is urgent.   The problem is amplified by the constraints that no major transients, be they operational or economic, can be tolerated in the existing system and that partial solutions favoring certain classes of users will, very likely, produce no appreciable improvements in the total system.

Since attempts to change the equipment in a large number of airplanes necessarily take a long time, and therefore the effects of these changes in the over-all system are long delayed, automation of ground procedures appears more attractive on first-order consideration. Therefore, there have been many suggestions for the employment of computers in the ATC ground system. As far back as 1947, the Special Committee 31 of the Radio Technical Commission for Aeronautics (RTCA) suggested the speedy introduction of "calculators" to provide automatic conflict detection and to expeditiously control flow of air traffic. There was no attempt made to experiment with this proposal. In addition, the military departments investigated a number of approaches which employed ground-based digital or analog computers mainly for improvement of traffic flow into the terminals or onto an aircraft carrier, and for instrument landing purposes. Although most of these experiments have been conducted for more than 5 years and with considerable effort and financial support, they have not yet produced convincing results that warrant operational introduction. Yet, the lessons gained from this experimentation are very valuable and have accelerated the emphasis on systems engineering principles for the introduction of improvements to a large existing system.

It appears that all of these, so far unsuccessful designs, have common deficiencies which originate from insufficient systems planning. The original planning treated the difficulties of eventual operational introduction into a large existing system too lightly and failed to recognize the over-all system difficulties of producing a very high flow of information between ground and controlled airplanes. On a systemwide basis this requires prohibitively complex equipment in the airplanes and hence defeats the objective of rapid introduction for all types of aircraft.

It is now common knowledge that thorough and complete analysis of the procedures of introduction into an equally well-analyzed existing system is necessary. This, of course, applies specifically to contemplated introduction of large-scale computers and their mutual communication requirements. Familiarization with the existing system, therefore, is necessary.

16.3　On the Present System

The present FAA air-traffic control system serves both civil and military air traffic. Physically it involves about 90,000 aircraft which enter or leave the air space from some 6,000 airfields. About 400 of these airfields employ air-traffic control towers. Most aircraft desire more or less random entrance into the system. Desire of entrance is announced by the pilot through the means of telephone, radio voice, or to some degree by teletype. Irrespective of weather, departing and arriving traffic is handled by the airfield tower. The area of jurisdiction of the tower is not standard but must be individually determined by the geometry of surrounding airfields, by the predominant air-traffic desires, and by the topography of the area. Pilots and controllers must be thoroughly familiar with these locally determined procedures. Elaborate charts and rather bulky manuals are the means of establishing this familiarity. Under good visibility conditions, visual flight rules (VFR) are in effect, and no further control is exercised after the airfield tower has controlled the take-off procedure and guided the aircraft into its en route phase of flight. If visibility conditions require continuation of the flight on instruments, instrument flight rules are effective (IFR). Control of such IFR traffic rests with a number of air-route traffic-control centers (ARTCC). There are 26 of these in the continental United States.

The communication network interconnecting the towers and the air-route traffic-control centers consists predominantly of leased telephone and teletype lines. For communication with the airplanes, two over-lapping radio-telephone systems operate on VHF and UHF frequencies. A total of some 2,000 channels of either 50- or 100-kc bandwidth is available.

Coordination of channels between ground controller and pilot is a complicated fixed system and has been mostly determined by geographical necessity and propagation requirements. Again, an elaborate manual of frequency charts is required in connection with accurate navigation to establish channel coordination between air and ground. Some routine information as, for instance, weather reports, is broadcast through additional means.

For navigation in instrument weather, four major ground-based systems are in use. All these systems delineate specific airways in air space and can not easily be applied for straight-line point-to-point navigation (area navigation). Accurate position determination is mainly feasible over the respective ground stations such as low frequency ranges, marker beacons, nondirectional beacons when used with air-borne radio compass, VOR stations, and the recently introduced VORTAC and TACAN stations.

Except for the use of prepared tables, or occasionally slide rules, flight following of the traffic in the traffic-control centers is completely manual. Information on the position of an airplane depends entirely on randomly arriving progress reports from the pilot. Reporting points (fixes) are separated by an average distance of 50 miles, hence, information suitable for traffic control purposes arrives intermittently and randomly in the control center only when airplanes cross these fixes. Conflict determination is based on estimated time of arrival at these fixes. The standard ANC regulations separate aircraft over fixes by a safety time of more than 10 min. Since none of the navigation systems facilitate area navigation, the entire IFR traffic is channeled over airways which are determined by the physical location of the ground-based radio aids.

In terminal areas, radar is applied to expedite arrivals and departures, and landing systems assist instrument approaches to the runway. The use of radar presents some problems mostly because of the inability to easily identify a specific aircraft. A navigation and communication procedure is therefore required to positively produce safe control of aircraft entering the vicinity of an airfield. Attempts to alleviate this situation by the introduction of transponder beacons have been proposed for many years. Expected effects on the over-all efficiency of the air-traffic system have been much disputed. Recently it has become necessary to manage military and airline traffic at high altitudes by other procedures. Military aircraft must be able to fly any arbitrary air route. A specific type of radar control at these high altitudes is now being exercised.

Under adverse weather conditions, the present airways system imposes restrictions on the free movement of air traffic in such a way and resulting in such an economic loss that it is urgently necessary to improve the capacity by an order of magnitude.

16.4 Preparation of Flight-progress Strips by Digital Computer

For the last three years the government has experimented with digital computers to determine their utility in air-route traffic control centers. For the first time these tests were conducted with operational traffic. The IBM 650 RAMAC computer, as well as the Remington-Rand UNIVAC FILE computer, were involved in this experimentation. These machines are to be used in air-route traffic control centers for the preparation of flight-progress strips. In the present air-traffic control system, flight plans and flight-progress strips constitute the key instruments for the determination of control actions. The flight plan is a standard form by which the pilot files, either verbally or in writing, his desired take-off, his destination, and his intended flight route over defined airways. The flight-progress strip is a handwritten, small paper form mounted in a holder for easy physical transportation within a control center. These strips contain flight plan information and are sequentially ordered in vertical rows on display boards. Usually each reporting point, or fix, has its corresponding row on display boards. The time of original posting of a strip is determined by the estimated time of arrival of the airplane over a fix, and precedes the airplane by about 30 min on its way through the center and from center to center. The progress strip is corrected according to the pilot's progress report.

Hand preparation of these progress strips is a major chore. Consider, for instance, the Indianapolis Air Route Traffic Control Center. It covers an area of approximately 350 by 250 n.m. There are 38 primary and about 110 secondary radio fixes used for posting of flights. On a peak day 6,000 fix postings are prepared per day. Six hundred of these are prepared during the peak hour. One of these digital computers is in operational use in the Indianapolis Air Route Traffic Control Center. The following functions are presently included in the program of the computer:

1. To receive and store flight plans
2. To compute estimated times of arrival over all the fixes of the route of flight
3. To print flight-progress strips
4. To detect conflicts over fixes
5. To transmit, via teletype, flight plans and flight-progress information to other facilities, such as centers, towers, air-defense command installations, airline offices, etc.
6. Correct flight-progress strips according to fix reports from air-borne aircraft

Flight plans are entered into the computer by typewriter. All fixes in the area and their mutual distances are in storage. The machine computes estimated time of arrival for each fix requiring posting of a progress strip and prints out these strips on perforated paper. The printed strips are manually placed into holders and then hand-carried to the proper display board in the control center.

16.5 Semiautomatic FAA Data Processing Central

The most systematic and accelerated effort in the improvement of air-traffic control that has ever been initiated by the federal government is currently under way. The semiautomatic FAA data processing central constitutes a complete system that introduces as much automation into the process of traffic management as seems practical and prudent at this time. It encompasses all activities of the controller from departure through en route flight to the transition into the terminal area and into the landing approach gate. Purposefully, it is designed to be introducible without transients in the present operation. It will produce improved efficiency of controllers and it will be capable of handling considerably more traffic, even before new equipment can be introduced into airplanes. However, the design is such that gradual introduction of, for instance, ground-air-ground automatic communication devices or of better air-borne navigation equipment will assist the over-all operation from the beginning, rather than postpone significant results until a large number of airplanes have been provided with new equipment. To shorten the development cycle appreciably, the decision was made to tailor the experimental equipment to the area where improvement is most needed, i.e., New York, and to perform the final test of the experimental system directly by operational employment with real, everyday traffic. This was possible since gradual introduction necessitates that the design must be capable of operating side-by-side with unequipped adjacent areas. This automatically makes it possible for the two systems to operate in the same area in a compatible manner. The core of the system consists of medium-large electronic computers. The central device servicing the entire air-route traffic control area is a transistorized general-purpose computer. For expedient sequencing of airplanes from en route flight through a transition phase into terminal areas containing possibly several satellite airports, a hybrid digital and analog computer will be used. The entire system design is based on a minimum of standard modules which can be assembled in the best economical combination to meet local civil and/or military traffic requirements.

The inputs into the central computer are flight plans. These may be directly introduced by teletype lines or by a special local controller who receives information from any source, including air-borne pilots, and who translates this into the proper format for the computer. The machine computes estimated times of arrival over all relevant fixes by assuming "standard" speeds of airplane types, but with consideration of known and continuously up-dated wind conditions. It formulates all flight-progress strips needed in the system and distributes this information to the working place of the user, such as sector controllers in the center, transition and terminal operators, towers, airline offices, military establishments, air defense installations, etc. When new fix report information is available on the progress of airplanes, all progress strips are continuously up-dated at the local operating place. The control function of the computer is based on standard separation regulations. The flight plan is extrapolated into the future and compared with other flight plans already in existence. If "conflicts" exist with the separation rules, the controller is alerted and, on request, presented with a planar view of the situation on a cathode-ray-tube display. If radar coverage is available, the information from the computer assists the controller in the identification of the airplane. Vice versa, the controller can feed radar information back into the system and thus up-date the knowledge of flight progress and of wind situations.

In transition and terminal control extensive use is made of radar. From the received flight-progress information, the transition area computer assists the controller to find and identify the radar target. An automatic tracking gate now preserves the identification. Times of arrival at the airport are computed and presented on a sequence display. If required, corrective actions are prepared automatically for execution by the sequence controller to prevent overloading of the airport while establishing smooth flow to prevent unnecessary delays to airplanes in holding patterns or stacks.

The applied control principle may be explained as follows: it is the basic assumption that a flight plan exists over the entire intended flight route, including the approach route to the final landing site. These plans are sequentially and intermittently checked against the actual progress of the airplane and simultaneously probed for potential violation of the separation rules. If no conflicts are developing in spite of deviation from the original plan, this plan is merely corrected in the computer in accordance with actual flight progress. Only in case of pending conflict will the controller be alerted to take corrective control action. This is essentially the procedure followed in the present manual system; hence introduction of the new system will not require serious or lengthy preparation.

In areas of radar coverage, specifically in high-density terminal areas, radar separation rules for departures and arrivals afford fairly high traffic rates. It is expected that this semiautomatic system will improve the air-traffic situation by a very significant amount.

The transistorized digital computer used in this system integrates electronic computing with a large-capacity magnetic drum storage. The arithmetic unit permits simultaneous operation of the drum file system and the very flexible input-output buffer system. The basic 64-character alpha-numeric structure, with a seventh bit for parity checking, is used. The internal core memory has a capacity of 4,000 eight-character words. File drums are provided in parallel for safety against loss of information. The drum capacity is two-thousand 64-character records. Ten drums are needed in the present system.

The data-processing central can process up to 400 flight plans per hour and can store 1,000 flight plans. A flight plan stored will be activated unless the airplane is actually ready to depart. Sixteen-hundred flight-progress strips per hour are printed or up-dated. The terminal equipment can sequence 60 aircraft per hour per runway and simultaneously permits the monitoring of 60 departures per hour.

16.6 Simulation in Air-traffic Control

Thirty years ago, Mr. E. A. Link convinced the world that a simulator has considerable utility for the training of instrument pilots. Since then, advancements in electronic computing have opened up an almost unlimited field for the application of simulation techniques. These applications may be classified into four major functional areas:

1. Training of persons or entire teams in the operation of new equipment or complete large systems

    2. Laboratory testing of design ideas during development of new equipment or systems

    3. Laboratory testing and evaluation of completed equipment or systems designs

    4. Laboratory experimentation for applied and basic research work in almost unlimited fields

The following discussion will not be concerned with the training aspects of simulation in air-traffic applications but will attempt to highlight the utility of simulators in testing systems and experimenting with concepts.

One reason for the historically slow development of air-traffic control as a total system was the inability of obtaining feedback of results to the designer. Large-scale flight testing is prohibitive for economic and safety reasons. Years of statistical observation of actual operational behavior are necessary to measure the effect of newly introduced equipment or procedures. This not only slows down the collection of new knowledge but has the potential of being an academic exercise because the time for possible corrections has often passed before the results of the analysis can be obtained. Experimentation, the powerful tool that is mostly responsible for the rapid advancement of equipment technology, has not been available to the system designer.

As a major example of the use of simulation in air-traffic control work, the testing and evaluation of the FAA Data Processing Central System will be described. Before this new evolutionary system can be introduced into operation it must be thoroughly tested. Without simulation this is not feasible. Hence, a large simulation system is under development for this specific purpose.

This simulator consists of four basic elements which are as follows: there are target generators, simulators, the communications system, and the data-collection system. The target generators represent airplanes and are operated by operators who simulate pilots. They manipulate their simulated aircraft in accordance with a prearranged script and in accordance with control instructions received through the communications system from the controllers. The outputs of the target generators feed into radar displays where they can be mixed with live radar targets.

The communications system simulates both air-ground and ground-ground communication. Air-ground channels provide communications between "pilots" and controllers, and the ground-ground system simulates communications between controllers and other operating personnel within the air-traffic control complex. Nonradar targets are introduced at special positions similar to flight-progress boards. These positions are used to simulate air traffic. Scripts are prepared for the operators of the "progress boards" to call into the system any number of en route airplanes and to also simulate fix-reporting procedures. The data-collection and -reduction system collects and reduces pertinent data during the testing to assist and speed up the evaluation of the particular test results. Information relating to conflicts, traffic density, landing rates, and changes in flight plans required by control communications is provided by this portion of the simulator, so that system performance can be determined a short time after a simulated test run has been completed.

The target generators, or "pilot" consoles, apply analog-computer techniques. The data collection and reduction machinery, however, employs predominantly digital techniques. The entire system is a special computer device and can be used for the analysis of a large number of air-traffic problems from take-off to landing. In addition to the improvements for flexibility of tests and proper human engineering of operating consoles, the data-reduction part is the major advancement over previous systems. For post-test analysis, considerable information is recorded in five different categories: general flight information, histogram over fixes, densities in special sector, conflict data, and communication data. The first four are punched on separate paper tapes, the last is recorded on magnetic tape in a manner which permits later reduction and analysis by such general-purpose computers as the IBM 704 or 709. For analysis purposes the flight history of each airplane is recorded, as well as statistical data on control actions, delay times, flight densities, altitude distributions, etc. Since communication constitutes a major burden to pilot and controller in the present air-traffic system, and also causes considerable delays, it is hoped that systematic analysis and experimentation with this simulator can shed some light on the problems involved.

The tape recording is suitable for analysis of such items as channel utilization, communication delays by mutual interference, effectiveness of control language, length of messages, etc. It is planned to add automatic communication features to the simulator as soon as more knowledge has been obtained from the simulation experiments with voice control.

There are other matters of great significance in the evaluation of new air-traffic control systems through real-time simulation. Consider, for instance, the difficulties involved in the design of an efficient, yet valid, test program requiring constant vigilance with respect to verity of results, or in the preparation of a large number of detailed input scripts to be used by simulator pilots.

It is hoped that a large digital computer will be an excellent instrument for preparing most of the scripts for simulator pilots. A considerable amount of information on these scripts concerns aircraft flight plans. It is required that random samples with definable distributions of aircraft types, airports of entry, desired rates of entry, desired altitudes, weather conditions, etc., be repeatedly sent through the test procedure. It is also desirable to have new samples available which can only be described after previous test runs have been analyzed. Since the simulated geographic test area is fixed, in this case the operating area of the New York Air Route Traffic Control Center, a variety of anticipated test programs can be stored on magnetic tapes in advance of the time that they will be needed. Analysis is yet required to determine the practicality of preparing these tapes with such flexibility that new samples can be adjusted to the knowledge gained from previous test runs.

To meet the requirement for verity, many simulator experts insist on extreme realism of simulation, specifically when human operators are in the system. Since the described target generators are rather crude imitations of real airplanes, there must be then some doubt as to the validity of the results. It will be possible, however, to introduce a small number of actual flights in parallel with the simplified target generators to validate results. To a certain degree this can also be accomplished by aircraft flight simulators.

In addition to the use of flight simulators with real pilots for checking the accuracy and validity of simplified target generator-human operator combinations, these flight simulators have been and will continue to be valuable research tools in the laboratory for solving a number of pilot problems in the air-traffic system. In recent years, the U.S. Air Force and the U.S. Navy have accelerated their research in improved cockpit designs. From the air-traffic viewpoint the workload of the pilot, who is alone in the cockpit and under IFR flight conditions, is an extremely serious problem. This problem has been discussed for many years. To actually realize high-density IFR traffic in terminal areas with the great variance of airplane performance and pilot efficiency, the accurate operation of aircraft by the pilot in terminal patterns must become an order of magnitude easier. This requires systematic redesign of the entire cockpit layout of instruments and switches in combination with research work on navigation systems and control procedures. Analog or digital flight simulators are well suited to extend the military successes in this area to civil applications.

Another unsolved problem is the disagreement on airport lighting systems. Undesirable lack of national and international conformity exists on standards of visual aids and lighting systems for airports.

Attempts are now under way to apply flight simulators in connection with optical attachments to project experimental lighting patterns onto a screen in front of the simulator cockpit. This may provide the capability for recording actual performance and thus obtaining some quantitative values for evaluation of results.

Another application of flight simulators to be mentioned concerns an experiment, again in connection with optical systems, to determine the possible utility of air-to-air collision avoidance, or proximity warning concepts. A modern F-101A flight trainer in connection with an elaborate modified fire-control training computer will be the basic tool for this simulation experiment.

Perhaps the most revolutionary fast-time simulation program for research in air-traffic problems was started by IBM in 1957. Over a period of almost two years a program was written for the FSQ-7 computer. Later the government decided to sponsor the extension of the program. The first promising results are now available, indicating an excellent potential of digital computers for air traffic and air-traffic control analysis work. The computer is programmed to exercise traffic control by the present standard regulations on randomly entered airplanes in the area of the New York Traffic Control Center. Flight-plan data are entered in plain text form similar to the way a pilot files a flight plan. As an example consider the following line:

E321 CVR 240 0900 LGA A2 COA A18 ALB 070 GNC

The above line means that the aircraft with number E321, a Convair, with indicated airspeed of 240 knots, will take off at 9 o'clock from LaGuardia. It will fly the route described by Airway number A2 to the Commack reporting point, change to Airway number A18, and leave the area of control at Albany. The pilot desires 7,000-ft altitude by the time he reaches the Glen Cove reporting point. Other data, for instance, geographical changes, can be entered in similar form. The traffic control computer program checks for conflicts, delays aircraft, clears for new altitudes, holds and lowers airplanes in stacks at terminal areas, introduces random navigation errors, and includes practically all other control functions of the real, present-day system. A traffic sample run of several hundred airplanes over a real-time period of 2 hr can be completed in the machine in 2 min. Other programs collect data on the parameters to be analyzed, for instance, for the purpose of preparing histograms.

Such parameters as loading of the system as to number and type of airplanes, distribution of entries, air-route structures, terminal capacity, control procedures, etc., can be controlled in the tests. For the analysis purposes, the effect of variation of such controlled inputs, or parameters of environment on performance results such as delays due to control, number of control actions, estimated load on communications, density of aircraft per unit volume or per altitude layer, collision hazard, etc., can be measured.

Provision is made in the program of the computer to skip the check for conflict. This permits direct comparison of the effectiveness of various control procedures with respect to collisions and with respect to penalties introduced by the control.

At the present time, checks against real-life results are under way to prove the validity of the analysis results obtained.   With positive results, it is obvious that a long list of air-traffic research problems can be investigated by such high-speed digital-computer techniques.   It is, of course, highly desirable that better ways be developed for the preparation of programs for such large simulation tests to further reduce the time and cost of analysis, so that research can be expanded to a much broader front.

16.7   Trends

In the preceeding discussion, significant developments of automatic means for air-traffic control have been described and the development of simulation instruments and methods for air-traffic problem analysis has been considered.   In addition, it appears appropriate to discuss the trends of air-traffic research as they appear at the present time. Although no factual results can be reported, the urgency of the problems involved seems to justify this otherwise premature attempt.

The tremendous advance in electronics, and specifically in radar during World War II, has caused considerable optimism in aviation circles. It was generally believed that many peaceful applications of the new knowledge could be found and that most problems of instrument flying were within reach of solutions.   Instrument landing, convenient navigation, terminal and en route traffic control by radar, even air-borne obstacle warning were considered to be completely sound and solvable objectives.   Efforts in these directions were started immediately after the war.   Since the average development cycle of electronic equipment surpasses a decade, recognition of partial defeat and reluctant admission of omissions in planning have come only relatively recently after test results became available.   It is interesting to note, as a matter of hindsight, of course, that the equally significant progress made during the war in operations research and systems planning has been neglected because of the enthusiasm for electronics.

Today we may observe a new surge of growing enthusiasm in the electronic field.   In this case it is a reverence for the electronic computer. However, the chance for a complete parallelism seems to be remote. Enough systems engineering experience has now been gained on other large-scale examples so that more systematic approaches can be predicted.   This is quite clearly expressed in the "Aviation Facilities Planning Report" of May, 1957, which is commonly known as the "Curtis Report."   This is also evident from the increasing activity in air-traffic systems research as a result of the recommendations of this report. Considerable operations analysis effort is under way to quantitatively describe the performance, or lack of performance, of the present system. Other efforts are directed toward the definition of yardsticks for measuring performance.   An agreement on a performance measure, of course, is required for comparison of the results of previously described simulation tests because delay times (or distribution of delay times), derived from mathematical models based upon theories of queuing, were heretofore nearly the only numerical measures of performance applied in air-traffic control studies.   However, delays by themselves are not a sufficient criterion for system performance.   Some finite probability of delay is quite acceptable if other factors, such as safety, higher over-all flow rate, convenience of operation, or lower operating costs are gained by accepting such delays.   The measure of effectiveness, therefore, will be a composite of several competing factors.

There is a close interrelation between data collection, data processing, decision making, communication, and navigation in an air-traffic control system and the complexity of the equipment to perform these functions. As an illustration of this, let us assume two absurdly extreme solutions. Visualize perfect navigation equipment in the airplane, so that a prearranged flight plan can be flown from take-off to landing with perfect spatial accuracy and timing.   This system requires no air-ground-air communications; however, a tremendous ground-to-ground data-collection, data-processing, and communication system is required if delays to arbitrarily desired take-offs are to be reasonable.

The opposite extreme would be no prearrangements before take-off. Under the assumption that air-to-air data collection and mutual avoidance are not possible in high-density traffic involving large speed variances, such a system requires no air-borne navigation, but a prohibitively high rate of data collection on the ground, data processing, fast decision making, and a high-capacity air-ground-air communication link.   It must be assumed that the solution is somewhere between these extremes. Yet in the past, most suggestions made came close to one or the other extreme.

There have been many discussions on the relative merits of specific control concepts, such as fixed block systems, moving block systems, time prediction methods, arbitrary radar vectoring, "first-come, first-served" regulations, etc.   It appears reasonable to assume that no decision on the merits of any one of these concepts can be made without a knowledge of the performance of the equipment necessary to operate in accordance with each of these (and other) concepts.

It is now becoming more and more accepted that neither such premature general abstractions nor relatively superficial considerations lead to useful actions or measurable progress.   It is understood that thorough understanding of the environment, detailed knowledge of technological performance potentials, and well-considered statements of realistic objectives are as necessary in the development of air-traffic systems improvements as in any other system.   It is conceded that this knowledge is not originally available but must be gained by detailed and diligent reconsideration and correction of an original intuitive concept after additional analytic and experimental results become available. A few examples will be used for illustration: a number of descriptive facts regarding the air-traffic environment, which will exist at the time when improvements can become effective, have been determined. Some of these have been mentioned previously in this paper, and additional examples will be reported here. There will be 125,000 airplanes. The majority of these will be small conventional types flown by one man. Most of these desire random access to the system from about 6,000 air-fields. A large number of aircraft supply very limited electrical power for the operation of electronic gear. The peak density in the most populated terminal area will be 0.1 aircraft/sq mile. This is the Los Angeles terminal area. In a circular area of 100 miles diameter, almost 800 air-craft will be in flight at the peak instant. Figures on en route density are not yet well known. Average peak densities of 0.001 aircraft/sq mile are estimated. This amounts to 1,000 airplanes over an area correspond-ing to a square with sides 500 miles long. The complexity of existing national and international rules and regulations, and the presently operating ground system, must be added to the description of the environ-ment. It is obvious that realistic consideration of this environment considerably restricts the choice of technical or procedural solutions. Objectives have been expressed only in a general manner. Access to the common air space must be possible for all potential users with equitable distribution of restrictions, and the control of air traffic must be expeditious yet safe. These are the primary objectives as stated. It is doubtful that it will be possible to quantitatively determine the restrictions which will not be acceptable or which will retard the desired expansion of air traffic. The hazards, delays, and inconveniences accepted in automobile traffic indicate that these factors are hard to judge. However, certain basic concepts of air-traffic control and techni-cal capabilities have changed and tend to crystallize into forms which become amenable to practical analysis or experimental investigation. Some examples follow: since we have traffic with relatively slow speeds requiring no other traffic control under VFR conditions than by rules of the road and regulations, it was considered for a while that by carrying electronic detection devices and computers in all aircraft, similar freedom from control could be obtained under IFR conditions. However, it has now been admitted that this is neither technically feasible nor a solution considering the density of present-day and future traffic. To produce orderly and safe flow, observation and control by a nonparticipating observer is required. Hence, a ground-based control system must con-tinue to be used.

The present air-traffic control system is a closed-circuit system with extremely high and variable time constants in all functions. It can be loosely compared with a sampled-data system. It should be considered, however, that all functions within the system are operated on discrete and random steps. This applies to inputs in the form of desired flight plans, to data collection by random position reports, to the determination of deviations from the plan, and to the transmission of information to the airplanes. It is quite reasonable to assume that increase of the capacity of the system will require marked reduction of the time delays and abolition of most of the randomness. It will also require the introduction of smoothing elements in the system.

In air-traffic-control language this means that the function of position determination by the ground environment must be improved, the communication system will require better reliability and quicker access to airplanes, the decision making of the controller should be faster, and the navigation capability of the aircraft improved to form the smoothing link in the system. Within the limits of technical feasibility and considering the problems of operational introduction, this leads to the following concepts. Position reporting by the pilot over fixes must be replaced by a system of position collection on the ground in a controllable cycle. A radar network alone is not sufficient for this purpose for two principal reasons. The required certainty of detecting all aircraft in all required areas cannot be obtained economically and the identification problem has not been solved. However, ground-based position-finding systems using the transmission from presently operational air-borne transmitters in the VHF and UHF bands appear technically feasible and, with the introduction of position computers, also practical. This position-finding system must be integrated properly with the radar system. One scheme proposes to employ improved direction finders in an existing network of ground-air-ground communications and to control the process by a digital machine. Determination of the position of an aircraft can then be made at any arbitrary time selected at the control center. The delay is expected to be in the order of 1 sec.

If successful, this scheme will reduce the communication load and hence the requirements on automatic communication. It is recognized that automatic communication is required. However, past efforts of experimentation and tests have not been complete enough to validate the assumption that a data link can be built that can be introduced into the majority of airplanes and still obtain the reliability of data transmission necessary for the automatic operation of computers. Since the complete loop of data transmission between airplane and ground includes a large ground network, it appears attractive to use a "teletype" compatible code which would afford a shorter time of introduction and economic savings. Instead of high-speed transmission over a wide band, this would require division of the wide band into smaller and slower channels.

Considerable fundamental experimentation is under way to find a solution for the needed automatic data transmission.

To speed up the decision-making process, it will be necessary to provide automatic means for the human controller. This, however, poses serious conceptual problems. It has been commonly accepted that the human operator must still be capable of backing up the automatic machine in case of failure, for obvious safety reasons. This could lead to a fateful paradox. Its literal application will very likely lead to frustrating disappointments. It is essential that the machine be more reliable than the human operator, otherwise it has no place in a safety system. The objective must be to produce increased safety by the use of machines and to leave the human operator with the role of expediting the process through judgment of the situation and ordering of the machine to apply new rules. Without smooth navigation, the sampling rates required for safe and expeditious control are prohibitively high with respect to technical and economical realization of the above-mentioned automation concepts, if the predicted traffic densities actually develop. It is, therefore, eventually necessary to improve the navigational capability in such a way that segments of flights to any arbitrarily selected point in space can be requested, and so that the pilot is able to do this within predictable tolerances. This is not presently feasible with the operating systems. Therefore, the introduction of new air-borne equipment cannot be avoided. Self-contained systems have the inherent capability of providing the required smoothness. However, the air-traffic systems engineer must recognize that the introduction of any new air-borne equipment is a slow and gradual process and that the system must retain the capability of serving unequipped airplanes.

The author believes that the expanding application of digital computers for en route and terminal air-traffic control should follow such functional concepts as indicated in Fig. 16.1.

Flight plans are received from a communication network and stored and processed in a digital flight plan processer, which in turn inserts the call letters of all airplanes into the call-distribution buffer. Through a radio communication network, airplanes are sequentially requested to automatically respond with the identity and perhaps the static pressure of the flight altitude. The returned message will be received by receivers with position finding capability. A slow code employing relatively long pulses would permit the network to neglect propagation time differences while employing space-diversity reception. The communication network delivers coded identity, altitude, and basic position information to the digital position computer. Output of this computer would be the identity of each called airplane attached to its X, Y, Z coordinates at time of call. This information is collected and stored in a first-order conflict filter and checked with previously stored data for first-order conflict: the separation rules or the conflict check is to be made in a basically simple form with the objective of obtaining simplicity and reliability of the computer.   Those airplanes passing this first-order check would automatically receive clearance by the control computer.   Others will be presented to a human controller.   He, then, would override the routine call procedure and selectively ask for special position determination for the airplanes involved. After inspection, the controller would determine the true and up-dated conflict situation and clear the aircraft through an automatic conflict

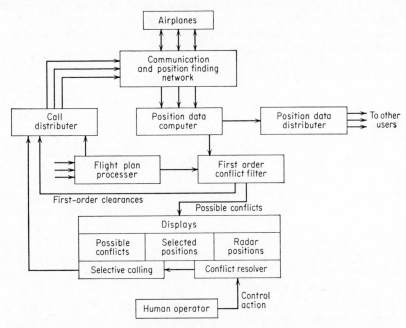

Fig. 16.1   Functional block diagram of air-traffic control computer system.

resolver that checks the validity of the controller's decision.   If the questionable targets can be identified on a radar scope, radar separation standards are applicable.   In this form, the automatic system would solve and clear the obviously simple cases, and the human controller would be alerted to judge only the possible conflicts and, with the assistance of a computer, resolve and expedite these cases, but with a final recheck by the machine.

16.8   Conclusion

It has been determined that the previous rate of progress in aviation activities might be retarded if we fail to significantly improve the nation's aviation facilities.   This is a formidable problem because a large system is in existence, and scientific knowledge regarding the interrelation of the large number of variables is at present insufficient. Modern computers are in use as analytical and simulation tools to attack these problems more thoroughly. The introduction of digital computers into the operating air-traffic-control system has been initiated.

REFERENCES

1. CAA Statistical Handbook of Civil Aviation, U.S. Dept. of Commerce, Civil Aeronautics Administration, Washington 25, D.C., 1958.
2. Air Traffic Control Paper 27-48/DO-12, prepared by RTCA Special Committee 31.
3. Aviation Facilities Planning, O-426455, Washington 25, D.C., 1957.
4. Modernizing the National System of Aviation Facilities, O-426460, U.S. Government Printing Office, Washington 25, D.C., 1957.
5. National Requirements for Aviation Facilities 1956–1975, vols. I–IV, U.S. Government Printing Office, Washington 25, D.C., 1957.

17

Optimalizing Cruise Control Systems

YAO TZU LI

PROFESSOR OF AERONAUTICAL ENGINEERING

MASSACHUSETTS INSTITUTE OF TECHNOLOGY, CAMBRIDGE, MASS.

17.1 Introduction

Optimalizing control is a device which automatically searches for the optimum performance of an operating system, such as an aircraft, a power plant, or an industrial plant. The performance of the operating system may involve the conversion of one form of energy or material to some other form of energy or material, following a function most desirable for the particular kind of operation. The need of an optimalizing control arises primarily because some of the critical parameters of the operating system change with the environment and thereby call for a new setting of some other controllable parameters. Programming techniques are frequently used to make proper settings based upon (1) the change of the critical parameters, and (2) some earlier knowledge of the necessary setting change of the controllable parameters for a given amount of change of the critical parameters. As a typical example, the cruise control of an aircraft is often done by a flight engineer based upon a flight handbook. This is in effect a programmed control, and can be done automatically by a program control system. It is usually when this type of program control becomes impractical that an optimalizing controller is desired. An optimalizing system requires no precise knowledge of the amount of the changing parameter nor the exact mutual relationship between this parameter and the controllable settings. One primary condition is that within the range of the controllable setting adjustment, there is one particular setting which yields the optimum performance. In operation, the optimalizing controller generates a proper variation of the controllable setting and then, by sensing the corresponding effect upon the performance, it would modify the controllable input setting in such a way as to keep the performance near the optimum point.

491

Figure 17.1 is a functional diagram showing the essential components of a generalized optimalizing controller applied in a typical system. In practice, optimalizing control action may be required for a number of inputs, but to facilitate the present discussion the controlled system of Fig. 17.1 is shown with a single output depending upon a single *controlled input*. The output is defined as the desirable performance to be optimized. Other outputs are shown as dashed lines. This means that the diagram applies only to situations in which all other inputs except the controlled input are constant or in which operation is primarily determined by a single input. The optimalizing controller appears as the feedback branch of a closed-chain operating system. This feedback branch may be considered as made up of three links. The first link is the *output signal generating system*, which receives the output to be controlled and produces a corresponding *output signal*.

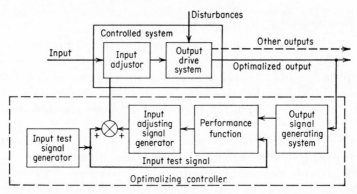

Fig. 17.1 Schematic functional block diagram of an optimalizing control system.

The second link is a performance function resolver which correlates the input test signal with the corresponding output signal to yield an indication of the system performance with respect to the optimum performance.

The third link is the input adjusting signal generator which drives the input adjuster in a direction and speed as determined by the performance function resolver. In proper operation the performance function resolver would manipulate the input adjuster to optimize the output.

The input test signal generator produces a test signal of suitable form which covers a frequency band faster than the input adjusting signal so that their effects upon the controlled system can be separated from each other. These two signals thus identified in Fig. 17.1 only serve as an illustration of the logic. In practice, they may come from the same source. For instance, a human operator may act as an optimalizing controller with the output indicated on a meter. The input adjuster may be a knob. By making trial twiddling of the knob and observing the corresponding change of output level, the operator would then know whether the system is operating near the optimum point or not. If the system is not doing so, then the operator would make proper adjustment of the knob until the system is operating near the optimum point. The optimalizing control system described in the above example thus includes an output signal generating system corresponding to the meter plus the optimalizing controller, which included the systematic test twiddling of the input knob and the corrective adjusting action, all performed by the operator.

Optimalizing controllers offer certain advantages over program type for the control of systems with complex performance characteristics. The primary characteristic of the optimalizing controller is that it uses the controlled system itself as an instrument for determining the existing relationship between its output and its controlled input. Beyond the assumption that some optimum performance condition exists, no knowledge either of the form of the input-output relationship or of quantitative data to describe this function for the controlled system is required for the controller design. This means that the optimalizing controller is always able to search out optimum performance, no matter how environmental conditions or the controlled system itself may change, as long as an optimum condition actually exists. This fact distinguishes optimalizing controller systems from program control systems because the latter require that the controlled system maintain the characteristics used in the system design.

17.2 Typical Performance Characteristics of Optimalizing Control Systems

Plots illustrating typical performance characteristics of a system adapted for optimalizing control are given in Fig. 17.2. The plot of Fig. 17.2*b* shows the variation of the *controlled input-output sensitivity characteristic of the controlled system* as a function of the controlled input. This sensitivity is, by definition, equal to the partial derivative of the output with respect to the controlled input and, as a consequence, represents the slope of the output-controlled input characteristic of the controlled system with all other inputs held constant. Because this slope has the nature of a derivative, it is independent of the shifts in location of the origin.

Optimalizing control may be applied to any operating system with a performance characteristic like that illustrated in Fig. 17.2*a*. The action of a controller must be to change the controlled input in such a way that operation is driven toward the *optimum point* which, in Fig. 17.2*a*, is the maximum point of the controlled input-output characteristic curve. At this point the tangent to the characteristic curve is horizontal, and the controlled system sensitivity is zero, as shown in Fig. 17.2*b*. This fact, and the circumstance that the controlled system sensitivity reverses its sign at the optimum point, make it possible to use a deviation signal based on sensitivity with zero for the reference level as the essential input for optimalizing controllers.

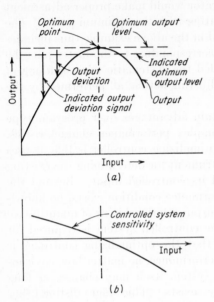

Fig. 17.2   Typical system performance characteristics suitable for optimalizing control. (*a*) Controlled system output and output deviation. (*b*) Controlled system sensitivity.

Optimalizing control may not only be made to depend upon the controlled system sensitivity but may also be based upon the *indicated output deviation signal*, as this quantity is defined in Fig. 17.2. This deviation may be used as the input to a controller which operates by changing the controlled input level in the proper direction to reduce the indicated output deviation.

Signals representing the output of a controlled system are ordinarily easy to obtain. Thus the principal problem in the design of a controller using output deviation as its input is to generate an *indicated optimum output signal* that is a close representation of the actual optimum output level as this quantity varies with controlled system operation. When controlled system sensitivity signals are used for control purposes, the reference level is naturally zero and, for this reason, is easy to realize in practice. On the other hand, the problem of generating signals that satisfactorily represent controlled system sensitivity is not simple. The several possible approaches to this problem lead to various types of optimalizing controllers.

In the generation of a signal to represent the performance characteristic of Fig. 17.2, one must realize that a curve of this kind usually represents the accumulation of earlier test data and is not readily available because of unknown environmental conditions. For this reason in actual operation this curve is generated by the following relationship:

$$\frac{\delta q_\text{out}}{\delta q_\text{in}} = \frac{\delta q_\text{out}/\delta t}{\delta q_\text{in}/\delta t} \tag{17.1}$$

For instance, in certain cruise control systems if a specific range is to be optimized by adjusting the speed, then a signal corresponding to the specific range may be obtained by dividing the forward speed of the vehicle by the flow rate of the fuel. This specific range is then the output to be optimalized. To get the sensitivity $\delta q_{out}/\delta q_{in}$ as represented by Fig. 17.2b and Eq. (17.1), the increment of the specific range must be divided by the change of speed, or the acceleration, of the vehicle. This means that unless there is a change of the controlled input there will not be any sensitivity signal. For this reason, in an optimalizing system the input level is always subjected to some variation for the purpose of generating a useful signal. This operation may be considered as a searching action. As a consequence of the searching action, a deviation signal is recognized and the input is then adjusted toward the optimum point. Thus there are two types of variations of the input that should be clearly distinguished. In principle, if the system is operating near the optimum point then the input needs no further adjustment. But

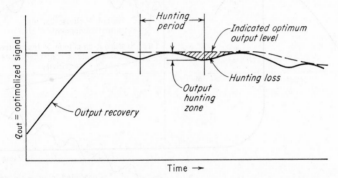

Fig. 17.3 Typical output function resulting from optimalizing control.

the searching action should be maintained to ensure an optimum operating condition when environmental conditions change. Searching can only be stopped temporarily by programming according to known environmental conditions. Without programming the searching action must go on continuously. As a result, all optimalizing control systems have a typical behavior, that is, the output hunts near the optimum condition. A hunting loss which represents the average output deviation from the optimum output is therefore associated with the operation. A typical optimalizing controlled output function is shown in Fig. 17.3. In the design of an optimalizing controller one object is to keep this hunting loss as small as possible. The size of the hunting loss may be expressed as a function of the input test signal and the interference signal or the noise. In order to minimize the hunting loss in a given system, a scheme to separate the input test signal from the interferences must be incorporated. Various methods designed to accomplish this goal are briefly described.[1]

A   Input-output   Sensitivity-operated   Controllers.   1 SIMPLE SENSI-
TIVITY SIGNAL INPUT CONTROLLER. This type of controller uses the
simple ratio of the input rate and output rate as the sensitivity signal.
Since the rate signal is obtained by a differentiator, it has a tendency to
boost the amplitude of high-frequency noise. This type of controller
is therefore not suitable for use in systems where high-frequency noise
prevails.

2 SINUSOIDAL TEST SIGNAL CONTROLLER. This type of controller
generates a sinusoidal test input signal which produces an output component equal to the product of the test input signal and the sensitivity

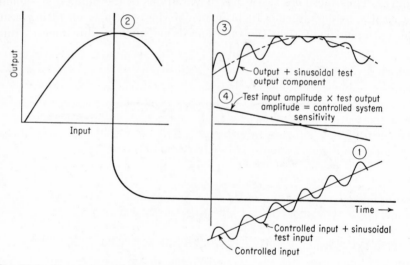

Fig. 17.4 Use of sinusoidal test input to determine control system sensitivity corresponding to various controlled input levels.

of the operating system. This relationship is illustrated in Fig. 17.4
When the input test signal and the corresponding output component is
properly correlated it is possible to resolve the sensitivity of the operating
system. One typical method is to use a bandpass filter to separate the
output test signal from all other components in the output signal. The
output test signal is then multiplied by the input test signal to yield a
rectified signal proportional to the product of the sensitivity of the
operating system and the square of the input test signal. The square
operation provides the rectifying effect. The rectified signal is then
used to close the control loop to reduce the sensitivity of the operating
system to zero.

3 OUTPUT SAMPLING CONTROLLER. This type of optimalizing controller utilizes a constant rate input drive to provide both the input test

function and the input adjustment. Since the input drive rate is constant, then the output rate is proportional to the sensitivity according to Eq. (17.1). In order to establish the output rate without being overshadowed by high-frequency interferences, the system incorporates an output signal sampler which integrates the signal over a fixed time interval and compares the integrated signal with that established during an earlier interval. The difference is then proportional to the sensitivity of the operating system. To complete the controller loop the direction of the input drive is to be reversed whenever the computed sensitivity changes sign. In effect, this is an on-and-off type of controller. It is possible to make this type of controller behave like a linear control system, but for most applications the dynamic characteristics of the operating system are dominated by time lags so that an on-and-off type control is generally adequate.

B   Peak Holding Controller. Unlike the controller described before which depends upon the input-output sensitivity of the operating system, a peak holding controller derives its information from the deviation of the present signal from the optimum or peak signal that has just been experienced. One form of the peak holding type of optimalizing controller utilizes a constant input drive. The basic controller operation is to initiate a reversal signal to alter the direction of drive when the deviation signal exceeds a preselected reversal zone. The reversal zone should be wider than the noise magnitude to avoid false reversal. Thus the noise magnitude determines the reversal zone and, therefore, the hunting zone. For this reason, a suitable filter is needed to smooth the signal before it reaches the controller.

Generally speaking, interferences of significant magnitudes are usually present alongside the useful signals for optimalizing control. These interferences must be separated from the signal to make the operation of the optimalizing controller successful. Various types of filtering schemes to remove the interference are available as discussed above. In addition to these schemes there must be a frequency range over which the interference amplitude of a system is sufficiently low to contain the signals used for the testing of the optimalizing controller. A typical interference spectrum of an operating system is shown in Fig. 17.5. In this diagram the high-amplitude low-frequency interference represents the effect of changes in environmental conditions. The existence of a certain amount of environmental change actually justifies the use of the optimalizing controller. The high-frequency interference, usually called the noise, is the operation problem. The wider the valley of the middle-range frequency with low-interference amplitude, the easier would be the design of the controller. This middle-frequency range should contain the testing frequency and/or the hunting frequency. This frequency also determines the rate of input correction adjustment, which determines the speed for the system to reach the optimum point from a large initial deviation as shown in Fig. 17.3.

Satisfactory optimizing control therefore depends upon the existence of such a frequency range substantially free from strong interference components in between the low- and high-frequency ranges. The corresponding controller design problem is to realize equipment based on test functions formed of frequency components that may be satisfactorily distinguished from the existing output interference without causing unacceptably large hunting effects. In general, the test function must be made up of input variations that are fast enough to be separable from drift interference and at the same time are slow enough to prevent

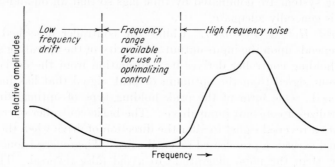

Fig. 17.5 Typical frequency spectrum of interferences acting upon an operating system.

confusion with high-frequency interference effects. The practical minimum limit for the output hunting zone is determined by the success achieved in meeting these conditions.

17.3 Types of System Output Performance to be Optimalized

The performance to be optimalized may have varied degrees of complexity with respect to the parameters of the controlled system. Some desirable performances are self-defined physical quantities and can be measured directly with suitable instruments; but some are relatively complex and a usable signal can only be obtained through the use of a computer based upon information of other measurable physical quantities. According to the degree of complexity, the performance of an operating system to be optimalized can be classified into three types:

1. A single direct measurable quantity
2. A performance which is defined as a simple algebraic function of the instantaneous value of several measurable quantities
3. The dynamic response of regular control systems

17.4 Direct Measurable Quantity as the Optimalized Performance

The simplest type of system performance to be optimalized is represented by single directly measurable quantities. This means that no computer is needed to establish the output signal. A typical example is the optimalization of the thrust of a turbo-propeller power plane in order to get an optimum fuel economy. For certain single-spool types of turbines it can be shown that the optimum thrust of the turbine for a given throttle setting bears a direct relationship with the optimum fuel economy, which is the ultimate goal of the control. Based upon this relationship an optimalizing controller for fuel economy may be designed with thrust as the quantity to be optimalized, and it is a single measurable quantity. In this particular example with a single measurable quantity the controller design is comparably simplified. For this reason, whenever possible, it is always desirable to examine the controlled system characteristic for a possible single measurable quantity prior to the design of the controller. One factor which must be considered however is the environmental and operational effects which might change the relationship between the selected measurable quantity and the true performance to be optimalized. Emphasis should also be placed upon the measurability of the selected quantity. For instance, in the above example thrust is a suitable quantity to be used to optimalize the fuel economy for certain types of turbojet power plant. But in flight, thrust measurement is not altogether simple. Elaborate setups are needed to make direct thrust measurement. For this reason there are proposals for making pressure measurement across the propeller blade to represent thrust. This means a two-stage conversion is involved from differential air-pressure indication to fuel economy. Of the two stages of correlation of optimum conditions, the conversion from optimum differential air pressure to optimum thrust is quite unreliable. This is because in practice the pressure distribution is not actually measured with a large number of pressure probes due to practical considerations. As a result, a small number of differential pressure probes are used to yield a rather unreliable information.

17.5 Optimum Performance Determined by Algebraic Computation

System performance most often to be optimalized are such criteria as economy, efficiency, and the like. These are not directly measurable physical quantities which normally pertain to the operation of a system and therefore must be established by a suitable computer. For instance, efficiency is the ratio of the quantity of a certain desirable output divided by the consumption of a certain critical input. A typical example is the efficiency of a power plant in terms of kilowatt-hours per ton of fuel. For cruise control of a long-range aircraft the efficiency may be the ratio of the distance covered per pound of fuel used, known as the specific range. This is especially important for a bomber because specific range determines its effective radius.

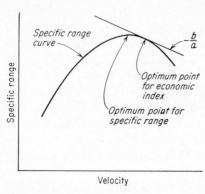

Economy usually has a broader meaning than efficiency. Frequently an economic index may be set up to represent the over-all efficiency of a series of intermediate stages of operation. On the other hand an economic index may depend upon the interlocking relationships of several controlling inputs and several outputs. In the case of cruise control for economy of an airline transport, the fuel economy is not the major operational object. The flying time is another factor

Fig. 17.6 Optimum points for economic index and specific range determined from specific range characteristic curve.

to be considered. For this reason an economy index may be set as represented by the following equation:

$$EI = a \times SR + b \times V = a \times \frac{V}{F} + b \times V$$

$$= V\left(\frac{a}{F} + b\right) \qquad (17.2)$$

where EI = economy index
  a and b = constants
  SR = specific range
  V = speed
  F = fuel flow rate

The condition for optimum economic index when velocity is used as the input adjustment is therefore

$$\frac{\delta EI}{\delta V} = 0 \qquad (17.3)$$

This means that

$$\frac{a}{F} + b = 0 \quad \text{or} \quad \frac{1}{F} = \frac{-b}{a} \qquad (17.4)$$

Now if the system performance is given in the form of specific range versus speed and the slope of the performance curve is

$$\frac{\delta(SR)}{\delta V} = \frac{1}{F} \qquad (17.5)$$

then by equating Eqs. (17.4) and (17.5) it shows that on the specific range curve the optimum economic index corresponds to the point where

$$\frac{\delta(SR)}{\delta V} = -\frac{b}{a} \qquad (17.6)$$

This fact is shown in Fig. 17.6. For similar reasons some people working in the optimalizing controller field have been considering the use of the off-peak point of a certain output-input curve as the optimum condition. This in effect is defining a new economic index other than the output. But to clear up the design concept it is better to start with a well-defined economic index and call that the output. Then there will be no confusion as to what is really to be optimalized.

17.6 Optimalizing of the Dynamic Response of Control System

For aircraft equipped with air-breathing power plant of relatively low capacity the cruise control is basically a fuel economy problem. This is because the operation of the airplane is limited to regions with sufficient air and with moderate rate of change of altitude. Under these restrictions, fuel economy is the only operation parameter which is sufficiently affected by environmental effects to require a cruise control. When the flight vehicle is used to cover a wider section of the atmosphere and is equipped with a powerful engine to make a fast change of altitude, then the dynamic characteristics of the control system would be affected by the rapid change of the air density and the fast rate of change of mass through consumption of the fuel.

The cruise control for this type of flight vehicle should therefore include systems to ensure desirable *flight control system dynamic characteristics* throughout the entire range of flight. This type of control system is now known as an adaptive control system because of its ability to adapt to changing environment. To be sure all cruise control systems are adaptive control systems. It may be a generalization to define cruise control systems as auxiliary systems to improve the adaptability of the primary system against operational and environmental effects.

In principle an optimalizing controller for maintaining the dynamic response of a control system to a desirable form is not much different from other types of application if a performance index indicator is made available to measure the performance of the system upon a suitable scale. When this is realized, then the complete system may be assembled as shown in Fig. 17.7. This schematic diagram shows a compensating network or system used in tandem with the controlled system. The compensating device is built with a few adjustable parameters. The adjustment of these parameters should produce similar changes of performance as the environment effects. For this reason, when environmental effects are taking place the adjustable parameter can be manipulated to bring the performance index up to the optimum condition.

Optimalization of the dynamic performance of a control system is considerably more complicated than similar control for economic index or its equivalent because of the difficulty involved in the design of two essential systems—the compensating system and the performance index indicator. Take the compensating system first which is relatively straightforward compared with the performance index indicator. The necessary condition for the design is the realization of an adjustable parameter or a set of parameters which can be incorporated in the compensating system and can be adjusted to offset the effects of the variant parameter in the controlled system. In the simplest case where the variant parameter is a change of sensitivity, the compensating parameter

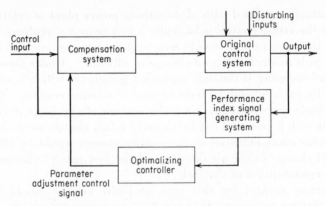

Fig. 17.7 Optimalizing control system for dynamic response by searching for the best performance index signal.

would be simply a gain adjustment. This is because the two parameters are conjugate quotients of a single parameter that appears in the over-all system dynamic characteristic equation. Complication results when each variant physical parameter affects all the dynamic characteristic parameters such as damping coefficients and natural frequencies of a higher-order system. To compensate exactly for these effects the controller should create a reciprocal dynamic characteristic function of the system to be compensated so that the shifting of the corresponding parameter of the controller may counterbalance exactly the effect of the variant parameter in the controlled system. In practice, this exact compensation may be impractical because of complication in design and possible limitation due to saturation of some of the components. For this reason a simplified compensating system is usually used. As a result, the optimum performance through the adjustment of the parameters of the simplified compensation system is not the absolute optimum for the controlled system. But, nevertheless, the optimalizing controller will be able to search for the optimum condition of the combined system.

The performance index indicator is a difficult problem because an exact definition of the performance index is hard to establish. A substitution method devised by P. H. Whitaker of MIT has been tested with satisfactory results. In Whitaker's system a reference system of simple second-order function is used to represent the desirable dynamic characteristics. Test inputs are applied to both the actual system and the reference system. The integrated difference of the outputs from the two systems is used as the performance index to be minimized by the optimalization controller. A schematic diagram of this system is shown in Fig. 17.8.

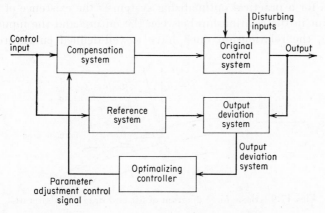

Fig. 17.8 Optimalizing control system for dynamic response by minimizing the output deviation with respect to the output of a reference system.

17.7 Design of a Specific Range Optimalizing System for Turbojet Aircraft

The specific range of an aircraft is defined as the instantaneous ratio of the speed divided by the fuel flow rate. Since it is impossible to maximize the total range for a specified total amount of fuel, the optimalization of the specific range is the best possible scheme aiming at the same object.

The reason that the aircraft cannot hold its setting for best specific range operating conditions is primarily due to environmental variations. The one single largest variating parameter is the weight of the aircraft which changes constantly as the fuel is consumed. Other factors are numerous, such as atmospheric conditions, deterioration of the aircraft through either aging effect or battle damage, or change of configuration such as the installation of external tanks.

Weight variation is a measurable physical quantity and its relationship with specific range is established during fly test.   For this reason it is possible to program the controllable operating settings in flight based upon weight information either manually or automatically.   The major drawback of this scheme is attributable to the presence of the other variations which are not in measurable form or do not have a known relationship with the controllable operating settings.

The controllable operating settings may involve certain engine parameters, such as compressor blade angle.   The two major aircraft performances that affect the specific range are the speed and altitude. Unless these factors are constrained, such as flying in formation, it is possible to hunt these variables to search for the optimum specific range, by one of the optimalizing systems described before.   One necessary condition for a practical optimalizing system is the existence of an optimum point in the relationship between the output and the input.   Furthermore, the relationship must have a well-defined curvature in the

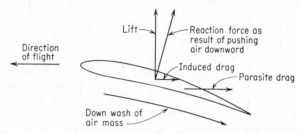

Fig. 17.9   Basic force diagram of lift and drag of an aircraft.

vicinity of the optimum point.   In the case of the specific range optimalizing system with altitude and speed as the inputs, we may specify the hunting of the speed to be not more than ± 10 knots and an altitude tolerance of ± 500 ft for 1 per cent deviation of the specific range.   This information can usually be obtained from preliminary flight tests.   For the present discussion it is interesting to examine the mechanics of the turbojet aircraft and realize the cause of the curvature of the input-output relationships.

For practical purposes the jet engine of the aircraft may be assumed as having a constant efficiency in terms of specific thrust which is equal to unit of thrust per unit amount of fuel per unit time.   The controlling factor for the specific range is then dominated by the drag characteristic of the airplane.   The drag of an airplane may be considered as the contribution from two sources.   The first one is the induced drag, and the second one the parasite drag.   Figure 17.9 shows that the induced drag is the component, in the direction of flight, of the reaction force acting upon the wing when the air mass is pushed downward to produce lift. At higher speed, more air is affected by the wing, and consequently a smaller angle of down-wash is needed.   As a result, less induced drag is produced for a given lift force. With the use of momentum concept it is obvious that the air mass affected is proportional to the forward speed and the down-wash is inversely proportional to the forward speed. For this reason the drag force is inversely proportional to the square of the forward speed. This means that if there is no parasite drag, the airplane should fly at higher and higher speed. But the parasite drag is directly proportional to the square of the airspeed. Therefore an optimum point for minimum drag is established at a certain speed as shown in Fig. 17.10. At this speed the rate of change of the parasite drag is just enough to balance the induced drag.

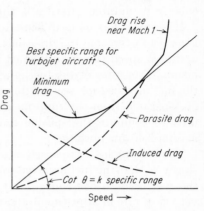

Fig. 17.10 Drag and specific range plot of a turbojet aircraft.

Specific range is defined as the ratio of velocity divided by the fuel consumption. For a turbojet the fuel consumption is proportional to the thrust or drag. For this reason specific range may be represented by the arc cotangent of the line drawn from any point on the drag curve of Fig. 17.10 to the origin. The maximum specific range is represented by the arc cotangent of the line drawn from the origin tangent to the drag curve as shown by the dashed line of Fig. 17.10. The drag curve of Fig. 17.10 also shows a sharp break at a critical speed close to Mach 1. This is the result of the creation of certain localized shock waves with the association of sudden increase in drag, known as drag rise. This drag-rise phenomenon changes the optimum cruise speed considerably.

The flying altitude affects the specific range through the change in air density. By similar reasoning we can see that the induced drag decreases with density because the down-wash angle is less for higher air density. On the other hand the parasite drag increases with density. For this reason there exists a balance between the two drags at a certain optimum altitude. For the present discussion only the optimum speed controller is to be considered.

The two basic instruments needed for the optimalizing controller are the specific range computer and an optimalizing controller such as a peak holding type. The basic design of these two instruments needs no detailed discussion. But the dynamic problem of the complete system as a whole warrants some consideration. By definition, the specific range is defined as the ratio of the speed divided by the fuel flow rate. As for the speed, conventional cockpit instruments are usually limited to air-speed measurement. But for optimalizing control, ground speed is the desirable information. However it can be shown that the result obtained by optimalizing the specific range based on airspeed is not appreciably different from the result when ground is used. The most important problem when airspeed is used is the error introduced by gust effect. A suitable filtering is thus needed to overcome this problem.

It is somewhat more difficult to measure the net fuel flow rate which is used to overcome the drag only. This is because in searching for the optimum speed the aircraft must hunt with a change of speed. At any instant a portion of the fuel is used to accelerate the aircraft. Ideally the fuel involved for accelerating or deaccelerating of the aircraft should be separated from the total measured fuel flow rate before the signal is used to compute the specific range. Three methods may be used to accomplish this purpose.

The first method is to accelerate or deaccelerate the airplane sufficiently slowly so that the fuel involved for doing this is small in comparison with the fuel used to overcome the drag. This scheme requires the use of very slow rate of adjustment and is inadequate when interference change is relatively fast. The second scheme involves the measuring of the acceleration and utilizing the known or estimated airplane mass and fuel needed for acceleration to account for this part of fuel expenditure. The third scheme involves a feedback control loop which maintains a constant acceleration of the aircraft during the speed-changing period. Assuming that the fuel needed for acceleration remains constant over each test period, then the addition of a constant amount of fuel would not alter the shape of specific fuel consumption in pounds per mile. For this reason the minimum specific fuel-consumption point corresponds to the same airplane speed with or without the constant acceleration. When the system is designed to optimalize the specific range with constant acceleration, then the maximum point will be slightly off because of the inclusion of a constant error in the denominator of the specific range computation. This error, however, is rather insignificant.

Of the three schemes, the first one tends to be slow. The second one requires the knowledge of the exact amount of fuel used in accelerating the aircraft. The third scheme does not require knowing the exact amount of fuel used for acceleration except that it maintained constant during the hunting cycle. This stands out as a very useful method not only for cruise control but for the kind of optimalizing system with a dynamic problem.

REFERENCES

1. Tsien, H. S.: "Engineering Cybernetics," chap. 15, Optimalizing Control, McGraw-Hill Book Company, Inc., New York, 1954.

18
Control Problems in Nuclear Reactors

E. RICHARD COHEN

RESEARCH ADVISER, ATOMICS INTERNATIONAL

CANOGA PARK, CALIF.

18.1 Introduction

A nuclear reactor represents a novel source of energy whose utilization will increase in coming years. Since the process of energy generation in a reactor is fundamentally different from what it is in a coal-fired or in a hydroelectric plant, the nature of the control problem is also different. It is the purpose of this discussion to outline the basic mechanisms of the reactor to the extent to which they influence the problem of control. We shall confine ourselves primarily to the reactor itself and not consider in detail the over-all system of the complete power plant. This restriction does not imply that the so-called "conventional" portions of the power plant will be exactly the same as in other power-generating systems, but only that the nuclear reactor plant behavior can be determined by conventional methods of analysis and can be designed with conventional components once the requisite parameters of the nuclear system have been determined.

A specific example of a nonstandard power plant is the SRE (Sodium Reactor Experiment of the U.S. Atomic Energy Commission Reactor Development Program). This reactor used liquid sodium as a heat transfer fluid to extract heat from the reactor. Because sodium becomes radioactive, this coolant loop cannot be run directly to the conventional side of the plant. Instead, an intermediate heat exchanger transfers the heat from the radioactive sodium loop to a nonradioactive loop. This heat exchanger is small (because of the excellent heat-transfer properties of liquid metals), and hence the system can be easily shielded against the radiation from the radioactive sodium. The nonradioactive sodium loop then exchanges heat with the high-temperature water loop which drives the steam turbines. This double heat exchanger system is a typical example of the type of nonconventional use of conventional

507

components which are common in reactor systems. The analysis of the performance of a double heat exchanger system is still within the area of conventional techniques, and we shall not explore it. We shall concentrate on the determination of the parameters only of the nuclear system itself and the extent to which the external (nonreactor) components alter the parameters of this internal (reactor) system.

18.2   Production of Neutrons—The Chain Reaction

A chain reaction is not a new mechanism developed by nuclear physicists; chain reactions have been known in chemical kinetics long before fission was discovered. The significant feature of the fission process is that it produces the agent required for its own propagation. When a fissionable nucleus (U^{233}, U^{235}, Pu^{239}, etc.) absorbs a neutron, it may undergo a fissioning—a breaking up into two approximately equal smaller fragments. The nucleus is composed of protons and neutrons in roughly equal numbers—but with the neutron-to-proton ratio increasing from approximately 1:1 in the lightest elements to 1:1.5 in the heaviest elements. The fission fragments therefore have an excess of neutrons. This situation is corrected primarily by a process in which a neutron changes into a proton. An average of approximately seven or eight such transformations are required to change each of the two fragments into stable fission products. It is the radioactivity associated with these transformations that is one of the principal products of fission.

There is, however, another process by which the neutron-proton balance in the fragment can be changed. This is the fairly obvious one of simply ejecting one of the excess neutrons, and this path is usually followed as the first step in the process of nuclear readjustment. On the average between two and three free neutrons may be produced in this way for each nucleus fissioned. Each of these neutrons can produce a fission if it is captured by a fissionable nucleus, and the object of reactor design is to ensure that, of the possible fates for the neutron, on the average one neutron per fission will produce a fission in its turn.

The preceding statement implies that other fates are possible. In broad terms we can define two other results: One depends on the composition of the reactor, the relative amounts of fissionable and nonfissionable material, and the probabilities of the neutron being absorbed in each material; the other depends on the size and shape of the reactor and hence on the probability that a neutron produced in the core (or fuel-containing regions) of the reactor will leak out and be lost to the system. We can then define an effective neutron multiplication factor for the reactor which we call k. This factor can be written as the product of three terms:

1. ν—the number of neutrons produced per fission
2. $\mathcal{L}$—the nonleakage probability or the fraction of those neutrons

produced in fission which are absorbed in the reactor as opposed to those which leak out of the reactor and are lost

3. $\mathfrak{F}$—the fraction of all those neutrons absorbed in the reactor which produce a fission

$$k = \nu \mathfrak{F} \mathfrak{L} \tag{18.1}$$

For the reactor to operate at a constant neutron level and hence at a constant power level, k must be exactly equal to unity. If $k > 1$, then more neutrons are produced in each cycle than were present at the start of the cycle. If we start with one neutron, then after 1 cycle, we have k neutrons, after 2 cycles we have k^2, after 3 cycles, k^3, and so on. Thus, depending on whether k is greater than or less than 1, the neutron population will grow or decay exponentially; $k = 1$ is therefore the critical value. After n cycles the neutron population will be k^n, and if we define a cycle lifetime l, the number of cycles in time t will be $n = t/l$, and the neutron population at time t will be

$$n(t) = k^{t/l} = e^{(t/l) \ln k} \tag{18.2}$$

However, we cannot assume that each cycle has a fixed lifetime any more than we can say that all biological lifetimes are the same length. The fissioning and multiplication of neutrons is a statistical process, and each neutron has a history which at each step is describable only in terms of probabilities. It is only because of the statistical certainty of the behavior of large numbers of neutrons that a continuous description is possible. We can, however, write a differential equation

$$\frac{dn}{dt} = \frac{(k-1)}{l} n \tag{18.3}$$

which states that the (average) rate of change of neutron population is proportional to the neutron population which is present at any time and to the change per cycle divided by the mean lifetime of a cycle. The integral of Eq. (18.3) is

$$n(t) = n(0) e^{(k-1)t/l} \tag{18.3a}$$

If $k \approx 1$ Eq. (18.2) and (18.3a) become equivalent.

18.3 Source Multiplication

If there is a source of neutrons, Eq. (18.3) is modified to

$$\frac{dn}{dt} = \frac{k-1}{l} n + S(t) \tag{18.4}$$

The solution of this equation is

$$n = n_0 e^{(k-1)t/l} + \int_0^t S(t-\tau) e^{(k-1)\tau/l} \, d\tau \tag{18.5}$$

If $k > 1$, the neutron level is divergent; but if $k < 1$, the initial neutron component will disappear, and after sufficient time the neutron level will be controlled entirely by the source. If S does not change appreciably over a time interval $l/(1 - k)$ we can write

$$n \approx \frac{lS}{1 - k} \tag{18.6}$$

If there were no multiplication, the neutron level would be lS and hence the multiplying medium acts as an amplifier with a gain of $1/(1 - k)$. If a constant source of neutrons is introduced into a multiplying medium (which may be some mixture of uranium-containing material), the neutron density in the system will rise initially linearly but will then level off to its equilibrium value. This behavior is shown in Fig. 18.1. If the multiplication is zero, the source increases the neutron population until the absorption rate (which depends linearly on the neutron population) just balances the production rate. If we have $k > 0$, the multipli-

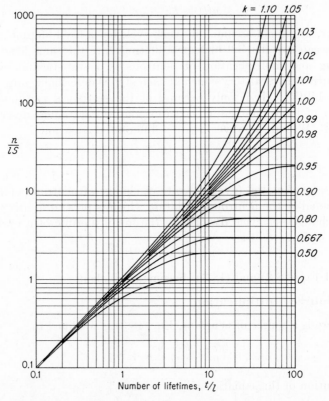

Fig. 18.1   Neutron population following the insertion of a source into a multiplying medium.   If the multiplication factor is greater than or equal to unity, no equilibrium is possible.   For $k = 1$ the neutron population increases linearly with time.   For $k > 1$ the population diverges exponentially.

cation adds to the neutrons which come directly from the source, and a higher equilibrium level is reached, but a longer time is required before this equilibrium is obtained. If the multiplication constant k is exactly equal to 1, there is a neutron produced on the average for each neutron lost; the neutron population therefore increases linearly with time, and no equilibrium is reached.

If we have $k > 1$, more neutrons are produced than are lost, and we have a divergent neutron population. No equilibrium is reached and Eq. (18.6) is no longer applicable. Instead one must return to Eq. (18.5). With no neutrons present initially, a constant source S is introduced at time $t = 0$; Eq. (18.5) becomes

$$n(t) = \frac{S}{k - 1} [e^{(k-1)t/l} - 1]$$

It is evident that for $k > 1$ the neutron level rises exponentially, and hence the neutron level can achieve very high values in a short time if the lifetime l is short.

18.4 Neutron Lifetimes

The lifetime of a neutron depends on the reactor design. A neutron produced in the fission process will have a mean free path between its collisions with the atoms of the uranium or other material in the reactor which is of the order of a few centimeters. Since the neutron speed is of the order of 10^9 cm/sec, it will therefore make 10^9 collisions/sec. If the neutron merely scatters but is not absorbed, the cycle is not ended. In the so-called fast reactor the cycle may require approximately ten collisions before the neutron is absorbed so that the cycle time is 10^{-8} sec. Most of the present power reactors, however, operate on neutrons that are slowed down from their initial high energies (and high velocities) and are in thermal equilibrium with the material of the reactor. These neutrons move more slowly and hence the collision rate is slower, perhaps only 10^6/sec. Furthermore, the neutron now makes a few hundred collisions before it is absorbed, and hence the cycle time is of the order of 10^{-4} or 10^{-3} sec.

The lifetime of a neutron is therefore strongly dependent on the type of reactor, but is always short compared to ordinary macroscopic physical processes. With a lifetime of 10^{-8} sec even an increase of only one neutron per million per generation ($k = 1.000001$) would give a multi-plication rate of $e^{100} = 10^{43}$ per sec. Such a system would be completely impossible to control. With the lifetime as long as 10^{-3} sec, a value of k only 0.1 per cent greater than 1 yields an increase of a factor of approxi-mately 3 per sec or an increase by 1 decade in 2.3 sec. This system, if not impossible to control, would be extremely difficult.

18.5   Delayed Neutrons

Nature, however, has been kind.   Not all of the neutrons produced in a fission are emitted instantaneously in the fission process (within less than 10^{-16} sec).   A small fraction of all neutrons is delayed.   These delayed neutrons are not emitted in the fundamental process of nuclear disruption but come instead from the fission products.   In the fissioning of U^{235} (the numbers are somewhat different for other fissionable isotopes) 1.80 per cent of all fissions results in fragments which emit delayed neutrons.   Not all of these precursors have been identified, but the fission product I^{137} will serve as an example.   This nucleus, which is formed in the fission process, is neutron-heavy and decays by the emission of a negative beta particle thereby converting a neutron into a proton and reducing the neutron-proton ratio.   The resulting Xe^{137} contains 83 neutrons and 54 protons.   The nuclear structure of 82 neutrons is, for reasons which are not fully understood, a particularly stable configuration, and the extra neutron is held only weakly in this nucleus.   The neutron is therefore ejected, and a residual stable nucleus of Xe^{136} is formed.   The process of neutron emission occurs in a time of the order of 10^{-14} sec and is therefore virtually instantaneous once the parent Xe^{137} has been formed.   Hence the neutron emission has the half-life (22 sec) of the radioactive decay of I^{137} to Xe^{137}.

Table 18.1   Delayed Neutron Data, Thermal Fission of U^{235}

Delayed neutron group, i	Half-life, $T_{\frac{1}{2}i}$	Decay constant, λ_i	Abundance	
			Relative, a_i	Absolute, β_i
1	55.72 sec	0.01244 sec^{-1}	0.033	0.00021
2	22.72	0.03051	0.219	0.00140
3	6.22	0.1114	0.196	0.00125
4	2.30	0.3014	0.395	0.00253
5	0.61	1.136	0.115	0.00074
6	0.23	3.014	0.042	0.00027
			1.000	0.00640

$$l_d = \sum_i \frac{\beta_i}{\lambda_i} = 83.2 \text{ msec}$$

$$\bar{\tau} = \sum_i \frac{a_i}{\lambda_i} = 13.01 \text{ sec}$$

$$\bar{\lambda} = \sum_i a_i \lambda_i = 0.405 \text{ sec}^{-1}$$

$$\frac{1}{\bar{\lambda}} = 2.468 \text{ sec}$$

In all, six groups of delayed neutrons have been identified by half-life. The decay constants and abundances of these groups are given in Table 18.1. It has now been quite well established that Br^{87} is the precursor of group 1 and I^{137} is the precursor of group 2. Unique identifications have not been established for the other groups, and they may well represent mixtures of several components. For a detailed description of the reactor these groups must all be considered; however, for general discussion of qualitative effects and even for many quantitative results, it is sufficient to consider the delayed neutrons to come from a single group of precursors with a single decay constant λ. The number of neutrons in the reactor at any time is then represented by the equation

$$\frac{dn}{dt} = \frac{k_p}{l} n + \lambda c - \frac{n}{l} \qquad (18.7)$$

The first term on the right is the rate at which neutrons are produced directly in fission; k_p is the number of neutrons produced promptly per generation (or the prompt multiplication factor). The second term is the rate at which neutrons are produced from the precursors which are present in a concentration c and decay with decay rate λ. The third term is the rate of removal of neutrons from the system. We must now also write an equation for the precursor concentration c

$$\frac{dc}{dt} = \frac{k_d n}{l} - \lambda c \qquad (18.8)$$

where k_d is the delayed multiplication constant, the number of precursors produced per neutron removed (by leakage or absorption). The multiplication constant k is the sum of the prompt and the delayed multiplication constants. It is common to use β to denote the fraction of all neutrons produced which are delayed:

$$\beta = \frac{k_d}{k_p + k_d} \qquad k = k_p + k_d \qquad (18.9)$$

If the reactor configuration is changed or if the physical parameters of the reactor (such as the temperature distribution) are changed, the multiplication constant k and the neutron lifetime l will also change. In general, however, the quantity $l_0 = l/k$ is much less sensitive to changes and in many cases is in fact constant with respect to changes in reactor parameters. It is common therefore to introduce l_0 in place of l and to assume that it is a constant of the reactor. If one also introduces the reactivity ρ by the relation

$$k = \frac{1}{1 - \rho} \qquad \rho = \frac{k - 1}{k} \qquad (18.10)$$

the equations become

$$\frac{dn}{dt} = \frac{\rho - \beta}{l_0} n + \lambda c \tag{18.11}$$

$$\frac{dc}{dt} = \frac{\beta}{l_0} n - \lambda c \tag{18.11a}$$

18.6 Reactor with Constant Reactivity

If ρ is a constant, these equations may be easily solved. We look first at the case $\rho = 0$ $(k = 1)$. Here we are producing neutrons at exactly the correct rate to balance losses. One solution is the steady-state situation

$$n = \text{arbitrary}$$

$$c = \frac{\lambda \beta}{l_0} n$$

in which the level in the reactor is constant. There is however a second solution, and the complete solution is

$$n = n_0 + n_1 e^{-\omega t} \tag{18.12a}$$

$$c = \frac{\lambda \beta}{l_0} n_0 - n_1 e^{-\omega t} \tag{18.12b}$$

$$\omega = \frac{\beta}{l_0} + \lambda \tag{18.12c}$$

The transient term disappears quickly, leaving only the constant component. That this constant value is arbitrary is a consequence of the homogeneity of the equations, and it points out the fact that an ideal reactor is only neutrally stable; any fluctuation in the neutron level is accepted by the reactor as a possible operating level.

Consider now a reactor with initial neutron level n_0 and equilibrium precursor concentration $c_0 = \beta n_0 / l_0$. Let the reactivity be altered instantaneously to the value $\rho \neq 0$. The solution of Eq. (18.11) is

$$\frac{n(t)}{n_0} = \frac{1}{l_0(\omega_1 - \omega_2)} [(l_0 \omega_2 - \rho)e^{\omega_1 t} - (l_0 \omega_1 - \rho)e^{\omega_2 t}] \tag{18.13}$$

where $\omega_{1,2}$ are the roots of

$$\omega^2 + \omega \left(\lambda + \frac{\beta - \rho}{l_0} \right) - \frac{\rho \lambda}{l_0} = 0 \tag{18.13a}$$

If $0 < \rho < \beta$ the two roots have opposite signs, and the positive root is smaller in absolute magnitude than the negative root. The two roots are approximately

$$\omega_0 \approx \frac{\rho \lambda}{\lambda l_0 + \beta - \rho} \qquad \omega_2 \approx - \left(\lambda + \frac{\beta - \rho}{l_0} \right) \tag{18.13b}$$

The negative root represents a fast-decaying transient which disappears rapidly leaving the more slowly varying term. For $|\rho| \ll \beta$ an adequate approximation is

$$\frac{n(t)}{n_0} = \frac{1}{\beta - \rho} \left\{ \beta e^{[\lambda \rho / (\beta - \rho)]t} - \rho e^{(\beta - \rho)/l_0} \right\} \tag{18.14}$$

Numerically let us consider $\beta / l_0 = 100 \sec^{-1}$, $\lambda = 0.1 \sec^{-1}$, and $\rho / \beta = 0.1$:

$$\frac{n(t)}{n_0} = \frac{10}{9} e^{0.0111t} - \frac{1}{9} e^{-90t}$$

$$= e^{0.0111t} + \frac{1}{9}(e^{0.0111t} - e^{-90t}) \tag{18.14a}$$

In comparison, if there were no delayed neutrons, a reactivity input of 0.1β would yield

$$\frac{n(t)}{n_0} = e^{\rho t / l_0} = e^{10t} \tag{18.14b}$$

The difference in neutron behavior is striking. Instead of increasing 4.3 decades/sec as it would without delayed neutrons, the level rises at this fast rate only for the first few hundredths of a second. By this time the neutron population has increased only 11 per cent. This increase is exactly the type of response exhibited in Fig. 18.1 if we consider the delayed neutron fraction to represent a source of strength βn. Since the total multiplication had been unity before the change, the prompt multiplication was initially $1 - \beta$. If this prompt multiplication is increased by ρ, the multiplication factor $1/(1 - k_p)$ increases from $1/\beta$ to $1/(\beta - \rho)$. In the short time however, the delayed neutron precursors, having a relatively long time constant, cannot respond to the change, and further increase in neutron population must now proceed at a slower rate determined by the delayed neutrons. The neutron population now levels off to a much slower rise of only 1.1 per cent per sec. The neutron level has run away from the delayed neutrons, and the reactor now acts like a subcritical multiplying system which is amplifying the delayed neutron source.

The delayed neutrons are therefore responsible for making feasible the controlled production of energy from fission. If this accident of nature had not occurred, the design of reactors, if possible at all, would be completely modified from what is now considered standard.

18.7 Kinetic Equations—Constant Reactivity

We now extend Eq. (18.11) and consider several delayed neutron groups. The equations are

$$\frac{dn}{dt} = \frac{\rho - \beta}{l_0} n + \sum_i \lambda_i c_i \tag{18.15a}$$

$$\frac{dc_i}{dt} = \frac{\beta_i}{l_0} n - \lambda_i c_i \qquad \sum_i \beta_i = \beta \tag{18.15b}$$

where β_i is the fraction of delayed neutron precursors produced per neutron disappearing in the system, and λ_i is the precursor decay constant.

If all of the coefficients are constant, these equations are most easily solved by use of Laplace transforms. With the usual notation we let $N(s)$ and $C_i(s)$ be the transforms of $n(t)$ and $c_i(t)$. Then

$$sN(s) - n_0 = \frac{\rho - \beta}{l_0} N(s) + \sum_i \lambda_i C_i(s) \qquad (18.16a)$$

$$sC_i(s) - c_{i0} = \frac{\beta_i}{l_0} N(s) - \lambda_i C_i(s) \qquad (18.16b)$$

Solving these equations for $N(s)$ gives

$$N(s) = \frac{l_0 \left(n_0 + \sum \dfrac{\lambda_i c_{i0}}{\lambda_i + s} \right)}{s \left(l_0 + \sum \dfrac{\beta_i}{\lambda_i + s} \right) - \rho} \qquad (18.17)$$

and the inverse transformation yields

$$n(t) = n(0) \sum_j A(p_j) e^{p_j t} \qquad c_i(t) = n(0) \sum_j \frac{\lambda_i A(p_j)}{\lambda_i + p_j} e^{p_j t} \qquad (18.18)$$

where p_j are the roots of the characteristic equation

$$\rho = s \left(l_0 + \sum \frac{\beta_i}{\lambda_i + s} \right) \qquad (18.18a)$$

and

$$A(s) = \frac{1 + (1/n_0) \sum_i \lambda_i c_{i0}/(\lambda_i + s)}{1 + (1/l_0) \sum_i \beta_i \lambda_i/(\lambda_i + s)^2} \qquad (18.18b)$$

Equation (18.18a) is known as the in-hour equation because it gives the reactivity of the reactor in terms of the easily observable time constant p_j which was recorded at the Hanford Plutonium Production Reactors in units of "inverse hours." To be precise, it is the most positive root of Eq. (18.18a) which is identified with the reactivity. If $|\rho| \ll \beta$, this root is given by

$$s = p_1 = \frac{\rho}{l_0 + \Sigma \beta_i/\lambda_i} \qquad (18.19)$$

Again one sees clearly in Eq. (18.19) the effect of the delayed neutrons. The neutrons have an apparent lifetime $l_{\text{eff}} = l_0 + \Sigma \beta_i/\lambda_i$. This is the average lifetime of all of the neutrons including the delay time of those neutrons which follow the precursor decay. The prompt neutrons have a mean lifetime l_0, and each group of delayed neutrons exhibits a longer lifetime $l_0 + 1/\lambda_i$. When these lifetimes are averaged over the abundances of prompt and delayed neutrons, one obtains the effective lifetime l_{eff}. For the thermal neutron induced fission of U^{235}, $\Sigma\beta_i/\lambda_i$ is approximately 0.083 sec so that the short lifetimes mentioned previously ($l_0 < 10^{-3}$ sec) are effectively increased by a factor of at least 100. More important the effective neutron lifetime is approximately 0.083 sec whether the prompt neutron lifetime is 10^{-3} sec or 10^{-8} sec, and hence the very short prompt lifetime of a fast reactor does not make it any more difficult to control than a thermal reactor with a prompt neutron lifetime several orders of magnitude longer.*

When the reactivity ρ is large compared to β, the time constant s will be large compared to all of the λ_i's, and one obtains in place of Eq. (18.19)

$$s = p_1 = \frac{\rho - \beta}{l_0} \tag{18.19a}$$

Here we see the reactor multiplying on prompt neutrons only and hence characterized by the prompt neutron lifetime. It is apparent that the value of β is fundamental to the description of the reactor and represents a division point in reactivity between the region of slow reactor response and fast reactor response. Hence it is convenient to measure reactivity in units of β and to define $r = \rho/\beta$. The quantity r is spoken of as the reactivity in "dollars."†

The principal root p_1 of the in-hour equation (18.18a) has the same sign as the reactivity; all of the other roots are negative and lie successively in the intervals $-\lambda_1 > p_2 > -\lambda_2$, $-\lambda_2 > p_3 > -\lambda_3$, . . . , $-\lambda_6 > p_7$, where the λ_i are ordered according to magnitude.

Curves for the determination of the roots of the in-hour equation and of the amplitude factor $A(s)$ are given in several references. Parts (a) and (b) of Fig. 18.2 constitute a chart for the response of an equilibrium reactor to a step change in reactivity. The initial conditions correspond to zero reactivity, and at $t = 0$ a sudden change in reactivity is made. To use the chart one reads the reactivity on the right-hand scale and locates the corresponding roots p_j from the $r(s)$ curve. From these values of s, one reads from the $A(s)$ curve the corresponding amplitudes.

---

* This statement does not apply to an accident situation in which a reactivity increase greater than β is introduced into the reactor. In such a case, with the reactor able to multiply on prompt neutrons only, the prompt neutron lifetime does determine the time scale. An accident in a reactor with a short prompt neutron lifetime may well be more serious than in a reactor with a longer prompt lifetime. As long as the reactor is "under control," the reactivity variations will ordinarily be kept less than β in order to avoid this situation.

† The term dollar originated at Los Alamos during the Manhattan Project. The etymology of the word is uncertain, and it is probable that it represents an arbitrary coinage for reasons of security. The use of the term however is now well established.

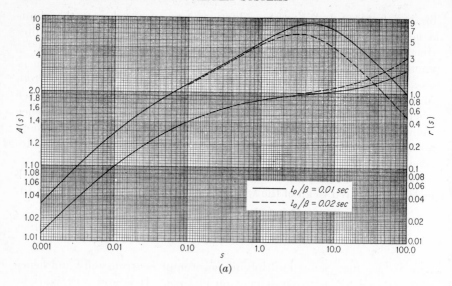

(a)

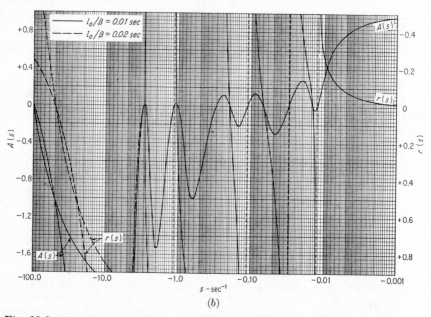

(b)

Fig. 18.2 Amplitude charts for the response of a reactor to a step change in reactivity. (a) Chart giving the positive root and corresponding amplitude for a positive reactivity change. Read reactivity on right-hand scale and read value of p_1 from abscissa on curve of $r(s)$; then read $A(p_1)$ from left-hand scale. (b) Chart giving all of the negative roots and corresponding amplitudes. Read reactivity on right-hand scale and read values of p_j from abscissa on curve of $r(s)$; for each p_j read corresponding $A(p_j)$ from left-hand scale.

The time response of the reactor is then calculated from Eq. (18.18). In general a different chart must be constructed for each new value of l_0/β, but in practice the prompt neutron lifetime has little influence on the response for $r < 1$ and hence one chart can serve reasonably well for most cases.

18.8 Reactor Start-up

If the reactivity of a reactor is set negative, all of the roots of the in-hour equation are negative, and the neutron level would apparently drop to zero after a long time.   This is not the case because of the presence of sources of neutrons which are not directly connected with the fission process or which come from spontaneous fission of U^{238}, or other heavy elements.   In addition to neutrons produced by cosmic rays, high-energy gamma rays from the radioactive decay of fission products can produce neutrons in the fuel either by stimulating fission or by the disintegration of light elements such as deuterium and beryllium which might be present as a moderator in the reactor.   In addition a neutron source is specifically inserted into the reactor in order to provide a background level of neutron flux in order that an indication is always possible in the control instrumentation.   The purpose of maintaining such a low level (which may in fact be 10^{-6} or 10^{-8} below the full operating power of the reactor) is to ensure that measurements of the reactivity of the reactor are possible at all times.

In the shutdown condition the reactor may be subcritical by 10 per cent or more so that k may be of the order of 0.9 and the reactivity may typically be $r = -15$ dollars.   The reactor then has a multiplication factor of the order of $1/(1 - k) = 10$.   In order to bring the reactor up to operating power level this multiplication must be increased to perhaps 10^6 or 10^8.   Typically this is done by removing control rods.

In a thermal reactor the control rods are often movable elements which contain cadmium or boron.   Both of these elements have large neutron-capture cross sections and therefore are quite efficient in absorbing neutrons.   Since a neutron which is absorbed in the control rod does not produce a fission, the factor $\mathfrak{F}$ of Eq. (18.1) is reduced by the presence of the rod, and hence the multiplication factor and the reactivity are reduced.   As the control rods are extracted, the reactivity increases, and the neutron level multiplies.   If the rate of insertion of reactivity is slow, the neutron level follows the reactivity change without a time lag, and the neutron level will be

$$n(t) = \frac{r(0)n(0)}{r(t)} \qquad r(t) < 0 \qquad (18.20)$$

where $n(0)$ is the initial level and $r(0)$ is the initial (negative) reactivity. In order for Eq. (18.20) to hold, the neutron level must change only slightly in a time corresponding to the time scale of the delayed neutrons.

Figure 18.3 indicates the neutron level as a function of the reactivity present in the reactor for various rates of reactivity insertion. The initial conditions represent equilibrium shutdown with the reactivity at −10 dollars. The control rods are then withdrawn, or by other means the reactivity is increased at a constant rate. If the reactivity insertion

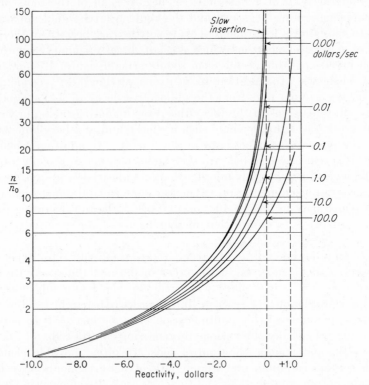

Fig. 18.3 Neutron level following ramp reactivity insertion from shut-down.

rate is infinitely small the neutron level would become infinite when the reactivity reaches zero. At finite rates of reactivity insertion, the delayed neutrons slow down the rate of increase.

From Fig. 18.1 it is seen that the time required for the neutron level to reach equilibrium with the source is $l_{eff}/(1 - k)$ or $l_{eff}/\beta|r|$. The prompt lifetime is in fact negligible compared to the delayed lifetimes in determining l_{eff}, and therefore from Table 18.1 this equilibrium, time is $13/|r|$ sec. If the period of the neutron level change, $n/(dn/dt)$, is small compared to the equilibrium time then equilibrium will be continuously established. Since the neutron level is proportional to $1/|r|$ the neutron period is given by

$$\frac{1}{n}\frac{dn}{dt} = r\frac{d}{dt}\left(\frac{1}{r}\right) = -\frac{1}{r}\frac{dr}{dt}$$

and hence the condition for equilibrium is

$$r^2 \ll \bar{\tau}\frac{dr}{dt} \qquad \bar{\tau} = 13 \text{ sec}$$

For slow insertions of reactivity a useful approximation neglects dn/dt with respect to $(\rho - \beta)n/l_0$ in Eq. (18.11). This is equivalent to saying that the prompt neutrons are in quasi-equilibrium with the delayed neutron source, and follow the delayed neutrons with zero time lag. With a source present, the one-delay-group equations become

$$0 = \frac{\beta}{l_0}(r - 1)n + \lambda c + S \qquad (18.21)$$

$$\frac{dc}{dt} = \frac{\beta}{l_0}n - \lambda c \qquad (18.21a)$$

This approximation is adequate if $r < 1 - 2\sqrt{\lambda l_0/\beta}$. It is most convenient to eliminate n from these equations and solve for the precursor concentration

$$n = \frac{l_0(\lambda c + S)}{\beta(1 - r)}$$

and

$$\frac{dc}{dt} = \frac{\lambda r}{1 - r}c + \frac{S}{1 - r}$$

The last equation can be easily integrated in explicit form

$$c(t) = c(0)e^{U(t,0)} + \int_0^t \frac{Se^{U(t,t')}}{1 - r(t')}\,dt'$$
$$U(t,t') = \lambda \int_{t'}^t \frac{r(t'')}{1 - r(t'')}\,dt'' \qquad (18.22)$$

When the neutron level has risen to a sufficiently high value, the source contribution will be negligible. For the case of a start-up from a sub-critical state with initial reactivity $r_0 < 0$, Eq. (18.22) becomes

$$n(t) = \frac{n(0)}{1 - r(t)}\left\{e^{U(t,0)} - r_0\left[1 + \lambda \int_0^t \frac{e^{U(t,t')}}{1 - r(t')}\,dt'\right]\right\} \qquad (18.23)$$

For a reactor initially critical ($r_0 = 0$), we have an obvious simplification. The case of a linear change in reactivity $r(t) = \alpha t$ gives

$$n(t) = \frac{n(0)e^{-\lambda t}}{(1 - \alpha t)^{(\lambda/\alpha)+1}} \qquad (18.24)$$

18.9   Linearized Equations

From an over-all control standpoint a reactor should operate a constant power level, and hence there is an important field of investigation in which the neutron level varies only slightly from a base value.   Under such circumstances it is useful to consider a linearized form of Eq. (18.15). We therefore let the neutron level be $n(t) = n_0 + n_1(t)$ in which n_0 is the steady-state level and $n_1(t)$ represents a small time-dependent term. There is of course an obvious difficulty here in defining exactly what one means by "small," but this is a question which may be postponed until later.   If the neutron level is to remain nearly constant, the reactivity of the reactor must be approximately zero, and hence the reactivity is itself a small quantity.

At steady state the equilibrium precursor concentration is $c_{i0} = \beta_i \lambda_i n_0 / l_0$, and hence for our linearized equation it is convenient to write

$$c_i(t) = \frac{\beta_i \lambda_i}{l_0} [n_0 + w_i(t)]$$

This is to be substituted into Eq. (18.15), and when the product of small quantities $n_1(t)r(t)$ is neglected, one obtains

$$\frac{dn_1}{dt} = \frac{\beta}{l_0} \left[r(t)n_0 - n_1(t) + \sum_i a_i w_i(t) \right] \qquad (18.25)$$

$$\frac{dw_i}{dt} = \lambda_i [n_1(t) - w_i(t)] \qquad a_i = \frac{\beta_i}{\beta} \qquad (18.25a)$$

The Laplace transformation of Eq. (18.25) yields

$$sN_1(s) = \frac{\beta}{l_0} \left[R(s)n_0 - N_1(s) + \sum_{i=1}^{6} a_i W_i(s) \right] \qquad (18.25b)$$

$$sW_i(s) = \lambda_i [N_1(s) - W_i(s)] \qquad (18.25c)$$

The transfer function of the reactor is defined as the ratio of the output (the variation in neutron level) to the input (the variation in the reactivity).   However the neutron level n_1 is linearly proportional to the constant level n_0, and hence it is much more convenient to define the transfer function in terms of the relative change

$$Z_0(s) = \frac{N_1(s)/n_0}{R(s)} = \frac{1}{s\left[l_0/\beta + \sum_i a_i/(\lambda_i + s) \right]} \qquad (18.26)$$

The zeros of the transfer function, as well as its poles, all lie on the negative real axis.   The zeros are at the points $-\lambda_i$; the poles depend on the value of l_0/β. For β/l_0, much larger than all of the λ_i's, however, only the most negative pole depends strongly on the value of l_0/β. This most negative pole lies approximately at $-[\beta/l_0 + \Sigma a_i \lambda_i]$. There is an obvious pole at $s = 0$. The other five poles lie between successive pairs of roots. For the specific case $l_0 = 10^{-4}$ sec the data of Table 18.1 give the following expression for the transfer function in canonical form

$$Z_0(s) = \frac{(s + 0.01244)(s + 0.03051)(s + 0.1114)(s + 0.3014)(s + 1.136)(s + 3.014)}{0.0156s(s + 0.01456)(s + 0.0682)(s + 0.1949)(s + 1.013)(s + 2.90)(s + 64.41)}$$

The limiting forms for small and large values of s are

$$Z_0(s) = \frac{1}{(l_0/\beta + 13.01 \text{ sec})s} \qquad |s| \ll 1 \qquad (18.26a)$$

$$= \frac{1}{1 + sl_0/\beta} \qquad |s| \gg 1 \qquad (18.26b)$$

In Eq. (18.26a) the prompt lifetime can be neglected since for almost all reactors the value of l_0/β will be of the order of or less than 0.01 sec, and it is seen once more that the slow response of the reactor is determined by the delayed neutrons only.

The behavior of the transfer function can be seen from its limiting forms. For large s the gain decreases as $1/s$ and the phase at high frequency goes to $-90°$. There is a break point at $s = \beta/l_0$ which corresponds to angular frequencies of the order 100 or 1,000 rad/sec. A second major break point occurs at approximately

$$s = 1/13.01 \text{ sec} = 0.077 \text{ sec}^{-1}$$

Between these two break points the gain is approximately constant, and the phase is between 0 and $-45°$. At values of s below the break point the gain is once more inversely proportional to s and goes to infinity at $s = 0$.

The pole of the transfer function at the origin is an indication of the instability of the ideal reactor. This instability is characteristic of the fact that the reactor equations in first approximation are homogeneous equations for the neutron level. Hence any solution will still be valid if multiplied throughout by an arbitrary constant or scale factor. The physical interpretation of this statement is that the reactor has no preferred operating level and would behave the same whether it were producing 1 watt of power or 1 megawatt. It is obvious where the approximation has been made. Although there may indeed be no difference between a reactor operating at 1 microwatt and one operating at 1 watt, if sensible amounts of heat are being produced, the temperature of the reactor components will increase above ambient and thereby affect the neutron behavior. Liquids in the reactor (either a coolant, such as water or liquid sodium, or a neutron moderator, such as heavy water or a liquid hydrocarbon) may boil. This boiling will have several effects. In addition to altering the heat-transfer properties of the system, the formation of vapor bubbles causes fluid to be expelled from the reactor. This can change both the rate at which neutrons can escape from the reactor core (in general increasing it) and the rate at which neutrons are absorbed in the reactor. The absorption rate is decreased since material which could absorb neutrons is removed from the reactor; but in general the number of neutrons produced per absorption will increase since the fraction of absorptions in the fuel is increased. The net effect of these changes may be either an increase or a decrease in reactivity of the system; but a properly designed reactor will utilize a negative temperature coefficient of reactivity in order to provide inherent stability.

18.10   Feedback Mechanisms

It is perhaps most convenient for a general discussion to consider the feedback mechanism to be expressed as an integral operator. In general this will be nonlinear in the neutron level; but if we consider small variations about a steady-state level, the feedback will be linear with respect to the magnitude of the variation. It may also depend on n_0, the steady-state level.

We assume therefore that the total reactivity of the reactor is given as the sum of two terms

$$r(t) = r_{\text{ext}}(t) + r_{\text{fb}}(t) \tag{18.27}$$

where r_{ext} is the externally impressed reactivity and r_{fb} is the feedback component. We assume that $r_{\text{fb}}(t)$ can be written as

$$r_{\text{fb}}(t) = \int_0^\infty K(\tau;n_0)n_1(t-\tau)\,d\tau \tag{18.27a}$$

If a constant small external reactivity change is impressed on the reactor steady state will be achieved only if the total reactivity is reduced to zero by the feedback. We will then have

$$0 = r_{\text{ext}} + \int_0^\infty K(\tau;n_0)\,d\tau\cdot n_1 \tag{18.28}$$

so that the required change in neutron level n_1 is

$$n_1 = \frac{r_{\text{ext}}}{-\displaystyle\int_0^\infty K(\tau;n_0)\,d\tau} = \frac{r_{\text{ext}}}{\alpha} \tag{18.29}$$

The reactor must therefore seek a new operating level $n_0 + n_1$ in order to compensate for the change in reactivity. A necessary condition for stability is that the steady-state coefficient of reactivity must be negative, or

$$\int_0^\infty K(\tau;n_0)\,d\tau < 0 \qquad (18.29a)$$

An increase in neutron level must therefore provide an inherent decrease in reactivity in order for stability. Although this is necessary, it is not sufficient. With reactivity feedback the transfer function of the reactor with respect to the external reactivity r_{ext} becomes

$$Z_{\text{fb}}(s) = \frac{Z_0(s)}{1 - n_0 H_{\text{fb}}(s) Z(s)} \qquad (18.30)$$

in which $H_{\text{fb}}(s)$ is the Laplace transform of the feedback function $K(\tau;n_0)$

$$R_{\text{fb}}(s) = H_{\text{fb}}(s) N_1(s) \qquad (18.30a)$$

the equivalent of Eq. (18.29a) in terms of the transform is the condition

$$H_{\text{fb}}(0) < 0$$

The full condition for stability is that the poles of Z_{fb} must all lie to the left of the imaginary axis of the complex s plane. The poles of $Z_0(s)$ lie in the left half-plane except for the pole at $s = 0$. A negative value for $H_{\text{fb}}(0)$ shifts this pole to the left half-plane; this will not ensure stability however unless the roots of $1 - n_0 H_{\text{fb}}(s) Z_0(s)$, which become additional poles of $Z_{\text{fb}}(s)$, are also entirely in the left half-plane.

Equation (18.30) is written in a form in which $H_{\text{fb}}(s)$ is often independent of n_0; the amount of feedback is therefore proportional to the neutron level and vanishes as the reactor power level goes to zero. Thus $Z_0(s)$ is often referred to as the zero power transfer function, and $Z_{\text{fb}}(s)$ is often written $Z_p(s)$ to indicate the transfer function at a finite power level.

The effect of feedback on the transfer function is shown in Figs. 18.4 and 18.5. The reactor is a small homogeneous solution reactor (KEWB) containing a uranium salt dissolved in ordinary water. The feedback mechanism is represented by the equation

$$r_{\text{fb}}(t) = -[bT(t) + gV(t)]$$

where $T(t)$ is the temperature rise of the reactor solution above its steady-state value and $V(t)$ is the excess volume of gas bubbles in the solution as a result of the radiolytic decomposition of the water. This decomposition of the water is produced by high-speed fission fragments which ionize and dissociate the molecules of the fuel solution. This process transfers the energy of the fission process to the water and represents the mechanism by which the energy of fission is converted into heat. The production of gas bubbles can be crudely visualized as a local boiling phenomenon produced by an intense thermal "spike" which is the track of the fission fragment.

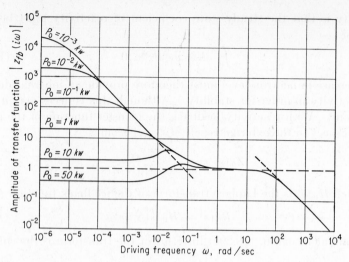

Fig. 18.4   Amplitude of the transfer function of a homogeneous solution reactor as a function of operating power.

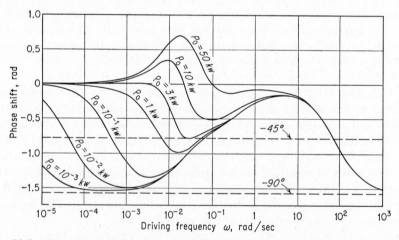

Fig. 18.5   Phase shift of the transfer function of a homogeneous solution reactor as a function of operating power.   At zero power the low-frequency phase shift is $-90°$; but at any finite power level the low-frequency phase shift is $0°$.

The temperature of the reactor solution is assumed to follow a simple cooling law

$$\frac{dT}{dt} + \gamma T = Kn_1 \tag{18.31a}$$

where $1/\gamma$ is the cooling time constant.   The gas-bubble formation is described by a similar equation

$$\frac{dV}{dt} + \sigma V = Gn_1 \tag{18.31b}$$

in which $1/\sigma$ represents the mean time a bubble remains in the reactor before it either collapses or escapes from the solution.

From Eqs. (18.30) and (18.31) the feedback transform is found to be

$$H_{\mathrm{fb}}(s) = -\left(\frac{bK}{\gamma + s} + \frac{gG}{\sigma + s}\right) \tag{18.32}$$

The steady-state reactivity coefficient is $\alpha = (bK/\gamma) + (gG/\sigma)$.

Figure 18.4 is the Bode diagram of the transform function. This diagram was constructed with the feedback constants $bK/\gamma = 0.0434$

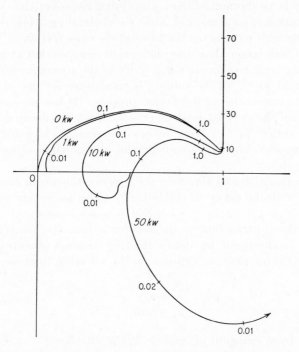

Fig. 18.6 Inverse transfer function of a homogeneous solution reactor-polar diagram. At any finite power the negative reactivity coefficients stabilize the system.

dollar/kw, $gG/\sigma = 0.00681$ dollar/kw, $\gamma = 0.01$ sec^{-1}, $\sigma = 0.5$ sec^{-1} which have been found to be a reasonable set of constants for the KEWB reactor. It is interesting to note that at power levels greater than 20 kw the low-frequency gain is less than 1. In its operating range (20 to 50 kw) this reactor is therefore quite stable. A more complete stability criterion is given in Fig. 18.6. The positions of the poles of $Z_p(s)$ represent the natural oscillations of the system. Stability of the linearized system therefore requires that all of the poles must have negative real parts in order that they represent damped oscillations. Hence the imaginary axis of the complex s plane must map into a contour which excludes the origin of the Z^{-1} plane. Figure 18.6 indicates that only at zero power is there any instability; this is the neutral instability at steady state which was pointed out earlier.

18.11 Xenon Poison

Shortly after the first Hanford reactor was put into operation, it was observed that the reactivity decreased sharply as the power level rose. This behavior was quite puzzling until its source was traced to the production among the fission products of unstable Xe^{135}, an element with an extremely large thermal neutron absorption cross section.

The absorption cross section of Xe^{135} for thermal neutrons is approximately 5,000 times as large as the absorption cross section of U^{235}, and ten million times larger than the absorption cross section of hydrogen. The extremely large cross section is a result of the strong nuclear binding which occurs in Xe^{136}. This stability is responsible for two of the most important characteristics of the fission process. It has previously been mentioned that the delayed neutron emitter Xe^{137} can decay by neutron emission to stable Xe^{136}. We now see the same seeking for stability from the opposite side; Xe^{135} captures an additional neutron in order to achieve stability.

Xe^{135} is radioactive and therefore the process of neutron capture is in competition with the decay to stable Cs^{135}. This Cs isotope has a relatively small absorption cross section and does not represent a significant poison. If the neutron flux in the reactor is low, the xenon poison is more likely to disappear by decay than by neutron absorption. The branching ratio for neutron capture or the effective fraction of poison produced is

$$\frac{nv\sigma_x}{\lambda_x + nv\sigma_x}$$

where λ_x = decay constant of Xe^{135} = 2.1×10^{-5} sec^{-1}

σ_x = thermal neutron absorption cross section = 3.5×10^{-18} cm^2

nv = neutron flux, neutron density multiplied by mean neutron speed

At low flux levels therefore only a small fraction of the xenon poison produced in the reactor actually contributes to the poisoning effect, and hence the existence of the xenon problem could not have been measured in the early experimental reactors which had operated only at low powers. If the neutron flux is equal to $\lambda_x/\sigma_x = 6 \times 10^{12}$ neutrons/sq cm/sec, the xenon disappears equally by capture or by decay, and half of the xenon produced in fission is effective as a poison. This flux level corresponds to a specific power of approximately 300 watts/gram of U^{235} or 2 megawatts/ton of natural uranium. Specific powers of this magnitude represent modest levels in present-day power reactors. The SRE at a total thermal output of 20 megawatts has an average flux in the fuel of 5×10^{12} neutrons/sq cm/sec and hence a poison branching ratio of approximately 0.45. A high-flux reactor such as the MTR at the National Reactor Testing Station in Idaho operates at fluxes close to 10^{14} neutrons/sq cm/sec and has a branching ratio of 0.94. Xenon is formed primarily by the radioactive decay of I^{135} which is produced in the amount of 56 nuclei per 1,000 fissions. The mean life of I^{135} is 9.7 hr, and hence when a high-power-level reactor is started up, the poisoning effect of the Xe^{135} is not evident until enough time has elapsed to allow for the decay of I^{135}. Then after approximately a day of operation an equilibrium is established between the rate of formation of Xe^{135} from the decay of I^{135} and the removal of Xe^{135} by its own radioactive decay to stable Cs^{135} or by the absorption of a neutron and the production of stable Xe^{136}. At steady state therefore we have the balance

$$\frac{y_I}{v l_0} n = \lambda_I I = \lambda_x X + \sigma_x v n X \qquad (18.33)$$

where λ_I is the decay constant of $I^{135} = 2.9 \times 10^{-5}$ sec^{-1}. Somewhat paradoxically the poisoning effect of xenon is largest after the reactor has been shut down. During operation of the reactor, the xenon is being destroyed by both the natural radioactive decay and by the absorption of neutrons. The equilibrium concentration is therefore given by

$$X = \frac{y_I n}{v l_0 (\lambda_x + n v \sigma_x)} \qquad (18.33a)$$

The poison contribution is proportional to $v \sigma_x X$ and hence is proportional to the factor $n v \sigma_x / (n v \sigma_x + \lambda_x)$. When the reactor is shut down, neutron absorption no longer removes xenon from the reactor. However the production of Xe from the radioactive decay of I^{135} does not cease instantly. If the reactor power is reduced (within a half-hour or so) to some low level, the iodine concentration will have decreased only slightly since the iodine mean life is 9.7 hr. Since the production rate of Xe does not change, whereas the destruction rate decreases from $\lambda_x + n v \sigma_x$ to λ_x, the concentration of xenon rises to a peak which is roughly in inverse ratio, and then finally decays as the iodine source decays. Thus after a reactor is shut down from high power levels, the strong poison buildup may make it impossible to start the reactor up again if start-up is delayed for an hour or so. If normal power level is restored shortly after shutdown, the neutron flux will again burn out the poison down to its equilibrium level; but if start-up is delayed for more than a few hours, the poison buildup may reduce the maximum multiplication constant to a value below unity so that criticality will be unattainable until the poison again decays after 20 to 30 hr.

This poisoning effect of xenon has of course also serious implications for the problem of reactor stability. A small increase in neutron level will burn out more xenon, but will also produce additional amounts of iodine. On a long time scale the net result of increased neutron level is an increase in the xenon concentration. This increases the poisoning effect and decreases the reactivity. Such a feedback would appear to produce stability. The short time behavior however is quite different; the immediate effect of an increase in neutron level produces iodine which must decay only slowly to xenon so that the xenon increase is not instantaneous. On the other hand the removal of xenon because of the increase in neutron level is immediate and hence the reactivity actually increases. There is in fact therefore a slow drift away from the fixed operating power unless a stabilizing feedback, such as the temperature coefficient, is sufficiently large to compensate for the instability. These conclusions can be quantitatively investigated by considering the complete transfer function of the reactor including the iodine and xenon equations.

The equation for the iodine concentration can be written

$$\frac{dI}{dt} = \frac{y_I}{vl_0} n - \lambda_I I \qquad (18.34a)$$

To be complete, the xenon equation must include the small effect due to prompt (or direct) Xe production in fission. This prompt Xe yield is $y_x = 0.0003$, which is only 5 per cent of the iodine yield $y_I = 0.056$.

$$\frac{dX}{dt} = \frac{y_x}{vl_0} n + \lambda_I I - (\lambda_x + v\sigma_x n)X \qquad (18.34b)$$

The neutron equation now includes a term which represents the absorption of neutrons by the xenon

$$\frac{dn}{dt} = \frac{\beta}{l_0}(r - 1)n + \sum \lambda_i c_i - v\sigma_x n X \qquad (18.34c)$$

The equation for the delayed neutron precursors is the same as before [Eq. (18.18b)]. There is therefore a new equilibrium reactivity for the reactor required to compensate for the xenon poison

$$\frac{\beta}{l_0} r_0 = v\sigma_x X_0 \qquad (18.35)$$

where the zero subscript indicates an equilibrium value. The equilibrium iodine and xenon concentrations are

$$I_0 = \frac{y_I n_0}{vl_0 \lambda_I} \qquad X_0 = \frac{(y_I + y_x)n_0}{vl_0(\lambda_x + n_0 v\sigma_x)} \qquad (18.36)$$

and hence

$$r_0 = \frac{(y_I + y_x)n_0 v\sigma_x}{\beta v(\lambda_x + n_0 v\sigma_x)} \qquad (18.35a)$$

so that, at fluxes above 10^{13} neutrons/sq cm/sec, the operating reactivity effect of xenon can be as large as 3.7 dollars.

If Eqs. (18.34a), (18.34b), and (18.34c) are now linearized in order to obtain equations for deviations from equilibrium, and Laplace transforms are taken, one obtains

$$s\left(1 + \frac{\beta}{l_0} \sum \frac{a_i}{\lambda_i + s}\right) N_1(s) = \frac{\beta}{l_0} n_0 R_1(s) - n_0 v \sigma_x X_1(s) \quad (18.37a)$$

$$(\lambda_x + n_0 v \sigma_x + s) X_1(s) = \frac{N_1(s)}{v l_0} \left(\frac{\lambda_x y_x}{\lambda_x + n_0 v \sigma_x} + \frac{\lambda_I y_I}{\lambda_I + s} - \frac{n_0 v \sigma_x y_I}{\lambda_x + n_0 v \sigma_x}\right)$$

$$= \frac{N_1(s)}{v l_0 (\lambda_x + n_0 v \sigma_x)} \left[\frac{(y_x y_I)\lambda_x \lambda_I - (y_I n_0 v \sigma_x - \lambda_x y_x)s}{\lambda_I + s}\right] \quad (18.37b)$$

The transfer function $Z(s)$ is defined again from the equation

$$\frac{N_1(s)}{n_0} = Z(s)R_1(s)$$

$$Z^{-1}(s) = s\left(\frac{l_0}{\beta} + \sum \frac{a_i}{\lambda_i + s}\right) + \frac{n_0 v \sigma_x [\lambda_I \lambda_x (y_I + y_x) - (y_I n_0 v \sigma_x - y_x \lambda_x)s]}{\beta v (\lambda_x + n_0 v \sigma_x)(\lambda_I + s)(\lambda_x + n_0 v \sigma_x + s)}$$

$$(18.38)$$

The inverse transfer function can therefore be reduced to the sum of two components—one, the "clean" reactor function; the other, the transfer function of the xenon effect

$$Z^{-1}(s) = Z_0^{-1}(s) + Z_x^{-1}(s)$$

The stability of the reactor is determined by the behavior of $Z_x^{-1}(s)$ near the origin $s = 0$, since the time scale of the xenon and iodine are measured in hours, whereas the time scale of $Z_0(s)$ is characteristically seconds. Hence, except for reactors with neutron fluxes which are beyond present engineering feasibility we can consider λ_I, $\lambda_x + n_0 v \sigma_x \ll \lambda_i$.

At $s = 0$ we have

$$\frac{\beta v}{(y_I + y_x)} Z_x^{-1}(0) = \frac{n_0 v \sigma_x \lambda_x}{(\lambda_x + n_0 v \sigma_x)^2} > 0$$

The positive value corresponds to the negative feedback effect of Xe in steady state. As we trace out the imaginary axis $s = i\omega$, $Z_x^{-1}(s)$ circles into the origin. For low neutron fluxes

$$n_0 v < y_x \lambda_x / y_I \sigma_x = 3.2 \times 10^{11} \text{ neutrons/sq cm/sec}$$

$Z_x^{-1}(i\omega)$ loops down and approaches the origin with a phase of $-90°$; for fluxes above this critical value, $Z_x^{-1}(i\omega)$ loops around the origin and has a limiting phase shift of $-270°$. This behavior is schematically represented in Fig. 18.7. The stability at low flux is a result of the prompt yield of xenon and would vanish if y_x were set equal to zero. At ordinary operating fluxes reactors are in the unstable region.   The neutron level will diverge from its operating level with a time constant of 1,000 sec at a flux of 3.10^{12} neutrons/sq cm/sec and 100 sec at a flux of 10^{14} neutrons/sq cm/sec.

To achieve stability a negative feedback is required.   Because of the difference in time scales between $Z_x(s)$ and $H_{fb}(s)$, we need only consider $H_{fb}(0) = -\alpha$, the steady-state reactivity coefficient.   Since the amplitude of $Z_x^{-1}(i\omega)$ decreases with increasing ω, it is sufficient to impose the requirement that the negative reactivity coefficient be greater than $Z_x^{-1}(0)/n_0$.   This will then shift the total transfer function an adequate distance to the right in Fig. 18.7 so that the contour will no longer enclose the origin.   For the solution reactor whose transfer function is displayed in Fig. 18.6 a power coefficient of less than 0.01 dollars/kw is sufficient to provide complete stability against xenon.

NOMENCLATURE

a_i	relative delayed neutron abundance, $a_i = \beta_i/\beta$
b	reactivity coefficient, dollars/degree
$c(t)$	delayed neutron precursor concentration
$C(s)$	Laplace transform of $c(t)$
$\mathcal{F}$	number of fissions produced per neutron absorbed in the reactor
g	reactivity coefficient, dollars/cu cm
G	gas-bubble production rate, cu cm/kw-sec
$H_{fb}(s)$	reactivity feedback function
$I(t)$	iodine concentration, nuclei/cu cm
k	multiplication constant
k_p, k_d	prompt and delayed multiplication constants
K	inverse equivalent heat capacity of reactor, degrees/kw-sec
$K(\tau, n_0)$	reactivity response at time τ following impulsive neutron flux change
l	neutron lifetime
l_0	equivalent neutron lifetime of nonstatic reactor
l_{eff}	effective neutron lifetime including precursor delay
$n(t)$	neutron density, neutrons/cu cm; total neutron population
$N(s)$	Laplace transform of $n(t)$
$r(t)$	reactivity measured in dollars $r = \rho/\beta$
$R(s)$	Laplace transform of $r(t)$
$S(t)$	neutron source strength per unit volume, neutrons/cu cm sec, or total neutron source rate, neutrons/sec
t	time, sec
$T(t)$	reactor temperature, °C

v	neutron speed, cm/sec
$V(t)$	volume of gas bubbles in the reactor, cu cm
$w_i(t)$	relative delayed neutron precursor concentration
$W_i(s)$	Laplace transform of $w_i(t)$
$X(t)$	xenon concentration, nuclei/cu cm
y	yield of fission fragment, nuclei/fission
$Z(s)$	reactor transfer function
α	reactivity insertion rate, dollars/sec; reactivity coefficient, dollars/kw
β	delayed neutron fraction
γ	cooling rate constant, sec^{-1}
λ	radioactive decay constant, sec^{-1}
ν	number of neutrons produced per fission
ρ	reactivity $(k - 1)/k$
σ	gas-bubble escape rate, sec^{-1}
σ_x	thermal neutron-capture cross section for xenon, sq cm
τ	time interval, sec
ω	time constant or frequency, sec^{-1}

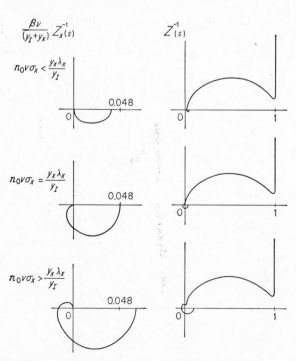

Fig. 18.7 Schematic representation of the xenon transfer function and its influence on the total reactor function.   The polar diagrams of $Z_x^{-1}(s)$ are on an expanded scale relative to $Z^{-1}(s)$.

REFERENCES

1. "The Reactor Handbook," (Physics), AECD-3645, 1955.
2. Murray, Raymond L.: "Nuclear Reactor Physics," Prentice-Hall, Inc., Englewood Cliffs, N.J., 1957.
3. Weinberg, A. M., and E. P. Wigner: "The Physical Theory of Neutron Chain Reactors," University of Chicago Press, Chicago, 1958.
4. Harrer, J. M., R. E. Boyer, and D. Krucoff: *Nucleonics*, vol. 10, p. 32, 1952.
5. Lundby, A.: *J. Nuclear Energy*, vol. 1, p. 53, 1954.
6. Grace, J. N., M. A. Schultz, and T. E. Fairey: *Proc. 1955 Conf. on Nuclear Eng. UCLA*, 1955.
7. Schultz, M. A.: "Control of Nuclear Reactors and Power Plants," McGraw-Hill Book Company, Inc., New York, 1955.
8. Skinner, R. E., and D. L. Hetrick: "The Transfer Function of a Water Boiler Reactor," NAA-SR-1948, Offices of Technical Services, Dept. of Commerce, Washington, D.C.
9. Cohen, E. R.: Some Topics in Reactor Kinetics, *Proc. 2nd U.N. Conf. on Peaceful Uses of Atomic Energy*, Geneva, 1958.
10. Keepin, G. R., T. F. Wimett, and R. K. Zeigler: Delayed Neutrons from Fissionable Isotopes of Uranium, Plutonium, and Thorium, *J. Nuclear Energy*, vol. 6, no. 1, 1957; *Phys. Rev.*, vol. 107, no. 1044, 1957.

19
Automatic Machine-tool Control

JACK ROSENBERG
CONSULTANT
LOS ANGELES, CALIFORNIA

19.1 Introduction

Machine tools are defined, in the "Encyclopedia Britannica," as "power-driven machines ordinarily not portable by hand which cut, shear, or press metal into desired forms." Since machine tools are the means by which other power-driven tools are manufactured, they are fundamental to the industrial process and therefore the most important of all power machinery. Archaeological evidence has shown that hand tools were developed by man during the Early Stone Age (35000 to 15000 B.C.). However, machine tools as they are known today were created and developed during the past 400 years.

While a lathe with manual drive was reported by Leonardo da Vinci to have been used in the sixteenth century, it required the availability of large mechanical power sources for machine tools in their present concept to be developed. Modern machine tools, therefore, first appeared during the Industrial Revolution of the late 1700s. A boring lathe was constructed by John Wilkerson in 1776 for James Watt, who needed its precision to develop his revolutionary steam engine. Henry Maudeslay, who produced the first all-metal lathe with sliding tool rests in 1794, adapted a lead screw to a lathe in 1810, and therefore set the stage for lathes, planers, milling machines, and all other screw-driven machines of today.

Machine tools may be defined in several ways. The U.S. Department of Commerce divides machine tools into two classes: metal cutting machines and metal forming machines. "Encyclopedia Britannica" lists six categories: (1) lathe, (2) drilling machine, (3) milling machine, (4) planer or shaper, (5) shearing machine and press, and (6) grinder. Since this chapter will be devoted to control problems, machine tools will be grouped according to control characteristics. Those machine

535

tools which perform their operations only at discrete points, such as drilling machines, punches, jig borers and boring mills, and shears, require only that the end position of the workpiece be controlled with respect to the cutting tool.   Other machine tools perform their operations on metal continuously, and require continuous path (contouring) control of the position of the workpiece relative to cutting tool.   In this class are milling machines, lathes, grinders, flame cutters, welders, and planers.

For an industry on which the productivity of our highly mechanized society is closely dependent, total annual sales are surprisingly low. Shipments in 1957, the highest on record, totaled \$1,265,000,000; \$863,- 000,000 was spent on metal cutting machines.   It is to this class that most numerical controls have so far been applied.

19.2   Definition of Numerical Control

In this chapter numerical control will be defined as the control of a physical process from a flexible, digitally recorded memory medium.   In the pure sense, numerical controls require that the information to be recorded be obtained by analytic means (computation); however, there are also control systems whose memory medium, although digital, has been obtained by empirical means such as the physical tracing and recording of a template or model.

To illustrate the difference between the flexibility of numerical control and other types of automatic control which are in widespread industrial use, let us consider the automatic screw machine.   By installing a series of cams on a control shaft, the setup man can prepare this lathe for the manufacture of dozens or thousands of identical parts, each complex and accurate, which will be produced automatically at a low cost. However, the screw machine would not be considered where only one, five, or ten parts of one type were desired.   The costs of setting up the machine are prohibitive for small runs.

Still another example of transfer machinery is the tracer lathe or tracer milling machine.   Here also operation is fairly automatic, and high accuracy can be achieved.   But it is first necessary for a complete physical model, accurate to the last detail, to be prepared manually or by some other means before the first part can be manufactured.   Costs and lead time of model preparation are high.

Probably the most sophisticated version of the transfer system is the transfer line, consisting of many different types of machine tools, together with automatic work transport and indexing equipment.   Automobiles could not be purchased by the average consumer without the economy of transfer machinery, which can manufacture a complete cylinder block from the raw casting without human intervention.   However, such equipment might be considered the ultimate in inflexibility, since a small change in part dimension or sequence of machining could create havoc in a transfer line. Changes are usually restricted to an annual model modification. This is in sharp contrast to a modern punched-tape-controlled drilling machine wherein a new memory tape for a completely different part, containing dozens of holes varying in size, can be programmed within 10 or 20 min.

19.3 History of Numerical Control (Open Loop)

To most people, the picture of a wide perforated paper tape brings to mind a player piano. Yet this device is of rather recent origin compared to other examples of physical process control from digitally recorded tape memories. The first automatic player piano, utilizing a 12-in.-wide roll of perforated paper through which air was passed to enable the appropriate keys to be actuated, was patented by M. Fourneaux in France in 1863. More than 100 years earlier, in 1725, M. Falcon constructed and patented a perforated-card-controlled knitting machine, also in France. Each hole which appeared in a wide card, whose motion was chain-synchronized to the action of the knitting machine, set up a mechanical linkage which caused a needle associated with this particular column on the card to pull a specific color of thread through the cloth at that location. Very complicated, multicolored fabric patterns could be programmed and woven by this system.

However, Mr. Falcon's invention was limited to fairly low production rates. In 1804, J. M. Jacquard invented (and received patents for) an improved card-controlled knitting and weaving machine permitting higher output and lower unit costs. Jacquard machines are still widely used today for the knitting of sweaters, bathing suits, tapestries, and draperies where short production runs are the rule. For higher-volume production, knitting machines utilizing disks with patterns of peripheral teeth (like gears) are usually employed. The latter machines are analogous to automatic screw machines or tracer machines in the metal industry.

Programming of cards for the Jacquard knitting machine is a fairly simple and rapid operation. The cards, of which twelve or more are employed on a single rotary knitting machine (each spliced into a continuous loop), are perforated on a small mechanical programming punch containing 42 control keys. From a full-scale colored drawing simulating the desired cloth pattern, the setup man can produce a complete card loop in a matter of minutes, and the entire knitting machine can be prepared for manufacturing the new cloth within an hour by a skilled operator. The card perforator follows mechanical logic similar to card punches for modern data-processing systems.

Turning now to music, it has been found that the musical octave was first divided into seven notes by St. Gregory in the eighth or tenth century.   The musical clef appeared in the twelfth century.   The earliest player pianos were able to produce only notes of uniform intensity and were incapable of simulating pedal control, amplitude variations, or other colorations which distinguish one pianist from another.   By the time the player piano reached the peak of its development, to be superseded by phonograph records (about 1930), it was versatile enough to record and duplicate almost all facets of the pianist's phrasing.   One of the last models produced contained eight extra hole channels on each side of the tape, with the eighty-two keyboard channels located in the center. These extra channels, just as auxiliary function channels on today's numerical control systems, were able to control the sound intensity, tone-pedal actuation, tape speed, and several other variables which affect the quality of reproduction.

19.4   Evolution of Modern Control and Computer Techniques

Modern digital controls for large, versatile machine tools would be impossible without two recent technologies, servomechanisms and automatic digital computers.   Simple, electrical positioning servomechanisms and the components which made them possible were developed in the United States starting in 1934.   Capable of achieving only moderate accuracy and of a slow and simple nature, these servomechanisms were only incompletely understood, and stabilization characteristics were relatively poor.   Basic components were developed to satisfy the requirements of these early systems.   Synchro and resolver transformers, precision potentiometers, torque motors, high-acceleration d-c and a-c variable-speed motors, and servo power amplifiers, such as vacuum tube, thyratron, and rotary d-c generator types, were brought into being in the late 1930s.   However, servomechanism capabilities were not appreciated at this time, and they were for the most part laboratory curiosities.

As in most phases of the Industrial Revolution, new devices and techniques were evolved in response to compelling needs.   The heavy dependence of the Allied Forces on radar and accurate fire control during World War II forced the servo art to graduate from the laboratory to front-line military installations between 1941 and 1943.   As high-power servo systems for the control of massive radar antennae and gun platforms began to be delivered in large quantities, techniques for the volume production of precision drive mechanisms were developed, as well as analytic tools for the theoretical analysis of servo performance.   Procedures for optimum stabilization of servomechanisms followed the theoretical progress, and field operation of these complex radar gun-laying systems became so reliable that aerial penetration by the enemy of locations guarded by these systems was discouraged.   Naval surface-to-surface artillery also became very deadly as a result of the integration of radar and gun controls.

Today's numerical controls would not exist without the great strides in automatic data processing which were occurring simultaneously with the evolution of the servo art. An early form of semiautomatic computer, the analog differential analyzer, first appeared at MIT in about 1932. This was a very elaborate mechanical device using ball and disk integrators, mechanical differentials, precision gear trains, and human operators to provide the mathematical input functions in mechanical form. About 1940 electronic versions of analog computers became available. The faster, more accurate, and more flexible digital computer was born in 1945 when the ENIAC was developed for the Army Ordnance Department. This was still a rather slow machine without internally stored programs, and therefore had to be sequenced from external information provided by the input medium.

The years 1945 to 1950 were marked by intensive laboratory development of computing systems aimed at specific scientific problems. Computing instruments such as EDVAC at the University of Pennsylvania, Harvard University's MARK II, and Von Neumann's MANIAC at the Institute for Advanced Study were developed under Government sponsorship for urgent military or scientific missions. It was not until 1951 or 1952 that the large manufacturers of mechanical data-processing equipment became interested in the commercial aspects of electronic computing. First came the card-programmed, magnetic-drum memory calculators. These were succeeded by the first generation of IBM 700 and Remington-Rand UNIVAC computers with internally stored programs and high-speed memories. Third-generation commercial computing and data-processing products are now being delivered (1959). At the present time universities have largely withdrawn, leaving the development of larger, faster, and more complex equipment to the commercial specialists.

American universities are now concentrating their efforts on problems of generating sophisticated program instructions for large computers, producing routines which will allow problems programmed for one type of machine to be automatically translated into the language of another type, and developing dramatically new computer components and techniques for the ultra-high-speed computing machines which will be required within the next 5 years.

Components and principles of logic important to modern numerical control came into being concurrently with digital-computer evolution. Digital shaft encoders (which are in reality analog-to-digital converters), rotary and linear high-resolution gratings of the magnetic and optical type, high-speed photoelectric punched-tape readers, magnetic tape handlers, special counter and indicator tubes, simpler and more reliable keyboard data input devices, and card-to-tape and tape-to-card converters were developed as adjuncts to computing systems beginning in about 1951.

19.5 Evolution of Controls for Machine Tools

Industrial demands for the removal of metal at high rates with great precision, on parts of high complexity, resulted in the development of

Fig. 19.1 Keller weight-controlled tracer. (*Courtesy, Pratt & Whitney Co., Inc.*)

tracer duplicating controls for machine tools in 1916. In that year the Keller Mechanical Engineering Company of Brooklyn, New York, built a weight-controlled tracer milling machine. By employing a weight hanging over a pulley to draw a cutter bar against a solid model, the cutting tool was fed into a die blank and made to machine a duplicate of the model. Keller machines were first used for making silverware dies, but gradually were applied to the machining of dies for other industries, such as bottle molds, small forging dies, and automotive crank shaft and connecting rod dies. Figure 19.1 is a photograph of an early Keller weight-controlled tracer milling a forging die for an automobile universal joint. A bronze casting of a wood pattern is mounted above, and the forging die being profiled is seen below.

Fig. 19.2   Keller electric tracer—automobile roof die. (*Courtesy Pratt & Whitney Co., Inc.*)

In 1920 an electric tracer, an ON-OFF type of servo follower, was conceived by Mr. J. F. Keller and John Shaw, chief engineer of the Keller Company. The first Keller electric tracer was purchased by Budd Manufacturing Company of Philadelphia, Pennsylvania, for making large automobile body dies. An electromagnetic clutch provided mechanical actuation of horizontal, vertical, and transverse tool motions, as in modern three-dimension tracers. Figure 19.2 shows an automobile roof die being profiled. Models for such products were generally made of plaster. From 1920 to the present day Keller profilers have been the mainstay of the automotive body and forging die manufacturers. Many early machines are still in use.

The Keller machines produced a granular surface finish which is characteristic of ON-OFF servo actuators. The Cincinnati Milling Machine Company introduced a line of tracer milling machines with proportional hydraulic actuators in 1935. The Hydro-Tel, now the most common tracer machine in job shop use, provided automatic depth control or

Fig. 19.3 Cincinnati Hydro-Diematic. (*Courtesy, Cincinnati Milling Machine Co.*)

vertical motion. A more sophisticated machine, the Hydro-Diematic, incorporated automatic control of longitudinal, transverse, and vertical motions from a single tracer finger.

Because the latter machine required an accurate, full three-dimensional master shape, and a more complex and expensive hydraulic system, the Hydro-Tel met with more widespread customer acceptance. Besides being appreciably lower in cost, the Hydro-Tel could work from simple, sheet-steel templates which were inexpensive to fabricate. A photograph of a Hydro-Diematic is shown in Fig. 19.3, and of a Hydro-Tel in Fig. 19.4.

In 1947 the General Electric Company first offered a record-playback system utilizing phase-modulated analog magnetic tape as the control medium. Under this concept, a master mechanic controlled a machine tool, such as a lathe or milling machine, throughout the cutting of a part. As his judgment and dexterity produced the first part, every motion was recorded on the multichannel, 1-in. magnetic tape. This tape was

Fig. 19.4 Cincinnati Hydro-Tel. (*Courtesy, Cincinnati Milling Machine Co.*)

able to duplicate his actions upon playback by employing phase-sensitive analog servo follow-ups, which were commanded by the previously recorded magnetic signals. However, productivity and accuracy were limited to that of the human operator, and accurate coordination of two or more feeds was still impossible. These limitations, and the cost of the control equipment, prevented widespread acceptance of this product.

In 1949 the MIT Servomechanisms Laboratory began the development of a true tape-controlled milling machine as subcontractor to the Parsons Corporation on an Air Force contract. Later Parsons withdrew, and MIT completed it as prime contractor in 1953. Still in operation, this numerically controlled three-axis Hydro-Tel proved the validity of many important concepts now embodied in industrial systems. Between 1950 and 1952 several other laboratory developments took place. One resulted in optical-film control of a gear shaper. Another project produced a turbine blade milling machine (for wind tunnel aircraft turbine models) commanded by signals on magnetic tape. This tape could be produced either by recording the shape of a steel spline whose contour was developed from positions stored on punched cards, or by synthetic processing of mathematical data.

Commercial product development in the numerical control field started in 1952. About this time General Electric began work on a table positioning system; Ferranti of Scotland, Bendix, and North American Aviation commenced the development of contouring control systems; and Hughes initiated work on a position control system. Concurrently, the Giddings & Lewis Machine Tool Company engaged personnel from the MIT Servomechanisms Laboratory to develop a digital interpolating computer to produce synthetically 1-in. magnetic tape compatible with the General Electric record-playback tape mentioned earlier. In 1953 Electronic Control Systems (Stromberg-Carlson) began work on a path control system. After 1953 the field mushroomed, and dozens of projects became active.

19.6 Point Position Controls

Many types of machine tools, such as drills, punches, jig borers, and boring mills, perform cutting operations only at discrete points on their workpieces. While highly accurate positioning of the workpiece under the cutting tool is required prior to the cutting operation, only the end position of the work must be controlled; the path taken is irrelevant. Consequently, controls for such machines require little data processing and fairly low servo power outputs (since there is no cutting load on the workpiece while it moves). Servo performance can be nonlinear without compromising the end product. As a result, numerical position controls contain simple logic, low data input rates, and are relatively low in cost. Over 30 different numerical position control systems have become available, and the potential field of application is very large because such machine tools are used in great numbers.

Because of the industrial advantages of compatibility, both the Electronic Industries Association and Aircraft Industries Association have proposed that their members adopt a 1-in.-wide, eight-channel (eight-level) punched tape as the input medium. Although it is not yet a formal standard, many manufacturers of position controls have accepted this mechanical standard for tape. A code standard for data contained in this tape, similar to the code employed on many industrially used typewriter-keyboard tape-punching mechanisms, has also been proposed and is now widely employed with 1 in. tape. A list of the codes for the various characters is shown in Fig. 19.5. Work is now beginning (in the middle of 1959) on the evolution of proposed format standards on these punched tapes. Involving the location of command information along the tape, this complex subject has a greater effect on system design and cost than mechanical and code standards; therefore acceptance of a single standard seems destined to be a slow process.

Before attempting to analyze the logic of a position control system, let us examine what it must do and with what existing machine shop procedures it must be integrated. Such an examination will review human engineering, information flow, and manufacturing procedures. Conventional drilling or boring machines are prepared for the manufacture of a batch of parts by being tooled. Work-holding fixtures are securely fastened at a designated location on the bed of the machine tool; the specified drilling or boring tool inserted in the spindle of the machine to a specified depth; and the machine adjusted to produce the desired feeds, coolant flow, and other peripheral functions by a setup man (or the machine operator, if he is sufficiently qualified). In the latter case the operator is an experienced machinist.

If the workpiece consists of a sheet of flat stock, however thick, in which must be drilled a number of holes at precise locations, perhaps of different diameters, and especially if a large quantity of such pieces must be manufactured, a drill jig (an overlaying plate containing holes with hardened walls of the desired diameter in the appropriate locations) is likely to be part of the tooling. Instructions to the operator would call for this jig to be superimposed on each fresh workpiece before the drilling operation commences. This would compel the operator to drill exactly in the correct locations with proper drill diameters.

A set of written instructions, called variously methods outline, manufacturing outline, process sheet, or process instructions, is delivered and explained to the machine operator by his supervisor before manufacturing is permitted to proceed. These instructions, those for the preparation of the fixtures and the tooling, as well as directions for the entire manufacturing sequence (which might include operations performed before it reaches the drilling machine), have been prepared when the part drawing was released for production by an experienced individual who occupies a key position in the organization. He might be called a process engineer, methods planner, or methods engineer; but in any case he is a qualified tool engineer. He receives his input information in the form of a part drawing, containing dimensional data and other pertinent data, from the design department.

During the course of manufacture, the machine operator is constantly called upon to exercise judgment in the performance of his duties. If at any time a situation arises which he feels unqualified to cope with,

Standard level numbers									
8	7	6	5	4	.	3	2	1	*Digit or letter codes*
		6			.				0
					.			1	1
					.		2		2
			5		.		2	1	3
					.	3			4
			5		.	3		1	5
			5		.	3	2		6
					.	3	2	1	7
				4	.				8
			5	4	.			1	9
	7	6			.			1	*a*
	7	6			.		2		*b*
	7	6	5		.		2	1	*c*
	7	6			.	3			*d*
	7	6	5		.	3		1	*e*
	7	6	5		.	3	2		*f*
	7	6			.	3	2	1	*g*
	7	6		4	.				*h*
	7	6	5	4	.			1	*i*
	7		5		.			1	*j*
	7		5		.		2		*k*
	7				.		2	1	*l*
	7		5		.	3			*m*
	7				.	3		1	*n*
	7				.	3	2		*o*
	7		5		.	3	2	1	*p*
	7		5	4	.				*q*
	7			4	.			1	*r*
		6	5		.		2		*s*
		6			.		2	1	*t*
		6	5		.	3			*u*
		6			.	3		1	*v*
		6			.	3	2		*w*
		6	5		.	3	2	1	*x*
		6	5	4	.				*y*
		6		4	.			1	*z*
	7	6		4	.		2	1	. (period)
		6	5	4	.		2	1	, (comma)
	7	6	5		.				+ (plus)
	7				.				− (minus)
		6	5		.			1	/ (check)
	7	6	5	4	.	3	2	1	Delete
8					.				End of block
				4	.		2	1	End of record
			5		.				Space
		6		4	.		2		Back space
		6	5	4	.	3	2		Tab
	7	6	5	4	.	3			Upper case
	7	6	5	4	.		2		Lower case

Fig. 19.5 EIA punched tape code.

he can stop the machine and ask the advice of an expert (who might be his supervisor or the tool engineer).   The operator's rate of pay is related to his competence and productivity rate, which is dependent on the degree of judgment of which he is capable.

Now what are the analogous operations in planning the manufacture of this part on a tape-controlled automatic drilling machine, with a turret containing as many different drill sizes (which can be automatically tape-selected) as there are hole sizes in the part?   The comparison may be made in many ways.   A convenient point at which to begin the examination is at the machine tool.   Again, the part must be securely fastened to the bed of the machine before drilling is initiated by some sort of work-holding device, which might be the same fixture as was referred to above.   In this case, a drill jig is not required.   Instructions for fixture installation and the installation of the proper drill sizes in the appropriate spindle positions to a specified depth are part of the process sheet.   Information to assure that the workpiece is fastened in the correct location with the proper orientation on the fixture must, of course, be included for the operator's benefit.

Assume the first workpiece has been properly mounted.   What comes next?   Of course, the tape containing commands for the machine-tool operation.   This tape must be properly coded with a visual tag to ensure that the tape appropriate to this part and fixture is installed in the tape-reading device.   Further, the leading end of the tape, right side up, must be properly installed in the tape reader by the operator.   This is by no means a trivial requirement, since both tapes and their readers can give trouble when not used correctly.   Now the tape has been installed. The machine-control system combination must be signaled to commence the machining process.   This command may be inserted via a button labeled START.   Thereafter, the control takes over, and the operation will proceed to completion unless a malfunction occurs or the operator is for some reason dissatisfied.   This state of affairs has its advantages and also its disadvantages.   On the one hand, the rate of machining is likely to be higher than in the manual case.   Likewise, the uniformity. However, the operator's judgment no longer plays a part in the machining phase.   All the judgment necessary must be exercised by the control or inserted in advance on the tape by the programmer.

The programmer now has the responsibility for machining judgment, formerly exercised by the operator, in addition to that of the methods engineer who has to decide on what machine, in what sequence, with what fixtures and tools, and at what machining rates the individual operations shall take place.   The programmer is therefore a tool engineer and operator combined (except for loading and unloading of the workpieces on the machine).

By this reasoning several characteristics of the control system have been defined.   For one thing, it becomes clear that the punched tape is part of the tooling for manufacture, as much so as the fixtures and cutting tools.   For another, the operator is not able to second-guess the tape, so that its information must be letter-perfect.   The programmer-tool engineer who originates the instructions entered on the paper tape must be meticulous, both in dimensional data, sequence of this data, and sequence and accuracy of the other data associated with the machining and received by the tool.   Examples are commands in proper turn for the various spindles, programmed stops for operator inspection or change of position or attitude of the workpiece, initiation or turn-off of various auxiliary functions, such as clamps, coolant, various tool speeds in rotations per minute, and so on.

To assist the programmer in the proper execution of his total responsibility, a highly organized form, often termed planning sheet, is suggested by the designer of the control system as a prelude to insertion of the data into the keyboard for punching the tape.   The program sheet or planning sheet must contain *all* the information received by the keyboard, which is to say all the information necessary to instruct the control in the complete machining cycle.   The planning sheet, then, is the only connecting link between the tool engineer-programmer and the machine-tool control. Preparation of the tape from the planning sheet is a clerical operation, usually assigned to a keyboard operator.

Since most position control systems require the locations to which the workpiece is to be positioned (prior to the drilling or other cutting) to be defined in positive absolute coordinates with respect to a single reference or orientation point, the dimensioning practices used by draftsmen do not satisfy the input needs of the control system.   The data conversion consists of nothing more than redimensioning, in the process of which dimensions on the normal drawing must have constants of offset either added or subtracted.   In some of today's shops where numerical control systems are being contemplated, designers may anticipate future needs by employing dual drafting standards, carrying along on drawings both conventional and absolute numerical types of data.   Frequently the new list of dimensions serves to reveal to the draftsman contradictions in his previous dimensioning habits, since arriving at the same end point via different sequences may result in quantities which do not coincide. In other words, as tolerances are usually specified, certain locations can be ambiguous.   In the absolute coordinate system of numerical control this condition does not exist.

The above considerations relate chiefly to the human engineering and communication requirements of numerical control.   One additional facet of the data input process deserves comment.   In the case of a manually operated drilling machine, blunders inserted in the list of instructions to the machine operator by the tool engineer are perceived quite readily, and critical comments are quickly passed along to the originator of the error. The numerical control is not nearly so articulate. Assuming that the tool engineer has prepared and accurately checked a planning sheet, there still exists a serious possibility of error before the instructions reach the machine. The clerical operation of inserting data from the planning sheet into the tape punch involves the orderly transmittal of many numerical and symbolic pieces of data. In the course of actuating in turn the hundreds of keys to complete this phase, the human operator is all too likely to commit errors, either of omission or commission.

Therefore, providing the keyboard operator with a printed record of his actual entries is a valuable addition to the system. It allows the operator to verify his actions against the instructions on the planning

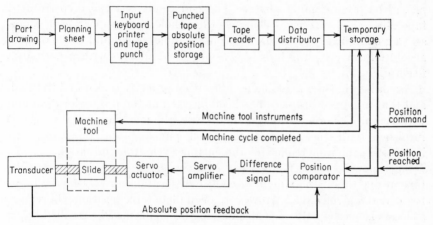

Fig. 19.6   Block diagram of typical position control system (closed loop).

sheet, either line by line or after the entire program has been completed. Sound control system design includes mandatory check-backs or closed loops around each step or group of steps. In some cases errors may be detected before they have been introduced into the punched tape, by providing line print-out for visual verification against the planning sheet, before the line of data is fed into the tape punch. In other cases, where printing and punching occur simultaneously, input errors are corrected by splicing the correct tape on the roll in place of the incorrect block.

Having reviewed the input data and its insertion, and defined the output product of a controlled machine tool as finished parts meeting the designer's specifications (just as output parts from manual machines), it is now logical to examine the individual pieces or blocks which comprise a typical position control system, from part drawing to manufactured workpiece. A block diagram is shown in Fig. 19.6. While position controls are available with open-loop logic, the closed loop has been selected as being more typical, more foolproof, and more flexible.

The part drawing is assumed to be the start point of the manufacturing operation. To produce a planning sheet from the drawing requires that data from the drawing be assembled in the proper sequence for the machining operation. The planning sheet is the prime responsibility of the programmer-tool engineer. Having satisfied himself of its accuracy, he passes it to the keyboard clerk, who enters the written digits into the keyboard mechanically. This keyboard, which may resemble that of a typewriter, an adding machine, or be a unique electromechanical device, converts mechanical key motion into electrical signals for punch-solenoid actuation, and drives the type-printer wheels mechanically or electrically. As the typist works, the punched and printed tapes emerge line by line. Verification of the printed sheet against the planning information completes the programming phase. The end result is a roll of perforated tape 1-in. wide, with eight channels where holes may appear, each representing one binary digit. It will contain dimensional and other data in absolute form, which is to say as a numerical address with respect to a fixed origin.

Assuming that the machine tool has been properly tooled and fixtured, and that a blank workpiece has been inserted at the proper location and with the proper orientation on the fixture, the machine operator who is furnished with the properly identified punched-tape program must install it in the tape reader for the cutting cycle to be initiated.

Since punched-tape readers can sample only a single line across the tape at one time, a maximum of eight hole locations or bits can be interrogated at a given time. However, a complete table position will require at least six (perhaps 12) new decimal digits. This may be recalled by an examination of the tape code proposed as an EIA and AIA standard, since it provides one decimal digit per line across the tape. Therefore, many lines of data from the tape must be read before a new table location can be commanded. Further, all the data in one block or word must be transferred to some type of intermediate storage, so that it can be made available simultaneously for the positioning phase. The temporary storage consists of a quantity of relays or stepping switches, with a total digit capacity equal to that of a slide position as presented digitally. To transmit the proper tape digits to the appropriate storage locations requires additional switching logic, here entitled "data distributor," which usually consists of a stepping switch.

Digital data representing one slide position has now been transferred and stored into the temporary storage register. It is not yet time to permit operation of the machine tool. Additional instructions must be conveyed as to which drill size must be brought to the ready position by the spindle turret. This involves storage of a different sort in the register, with data received also from the tape. The machine tool may receive these commands either before, during, or after the positioning sequence, but in any case before the cutting operation is initiated.

Now that the position and machine information have been introduced into the temporary storage register, the control is at last prepared for the machining cycle. The new slide position command, in absolute or address form, is presented continuously from storage to a position comparator as one of its two inputs. The other input is the actual slide position, as monitored by a transducer mechanically attached to the slide. The transducer in the typical system measures position in the same units or code as it is commanded from storage. As command and feedback are compared, the difference is produced at the output of the comparator as an error signal into the servo amplifier. The error may only denote the sign of the difference, or both the sign and the amplitude. In the former case an ON-OFF servo is implied; in the latter, proportional servo drive.

The error signal, which is a continuous function changing as the slide is moved under servo action, is furnished at a low electrical power level, perhaps 1 watt. Considerable power is required to move the slide 100 watts or more on a typical machine table. The error signal must therefore be amplified, which is the function of the block titled "servo amplifier." This may denote vacuum tubes or thyratrons, relays for an ON-OFF servo, or an electromechanical d-c generator-amplifier system.

An error power signal is now available to excite the servo actuator. The actuator may be an electrohydraulic valve, a d-c motor, an a-c motor, differential magnetic clutches, or some other type of prime mover appropriate to the accuracy and speed required. The most common form of mechanical output from the actuator is a rotating shaft, which is coupled to the slide through a reduction gear box and an antibacklash precision lead screw. Rack-and-pinion drive is employed where large strokes are required, so that the moment-of-inertia of the driven system is minimized. The nut on the screw is physically coupled to the table slide being positioned. If the transducer is rotary, then the screw may be used as the mechanical input. If the transducer is linear, mechanical coupling is from the slide itself.

Motion of the slide occurs until transducer and temporary storage data are precisely matched, at which time the difference signal is reduced to zero, the slide is clamped, and the storage register is signaled that the desired position has been reached. This in turn triggers a command to the machine tool that it is now appropriate for the metal-cutting operation to proceed; so that, in the case of a drill, the down-feed of the spindle is enabled. When the drill has reached the bottom of its stroke and been retracted, a completion signal is initiated on the machine-tool spindle and fed back to the storage register.   One cycle of machining has been completed, and the register commands the tape reader to interrogate the data on the next block of tape.   The cycle is repeated, block by block and point by point until the machine has gone as far as it can automatically, at which time the tape has either been completely read or it has stopped the proceedings and set off a signal which commands the operator to intervene, perhaps to insert a new workpiece or change the surface presented to the machine tool.   The operator signals completion of his function by pressing a button.

When industrial position control systems were first presented for sale, in 1954 and 1955, a variety of memory input media was employed.   A few systems used special punched tapes, 4 to 12 in. wide, and others used punched cards of the types employed in data-processing equipment (IBM and Remington-Rand).   Since one line of the wide tape could provide simultaneously all the instructions for one slide position, such nonstandard tapes had the advantage of being able to eliminate part or all of the data distribution and storage portions.   However, these tapes were slower to prepare and read, and the punching and reading mechanisms, being highly specialized, were costly and often troublesome.   In the case of punched cards, the readers were also rather expensive, and the sequence was not fixed, so that it was possible for cards to be read in an order other than that originally programmed.

The selection of eight-hole, 1-inch punched tape by the Aircraft Industries Association (the largest first-user group) and the Electronic Industries Association (representing the systems suppliers) resulted from the familiarity of members of both groups with perforated tape for data processing, data transmission by wire, and the widespread availability of standard tape-punching and reading mechanisms throughout industry from these previous applications.

Several of the early systems designers adopted a binary code for the input information.   While this simplified the internal design of the control, and reduced the number of bits which had to be stored on the tape, it forced a difficult decimal-to-binary code conversion on the machine programmer.   It slowed him down and tended to introduce many errors.   Binary-coded decimal is now the proposed standard, and represents an efficient compromise of the requirements of the programmer, the tape punch and reading mechanisms, and control design.   One complete line of eight-hole punched tape is allocated to each alphabetic letter or decimal numeral.   A new position in X and Y, at any point in a plane up to 100 by 100 in. (with a resolution of 0.001 in.) requires for each axis one letter and five decimal digits, a total of six lines of tape per axis and twelve lines per position (independent of machine-tool operation commands).   The speed of most present-day tape-reading mechanisms is about 10 lines/sec; the reading of the new location from tape therefore requires approximately 1.2 sec. Positioning of the slides may require from 2 sec up to 1 min or more, depending upon the distance to be traveled and the acceleration and deceleration characteristics of the servomechanisms.

The small appetite of position controls for new information has permitted the use of absolute positional data, as distinguished from incremental. The absolute or address philosophy eliminates the possibility, in closed-loop systems, of an accumulation of error which is inherent in incremental systems. In present-day combinations of controls and positioning tables, a positioning accuracy of ± 0.001 in. and a repositioning accuracy of ± 0.0003 in. are typical. The largest factor in systematic error, which controls the initial positioning accuracy, is the mechanical coupling between linear slide motion and rotary input to the transducers used in most systems. Nonlinearity of the transducers is also a contributing factor.

As for control philosophy, some designers have employed analog transducers, such as resolvers, synchro transformers, or potentiometers. In these cases the temporary storage register performs the conversion from the digital data input to analog voltage output (either amplitude or phase-modulated voltage). Other designers have chosen an all-digital approach, in which case the transducers are of the digital shaft encoder (address information) type. In these cases the input and the comparator are also digital. There are also examples of systems which utilize a combination of digital and analog philosophies in input, comparator, and transducer sections.

Prospective users of machine tools with position controls approach the problem of justifying these new, costly tool combinations from several viewpoints. As items of capital equipment, these novel systems are expected to pay their own way, in reduced over-all costs, within 3 to 5 years. In those industries where small and medium production batches are the rule, reduction of tooling or get-ready costs can be appreciable. The manufacturing phase may also play a part in the cost justification. Besides tooling and manufacturing cost advantages, justification may include reduction in lead time, improved flexibility to accommodate part design changes, greater accuracy and uniformity of the manufactured product, lower scrap percentages, longer tool life, and reduction in paperwork.

Combinations of these factors can, in turn, produce increased over-all manufacturing efficiency. With higher accuracy and shorter lead time, production scheduling becomes easier, since manufacturing rates are predictable and uniform. Engineering changes need no longer be delayed because of reluctance to interfere with shipping schedules. Better finished products, as well as smoother production rates, are important indirect advantages.

19.7 Path Controls

Contrasted to drills, jig borers, punches, and boring mills, there is another class of machine tool which performs continuous metal removal. Included are milling machines, profilers, lathes, grinding machines, broaching machines, shapers, and planers. They require, to achieve maximum productivity, numerical path controls (also known as contour controls). Milling machines and profilers (large milling machines) represent the largest single group to which contour controls have been initially applied. These machines have been employed both in the manufacture of production parts, and in the machining of patterns or templates to be used on other manufacturing machines. The latter case is considered a tooling or toolroom application.

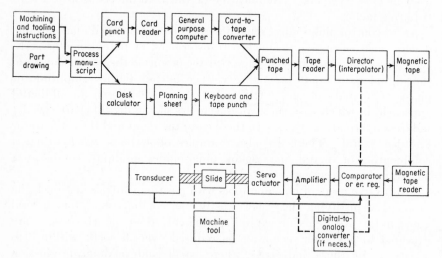

Fig. 19.7 Typical path control flow diagram (closed loop).

Special applications of path controls have also been made. Three-dimensional cam milling (a spiral cam), turbine blade milling and grinding, lathes for the broaching of nonlinear gun rifles, and the carving of scale models of map terrains have been among the earliest of these unusual applications.

Before examining in any detail commercial contour control systems, it will be instructive to review the major functional elements necessary in any closed-loop path control. Figure 19.7 is a flow diagram of a typical path control system. As in the case of positioning control, punched tape represents a common command medium for most controls. However, a comparison with the previous block diagram will quickly reveal the presence of a number of blocks relevant to computing or data processing, which did not appear between the part drawing and punched tape in the earlier diagram.

Since contouring requires that all portions of the path traversed by the cutting tool relative to the workpiece be accurately controlled, it follows that continuous command data must be made available to the control. Such commands require a vast amount of information, if high resolution and accuracy are to be attained. Quickly comparing the data volumes demanded by the two types of systems, position controls require approximately 4 bits/decade, or 40 bits of information for each positioning cycle for two axes. Such cycles may occur as frequently as one every 2 sec, so that a maximum data input flow would be 20 bits/sec. For path controls, input commands may be required simultaneously, for each of three axes, at a rate of 5,000 bits/sec per axis, a total of 15,000 bits/sec. Thus contouring systems have a data appetite perhaps 750 times as great as positioning machines.

Conventional part drawings can contain only general instructions defining the paths or contours of the finished part, and therefore a very small fraction of the total data to be generated. Drawings typically contain only the critical dimensions of the part, which might also be termed the break points in the contour. To this data must be added the tool engineer's decisions relating to the type and size of the cutting tool, rate of material removal, which may be defined as the number of cuts or passes chosen to reach the finished dimensions, spindle speeds, feed rates of the cutting tool with respect to the workpiece, machining tolerance, sequence of operations, type of coolant, and instructions as to when in the sequence the cutting tools or holding fixtures must be changed by the operator.

We see then that machining instructions and part drawing dimensional data are the two basic data sources which merge into a process manuscript, an organized form which serves as the starting point for the data-processing phase. Because there are two dissimilar data-processing functions to be accomplished, all current systems require that these be accomplished in two separate phases and by two different computing devices.

Existing path controls monitor the location of the workpiece with respect to the center of the cutting tool, not the final part dimension. Accordingly, one of the major computing functions is the calculation of the path of the tool center offset by the radius from the desired finished part dimensions. This usually involves only the application of trigonometry. In addition, it is frequently necessary for the exact tool offset path to be broken down into a number of linear or circular segments which will approximate the finished part within acceptable dimensional and finish tolerances. To put it another way, many part contours are too complex to be accurately generated by practical processing equipment, and present-day systems can perform only linear cuts, or at the most circular ones. Still other tasks for the initial data-processing phase are calculations of points at which acceleration or deceleration must be commanded to prevent undercutting, tool breakage, or loss of servo synchronization; time block lengths for acceleration or deceleration commands; pulse frequencies to produce the desired vector tool feed rates; automatic pocket cleanup routines; and possibly compensations for tool or workpiece deflection.

In the second phase of data processing the critical or break points of the tool offset path are converted into simultaneous continuous command information for all the slides to be servo-controlled during the cutting cycle. This interpolation function requires the very high data output rates (up to 15,000 bits/sec) referred to earlier, as well as high accuracy.

The process manuscript is prepared by the part programmer. It contains raw data, both with respect to part specifications or dimensions and the tooling decisions. In a large plant, such as an aircraft factory, where there is available both a general-purpose computer and a library of computer routines for numerical control data processing, the part programmer orients his manuscript around the automatic routines of the computer, which is likely to be of medium or large size (IBM-650 or 704, or UNIVAC-III). In this case, a clerical employee will insert the manuscript data into a keypunch and produce a series of punched cards from the manuscript. These cards will then be fed into the general-purpose computer, which will perform all the calculations required by the manuscript and the data-processing routines, translating its results into a stack of output punched cards. To be of use for the special-purpose computer-director in the next phase, the card data is automatically converted to 1-in., eight-channel punched tape, either by the computer itself, or more likely by an off-line card-to-punched-tape converter.

If, on the other hand, the part programmer is employed by a small machine shop, such as a job shop or subcontractor, or if the part to be manufactured is a simple one, the manuscript is prepared with a desk calculator in mind. The calculations necessary to derive the path of the tool center from an outline drawing of a simple part, which contains a series of linear or circular segments, can be expeditiously accomplished by simple routines on an electric calculator. Simple curve-fitting as well as data for control of acceleration and deceleration to minimize overshoot, and feed rate information can also be prepared by this method. The operator of this machine will record the results of his efforts on a second organized manuscript, or planning sheet, which now contains in proper order the complete series of data required by the Director for machine-tool control. Afterwards, the planning sheet information is entered into the keyboard of a tape-punching mechanism, which may be the typewriterlike input of a Flexowriter or the adding machine format of a posting machine.

Whether the upper (automatic computer) path or the lower (manual computer) path has been chosen, the same punched tape will result, and will be verified before the computing phase is considered complete. The punched-tape may be as short as 2 or 3 ft, in the case of a simple part and tape intended for a Director capable of first- and second-degree interpolation, or tape may be several hundred feet long, if the part is sizable, complex, and intended for a linear segment-interpolating Director.

For the typical Director, the information residing on the punched tape consists of instructions to the Director for control of vector feed rate, and the displacement to be produced simultaneously during the interpolation interval for each axis or feed to be controlled, ΔX, ΔY, and ΔZ. One machining interval or segment is defined by one block of tape data, so there will appear as many blocks of data as there will be machining intervals. It is the number of blocks which determines the length of the tape. For the average Director, a block requires approximately 2 in. of the standard eight-hole paper tape.

For optimum control of the machining process, each servomechanism which must be coordinated during the cutting interval requires that it be fed data continuously, the data for each channel being coordinated or synchronized with the other channel or channels involved in the cutting. The interpolation process consists of the generation of simultaneous coordinated command data for the machine servomechanisms, and is usually performed by a special-purpose digital interpolator which provides incremental digital pulse trains, with as many outputs as there are slides to be displaced. As far as possible, the pulses for a single slide are spaced uniformly in time, providing periodic commands (the optimum type for smooth servo action).

A short consideration of accuracy is in order, to provide some background for an understanding of the interpolation function. Most machined parts will require that some dimensions be held within a tolerance of 0.002 to 0.005 in., no matter what the maximum size of the part. The total machining path may be 1,000 in. or more, but the accuracy is specified on an absolute basis. An accuracy of 0.002 in a traverse of 1,000 in. represents a tolerance of one part in 500,000. A very good analog computer may achieve an accuracy of one part in 10,000. It is evident that the Director cannot utilize standard analog techniques. As will be seen later, most interpolators are digital in logic; however a special type of analog interpolator, making use of digital reference or calibration principles, has been developed for one of the control systems.

As mentioned above, the Director will usually produce simultaneous incremental pulse trains for servo control. The total amount of data required by a part is indeed very great, often exceeding 1 million bits. The logic of the Director is quite different from that of a computer, which can only produce a single output at any time, and in absolute rather than incremental form.   Directors in present-day use require several hundred vacuum tubes.   It is therefore complex, costly high-speed equipment.   Some manufacturers have chosen to perform interpolation within the machine tool itself, thus providing a Director along with each control unit.   Others have chosen to separate the Director and the control functions, by utilizing a Director to make preinterpolated magnetic tapes and using magnetic tape input to the machine control on the shop floor.

There are advantages and disadvantages in each case.   Magnetic tape is the only medium capable of storing and reproducing the vast amount of information necessary for path control at a reasonable price.   However, it is a fairly fragile memory for shop use.   Dirt and other forms of contamination can easily produce loss of information.   Where properly handled, magnetic tape has proven to have adequate reliability; in other cases, where proper precautions against contamination and damage were not taken, it has proven troublesome.   However, the advantages of removing interpolation from the machine tool are undeniable; the cost of the control can thereby be cut by at least 50 per cent, and the amount of equipment and the service problems on the shop floor are diminished by an even greater percentage.   The cost reduction may be in the order of $30,000 to $40,000 per control, so that where three or five machine controls are involved, large economies can be effected by separation of the Director from control.

Incremental data for each servo slide arrives at the comparator or error register in the control unit either by direct wire from a built-in Director or as the amplified output of a magnetic tape reader.   The comparator of a path control unit receives information continuously and must provide a difference signal representing instantaneous error between transducer and input commands continuously and at a high comparison rate.   It is therefore a much higher-speed device than the typical position comparator.   Frequently it is a reversible digital counter, which contains only the instantaneous or dynamic difference between command and response.   Where such a digital error register is employed, a high-speed, continuous digital-to-analog converter is necessary to provide a continuous signal to the amplifier.   Several types of amplifiers have been selected in path controls. High-speed magnetic amplifiers, which operate at power-line frequencies, rotary d-c motor generator sets of the amplidyne type, and high-pressure hydraulic servo valves have been used.   As servo actuators we find a-c high-response electrical servo motors, d-c motors, hydraulic linear rams, and rotary hydraulic motors. Power requirements imposed by the load, cost, mechanical response desired, service problems, and other economic factors have influenced actuator selection.

Since the slides are under continuous servo actuation, while a cutting load is imposed by the tool, the servo actuators are called upon to deliver both higher horsepower outputs and greater bandwidths (faster response) than actuators in positioning systems. Furthermore, the entire servo system, composed of the comparator, amplifier, and actuator, must be highly linear, so that both during steady-state motion and during acceleration and deceleration the two or more slides which must be coordinated to produce an accurate path may remain synchronized. This linearity is achieved with highly nonlinear components, represented by the amplifiers, actuators, and slide mechanisms, with great effort and considerable expense. Friction and stiction in the mechanical portions of the system are especially troublesome obstacles to linear servo loops.

The actuator usually produces a rotating shaft output which is coupled to the slide by a precise reduction gear box with low moment of inertia and low backlash, and a recirculating ball-bearing lead screw with split nuts for backlash reduction. The ball screw is required to have a highly linear pitch, since the feedback transducer is frequently coupled to the screw mechanically.

Where comparators receive incremental command data, the transducer also generates incremental information. Transducers may be rotary digitizers of an electromagnetic or optical type, linear optical gratings, synchro transformers, resolvers, or precision potentiometers (in the case of a combined digital-analog comparator). In the sections to follow, the path control systems in most general use will be considered, and the specific details of the various blocks will be described. The relationships between transducer and comparator types will then become more apparent, as will the actuators employed.

19.8   The MIT Milling-machine System

Developed by the MIT Servomechanisms Laboratory on an Air Force contract, this system was begun in 1949 and completed in 1953, although machine-tool operation was begun in 1952. This, the first true numerical control, was applied to a 28-in. Cincinnati Hydro-Tel vertical-spindle milling machine, with a work capacity of 60 by 30 by 15 in.

The MIT machine system utilized as an input mechanism a Flexowriter automatic typewriter and tape punch. This produced paper tape $\frac{7}{8}$ in. wide with true binary coding, each binary dimension being located in a single channel parallel to the edge of the tape, and was therefore read serially. Since the logic was based on an incremental motion of 0.0005 in. for each pulse command to any one slide, there appeared in each tape block a binary equivalent of the displacement ΔX, ΔY, and ΔZ for the three slides, each quantity representing the number of thousandths of an

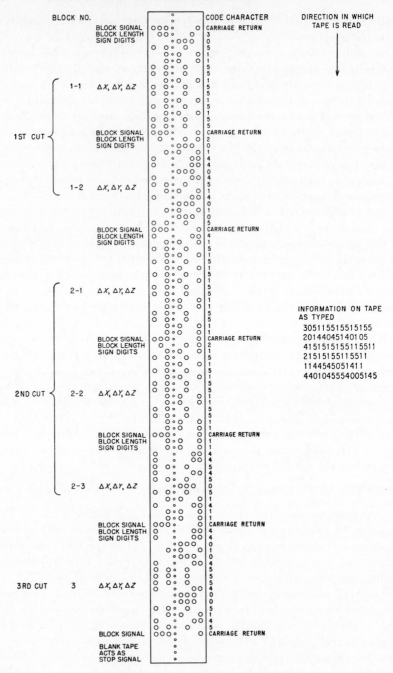

Fig. 19.8 Sample of MIT coded paper tape.

inch of motion multiplied by two.   Figure 19.8 shows a sample of the coded tape.

A block diagram appears in Fig. 19.9, while a functional diagram is shown in Fig. 19.10.

In operation, a block of punched tape was read by the tape reader and distributed into a relay register or buffer memory.   Each block defined a straight-line motion in space, produced by coordination of the three slides during the same time interval.   Since the Director contained two relay buffer stores for each axis, while one was controlling the operation of the machine (the active store), the other was available to receive the command information from the next block of tape, which was distributed while the machine tool was under command of the first register.   The

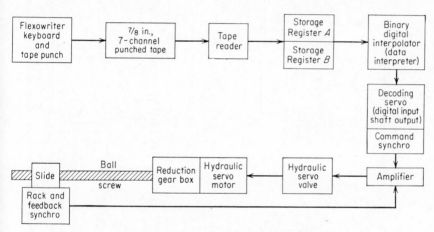

Fig. 19.9   Block diagram—MIT milling machine.

Director included a binary digital interpolator, which produced simultaneously on each of three output channels a sequential pulse train which commanded the displacement of a servo-powered slide.   As many pulses appeared on a single output line during an interval as there were half-thousandths of an inch of motion.   The Director was therefore a special-purpose digital computer, performing first-degree interpolation, with a maximum of three simultaneous outputs.

Each pulse train was transmitted to a reversible binary counter.   The contents of this counter were continuously converted into an analog voltage, which was amplified and applied to an electrical instrument servo motor attached to a disk called a position coder.   As the coder rotated under actuation of the servo motor, brushes sensed its displacement and produced pulses, one pulse for each $\frac{1}{120}$ revolution.   These output pulses were fed back in an opposite sense to the reversible counter, so that at rest the counter stood at zero after having caused the position

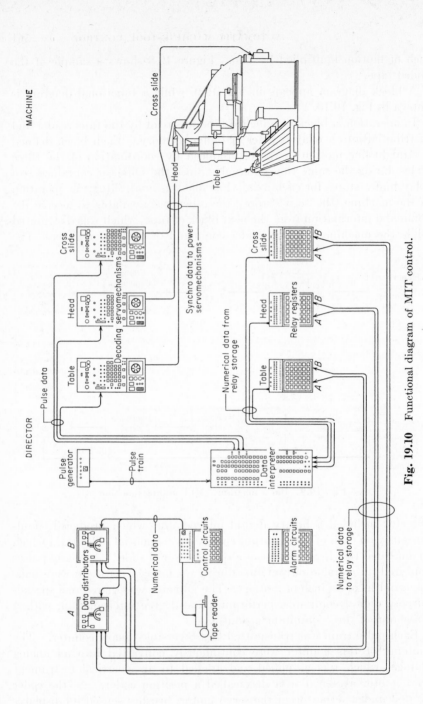

Fig. 19.10 Functional diagram of MIT control.

coding wheel to rotate an amount exactly proportional to the total number of pulse commands received. This subsystem (decoding servomechanism) was in effect a digital-to-analog converter, whose output was a shaft displaced in rotation by $\frac{1}{120}$ revolution for each command pulse, which in turn represented an ultimate slide displacement of 0.0005 in.

Attached to the output shaft was a synchro transformer used to command a power servomechanism follow-up. From mechanical shaft input, the synchro rotor produced a phase displacement of a carrier signal exactly proportional to the number of pulses received by the position coder. The synchro output signal was fed into a servo amplifier, whose output drove an electrohydraulic servo valve. The hydraulic fluid metered by the valve powered a rotary hydraulic servo motor, which through a reduction gear box actuated a special lead screw with recirculating ball bearings and two nuts preloaded against each other. This ball screw provided a rotary to linear power conversion without backlash and with high mechanical efficiency. The slide was coupled to the output nut of the screw; as it moved, a precision rack mounted on the slide produced rotation of a feedback synchro transformer which monitored slide displacement. The rotor of the feedback synchro served as the other input to the servo amplifier. The power servomechanism system was connected in a sense to cause the slide to be displaced and produce a feedback synchro output equal to the command synchro input.

Thus the Director consisted of a digital interpolator, an instrument servo system organized as a digital-to-analog converter, and an analog power servomechanism in cascade. The comparator was a servo amplifier comparing the phases of the command and feedback synchro transformers. The amplifier was an electrohydraulic valve, and the servo actuator a rotary hydraulic motor. There were, of course, three such systems, each consisting of an instrument and power servo, one for each of the slide motions on the machine tool. No magnetic tape was used, and the Director operated in real time as the milling machine performed metal removal.

The feed rate for each axis was infinitely variable from zero to a maximum of 15 in./min, controlled by the pulse rate generated by the Director. This pulse rate was dependent on an entry in each block of punched tape which determined the rate at which clock pulses were fed to a special multiplying counter, whose operation will now be described.

A chain of binary counters is commonly employed to reduce a train of input pulses by successive powers of 2. Each binary flip-flop stage produces 1 output pulse for 2 input pulses. If we assume the counter is initially in the zero condition, the first input pulse changes the state of conduction and causes the flip-flop to assume the one condition. When the second pulse enters, it changes the flip-flop back to its initial zero condition, and causes an output CARRY pulse to emerge. If the output line is connected as the input to a second binary flip-flop, it in turn will be changed to the "one" condition by the output carry pulse. In this manner as many binary stages as desired can be connected in cascade. If there are n flip-flops in the chain, any number of input pulses divided by 2^n will appear at the output of the last counter stage.

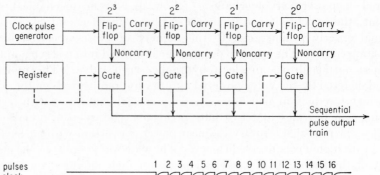

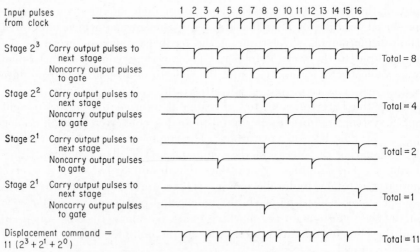

Fig. 19.11 Block diagram of binary rate multiplier.

A binary counter chain possesses another important property, seldom used in computer practice. It was first employed in the MIT project, and later utilized in identical or modified form by commercial path controls. Because of its widespread application, the principle will be explained here in some detail.

A block diagram of this device, called a "binary rate multiplier," is shown in Fig. 19.11. In this case a clock pulse generator feeds input pulses to a chain of four binary flip-flops connected in cascade. Below each flip-flop is shown a gate, and the outputs of the four gates are connected together to indicate a summation process. In the normal binary counter chain, only the flip-flops would be included; gates would be absent.

A pulse timing diagram appears in the lower half of Fig. 19.11. The top line of the diagram shows a sequence of 16 input pulses from the clock generator. Since the counter chain contains four flip-flops, the sequence of operation will be exactly repeated each time 2^4 or 16 clock pulses have been introduced. A single train of 16 pulses therefore serves to illustrate the entire sequence of operations. As can be noted, a clock pulse occurs at each time interval denoted by a vertical graph line, and therefore the clock pulses are uniformly spaced in time.

Below the clock pulse train are shown two pulse trains (one above the other) associated with the first binary counter stage, labeled "Stage 2^3." The top line, labeled "Carry output pulses to the next stage," shows when a clock pulse changes flip-flop 2^3 from the one condition back to the zero condition, causing a CARRY pulse to be emitted. Immediately below is shown a line, "Noncarry output pulses to gate," each pulse occurring coincidentally with a flip-flop change of state from zero to one. It can be observed from a comparison of these two lines that CARRY pulses occur simultaneously with each even-numbered input pulse from the clock pulses 2, 4, 6, 8, etc. On the other hand, NONCARRY pulses occur simultaneously with each odd-numbered clock pulse, 1, 3, 5, etc. For stage 2^3, there is a total of 8 CARRY pulses and a total of 8 NONCARRY pulses. For any stage the total of CARRY plus NONCARRY pulses is exactly equal to the total number of input pulses; so it may be concluded that for any binary stage there is available a NONCARRY pulse output equal to one-half the input total.

For the next stage 2^2 there may be seen a series of 4 CARRY output pulses, occurring on input pulse numbers 4, 8, 12, and 16, and another total of 4 NONCARRY pulses on clock-pulse numbers 2, 6, 10, and 14. Two other details are worth noting: for stage 2^2 the CARRY output pulses occur simultaneously in time with CARRY output pulses from 2^3 stage immediately above, while the NONCARRY output pulses from stage 2^2 occur noncoincidentally with the NONCARRY output pulses from the 2^3 stage.

Similar circumstances prevail for the last two counter stages, labeled 2^1 and 2^0. In all cases, CARRY output pulses occur from two or more stages simultaneously, while NONCARRY output pulses always occur individually. It is this last characteristic which makes the binary rate multiplier so useful in generating command trains for path control systems. A digital servomechanism employing a reversible counter as a comparator or error register can recognize only one command pulse at a time, and therefore a displacement command train must occur sequentially (incrementally). It can be seen that for each 16 clock pulses, there will be a total of $8 + 2 + 4 + 1$, or 15 NONCARRY output pulses. The first stage will produce 2^3 or 8; the next stage 2^2 or 4; the third stage 2^1 or 2; the last 2^0 or 1.

It is therefore possible to produce any desired command pulse total, up to 15, for a group of 16 clock pulses. The total generated will be determined by those gates which are enabled by static commands from the register, and therefore permit NONCARRY pulses from the appropriate flip-flop to be passed through and summed at the output of the gates. As an example, at the bottom of Fig. 19.11 there has been diagrammed the output pulse timing train for a command of 11 counts, representing the enabling of the gates in stages $2^3 + 2^1 + 2^0$. A total of 11 pulses, occurring sequentially, may be counted on the bottom line. It may be noted that the pulses occur in bunches of varying size, in this case one pulse, three groups of three pulses each, and finally a single pulse.

This aperiodicity is inherent, and undesirable, because these groups may occur so spaced in time as to permit the servomechanism which receives them to resolve the individual groups, and in some cases to resonate at the group frequency. The latter event can lead to servo instability, poor cutting accuracy, and poor surface finish of the cut material. For this reason some control builders smooth pulse rates by employing a clock rate much higher than the output pulse command rate, multiplying by a constant the frequency and the total of clock pulses to the binary rate multiplier, and then dividing the output pulses by the same constant in a separate conventional binary counter chain. Even with appreciable smoothing factors, such as 2^4, for most incremental values and slide feed rates employed in normal machining the clock-pulse frequencies are well within the limits of an ordinary binary counter. A triode flip-flop stage can easily resolve a pulse frequency of 100,000/sec, so that a smoothing factor of 16 permits a 16,000-pulse/sec output rate. Even for a slide displacement of 0.0002 in. per pulse, this can produce a feed rate over 3 in./sec or 180 in./min. higher than the maximum cutting feed rates used today in light materials such as aluminum and magnesium.

The binary rate multiplier utilizes a single chain of flip-flops, and as many separate groups of gates as there are separate slides to be controlled, to produce as many simultaneous pulse trains as will be necessary. The rate multiplier can therefore be recognized as a simple and economical device, in which all clock pulses, up to the capacity of the counter chain minus one, are potential command output pulses. Another characteristic should also be mentioned. The rate multiplier as described above performs only first-degree or linear segment interpolation. In the MIT system, as in all the later systems which employ this type of logic, where a curved surface must be generated, data processing is necessary to define the parameters of each linear segment, the number of segments increasing as more accurate and smoother curves are demanded. Where high accuracy and smoothness must result, the size of each segment decreases, the total length of punched-paper tape becomes great, and the rate at which information can be read from tape and transferred into registers to control interpolation becomes the limiting factor in the cutting feed rates which can be produced.

The employment by MIT of two servomechanisms in cascade—a low-power command servo, and a high-power machine servo—introduces the possibility of undesirable interaction. To avoid this hazard, modern path controls employ only a single servo loop, wherein slide displacement is monitored by transducers which transmit feedback signals directly to the comparator.

19.9   The Bendix Path Control System

Figure 19.12 is a block diagram of the Bendix machine control unit. It utilizes philosophy similar to that of the MIT system described above. Including the interpolator within the machine control equipment, the Bendix control also employs binary-coded punched tape as the input medium, a seven-channel tape again being used. A diagram of the control-tape format is shown in Fig. 19.13.

In the Bendix system each pulse represents a slide displacement of 0.0002 in. The maximum length of a single information block on tape is 22 lines (2.2 in.), corresponding to a maximum slide displacement in excess of 400 in. A feed rate of 240 in./min, or 20,000 pulses/sec, can be generated. To produce high feed rates during machining, the Bendix control reads the input tape photoelectrically. This permits a tape reading speed ten to twenty times that of a conventional mechanical reader.

As in the interpolator portion of the MIT Director, the feed rate in the Bendix interpolator is controlled by a number contained in a separate channel on the punched tape. This feed rate number controls both the pulse rate fed into the interpolating counter and the counter stage into which the clock pulses are introduced.

Interpolation is produced by a binary rate multiplier, similar to that of MIT. However, the Bendix implementation of this logic is somewhat different, in that it uses magnetic-core shift registers instead of an ordinary binary counter. Each register is 22 stages (bits) long. There are two registers used for each binary operational multiplier; one operates in straight binary fashion, producing at its output NONCARRY pulses which are potential command pulses. The other register is controlled by the displacement of the axis during the segment, a quantity stored in the active storage block from data received from the punched input tape. Whether or not an individual NONCARRY pulse is gated through to the output line as a command is determined by the number held in the active storage magnetic-core shift register. The latter therefore corresponds both to the register and the gate in the MIT Director. The net result is a series of sequential pulses for each feed of the machine tool, the total

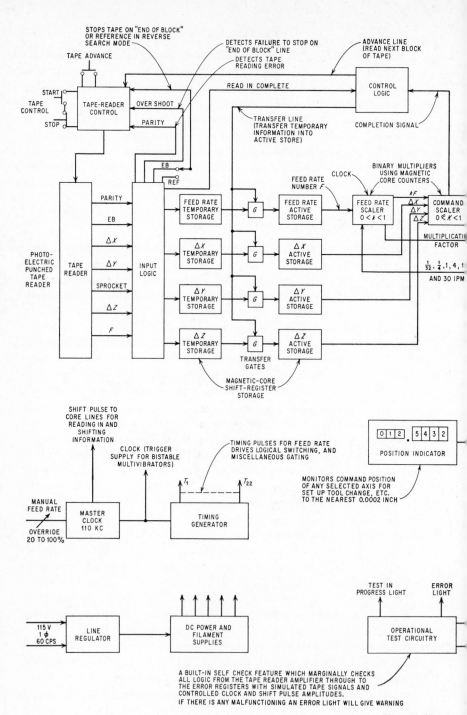

Fig. 19.12

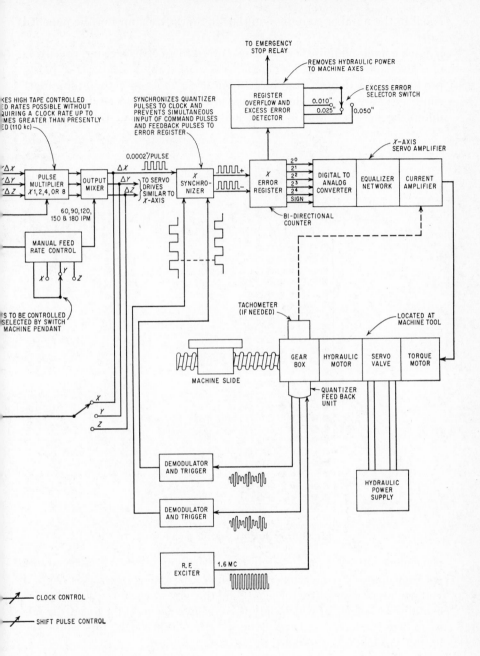

Bendix control.

equal to the number contained in the appropriate channel of the punched tape.

Each command pulse train is transmitted to an error register, consisting of a reversible binary counter chain, whose other input is a series of pulses produced by a digital transducer monitoring motion of the appropriate slide. At any instant the quantity in the error register represents the difference between total commanded displacement and the actual dis-

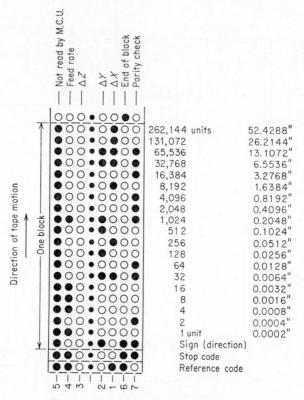

Fig. 19.13   Bendix control tape format.

placement which has occurred up to that instant. The register contents are continuously converted, via a digital-to-analog converter, into a voltage proportional to the count in the error register. The register contains 11 stages, of which only the first five are used for linear digital-to-analog conversion. Larger counts are not decoded, but cause the output voltage to be clamped at a saturation level.

The error voltage is fed into a current amplifier, which excites a torque motor that controls a servo valve from a constant-pressure hydraulic supply. The fluid metered by the valve drives a piston-type rotary hydraulic servo motor, whose output shaft speed is reduced through a gear box before being applied to the drive for the machine slide.   Slides with a short stroke are actuated by a recirculating ball lead screw; for larger strokes a rack-and-pinion drive is utilized, so that the rotating moment of inertia will be low, and a high stiffness achieved.

The feedback transducer employed is a rotary electromagnetic grating called a quantizer.   The quantizer has one rotor winding and two stator windings, spaced to give outputs 45 electrical degrees apart from each other.   Each rotor and stator winding has 250 poles, and each stator output signal is therefore modulated 250 times per revolution of the quantizer shaft.   The rotor is fed a signal from a 1.6-megacycle oscillator, so each output is an a-m 1.6-megacycle carrier.   Both outputs are amplified and demodulated to produce rectangular output signals.   The time relationship between the zero crossings of the two outputs of a quantizer determines the direction of rotation of the input shaft, and therefore the direction of slide motion.

The entire control contains about 400 vacuum tubes, 2,800 diodes, and 200 magnetic cores.   The hydraulic servo valve has a bandwidth of about 200 cps, and the valve and hydraulic servo motor, including the slide load, has a servo bandwidth of 7 to 10 cps even for large slide loads.

19.10   The North American Numill Control

Another system which combines a linear binary digital interpolator and machine servomechanisms in a single machine control unit is the Numill control.   Utilizing binary-coded punched-paper tape at the input, with a different format than that of MIT and Bendix, Numill also employs a binary rate multiplier for interpolation.   A block diagram is shown in Fig. 19.14.

North American has implemented both the interpolator and servo portions with transistor logic.   An all solid-state control, the package is more compact than any of the other path systems described in this chapter.   Numill departs in another important respect from the systems previously described.   The transducer is not rotary, but a linear optical grating which modulates the illumination to a semiconductor photo-electric cell.   The grating is ruled with 1,250 lines/in.   This optical resolution is increased by a factor of 4 by electrical multiplication, so that one pulse is generated for a slide displacement of 0.0002 in.   Since the optical linear transducer is not dependent on a screw or a rack for its output signals, transducer accuracy can be independently controlled. The transducer signals are not affected by such factors as wear in the threads of a screw or torsional deflection (called wind-up) of a screw due to dynamic loads imposed either by slide bearing friction or heavy cutter loads.

The servo amplifier, which receives a decoded (analog) voltage from the digital error register, performs an integration as well as amplification operation on it.   This permits each servo to operate with zero average velocity error during a constant-velocity cutting interval.   The output of the amplifier drives a servo valve, which in turn controls a hydraulic motor.

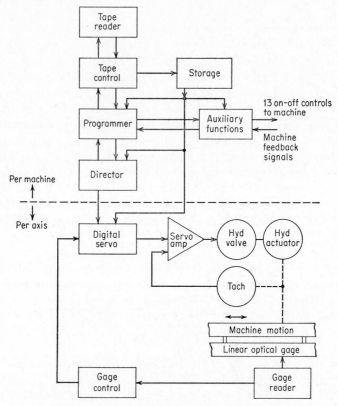

Fig. 19.14   Block diagram of Numill control.

19.11   The Giddings & Lewis Numericord System

This system employs a digital Director (interpolator) to generate incremental pulses.   These are converted to analog phase-modulated carrier signals and recorded on magnetic tape to serve as commands to an analog control unit similar to that of the playback portion of the original General Electric record-playback control.   The Giddings & Lewis Machine Tool Company developed and provides the Director, while the machine control unit is furnished to Giddings & Lewis by the General Electric Company.

A block diagram of this system appears in Fig. 19.15.   Since the interpolation and control functions have been physically separated, a preinterpolated magnetic tape serving as the link, the complexity of the machine control has been reduced. Furthermore, a single Director can prepare tapes for several control units.

A modified form of binary-coded decimal is used both in the punched tape and in the interpolator; a 5, 2, 1, 1 code was chosen. Each block of punched tape contains command-time and command-distance information, and incremental distances for the displacement of up to five machine-tool axes of motion. The displacements are programmed in multiples of 0.0005 in., and the director has a capacity of 399,9995 in. for

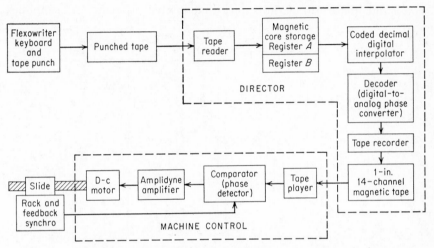

Fig. 19.15 The Giddings & Lewis Numericord system.

a single interpolation segment. While the resolution of the input information is 0.0005 in., the resolution of an output pulse from the interpolator is 1/8,000 (0.000125) in. Thus, 8,000 command pulses are produced per inch of slide motion.

Each axis displacement command is transferred from the punched tape into a magnetic-core shift register. The cores of this register function as gates for a binary rate multiplier. NONCARRY pulses from a chain of binary-coded decimal counters are used to interrogate the gates, and a pulse output is produced where the interrogation pulse finds a 1 stored in the core. The core storing the information corresponding to 0.0005 in. is interrogated four times during the processing of a block of information. The next core, weighted at 0.001 in., will be interrogated eight times during the period of a command time; the 0.002-in. core interrogated 16 times, the 0.005-in. core 40 times, etc. A block diagram of the counter chain and gating cores for one axis is given in Fig. 19.16. As in the previous systems described, a CARRY occurring from the binary counter stage at the right end denotes the completion of an interpolation cycle and is used to disable the clock-pulse generator. Since NONCARRY pulses from the counter are used for interrogation, no two cores of any axis can be simultaneously interrogated, and the summed output pulses are non-coincident in time.

A 16-kc clock frequency is employed; the location in the counter chain at which these pulses are inserted depends on the command time or interpolation interval. The command number sets up one of nine gates which selects the insertion point.

A separate clock oscillator and cascaded chain of binary and decade counters is used in the decoder portion of the director, to convert the command pulse trains into phase-modulated carriers. A simplified

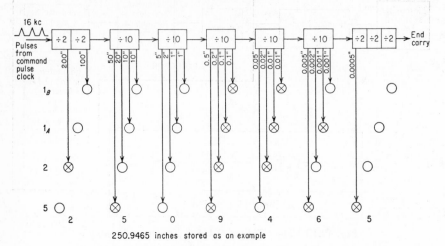

250.9465 inches stored as an example

Fig. 19.16 Block diagram of Numericord rate multiplier.

version of the decoder for one axis appears in Fig. 19.17. There may be seen two six-stage binary counter chains, each receiving input signals from a carrier clock oscillator. The lower chain also receives pulses from one output of the digital interpolator. A positive command pulse is inserted as an input in addition to the clock pulses, while a negative command pulse causes one clock pulse to be deleted from the input to the lower counter. Consequently positive commands cause the transitions of the output stage to be advanced; negative commands produce retardation of the output signals. The upper counter chain, which receives all clock pulses without interference, generates a reference square-wave signal. As command pulses occur, the zero crossings or transitions of the lower chain output are advanced or retarded in a manner analogous to that of the output of a command synchro.

A synchronizing gate, called a chronizer, is used to prevent pulses from the carrier oscillator and the command generator from entering simultaneously, since the decoder counter could not process both pieces of information. In the Numericord Director, there are one reference counter chain and five command counter chains, to permit simultaneous output commands for five axes of motion. The reference counter divides the 160-kc clock frequency by 800, producing a reference output frequency of 200 cps, for which the comparator and synchro in the machine control unit were designed. Each command pulse from the interpolator shifts the output phase of the decoder for this axis by $\frac{1}{800}$ of a carrier cycle or 0.45°. Thus 800 command pulses cause 1 cycle of carrier phase shift and correspond to a displacement command of 0.1 in. The maximum interpolator output rate of 16 kc, which would occur in the event

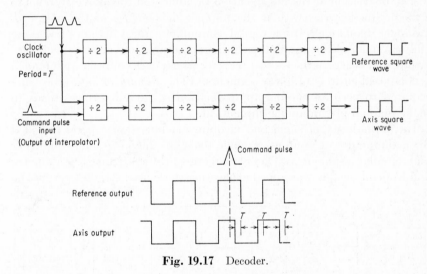

Fig. 19.17 Decoder.

the maximum 400-in. displacement has been called for, would cause a modulation of the output phase of a decoder channel of 7,200°/sec, corresponding to a frequency modulation of 20 cps. This is $\frac{1}{10}$ the frequency of the reference carrier. The decoder output signals are recorded on separate channels of 1-in. magnetic tape.

In the machine control unit, each phase-modulated command signal is amplified, then inserted as an input command to a comparator, which is a phase detector. The other comparator input is produced by a feedback synchro whose shaft is rotated by a precision instrumentation rack attached to the slide of the machine tool. The comparator output is a d-c voltage proportional to the instantaneous displacement error between command and feedback, and is amplified in power by an amplidyne (d-c motor generator) amplifier. Its output signal excites a variable-speed d-c motor, which is coupled to a ball nut lead screw or drive rack through a precision reduction gear box.

In summary, the Numericord system embodies the linear digital interpolation and analog power servomechanism philosophy included in the MIT approach; it differs primarily in the separation of the interpolator and control functions, using as the connecting link analog magnetic tape. A secondary point of departure is the employment of a coded decimal language for the input punched tape and the linear interpolator. This permits the use of a decimal keyboard for tape preparation and makes a more efficient link with the human programmer, who has been taught to think from childhood in the decimal language.

19.12   The Stromberg-Carlson Digimatic System

The restriction of the interpolation capability in the above systems to straight lines carries with it the implicit dependence of the part programmer upon an electronic digital computer to assist in data processing. Only a small percentage of parts manufactured on milling machines, lathes, and others in the class of tools for which path controls are intended is composed entirely of linear segments. The amount of data processing required to perform chordal approximation to curved surfaces tends to make manual programming impractical.

In the majority of small and medium machine shops, parts intended for manufacture on contour machine tools are composed mainly of linear and circular segments. The Stromberg-Carlson Digimatic Computer and Control System was aimed at meeting these needs, and to permit the

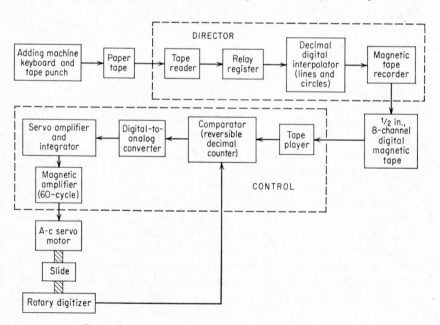

Fig. 19.18   The Stromberg-Carlson digimatic system.

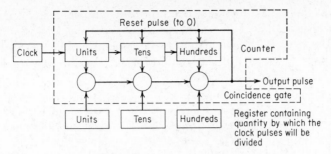

Fig. 19.19   Divide counter.

programmer of such parts to remain independent of general-purpose computers, which are seldom available in small business organizations.

A diagram of the Digimatic system is shown in Fig. 19.18.   Data entry is accomplished on a multicolumn adding machine keyboard, to which is attached a tape punch.   A modified binary-coded decimal is perforated on the paper tape, representing the machine vector feed rate (in inches per minute), and the slide displacements ΔX, ΔY, and ΔZ for a given interval.   Where a circular arc is to be cut, information referring the two ends of the arc to the circle center is also included.

The Director, which interpolates digitally in the pure decimal code, departs from the binary rate multiplier of the previous systems and is instead a special form of digital differential analyzer.   It is organized as a first- and second-degree parametric function generator, capable of solving the following equations:

$$y = mx + b \tag{19.1}$$
$$(x - a)^2 + (y - b)^2 = r^2 \tag{19.2}$$

It accomplishes these functions by setting up the differential equal to the slope of the line, and adding successively constant increments for the linear case and increments of variable slope for the circular case.

A decimal electronic counter, using magnetron beam switch tubes, has been organized to divide any number of clock input pulses by an amount equal to a number statically presented at the input to coincidence gates attached to each decade.   As shown in Fig. 19.19, this device can divide clock pulses by any desired integral quantity, producing at the output the quotient.   When pulses from the same clock are fed to two such counters in parallel, and the counters are instructed to divide by quantities representing Δx and Δy respectively, then the two output pulse trains will have a frequency ratio equal to the slope of the line to be machined (the hypotenuse of the triangle whose legs are Δy and Δx).   The process continues until the output pulses, which are summed in separate counters, reach a total equivalent to the desired displacement in increments of 0.001 in.   The pulses are recorded incrementally on multichannel magnetic tape.   A functional diagram of a straight-line generator may be seen in Fig. 19.20.

For the case of the circular arc, the general circular equation (19.2) given above is reduced by differentiation to its instantaneous slope

$$\frac{dy}{dx} = -\frac{x-a}{y-b} \tag{19.3}$$

By arranging for the totals $x - a$ and $y - b$ to be accumulated in separate reversible decade counters, and presented continuously as inputs to respective divide counters of the type described above, a digital representation of the desired circle is generated and recorded on magnetic

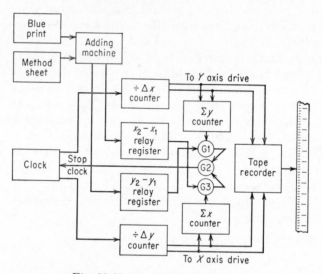

Fig. 19.20   Straight-line generator.

tape.   A functional diagram of the Director connected to produce circular interpolation is given in Fig. 19.21.   The Director is converted from a first-degree interpolator to a second-degree interpolator by a multipole relay, which switches the input lines of the divide counters to either a relay storage register (linear) or a reversible summing counter (circular).

Pulse command rates are controlled, to produce the desired vector feed rate, in a manner different from that associated with the binary rate multipliers.   A separate internal electronic analog servo loop controls the frequency of the clock-pulse generator in accordance with the feed rate contained in digital form in a separate portion of the relay register. The output pulses along each of the three axes command lines are monitored, converted to analog voltages, and added vectorially, after which they are compared to the commanded feed rate.

As in the case of Numericord, the interpolation is carried out independent of the control function. In Digimatic, $\frac{1}{2}$-in. digitally recorded magnetic tape is the connecting link. In the control the incremental pulse commands are fed into a reversible digital decimal counter. The contents of this error register are continuously converted to an analog voltage, which is both amplified and integrated, then introduced into a high-speed, 60-cycle magnetic amplifier. The output of the latter excites an a-c servo motor, which in turn drives the slide through a reduction gear box and a ball nut lead screw. A rotary digitizer, an electromagnetic grating similar to that described in the Bendix system, provides feed-

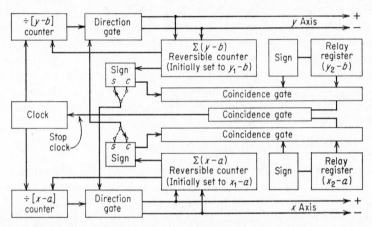

Fig. 19.21 Circle generator. Note 1: In sign block of reversible counters, the letter s refers to the true sign, the letter c refers to the complement of s. Note 2: With switches on the sign outputs of the above counters set as shown by the solid lines, the circle will be generated in a clockwise direction. If they are set as shown by the dashed lines, the circle will be generated in a counterclockwise direction.

back pulses which are introduced as the other input to the comparator.

Although the pulse commands of 0.001 in. represent larger displacements than the quanta associated with the previous systems, the smoothing action of the integrator, magnetic amplifier, and servo motor is such as to produce paths which are continuous along either linear or circular paths. As in the case of Numill, the addition of an integrator in the servo amplifier permits operation at constant feed rates with zero average difference between commanded and instantaneous locations. Circular paths are cut smoothly and accurately, in spite of the continuous acceleration in each axis.

The use of digitally recorded tape permits the program to be recorded at a standard tape speed, and played back at any tape speed over a considerable range. The machine operator therefore has the privilege of second guessing the part programmer and can optimize the playback feed rate for cutting-tooth load in accordance with the characteristics of the work and condition of the cutter. This freedom can be a blessing or a curse, however, since the part programmer should be an expert at predicting optimum cutting conditions, and the machine operator is often a novice in these matters. As in the case of most of the features which numerical control offers the manufacturing function, each innovation has potential advantages which can be turned to disadvantages with careless use. Production control must be organized in a new way to capitalize on the flexibility of numerical machining.

The ability to perform first- and second-degree interpolation has permitted many simple parts to be manually programmed without the use of a desk calculator. However, in the case of aircraft parts, to which most of the contouring systems have been applied, the general-purpose computer is an indispensable part of the data-reduction phase. Digimatic part programs, as well as programs for the preceding path control systems, have been produced almost without exception by IBM-704 computers. Punched tapes containing programs for insertion in the Digimatic Director are usually shorter than tapes programming the same parts on other Directors, by factors of 5 or 10.

19.13   The Ferranti Contouring System

Control development in Great Britain paralleled efforts in the United States, both in time and philosophy. In 1952 the Ferranti Research Laboratories initiated developments in the control of machine tools. This company evolved a digital path system which is remarkably similar to the Stromberg-Carlson system in that a digital interpolator producing incremental digital magnetic tape is employed. The machine control unit has as a comparator a reversible binary counter, whose output, after conversion to an analog voltage, drives a 400-cycle magnetic amplifier

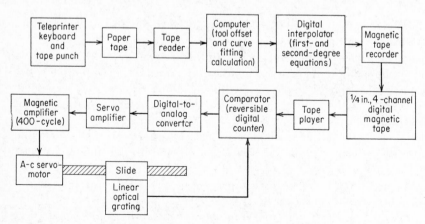

Fig. 19.22   The Ferranti contouring system.

and a-c servo motor. The transducer is a linear optical grating, which can produce a pulse for each 0.0002 in. of motion. Instead of ½-in. eight-channel magnetic tape, Ferranti commands the machine control from ¼-in. four-channel magnetic tape, deriving positive and negative drive signals from a single recorded channel.

The chief difference between this and the American system lies in the combination of data-processing and interpolation functions within a single computer. This combination performs the functions of curve-fitting, tool offset calculation, and first- and second-degree interpolation, so that the burden on the programmer is lower than in any other system. It represents in most respects the most sophisticated solution yet available. The major elements of the system may be seen in Fig. 19.22. The interpolator can automatically generate lines, circles, ellipses, parabolas, or hyperbolas. A special command to the computer causes a curve-fitting routine to be initiated.

19.14 The Cincinnati Numerical Control System

Concurrently with the system developments enumerated above, EMI Electronics Limited in England developed a continuous contour control. Unique because of its analog nature, it is furthermore an absolute rather than incremental system, using carrier voltage amplitudes for both command and feedback functions. In the United States the Cincinnati Milling and Grinding Machines Company evolved a special adaptation of the EMI system, which it is distributing in this country.

Figure 19.23 is a simplified block diagram of the Cincinnati system. Punched cards are used as the input medium to the control unit. Information from the cards is loaded into a storage unit consisting of rotary stepping switches which set up in cascade a bank of precisely wound toroidal transformers. These transformers, excited by a reference carrier with a frequency of 1,000 cps, produce at their combined output a

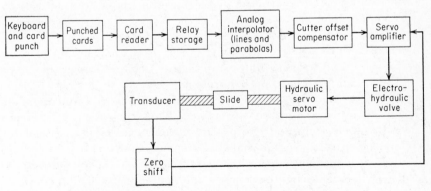

Fig. 19.23 The Cincinnati numerical control system.

voltage amplitude which corresponds to the location of the slide for which they are producing the displacement command.   With a stated accuracy of one part in 100,000, an absolute position command accuracy of 0.001 in. in 100 in. is made possible.

A schematic of a typical memory unit, including rotary stepping switches and a group of five toroidal transformers, is given in Fig. 19.24. Transformer $T1$ has 10 output taps, which feed in parallel the corresponding taps on the five stepping switches.   The impedances of the trans-

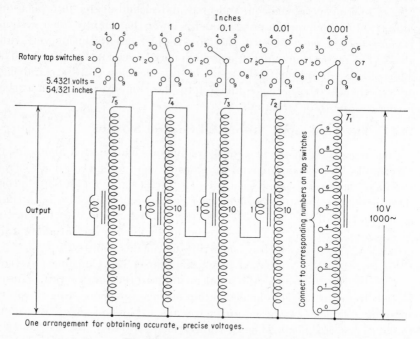

One arrangement for obtaining accurate, precise voltages.

Fig. 19.24   Typical memory unit.

formers must be so controlled that connecting the outputs in cascade will not result in any degradation of the total voltage, independent of the taps to which the switches may be connected.

There are five such memory units in the storage register for one control axis.   Each memory unit establishes a single coordinate point for its slide.   The interpolation performs its operation on a single segment or "span" at one time.   Each span is defined by three coordinate points, one at each end and one at the center.   Thus three memory units are used to supply command information for one span to the interpolator. While one span is being interpolated, the two unused memory units are loaded with information for the next span from the punched cards. When switching occurs, the memory unit containing the end point of the first span becomes the unit commanding the start point of the next span.

The interpolator can generate continuously changing command information for either linear or parabolic span segments.   To accomplish this process smoothly, it makes use of induction potentiometers, rotary switches, and additional toroidal transformers with special turns ratios on the transformers to permit the establishment of several discrete points along the desired parabola.   Figure 19.25 is a simplified functional dia-

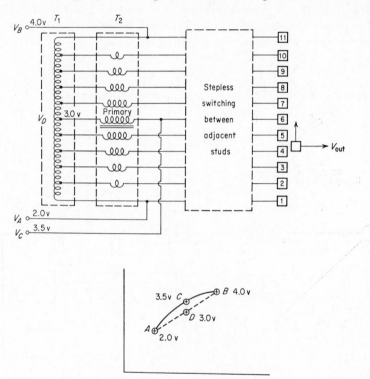

Fig. 19.25 Functional diagram of interpolator.   Turns ratios for parabolic compensating transformer:

$$\text{Primary: } N^2 = 25 \text{ turns}$$
$$\text{Sec. 1: } N^2 - 1^2 = 24 \text{ turns}$$
$$\text{Sec. 2: } N^2 - 2^2 = 21 \text{ turns}$$
$$\text{Sec. 3: } N^2 - 3^2 = 16 \text{ turns}$$
$$\text{Sec. 4: } N^2 - 4^2 = 9 \text{ turns}$$
$$\text{Sec. 5: } N^2 - 5^2 = 0 \text{ turns}$$

gram of an interpolator.   The span to be commanded is that lying between points A and B on the graph.   The absolute voltage corresponding to point A is applied to the bottom of transformer $T1$, and that corresponding to point B to the top of $T1$.

If the straight line ADB were desired, transformer $T2$ would be bypassed; since the taps on $T1$ are equally spaced, voltages on taps 1 through 11 would lie along the straight line ADB.   In the event the parabola ACB is desired, transformer $T2$ is inserted. With turns ratios as described in the table included in Fig. 19.25, the voltages induced in the multiple secondaries of $T2$ will cause the potentials on taps 1 through 11 to lie on the parabola ACB. In either the linear or the parabolic case, 11 discrete points on the span are presented at the output taps.

To enable the output line, labeled V_{out}, to vary smoothly instead of discontinuously, a process called stepless switching has been worked out. This consists of an array of additional toroidal transformers, rotary transformers, and induction potentiometers, as depicted in Fig. 19.26.

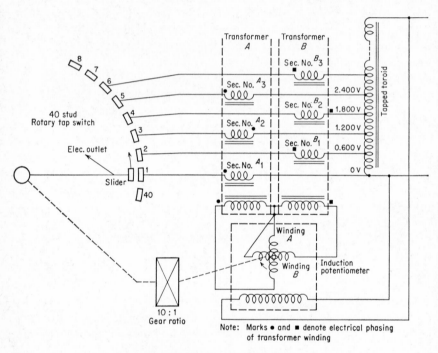

Fig. 19.26 Stepless switching.

A mechanical gear reducer of a 10:1 ratio has been included between the shaft of the rotary switch and that of the induction potentiometer.

The potentiometers have a transfer function that gives a linear output voltage over a shaft displacement of $\pm 60°$ from null. By proper phasing of the potentiometer rotors, and the stepping switch rotor, the slider voltage on the stepping switch can be made to lie at exactly the mid-point of stud 1 when potentiometer winding A is at null. The output voltage at stud 1 is then exactly equal to the voltage from the tapped toroid, shown in the previous diagram. As the rotors of the switch and potentiometer rotate simultaneously, the switch slider moves toward stud 2, and rotor A of the potentiometer generates a voltage which increases with time, and is added through transformer A to the voltage from the toroid tap. Simultaneously, rotor winding B is introducing a subtracting voltage to the voltage from tap 2. When the shaft of the potentiometer has rotated 45°, the slider on the switch will be midway between studs 1 and 2. This inductive continuous interpolation, when properly organized, will provide stepless switching, so that as the slider of the switch reaches a stud, the voltage generated by the array of potentiometers and transformers A and B will stay in synchronism with the voltages provided by the toroidal transformers $T1$ and $T2$ previously described.

The transducer or feedback unit consists of an array of toroidal transformers, rotary switches, and stepless switching analogous to that in the interpolator. The feedback unit is coupled either mechanically or electrically to the motion of the slide, and serves as the second input to the servo amplifier. The difference between commanded voltage and transducer voltage is, of course, the error signal which excites the electrohydraulic valve and hydraulic servo motor.

The analog interpolation philosophy permits two features which are not practical in digital systems to be added conveniently. One is the cutter offset compensator, which in an analog manner erects a perpendicular to the slope of the interpolated span and displaces the voltages by an amount equal to the radius which has been inserted in the compensator. Thus a path offset to the programmed span can be erected. Zero shift provides a fixed displacement along an axis, such as might be desired to provide offset from an orientation point.

19.15 Summary

In 1956 the Air Materiel Command of the Air Force let contracts for the procurement of about 100 numerically controlled profilers and skin mills. The machine-tool manufacturers who received prime contract awards were Giddings and Lewis, Kearney and Trecker, Cincinnati, and Morey. Machine tools were delivered to Air Force contractors and were installed and put into operation during 1958 and 1959. Controls purchased on subcontracts were those of Numericord, Bendix, Stromberg-Carlson, and Cincinnati. Directors were also purchased from Giddings and Lewis and Stromberg-Carlson.

Some of these machine-tool systems have been used to make tooling for conventional and numerical milling machines, while others have been put into manufacturing use. Although a true assessment of the costs of manufacturing by numerical control is difficult because of cost-accumulation practices within the aircraft plants, reduction in machining times of 50 to 80 per cent have been reported by several of the users. Cost improvement of 30 to 50 per cent has also been reported (these numerical machine systems represent a higher capital investment than the conventional machining systems and therefore a higher cost per hour).

Improvement in the lead time has been even more impressive. The cycle from drawing to the first finished part has been reported to have been reduced from 50 to 90 per cent. This is a reflection of the complexity of getting ready to manufacture by conventional methods. The design and fabrication of tools and jigs to permit the cutting of complex parts, such as those in military aircraft, is a laborious procedure, both in terms of engineering design, metal fabrication, and information dissemination. Numerical systems have made possible the elimination of many tooling fixtures and have simplified others.

From this preliminary data, it is possible to draw some tentative conclusions pointing toward a new manufacturing philosophy. Most users agree that the introduction of numerical control does not involve doing things in the same way as before, either better or faster, but doing things in entirely new ways, with new people and devices. Unless the design, tool engineering, and work and machine setup are organized to match the unique characteristics of the numerical system, higher rather than lower costs may result. Scheduling must be performed differently, since the new machines offer a much lower floor-to-floor time. While by no means all elements in the user plants are enthusiastic, most personnel charged with the use of these exotic systems are optimistic about the results. As they become better qualified to employ the systems, efficiency improves rapidly. Opinions concerning the merits of numerically controlled manufacturing are sharply divided; personnel are either strongly in favor or strongly opposed, with few who are noncommittal. The introduction of these systems represents something of a revolution in the aircraft industry, and it is likely that design and manufacturing practice will change rapidly within the next three years as the secondary effects become apparent.

To support the very difficult data-processing phase of numerical control, the Air Force also sponsored the development of a large library of programming routines for the IBM-704 Computer, a machine common to most plants receiving the tape-controlled machine tools. This programming project, titled APT-II, was coordinated by MIT; many of the aircraft plants contributed mathematicians who participated in the evolution of APT. It permits the part programmer, who need not be a mathematician and is usually a specially trained tool engineer, to address the 704 in English or Englishlike words, to perform the various functions associated with producing the desired instruction tapes for a Director from the part drawing information with which the programmer is supplied.

APT instructs the 704 to perform tool offset, curve approximation, pocket cleanout, tool acceleration and deceleration, and other functions common to all the control systems. Since each of the four systems requires different information, both in total and in code and format, four different post-processing routines for the 704 computer have also been developed, so that the data resulting from the basic computation phase can be automatically translated into the punched tape or cards for any of the control systems on which the part is to be manufactured.

19.16   New Developments

Machine tools with numerical controls for cutting are now islands of automaticity in factories which are inherently manual. Numerical control has thus far supported only the metal-cutting phase of production. There are already becoming available control systems aimed at reducing the noncutting intervals on numerically controlled tools. Most of the down time on a machine tool occurs because workpieces must be loaded and unloaded by manual means, and cutting tools inserted and replaced by the human operator. Kearney and Trecker has introduced a machine intended as an automatic system rather than an automatic metal-removal device. Their Milwaukee-Matic includes tape control of tool selection and change, automatic workpiece and fixture loading, unloading, and reorienting, as well as tape control of the cutting process.

Automatic controls to assist the design engineers are widely discussed. Automatic drafting machines, three-dimensional simulators, and computer systems programmed to make many simple engineering decisions are technically feasible and will undoubtedly emerge as soon as an economic need is evident. Few engineers will deny that much of their time is spent on routine work which could easily be subcontracted to a simple control or computer.

Even prior to the advent of numerically controlled cutting machines, there have been numerous examples of complex, precise parts which required more time and cost to inspect than to manufacture. Precision inspection is a tedious, manual, and subjective process. There have been announced two tape-controlled automatic-inspection systems, one by Warner and Swasey and another by Stromberg-Carlson. In each case, a probe positioned by tape is advanced until it contacts the desired portion of the finished part. The probe location at the time of contact can then be converted into an electrical READ-OUT, such as on a chart recorder. Either deviation from nominal (part error) or actual position can be automatically printed or recorded in a memory medium. Inspection of mechanical products is now an OFF-line function; with sufficiently flexible and efficient automatic devices, inspection could become an ON-line true quality-control function. Rapid developments in this area can be expected within the next 3 years. Numerical inspection controls could have a greater eventual effect on industry than numerical manufacturing controls.

As the number of stations under numerical or computer control increases, the flow of instructions through the factory will take on a different character. Presently drawings, written procedures, written schedules, and large volumes of paper must carefully precede parts in their flow through the factory. Tapes represent comparable instructions to automatic stations. It can therefore be expected that for several years both numerical and written process instructions will be generated and transmitted in parallel. Later the written sheets for human consumption will diminish and the unambiguous, mathematical descriptions will take their place.

New products will become economically feasible. Automatic processing of data recorded by various inspection, manufacturing, and conveyer and storage locations will permit close control of inventory, quality control, raw material procurement, and completed material to customers. Numerical control of warehousing, partially manufactured inventory, and perhaps even scheduling are probably no more than 5 years away. Accounting, billing, and cost control are already largely computer controlled. Economic and social pressures will force the introduction of computers and servo controls to many of the routine functions in the factories of 1965.

GLOSSARY

Analog   a quantity or function (often an electrical signal) which can vary continuously in some respect, such as amplitude, frequency, phase or time.

Bit   an abbreviation of *binary digit*. The smallest unit of digital information.

Comparator   a circuit which compares two signals (such as commands from tape and slide displacement from the transducer) and produces an output signal representing the difference between the inputs.

Differential analyzer   a type of computer which performs the mathematical operation of integration by adding successive increments representing the instantaneous value of the differential of the function to be integrated. This can be done in analog fashion either mechanically (shaft rotation) or electrically (continuously variable voltages). Digital computers can also perform this operation by using discrete digital approximations of the true mathematical analog function.

Interpolate   to produce data which fills in gaps between given information. If the location of two points in a plane is defined, then a ruler can be used to draw a continuous straight line between them. This represents linear interpolation. Loft lines are a form of nonlinear interpolation.

Nonlinear servo   a servo in which the relationship between input signal and output power or motion is not a fixed ratio; a nonproportional servo.

ON-OFF servo   a servo system in which the load has only two possible velocities, stand-still or full speed.

Phase   the fraction of an a-c cycle period that has elapsed since the instantaneous voltage or current passed through zero.

Phase modulation   a method of transmitting information by varying the phase of an a-c signal with respect to a reference a-c voltage.

To program   to prepare a list of coded instructions, containing numerical data and operation instructions, for a digital computer.

Proportional actuator   an actuator which can produce a continuously variable output speed.

Servo   a device which compares the output of an apparatus to its input, and uses the difference to control the apparatus.

Servo actuator   the prime mover which generates the force that moves the physical load in a control system.

Shaft encoder   a transducer which converts shaft rotation into an absolute digital number.

Shift register   a digital register in which a fixed pattern of digits can be shifted intact to different locations in the register.

Storage register   a memory to hold electrical information.   In digital systems, this may consist of relays, stepping switches, flip-flops, magnetic cores, or delay lines.

Synchro   a motor wound for single-phase rotor and three-phase stator operation.   When two such motors are connected in parallel, and both rotors excited from a single-phase line, if the rotor of one is turned mechanically the rotor of the other will turn to align itself with the angular position of the first.   This follower motion occurs because of magnetic field rotation produced by shifting of stator phases as the first rotor is turned.

Tape code   a set of symbols, such as holes, which convey numerical or alphabetic information.

Tape format   the order in which code symbols are arranged on tape.

Transducer   a device which transforms power or information from one form to another; examples are the loudspeaker (electrical to acoustic), motor (electrical to rotary mechanical motion).   In a machine control, the transducer is usually defined as a device which converts displacement of the load into electrical information.

20

Computer Control in Process Industries

GARY K. L. CHIEN
INTERNATIONAL BUSINESS
MACHINES CORP.

20.1 Introduction

Feedback control engineering has been considered the backbone of automation. It is of interest to note that, compared with most of the other branches of engineering sciences, feedback control seems to distinguish itself in the fact that it seldom involves economic considerations. The factor of efficiency, normally an important consideration in other engineering design problems, is generally not considered as part of a feedback control system design problem. The applications of feedback engineering in the process industry have the same characteristics. The design of process instrumentation and automatic controllers deals mainly with problems of system accuracy and stability. The automatic controllers on a process bear little or no direct relationship with the economy of over-all process operation, except that they are considered as necessities for the operation of the process.

On the other hand, with the advent of the branch of science called operations research, the process industries have benefited economically by applying operations research concepts and techniques to process design and operation. Operations research is the science concerned mainly with optimum utilization of resources. One good example of its application in a process industry is the solution of the gasoline-blending problem by the method of linear programming.[1] However, the present status of the application of operations research techniques in processing industries has been limited to the optimization of steady-state problems. The implications of their extension to the dynamic situation, when the results of optimization are to be used to affect the control of the process on a feedback basis, have not been fully investigated.

The objective of this paper is to discuss the application of computer

590

control in the process industry where the problems have to be treated from both the control engineering and operations research point of view. It can be considered as the extension of either control engineering into the economic domain or operations research into dynamic and feedback situations.

The process computer control problem is first discussed in terms of its characteristics. The basic methods of solution which can be applied to this problem are then summarized. Various aspects of the problem will be considered with greater detail in the form of three examples.

20.2   Characteristics of Process Computer Control Problems

The complexity of the present-day automation in a process plant can be characterized by the large number of recording controllers interconnected by the flow diagram on the centralized control panel board in a process control room. On the control board, the process is divided into several interconnected unit operations, such as reactor, heat exchanger, etc. Associated with each unit operation, there are a number of measured variables, such as temperatures, pressures, and flows. Some of these variables are also controlled by individual controllers and can be controlled within a certain range by adjusting the controller set points on the control panel. Although the number of variables being controlled this way is relatively large, there are still process disturbances which cannot be controlled, such as ambient temperature, variation of feed quality, and aging of catalyst. The optimum way to operate the process is generally a function of these disturbances. It is the operator's job to sense these disturbances, estimate the new optimum operating conditions, and readjust the set points of the controllers accordingly. This describes the function of the present-day controllers in a process plant and their relation to the operator.

The characteristics of modern controllers, such as the three-mode type, are such that each can control only a single variable and is therefore functionally independent of the controllers being used in other parts of the process (except in the case of simple cascade controllers). Furthermore, they are mainly regulators, in that their function is to maintain the process variable at a preset value. Although three-mode type controllers include differentiators and integrators similar to analog-computer elements, they are relatively simple and are not considered as computers in our discussion. The computer control problem to be examined here has a somewhat different scope than the conventional process control problem. Its scope can be best defined by the following discussion of the characteristics of the problem which it must handle.

A   Optimization. The fundamental objective of a process operation is to make a profit. The optimum operating condition is defined as a particular combination of process variables which causes the process to yield maximum profit.   Because of the uncontrolled disturbances, the optimum operating condition may change from time to time.   The conventional regulating control philosophy is based on the assumption that either the optimum operating condition does not change much or the effect on profit resulting from the change of the optimum is small.   However, this assumption is not always valid.   It is true that percentagewise this effect on profit may not be very large; but because of the large throughput or high product value of a process, a relatively small percentage difference can still mean an appreciable loss if the process is not kept at an optimum operating condition all the time.

Unlike conventional feedback control problems where the desired value for the controlled variable is given, the process computer control problem generally is concerned first with locating the desired values which correspond to the optimum operating conditions.   Once the desired values are determined, the primary control variables of the process will be adjusted to move the controlled variables to the optimum point.   This optimizing procedure has to be repeated often enough to compensate for all the effects of the disturbances to the process so that the process is always at the optimum operating condition and, therefore, the maximum profit is obtained.

B   *Multivariable System*.   The basic control philosophy in applying a process control computer is to control the process as a whole.   Since the performance of a process is generally dependent on a number of important process variables which are not independent of each other, the control problem falls into the category of multivariable systems. The multivariable problem distinguishes itself from the single-loop control problem by the fact that each output variable is a function of all the input variables, and a change in any input variable causes changes in all the output variables.   Because of this interaction between variables, the problem cannot be simplified to the form of single variable control loops.   The need for a process operator to examine several recorders simultaneously, make decisions based on the particular combination of the readings, and then adjust the set points of a number of controllers, illustrates the multivariable control problem.   Due to the operator's inability to grasp the combined effects of simultaneous adjustment of all the controllers, these adjustments are usually done in a serial manner. The operator adjusts one controller at a time and waits until all the effects have settled down before he starts to adjust the next variable based on the new set of readings.   Such a procedure is not only time-consuming and therefore inefficient, but also can lead to an unstable condition in the sense that the operator may have to re-adjust the first variable as a result of the adjustment of the second variable, and vice versa.   One of the control problems the process computer must solve is how to handle this multivariable operation in a logical and optimal manner.

C   Constraints on Process Variables.   Constraints are defined here as the upper or lower limits set for each process variable under normal operating conditions.   There are two basic types of constraints to be considered.   One kind is the constraint due to physical or equipment limitations and the other is that due to product specifications.   For example, the maximum wall temperature of a furnace is a physical constraint and the minimum octane number of gasoline is a product specification constraint.   During normal operation, a basic requirement of the process control system is that neither type of constraint be violated.

As we discussed before, one characteristic of the process computer control problem is that a large number of process variables have to be measured, correlated, and manipulated simultaneously as a single unit. An important type of process variable which must be taken into consideration is that which is constrained within the operating range.   Since a prominent objective in any design study is to distribute the load evenly among all elements in the system, and not to overtax one element or overdesign another, it can be expected that the constraints on most process variables are not very far from the normal operating point.   Therefore, in many cases, the optimizing control of a process becomes a problem of determining the right combination of constraints to be met simultaneously, and to determine the new optimum combination wherever it is shifted by the disturbances affecting the process.

D   Estimation of Process Variables.   One of the basic requirements of a good feedback control system is accurate measurement.   The measurement problem encountered in process control has been a continuing challenge to the instrument industry for a long time.   To date, there are still serious limitations on the scope of process control due to lack or inadequacy of measurements.

Although measurement is the most direct method for determining the state of a variable, it is not the only one.   One alternative is the model method.   A model can be built to approximate the operation of a real process.   Instead of having to measure a variable directly from the process, it is possible to estimate its value from the model.   There are various ways an approximate model of a process can be constructed.   A model may be a scaled-down pilot plant of the process, a direct analog using a different physical system to simulate that of the actual process, or a set of mathematical relationships describing the process.   The use of a mathematical model for estimating some process variables can, in many cases, supplement direct measurements for process control purposes.

As an example, one of the limitations on the throughput rate of a distillation column is the maximum vapor velocity at certain trays in the column.   If this maximum vapor velocity is exceeded, flooding will occur and the separation efficiency of the column will become very low. Therefore, in the case where the throughput can be considered as a good optimization criterion, the amount of material passing through the column should be kept at a maximum subject to the constraint on maximum vapor velocity.   However, the instantaneous vapor velocity in a distillation column is a quantity very difficult, if not impossible, to measure.   One way to solve this problem is to build a mathematical model of the distillation column and use it in the computer control scheme.   First, this model will be made to fit the boundary conditions of the process operation wherever they can be measured: e.g., feed and draw-off temperature, composition, etc.   Next, the model can be used to estimate continuously the vapor velocity at certain critical trays inside the column.   It is then possible to use this information to decide how the process should be controlled to keep its throughput at maximum without causing the column to flood.

Other process variables which sometimes require estimation are feed and product compositions.   Although important advances have been made in the development of stream analyzers in recent years, composition analysis remains the most difficult class of measurement.   If, however, a good correlation can be found between composition and some other secondary variables, it can be used to estimate the composition by measuring the secondary variables.   It should be noted that since the estimation scheme of this type is used to supplement measurements, its effect on the accuracy of the control system is just as important.   The estimation step is by definition an "open-loop" operation in the sense that it lacks the ability to verify.   The over-all accuracy of the control system is directly affected by the accuracy of the estimation scheme. Therefore, it is important to have an accurate mathematical model for the purpose of estimation.

E   Disturbances.   The need for any feedback control system arises mainly because there are unpredictable and uncontrollable disturbances affecting the operation of the process.   Therefore, the characteristics of the disturbance have a very important effect on the nature of the computer control problem.

If we qualitatively characterize the disturbance by the frequency and amplitude of its time function, some general comments can be made regarding its effect on the formulation of the control problem.   For slow disturbances, such as a slow aging process of catalyst in a reactor, which may last for months, the control problem is not much different from the process design problem.   Process data can be collected manually and analyzed on an OFF-line basis for the purpose of determining an optimum operating condition.   The set points of the controllers can then be readjusted wherever the effect of the change in the catalyst activity becomes significant.   Since this will have to be done only at infrequent intervals because of the slow rate of catalyst aging, the process will be in a steady-state condition most of the time.   Therefore, an optimizing control scheme based on a steady-state model of the process would probably be sufficient for realizing most of the benefits of improved control.

For cases where disturbances occur frequently, manual collection of data and OFF-line analysis may not be sufficient. For example, if the hourly variation of the feed composition becomes an appreciable disturbance to a process, then a scheme of using an OFF-line approach—which may take a large portion of an hour to collect, transmit, and analyze one set of data—will not be adequate. In this case, an automatic data-collection system with an ON-line control computer may be necessary to reduce the amount of time required for data handling. In other words, the sampling rate of the control system, which is inversely proportional to the time required to collect and process each set of data, has to be compatible with the highest-frequency component in the disturbance whose effect is to be compensated by the control system.

When the effect of frequent disturbances becomes significant, another problem which must be considered is the relationship between the average time period of the disturbances and the time constant of the process. In the case where the disturbance period is much greater than the process time constants, the effect of adjusting the controllers will settle down long before another readjustment is necessary. Therefore, the process is in a steady-state condition most of the time, and a steady-state model can be used for optimization. However, in cases where the disturbance period is comparable with the time constants of the system, the process will no longer be in a steady state most of the time, and an optimization scheme based on the dynamic model will be required.

20.3   Methods of Solution

Based on the above discussion of the characteristics of the process computer control problem, a typical process control system can be described by a functional block diagram as shown in Fig. 20.1. The three basic functions required of the computer control system are estimation, optimization, and control. Estimation represents the ability to estimate from a mathematical model some dependent variables which cannot be directly measured from the process. Optimization means the ability to determine an optimum operating condition from knowledge of the process status and economic objective. The control function is the ability to manipulate the control variables of the process in such a way that the optimum operating condition is achieved and maintained at all times. In order that the computer can perform these three functions, the computer has to be instructed as to (1) how the process works (process characterization), (2) how to optimize (optimization), (3) how to feed back the control signals (control).

A   Process Characterization.   One common basis needed so that the computer will know how to estimate, to optimize, and to control is a mathematical model which characterizes the process. The model is a set of mathematical functions relating the important dependent variables to the independent variables of the process. A model can be used to describe the steady-state relationships between the process variables (static model) or these relationships as a function of time (dynamic model). It can be built merely based on operating data of the over-all process (experimental method), or it can be established mainly from a fundamental understanding of the different parts of a process and their interconnection (analytical method).

1 ANALYTICAL METHODS. The techniques required to analyze rigorously the unit operations in various processes probably encompass the whole fields of physics, chemistry, and mathematics. A dynamic

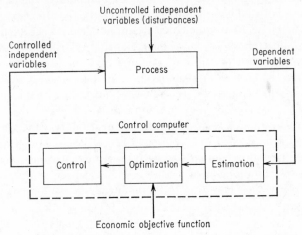

Fig. 20.1   Functional block diagram of a process computer control system.

analysis of even a simple process will become an impossible task if the exact description of the process is to be derived. The first important job for the system analyst is to choose the right set of assumptions to simplify the analysis. After the various parts of the process are described analytically based on these assumptions, the next step is to interconnect these parts and obtain a consolidated description of the whole process. During this step, various simplifications have to be applied in order to be able to handle such difficulties as nonlinearity and partial differential equations.

One of the major advantages of the analytical approach to process analysis over experimental methods is the opportunity for generalization. If a process is treated as an assembly of a number of basic functional elements, a strong resemblance can be found between processes due to the similarity between their functional elements although they may be arranged differently or used to produce different products.

However, a model developed by analytical methods generally has to be verified by experimental data. Some of the basic unit operations of interest for dynamic analysis of process plants are fluid flow, thermal processes, mass transfer, and chemical process dynamics. Discussions of the dynamic analysis of various unit functions have been published in numerous articles and will not be treated here.[2] However, some of the techniques of simplification will be discussed since they have a determining effect on the practicality of the analytical approaches when they are to be applied to a complete process where a large number of unit operations are interconnected.

The dynamic analysis of a steam generating plant will be used as an example of applying analytical methods to build a mathematical model of a complex plant from the knowledge of its unit operations.

2 EXPERIMENTAL METHODS. Sometimes the analytical approach to the analysis of a process plant becomes impractical. This could be either because some of the basic relationships between process variables are unknown or because the computational problem becomes prohibitive as a result of the complexity of the system. In this case, the experimental approach may be the only practical way to obtain a mathematical model of the process.

Various experimental methods have been developed to determine the dynamic characteristics of a system. Most of these methods require that the system be excited by known inputs. By correlating the output responses with the known inputs, the system dynamic characteristics can be determined. The excitation used for this type of dynamic test can be sinusoidal, step, impulse, or ramp function. The correlated results could be in the form of either frequency or transient response curves. These methods can be extended to investigate the system dynamics of a complex multivariable system such as a process plant. Generally the independent variables of the system can be excited one at a time, and the individual elements of the system transfer function matrix can thus be determined. In practice, however, there are difficulties in applying these types of experimental methods for process characterization. Large excitation of inputs is not usually permitted on a process under normal operation, and excitations with insufficient amplitude are generally indistinguishable from measurement noise or other disturbances. Methods have also been developed to obtain the dynamic model of a process without introducing arbitrary input excitations. These are the statistical methods using auto- and cross-correlation functions. These methods provide a means for developing a dynamic model of a process from its normal operating data.[3]

The techniques discussed above, such as frequency and transient analysis and statistical correlation methods, are generally limited to analysis of linear systems. When the nonlinearities existing in the process characteristics become significant, the problem becomes more difficult. A general experimental method for obtaining a nonlinear dynamic model of a multivariable system is not available. An alternative is to approximate the system characteristics with piecewise linear models and then apply linear techniques. Piecewise linearization consists of dividing the process operating range into several regions and approximating each region with a different linear dynamic model. A gross steady-state model of the process can then be used to relate the average steady-state conditions of different regions.

A steady-state model of the process is also required for the purpose of process optimization. Various statistical techniques have been developed to determine the steady-state model of a process from experimental data.[4] In general, before the collection of process data, systematic experimental procedures should be carefully designed. The independent variables of the process can be changed sequentially or as a group. The one-at-a-time methods or the steepest ascent approach can be used in connection with the sequential method, whereas the factorial methods can be used if the inputs are changed as a group. After the experiments are conducted and data collected, various techniques can be used for data analysis. The most commonly applied is the method of least squares.[5] This is the method of fitting the test data with a mathematical model such that the sum of the squares of the errors at all test points is minimized by properly adjusting the parameters in the model. If the parameters appear only in linear form in the model, it is referred to as a linear statistical model. The linear regression method, which belongs to the class of linear statistical methods, is the most commonly used technique for steady-state process model development.

B   Economic Objective Function.   So far we have discussed the methods for process characterization from the physical point of view. Since, as it was mentioned before, the basic objective of a process operation is to make a profit, the other important aspect of the process characterization problem is in the process economics. The economic objective function of a process operation can generally be expressed as the difference between the value and the cost of the process operation. The value of the operation is a function of the quantity and unit prices of the output products. The cost of the operation involves such items as raw material, energy input and labor. Problems encountered in evaluating the value or cost of all factors in a process operation can become very complex. To determine the value of a product from a process which is only an element of a large production complex may require complete analysis of its economic interaction with all the other processes in that complex. Other factors which may complicate the economic analysis are nonlinearities and discontinuities in the value and cost functions. However, incremental techniques can generally be applied to simplify the economic objective function to linear forms.   Just as in constructing a physical model of the process, intelligent assumptions must be made to simplify the economic model.   Sensitivity tests should be made to determine the effects of incremental changes in the various factors of the objective function. The less significant ones can be omitted in order to minimize the computational requirement.

C   Optimization.   Once a process is characterized by a mathematical model and an economic objective function is specified, it is then possible to determine the optimum operating condition.   In general, the objective function is expressed in terms of both independent and dependent variables of the process.   For control purposes the optimum operating condition has to be determined only in terms of controlled independent variables.   Therefore, the objective function has to be solved in connection with the model of the process so that an objective function in terms of only the independent variables can be obtained.

It should be noted that the independent variables can be either controlled or uncontrolled.   The various disturbances to the process are the uncontrolled independent variables which have a direct effect on the behavior of the process response and, therefore, the process economics. Consequently, the optimum set of operating conditions has to be determined at least as frequently as the disturbances occur.   This is the main reason why the optimization function has to be considered as an important part of the real-time control problem.   Because of this optimization requirement, the effects of the disturbances on the responses and constraints have to be known.   They must be either measured directly or estimated from the mathematical model of the process.

In general, there are two types of optimization problems encountered in process control, constrained and unconstrained. Unconstrained optimization deals with the process whose response surface is nonlinear with an extremum inside the permissible operating region.   Constrained optimization deals with processes where the response surface does not reach its extremum within the operating region.   The permissible operating region is generally bounded by constraints either on the dependent or the controlled independent variables.   The optimization problem in this case is to determine the intersection of the constraints at which the objective function is a maximum.

1   UNCONSTRAINED OPTIMIZATION.   The classical method of finding the optimum of a differentiable function by finding the point at which the first derivatives of the function are zero is the most useful technique for the unconstrained case.   When the objective function is not available in analytic form, a numerical gradient method may be used.[6]   Here the first derivatives are approximated at some base point by evaluating the function at small increments Δx_i away from the base point with respect to each independent variable and calculating $\partial y / \partial x_i = b_i$ for each inde-

pendent variable. A new base point is then found by changing each independent variable an amount proportional to its corresponding b_i. As a local optimum is approached, all the b_i's will approach zero. The magnitude of the Δx's may then be reduced and the process repeated until the optimum is located with sufficient accuracy.

2 CONSTRAINED OPTIMIZATION. The addition of constraints to the problem of optimizing an objective function usually adds considerable complexity. Optimization problems involving constraints were first studied under the subject title of linear programming. This technique was developed to treat problems where both the response and the constraint functions are linear.

Process responses are generally nonlinear, but in some cases where the permissible operating regions are tightly bounded by constraints, the response surface of interest will be only a small area and may be approximated by a linear surface without introducing serious error.

If a single linear model cannot approximate the entire operating region accurately enough, piecewise linearization may be employed. Linear programming with artificial constraints or a gradient method can be used to climb along the response surface until a constraint is encountered. The response surface can then be linearized and linear programming applied locally. This procedure can be repeated until the true maximum is reached.

As was mentioned above, the normal operation of a process generally is limited by a large number of constraints. Therefore, the methods of constrained optimization, such as linear programming, are important tools for optimization in process control systems using digital computers.

The simplex method of Dantzig is a well-known general method of solving linear-programming problems.[7] It follows from the linearity of the objective function and the constraints that the optimum value will be attained at a vertex of the feasible region defined by the linear constraints. It is, therefore, at worst only necessary to evaluate the objective function at all the vertices of the constraint region to identify the optimum. The simplex method not only makes use of this fact, but also by further restricting the search considerably simplifies the computational procedure. Starting from any vertex of the feasible region, it is an algorithm for selecting an adjoining vertex with an improved value of the objective function. There will always be such an improved vertex unless the optimum has already been reached. The simplex method thus proceeds in a stepwise manner, always improving the value of the objective function with each iteration until the optimum is achieved, without the necessity of evaluating the objective at all possible vertices.

D Control. So far we have discussed the problems in determining the present process status (characterization) and the desired process conditions (optimization). The next question is how should the process be manipulated from the present to the optimal condition. The scheme for determining how the independent variables of the process should be manipulated so that the process will be moved to and maintained at its optimum is defined here as the control function.

The type of control scheme required is largely a function of the characteristics of both the process and the disturbance. For instance, if all the disturbances to a process are well defined and measurable, the optimal conditions can be determined a priori and tabulated against the values of the disturbances. Therefore, the control scheme is, at least in principle, merely to set the manipulated variables based on the measurement of the disturbances according to this tabulation. This is the open-loop type of control.

In the case where not all the major disturbances are well defined and measurable, feedback control has to be applied. Feedback control consists of measuring the output of the process, comparing it with the desired value and applying the difference as a signal to manipulate the process in such a way that the difference between the measured and desired values tends to vanish. The inherent ability of a feedback control scheme to monitor the output eliminates the need for exact knowledge of all the disturbances. The effect on the process output due to any disturbances which have not been taken into account in the model must be compensated for by feedback type of control.

Another factor which has an important effect on the type of control scheme required is the frequency of disturbance. In the case where disturbance is infrequent, the process will stay at a steady-state condition most of the time. Since the need for adjusting the control variables is infrequent, the total amount of time it takes for the process to move from one state to the other may be insignificant compared to the total time the process is in a steady state. Therefore, the need for knowing exactly the dynamic characteristics of the control scheme is not very critical in this case. The scheme could be simply to set the control variables according to the result of the optimization procedure, i.e., the magnitude of the control variables which produce the optimum steady-state process condition based on the present status of the process. The approach is defined here as steady-state optimization. In other words, the control function has a gain of one for all control variables. In some cases, the gain could even be made less than one if the disturbance frequency is very low and an extra safety factory is required to ensure stability of the process operation. As in all feedback systems, stability increases with decreases of system gain; however, the system response time is acceptable only if it is still short compared to the average period of the disturbance.

For the processes where the disturbances are relatively frequent, some dynamic optimization procedure may become necessary in the control function.   Dynamic optimization is defined as a method by which the dynamic response of a feedback system is optimized according to some predetermined criterion.   When the disturbance becomes frequent compared to the time constant of the process, just to know the optimum steady-state operating condition is not sufficient.   We also have to consider the question of how to change the control variables in such a way dynamically that the process will be brought to the optimum condition as fast as possible.   Since there is a loss of profit all the time that the process is away from the optimum, dynamic optimization becomes valuable if disturbances frequently either move the process away from an optimum or cause the optimum to move to a new position.

The disturbance can be characterized by a quantized time function of the form shown in Fig. 20.2a, where the time periods between significant disturbances are T_1, T_2, ...   We can define the mean free time between disturbances as T which is the average of all the time periods. This quantity represents the frequency characteristic of the disturbance. In the meantime, we can qualitatively represent the bandwidth of the process by a typical time constant t, as shown in Fig. 20.2b.   Thus t may be defined as the longest time constant existing in the process.   In other words, if we excite all the independent variables of the process simultaneously, with a step function input, t would be the amount of time required for the last dependent variable to settle down.   The ratio T/t can be used as a criterion to determine the amount of sophistication required in the design of the control scheme for a specific process with known disturbance characteristics.   A qualitative relationship between the effectiveness of the control system and this ratio T/t is shown in Fig. 20.2c for the control schemes with steady-state or dynamic optimization.

For very large T/t, the advantage of any sophistication in the control program diminishes, and the two curves merge into one.   This is because the transient period is altogether negligible compared with the period between disturbances.   When T/t becomes small and close to unity, the difference between the dynamic and steady-state optimization procedures again diminishes.   In this case, the frequency of the disturbance becomes greater than the bandwidth of the process, and therefore the effect of the disturbance diminishes because of the filtering effect of the process.

When the ratio T/t is in the middle range, a dynamic optimization scheme may show significant advantage over the steady-state optimization approach; in other words, the transient response characteristics of the control system become important.

All the conventional servomechanisms and feedback system design concepts and techniques become useful for process control system design problems where dynamic optimization becomes necessary.   The basic concepts of stability and control system error as functions of the loop gain of the system will still be of main interest.   The fact that a process control problem almost always involves a multivariable system does somewhat distinguish itself from the convention servomechanism design. However, similar problems have been treated in connection with turbo-jet engine control.[8] The requirement of a balanced combination of optimization and control functions in a process control problem is another distinguishable characteristic.   A similar problem was first analyzed as

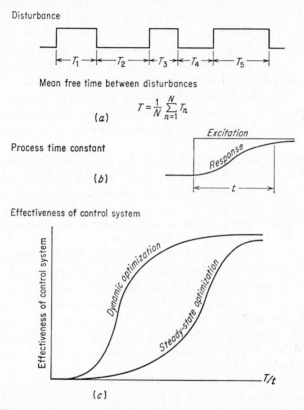

Disturbance

Mean free time between disturbances

$$T = \frac{1}{N} \sum_{n=1}^{N} T_n$$

(a)

Process time constant

Excitation

Response

(b)

Effectiveness of control system

Effectiveness of control system

Dynamic optimization

Steady-state optimization

T/t

(c)

Fig. 20.2   Effectiveness of control system as function of the characteristics of disturbance and process.

an optimizing control system for internal combustion engines.[9]   These examples are techniques which are effective in dealing with various portions of a process control problem.   They are problems suitable for applying analog-computer type of equipment as the control element.

When all the aspects of a process control problem—namely, estimation, optimization, and control—are considered as a whole, then the digital computer becomes more attractive because of its advantage in the relative ease of problem expansion and alteration.   In this case, we will no longer deal with continuous time functions in the control system, but rather with discrete information on a sampled basis. The sampled-data control concepts and techniques have been developed and used effectively for the analysis of control systems involving digital computers.[10]

20.4   Examples of Computer Control Problems in Process Control

The three examples given here illustrate the various aspects of the process control problem under discussion. The first example deals mainly with the steady-state optimization problem involving constraints. The problems of linearization and identification will be discussed in detail. The second example illustrates the control problem with consideration of the constraints on a dynamic basis. The third example shows an optimal sampled-data system for process control.

All three examples begin with building a model of the process. The second example is used especially to illustrate the problems in constructing a dynamic model of a process consisting of a number of unit operations.

A   Example 1: Steady-state Optimization of a Catalytic Cracking Unit.[11] Catalytic cracking of crude-oil fractions is an important operation in every large-scale modern petroleum refinery. In several respects it can be considered typical of the many processes of extensive commercial significance which are suitable candidates for computer control; there are a relatively large number of important process variables (several of which cannot be measured) which interact in a highly complex manner; there are numerous constraints which must be observed; and the nature of the disturbance is such that the optimum operating point varies appreciably. Consequently, a detailed examination of the problem of optimizing the operation of a catalytic cracking unit should prove instructive in revealing the type and magnitude of the difficulties to be encountered in a typical process, and provides an opportunity to apply various methods to their solution.

1   PROCESS DESCRIPTION.   Catalytic cracking is a continuous process for converting high-boiling, high-molecular-weight components of distilled crude oil into lower-boiling, lower-molecular-weight materials such as gasoline. This processing adds economic value to the oil. A catalyst is used to effect the reaction, and in fluid catalytic cracking, the catalyst is in a fine powder form and behaves like a liquid in its flow properties.

The diagram of the process is shown in Fig. 20.3 with the various symbols explained in Table 20.1. Three different streams of recycle oil from a fractionator downstream are fed into the reactor section, along with two streams from storage tanks. The incoming oil is vaporized upon contact with the hot fluidized catalyst, and the reaction (an endothermic one) takes place in the gas phase. The product vapors pass overhead to the fractionator. And the catalyst, which has a layer of coke deposited on it as a result of the reaction, passes continuously into the regenerator section. Here the coke is burned off the catalyst surface by a stream of air blowing through it. This reaction is exothermic, and the hot regenerated catalyst flows back into the reactor section and provides the necessary heat for the cracking reaction.

The problem is to select the set of conditions which will result in optimal steady-state operation of the process.

2 MATHEMATICAL MODEL. (a) The first step in approaching the problem is to construct a mathematical model of the process by considering the fundamental chemical and physical phenomena which govern it.

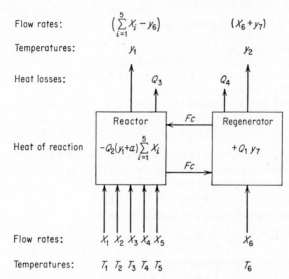

Flow rates: $\left(\sum_{i=1}^{5} X_i - y_6 \right)$ $(X_6 + y_7)$

Temperatures: y_1 y_2

Heat losses: Q_3 Q_4

Reactor F_c Regenerator

Heat of reaction $-Q_2(y_1 + a)\sum_{i=1}^{5} X_i$ $+Q_1 y_7$

F_c

Flow rates: $X_1\ X_2\ X_3\ X_4\ X_5$ X_6

Temperatures: $T_1\ T_2\ T_3\ T_4\ T_5$ T_6

Fig. 20.3 Block diagram of a catalytic cracking unit.

There are six independent variables, x_1–x_6, which can be varied at will; plus seven dependent variables, y_1–y_7 (of which only y_1, y_2, and y_4 are measurable); therefore, seven equations are needed for the model. These are shown in Table 20.2.

Equations (20.1) to (20.3) are dynamic equations; at steady-state conditions, the left sides (accumulation terms) are equal to zero. The heat-balance equations (20.1) and (20.2) may be derived readily by inspection of Fig. 20.3. The rate of coke accumulation [Eq. (20.3)] is obviously equal to the difference between the rates of formation and consumption of coke. Equation (20.4) may be derived from a knowledge of the regenerator effluent gas composition, the coke composition, and the stoichiometry of the reactions.

In order to derive the yield equations (20.5) to (20.7), a semiempirical approach obtained from the literature was used.

Table 20.1 Symbols Used in Diagram of a Catalytic Cracking Unit

x_1
x_2 flow rate of incoming recycle stream in units of weight/unit time
x_3

x_4 flow rate of incoming streams from storage
x_5

x_6 flow rate of air into regenerator

F_c flow rate of catalyst between reactor and regenerator

T_i temperature of the ith ingoing stream

Q_1 exothermic heat of combustion of coke, heat/weight of coke

Q_2 endothermic heat of reaction, heat/weight, degrees

Q_3
Q_4 heat losses to surroundings

Q_5 net heat from regenerator to reactor

y_1 reactor temperature

y_2 regenerator temperature

y_3 yield of reactor by-product, weight/unit time

y_4 volume fraction of oxygen in regenerator effluent gas

y_5 yield of desired product from reactor

y_6 rate of formation of coke in reactor

y_7 rate of burning of coke in regenerator

q_i average specific heat over the given temperature range of the ith incoming stream; $i = 1$–6

h_j average specific heat of the jth outgoing stream; $j = 1, 2$

m_1 constants representing amount and specific heat of material in the reactor
m_2 and regenerator respectively

H weight fraction of hydrogen in the coke

M_H molecular weights of hydrogen and carbon
M_c

k mole ratio of carbon dioxide to carbon monoxide in the regenerator effluent gas

ρ_i density of ith incoming stream

a
b various constants which include air density and composition factors, and
c miscellaneous empirical constants

K'
K_1
K_2
K_3 constants which must be evaluated empirically for each different oil stock
m
n_i
A

W_c weight of catalyst in the reactor

h F_c/W_c

C_D weight per cent coke deposited on catalyst

P weight per cent of catalyst in reactor for up to θ time units

ΔP weight per cent of catalyst in reactor for time period θ to $\theta + \Delta\theta$

Table 20.2 Equations Describing System of Fig. 20.3

Reactor heat-balance equation

$$m_1\dot{y}_1 = \sum_{i=1}^{5} q_i T_i x_i - \left(\sum_{i=1}^{5} x_i - y_6 \right) y_1 h_1 - Q_2(y_1 + a) \sum_{i=1}^{5} x_i + Q_5 - Q_3 \quad (20.1)$$

Over-all heat-balance equation

$$\dot{Q} = m_1\dot{y}_1 + m_2\dot{y}_2 = \sum_{i=1}^{6} q_i T_i x_i - \left[\left(\sum_{i=1}^{5} x_i - y_6 \right) y_1 h_1 + (x_6 + y_7) y_2 h_2 \right]$$

$$+ Q_1 y_7 - Q_2(y_1 + a) \sum_{i=1}^{5} x_i - (Q_3 + Q_4) \quad (20.2)$$

Over-all coke-balance equation

$$\dot{C} = y_6 - y_7 \quad (20.3)$$

Steady-state coke-burning equation

$$y_7 = \frac{(b - cy_4)x_6}{(cy_4 + 1)\dfrac{H}{M_H} + \dfrac{(1 - H)}{M_c}\dfrac{(2k + cy_4 + 1)}{k + 1}} \quad (20.4)$$

Rate of formation of coke

$$y_6 = \frac{K'F_c}{\displaystyle\sum_{i=1}^{5} x_i} \left(e^{-A/y_1} \right) \sum_{i=1}^{5} \left[\frac{\Gamma(n_i + 1)}{h(n_i + 1)} x_i \right] \quad (20.5)$$

Product-yield equation

$$y_5 = K_1 \sum_{i=1}^{5} \frac{(x_i)}{\rho_i} \frac{(y_6)^m}{\left(\displaystyle\sum_{i=1}^{5} x_i \right)^m} \quad (20.6)$$

By-product-yield equation

$$y_3 = K_2 y_5(y_1 + K_3) \quad (20.7)$$

Crawford and Cunningham[12] provide the equations

$$C_D = K e^{-A/y_1} \sum_{P=0}^{100} \Delta P \theta^n$$

$$P = 100(1 - e^{-h\theta})$$

where n depends on the feed characteristics and is usually in the range 0.38 to 0.53. Therefore, for five different feed streams, the first equation may be rewritten as follows:

$$C_D = K e^{-A/y_1} \sum_{i=1}^{5} \left[\frac{x_i}{\displaystyle\sum_{i=1}^{5} x_i} \left(\sum_{P=0}^{100} \Delta P \theta^{n_i} \right) \right]$$

Upon substituting for ΔP and changing the summation sign to an integral, we obtain

$$C_D = \frac{K_e^{-A/y_i}}{\sum\limits_{i=1}^{5} x_i} \cdot \sum_{i=1}^{5}\left(x_i \int_0^{\infty} 100 \, he^{-h\theta}\theta^{n_i} \, d\theta\right)$$

which is integrated and multiplied by W_c to give Eq. (20.5).

Inserting this result into Voorhies' equations leads to (20.6) as the equation for yield of product.[13] Finally, since the by-product yield is proportional to the product yield, it may be approximated by Eq. (20.7).[14]

(b) Constraints.   In addition to the relations in Table 20.2, a complete mathematical description of the problem must include the restrictions on the range of many of the variables.   For example, limitations on the size and capacity of pipes, pumps, etc., impose constraints on the independent variables; these can be represented as follows

$$
\begin{aligned}
0 &\leqslant x_1 \leqslant U_1 \\
0 &\leqslant x_2 \leqslant U_2 \\
x_1 + x_2 + x_3 &\leqslant U_3 \\
L_4 &\leqslant x_4 \leqslant U_4 \\
x_4 + x_5 &= U_5 \\
L_6 &\leqslant x_6 \leqslant U_6
\end{aligned}
\tag{20.8}
$$

In addition, there are constraints on several of the dependent variables. The oxygen level in the regenerator, for example, must be maintained within rather narrow limits to avoid undesirable effects.   Also, temperatures must be kept below the point where damage might occur.   Similarly, by-product yield must be compatible with the capacity of other processing units downstream.

$$
\begin{aligned}
L_7 &\leqslant y_1 \leqslant U_7 \\
L_8 &\leqslant y_2 \leqslant U_8 \\
L_9 &\leqslant y_3 \leqslant U_9 \\
L_{10} &\leqslant y_4 \leqslant U_{10}
\end{aligned}
\tag{20.9}
$$

(c) Objective Function.   In any optimization problem, a management decision must be made as to precisely what criterion is to be used to define the optimum.   In this case it was decided to strive for maximum product yield y_5.   That is, Eq. (20.6) itself is the objective function and is to be maximized.

(d) Disturbances.   The only justification for on-line computer control of a process is the occurrence of disturbances.   Furthermore, the disturbances must be of such a nature that when they occur, a different set of conditions is needed for optimal performance.   The principal disturbance which affects the operation of this process is the fluctuation of feed properties.   This results from the unavoidable necessity of processing several different crude-oil stocks during a relatively brief period.   As was mentioned in Table 20.1, several of the parameters in the model depend on the properties of the particular crude oil being processed at that time, and must be determined empirically for each of the different types of petroleum usually processed in this unit. If the process is operating at optimum and a disturbance occurs, the correct set of parameters corresponding to the new crude-oil composition must be inserted into the model equations and the new optimum must be found in the manner described below.

3   METHOD OF OPTIMIZATION.   (a) Linear Programming Approach. (1) *Development of a completely linear model.*   Examination of the mathematical model, with the explicit constraints on dependent and independent variables and with a rather straightforward objective function, immediately suggests the method of linear programming.[7]   Indeed, if the model or its approximation is sufficiently linear; i.e., if the constraints and the objective function can be approximated by linear functions of the independent variables, then linear programming can be used directly to solve for the optimum values of the independent variables.

This approach was applied to the problem at hand in the following manner: a computational technique was devised to solve the set of seven simultaneously steady-state equations   [(20.1) to (20.7)] in an iterative manner for the seven dependent variables, given the independent variables.   (Direct analytical solution was found to be exceedingly difficult, if not impossible.)   Using this scheme, the dependent variables were evaluated at many selected points throughout the entire permissible operating region.   Then linear equations were fitted by regression to this accumulated data.

$$y_i = \sum_{k=1}^{6} b_{ik}x_k \qquad i = 1, 2, 3, 4, 5, 6$$

In other words, the "true" nonlinear steady-state model can be used to generate points which are then fitted by linear equations.   If this linear steady-state model approximates the nonlinear model within the accuracy requirements, a large saving in computation time may be realized. If the model is not sufficiently accurate, another method, such as the one discussed below, must be used.   Nevertheless, the linear model may still prove useful in examining the effect of disturbances on the location of the optima, indicating which of the constraints limit the process.

(2) *Local linearization of the nonlinear model.*   Returning to the original model, it is obvious that linear programming cannot be applied directly. However, it is still possible to obtain the advantage that linear programming provides in its handling of constraints.   The steady-state model can be linearized in a small region about the current operating point, and instead of using the real constraints which bound the permissible operating region, artificial constraints can be defined to form the bound-

aries of the small region wherein the linearization is valid. Linear programming can then be applied to find the optimal point in this subregion. Now the model may be relinearized about the new point, a new region can be bounded by a new set of temporary constraints, and the linear program again performed. This procedure may be repeated until real constraints are encountered or no further significant moves are called for by the program.

One way to begin the requisite linearization is to take the partial derivatives of each of the six dependent variables ($y_7 = y_6$ at the steady state) with respect to each of the six independent variables, a total of 36 partial derivatives. Ideally, this would be done by solving the equations for the dependent variables in terms of the independent variables so as to obtain a set of relations of the form

$$y_i = f_i(x_1, x_2, x_3, x_4, x_5, x_6) \qquad i = 1\text{--}6 \qquad (20.10)$$

followed by differentiation in a straightforward manner. However, as was mentioned above, such an attempted solution proved hopelessly complex. Instead, the steady-state equations were differentiated implicitly.

$$f(x_1, x_2, x_3, x_4, x_5, x_6; y_1, y_2, y_3, y_4, y_5, y_6) = 0 \qquad (20.11)$$

$$\frac{\partial f_i}{\partial x_j} + \sum_{k=1}^{6} \frac{\partial f_i}{\partial y_k} \frac{\partial y_k}{\partial x_j} = 0 \qquad \begin{array}{c} i = 1\text{--}6 \\ j = 1\text{--}6 \end{array} \qquad (20.12)$$

The ensuing set of relations, although large and complicated, could nevertheless be solved algebraically for the 36 partial derivatives.

$$\frac{\partial y_i}{\partial x_j} = g_{ij}(x_1, x_2, x_3, x_4, x_5, x_6; y_1, y_2, y_3, y_4, y_5, y_6) \qquad \begin{array}{c} i = 1\text{--}6 \\ j = 1\text{--}6 \end{array} \qquad (20.13)$$

Thus, by inserting the values of the independent and dependent variables at a given point into this last equation, the derivatives may be evaluated at that point.

Finally, in a small region about the chosen point, we can say that

$$\Delta y_i = \sum_{j=1}^{6} \frac{\partial y_i}{\partial x_j} \Delta x_j \qquad i = 1\text{--}6 \qquad (20.14)$$

which is a linear function expressing the change in a dependent variable as a sum of changes in the independent variables.

(b) Identification of the Operating Point. (1) *Correcting for transient condition.* The next step is to identify the current operating status of the process to use as a starting point for the optimization. This immediately presents two distinct problems. First, if the process is in a transient condition, not at a steady state, this must be recognized and treated accordingly; i.e., a steady-state starting point is necessary for sequential static optimization.   The second problem is that the mathematical model inevitably differs from the true process, and there is a question about how to handle the discrepancy.

One approach would be to measure the accumulation terms Q and C directly from the process.   Nonzero values indicate that the system is in a transient condition.   Then, by adjusting the values of the independent variables on the right-hand side of (20.2) and (20.3), the left sides may be made to equal zero.

In the present case Eqs. (20.3) and (20.5) can be combined and represented by

$$\dot{C} = y_6 - y_7 = \rho \sum_{i=1}^{5} B_i x_i - y_7 \qquad (20.15)$$

where

$$\rho = \left(K'F_c / \sum_{i=1}^{5} x_i \right) e^{-A/y_1}$$

$$B_i = \frac{\Gamma(n_i + 1)}{h^{(n_i-1)}}$$

Since C can be evaluated directly from process measurements, it follows that setting

$$x_3' = x_3 + \frac{\dot{C}}{\rho(B_2 - B_3)}$$

and

$$x_2' = x_2 - \frac{\dot{C}}{\rho(B_2 - B_3)} \qquad (20.16)$$

will lead to the balanced-coke equation

$$0 = y_6' - y_7 = \rho \sum_{i=1}^{5} B_i x_i' - y_7 \qquad (20.17)$$

The choice of which variable to adjust is based principally on convenience of algebraic manipulation.   In this case two variables are adjusted by equal amounts in opposite directions so that the summation term in ρ remains constant.

It should be stressed that these changes need not be imposed on the plant; they merely provide a computational starting point.   If x_2 and x_3 were to be physically changed in the indicated fashion, and if the model is accurate, particularly in the functional form of the x_2 and x_3 terms, the rate of making coke would instantaneously become equal to the coke-burning rate, thus placing the system in equilibrium as far as coke is concerned.

In an analogous manner, the heat imbalance can be eliminated.

$$\dot{Q} = m_1\dot{y}_1 + m_2\dot{y}_2 \equiv D + \sum_{i=1}^{6} q_i T_i x_i \qquad (20.2a)$$

$\dot{Q}$ is evaluated directly by measuring $\dot{y}_1$ and $\dot{y}_2$ from the process. Taking into consideration the hypothetical changes that have already been made to x_2' and x_3', x_4 and x_5 may be manipulated so that

$$0 = B + \sum_{i=1}^{6} q_i T_i x_i' \tag{20.18}$$

where
$$x_4' = x_4 + \frac{\dot{Q} - [\dot{C}/\rho(B_2 - B_3)](q_2 T_2 - q_3 T_3)}{q_5 T_5 - q_4 T_4}$$

and
$$x_5' = x_5 - \frac{\dot{Q} - [\dot{C}/\rho(B_2 - B_3)](q_2 T_2 - q_3 T_3)}{q_5 T_5 - q_4 T_4} \tag{20.19}$$

(x_1 and x_6 remain unchanged; $x_1' = x_1$, and $x_6' = x_6$.)

(2) *Correcting for model error.* Here the errors in the model enter the problem. If the observed y_i and the adjusted x_i' are inserted into (20.2) and (20.3), the left sides would, in general, not equal zero, despite the fact that the modified system is now in a steady state. The magnitude of the discrepancy is a measure of the inaccuracy in the model. In a manner entirely analogous to the foregoing, adjustment of x_i to x_i' may be further changed to x_i'', which is equivalent to changing the model from

$$f(x_i', y_i) = 0$$

to
$$f[(x_i' - \Delta_i), y_i] = 0$$

This treatment may be clarified considerably by referring to Fig. 20.4, which, although only a two-dimensional case, is quite adequate.

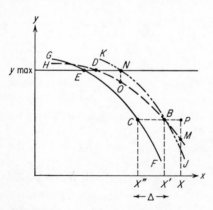

Fig. 20.4 Correction of transient condition and model error.

Let us suppose that a process is defined by the true (unknown) steady-state curve $HDBM$ and is approximated by the model $y = f(x)$, curve $GECF$. The objective is to maximize y subject to the constraint $y \leqslant y_{max}$. The true optimum is therefore at D, but according to the model it is at E. Point P, with coordinates x, y is observed on the process at a given time and x is adjusted to x' in order to obtain the corresponding steady-state point B. Because of the error in the model, B does not fall on the curve $y = f(x)$ so the latter is moved a distance Δ to position $KNBJ$. Now the stepwise optimization scheme calls for an x setting corresponding to N; but when the system reaches steady state, it is observed to be at point 0 instead.

By repeating the above procedure, i.e., adjusting $f(x)$ to pass through point 0, it can be seen that in this case the solution converges toward the true optimum D.

It should be noted that in this discussion, y was kept unchanged from its observed value. It would be possible by the exact same reasoning to adjust y and keep x unchanged, i.e., by adjusting from P to M, etc. Now, in general, the constraints on the dependent variables are more significant than constraints on the independent variables for it is often physically impossible to violate the latter. Therefore, the advantage in the original method (not changing y) is that the true distance from the constraint $y_{max} - y$ is retained and used in the calculations.

A further advantage of this treatment is that since the Δ's represent a measure of the model inaccuracy, they may be analyzed in a systematic manner and used to update the model.

(c) Optimization. At this point we are finally ready to apply linear programming to the problem, and the Simplex formulation[7] is a convenient method of doing so. The constraint equations (20.8) on the independent variables are already in the proper format for the Simplex tableau; these may be combined with the artificial constraints which limit the step size or—putting it another way—which bound the region of valid linearization. Furthermore, the objective function and the dependent variable constraints can be transformed to the necessary format in the manner illustrated:

Let one of the constraints from Eq. (20.9) be written

$$y_n^* \leqslant U_n \qquad (20.20)$$

where the asterisk denotes the value of the associated variable at the optimum steady state, and the same variable without an asterisk refers to its current value. Then

$$y_n + \Delta y_n \leqslant U_n \qquad \Delta y_n \leqslant U_n - y_n$$

Substituting for Δy from (20.13) and (20.14)

$$\sum_{j=1}^{6} g_{nj}\, \Delta x_j \leqslant U_n - y_n \qquad (20.21)$$

$$\sum_{j=1}^{6} g_{nj}(x_j^* - x_j') \leqslant U_n - y_n \qquad (20.22)$$

$$\sum_{j=1}^{6} g_{nj}x_j^* \leqslant U_n - y_n + \sum_{j=1}^{6]} g_{nj}x_j' \qquad (20.23)$$

or $$\sum_{j=1}^{6} g_{nj}x_j^* \leqslant U_n' \qquad (20.24)$$

With all the constraints and the objective functions now expressed as linear functions of the independent variables, the starting tableau can

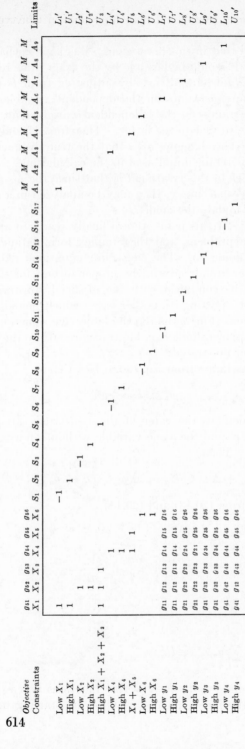

Fig. 20.5 Initial simplex tableau for optimization of catalytic cracking unit.

be prepared and is shown in Fig. 20.5. The total of 18 constraints leads to an 18×32 Simplex matrix when it is augmented with appropriate slack and artificial variables.

This linear-programming problem is solved on an ON-line digital control computer, in real time, for optimal x_i^*, from which y_i^* can be calculated as follows:

$$y_i^* = y_i + \sum_{j=1}^{6} g_{ij}(x_j^* - x_j') \qquad i = 1\text{-}6 \qquad (20.25)$$

In order to linearize about the new point (x_i^*, y_i^*), it is merely necessary to substitute these values in place of x_i' and y_i in Eqs. (20.13) and (20.23), enter the modified quantities into the Simplex matrix, and solve again. As discussed above, this repetitive procedure is continued until no further changes are called for by the program. Such a condition will occur either when an internal (unconstrained) optimum is found, or, more commonly, when several constraints (equal in number to the independent variables) are encountered simultaneously. The final x_i^* reached in this manner constitute the solution to the static optimization problem: they are the values which the control variables of the process must assume for the optimal steady state; the intermediate x_i^* calculated at each step of the iterative progression need not be imposed on the process.

4   DISCUSSION.   The mathematical model and a steady-state optimization of a catalytic cracking process has been outlined. As was discussed previously, if the mean free time between disturbances is very large compared to the process time constant, the above steady-state optimization scheme would be sufficient for optimizing control of the process. In cases where the disturbances are relatively more frequent, then some dynamic optimization scheme would be required. A different process, a steam-generating plant, will be used next as an example of dynamic model building and computing control system design.

B   *Example 2: Dynamic Analysis and a Noninteracting Control System for a Steam-generation Process.*[15]   A conventional boiler process is shown in a simplified block diagram in Fig. 20.6. The control problem to be considered here is as follows:

1. Objective—to keep the steam pressure and temperature at their maxima at all times so that the over-all plant efficiency is maximized

2. Constraint—to keep water level in the drum within a certain limited excursion

3. Disturbance—to compensate for large variations in steam demand

It is assumed, in this problem, that the optimum operating condition of the process is at a fixed constrained point, namely, maximum steam pressure and temperature. The effect of the disturbance only tends to move the process away from its optimum but does not shift the optimum point.   Therefore, optimization is not required as a continuous part of the control function.   This example will be mainly concerned with the dynamic analysis of the process and the feedback system design required to meet the objective and constraint requirements.   The control system in this example will be referred to as a noninteracting controller because of its characteristics in decoupling the pressure and the water level due to changes in steam demand.   The result is a computing controller which has superior performance compared to the conventional single-variable type of proportional plus reset type of boiler control system.

1   PROCESS DYNAMIC ANALYSIS.   The major difficulty in boiler control studies is that the mathematical description of the whole system is highly complex, containing numerous nonlinear variables and uncer-

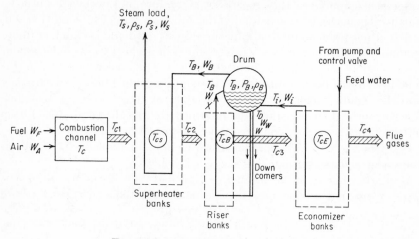

Fig. 20.6   Simplified boiler diagram.

tainties in some physical phenomena.   Simplifying assumptions must be made to facilitate problem solution, but oversimplification results in solutions that do not describe dynamic behavior properly.   Simplifying assumptions are of two types: (1) Simplification of certain physical phenomena too complex for exact mathematical description.   Examples of such phenomena are heat-transfer equations in nucleate boiling, evaporation or condensation rates in the drum, and turbulent heat transfer from hot combustion gases to the tube wall.   Some semiempirical or approximate equation is required.   (2) Simplification of equations, either exact or approximate, to eliminate nonlinearities.   Partial differentiation through difference-equation or numerical-analysis methods yields a set of linear ordinary differential equations for the dynamic behavior of the boiler.

Figures 20.7 to 20.9 show that the boiler dynamics can be analyzed in four sections: superheater, downcomer-riser loop, drum, and gas path.

With simplifying assumptions for this boiler in mind, three basic types of equations—flow, heat-transfer, and steam-state—are derived analytically or approximated empirically.   The flow and heat-transfer equations involve partial differentials and contain nonlinearities; therefore, in order to permit the use of linear technique, they must be linearized by perturbation and difference-equation techniques.

   (a) Linearizing Techniques.   Suppose an equation of the form

$$f\left(x,\ y,\ z,\ \ldots\ ,\ \frac{\delta x}{\delta t},\ \frac{\delta x}{\delta l},\ \frac{\delta y}{\delta t},\ \frac{\delta y}{\delta l},\ \cdots\right) = 0 \qquad (20.26)$$

is to be reduced to linear ordinary differential equation form where $\delta/\delta t$ indicates time derivative and $\delta/\delta l$ is the derivative with respect to the space variable.   For small space intervals L, variables $x,\ y,\ z,\ \ldots$ may be written as linear functions of the variable such that

$$\frac{\delta x}{\delta l} = \frac{x_2 - x_1}{L} \qquad \frac{\delta y}{\delta l} = \frac{y_2 - y_1}{L} \qquad \frac{\delta z}{\delta l} = \frac{z_2 - z_1}{L}$$

where $x_2,\ y_2,\ z_2$, and $x_1,\ y_1,\ z_1$ denote the value of the variables $x,\ y$, and z at the end and beginning of L.

   Even though $x_1,\ y_1,\ z_1$, and $x_2,\ y_2,\ z_2$, are no longer functions of l, they are still functions of time. $x,\ y,\ z,\ \delta x/\delta t,\ \delta y/\delta t$, and $\delta z/\delta t$, are now assumed to be the value of the variables at the beginning of the space interval L; hence, Eq. (20.26) can be written as

$$f\left(x_1,\ y_1,\ z_1,\ \ldots\ ,\ \frac{dx_1}{dt},\ \frac{x_2 - x_1}{L},\ \frac{dy_1}{dt},\ \frac{y_2 - y_1}{L},\ \cdots\right) = 0 \quad (20.27)$$

Equation (20.27), then perturbed about its steady-state operating condition to eliminate the nonlinearities, can be written as

$$\frac{\delta f}{\delta x_1}\,\Delta x_1 + \frac{\delta f}{\delta y_1}\,\Delta y_1 + \cdots \frac{\delta f}{\delta x_2}\,\Delta x_2 + \frac{\delta f}{\delta y_2}\,\Delta y_2$$
$$+ \frac{\delta f}{\delta(dx_1/dt)}\,\Delta\,\frac{dx_1}{dt} + \cdots = 0 \quad (20.28)$$

where $\Delta(dx_1/dt),\ \Delta(dy_1/dt),\ \ldots$
can be replaced by

$$\frac{d(\Delta x_1)}{dt},\ \frac{d(\Delta y_1)}{dt},\ \cdots$$

for small perturbation.

   It is seen from Eq. (20.28) that time derivatives $dx_1/dt,\ dy_1/dt$, and dz_1/dt are treated as independent variables, and second- or higher-order terms in perturbed variables are neglected.   The partial differentials $\delta f/\delta x_1,\ \delta f/\delta x_2,\ \delta f/\delta y_1$, forming coefficients of the perturbed variables, are evaluated at the initial steady-state operating conditions about which the dynamic behavior of the boiler is to be analyzed.   As a result of these simplifications, Eq. (20.28) becomes a linear first-order ordinary

618 APPLICATIONS TO COMPLEX SYSTEMS

differential equation with constant coefficients in perturbed variables $x_1, x_2, y_1, y_2, \ldots$.

The linearizing method will now be applied to the four boiler parts mentioned previously. In the initial analysis the space interval L is taken to represent the total length of the superheater and riser tube banks.

(b) Superheater Bank. Figure 20.7 shows the superheater bank, which is considered as a single capacitance with one restriction at the entrance and another at the exit. Variables ρ_s, T_s, and P_s are taken lumped parameters, and thus in an actual case represent the superheater

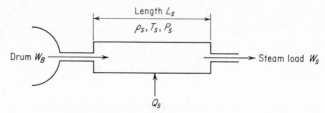

Fig. 20.7 Simplified single section superheater.

output density, temperature, and pressure. The length of the superheater tubes is taken as L_s and the total cross-sectional flow area of the bank as A_s.

Continuity equation:

$$w_B - w_s = \frac{d}{dt}(L_s A_s \rho_s) = L_s A_s \frac{d\rho_s}{dt} \qquad (20.29a)$$

or in perturbed form

$$\Delta w_B - \Delta w_s = L_s A_s S \, \Delta \rho_s \qquad (20.29b)$$

where d/dt is replaced by its equivalent Laplacian operator S.

Momentum equation:

The superheater's inertial terms are assumed neglected, compared with frictional terms. The validity of this assumption can be shown both analytically and experimentally. Hence

$$P_B - P_s = f_s \frac{w_B{}^2}{\rho_B} \qquad (20.30a)$$

W_B is the steam-mass flow rate and ρ_B is the saturated steam density corresponding to drum pressure. Since the pressure drop across the superheater $(P_B - P_s)$ is known from steady-state conditions, the friction coefficient for Eq. (20.30a) can be calculated. Writing Eq. (20.30a) as a perturbation equation about its steady-state conditions,

$$\Delta P_B - \Delta P_s = 2f_s \frac{\bar{w}_B}{\bar{\rho}_B} \Delta w_B - f_s \frac{\bar{w}_B{}^2}{\bar{\rho}_B{}^2} \Delta \rho_B \qquad (20.30b)$$

The bars (—) above the variables indicate the steady-state values.

Energy equation:

$$Q_s + w_B h_B - w_s h_s = \frac{d}{dt}(A_s L_s \rho_s h_s) \qquad (20.31a)$$

or
$$\Delta Q_s = (A_s L_s \bar{\rho}_s S + \bar{w}_s)C_{ps}\,\Delta T_s + (\bar{h}_s - \bar{h}_B)\,\Delta w_B \qquad (20.31b)$$

To get Eq. (20.31b) the term $A_s L_s d\bar{\rho}_s/dt$ is replaced by its equivalent from Eq. (20.29a). It is also assumed that $\Delta h_B = 0$ and $\Delta h_s = C_{ps}\,\Delta T_s$ are valid for small variations about steady-state values.

Heat input to superheater:

The empirical equation for heat-transfer rate into a turbulent gas flowing within a pipe is

$$Q_s = k_s(w_B)^{0.8}(T_{ws} - T_s) \qquad (20.32a)$$

where T_{ws} is the superheater wall temperature. k_s is again determined from steady-state conditions since Q_s, W_B, and T_s are known, and T_{ws} can be calculated. Hence

$$\Delta Q_s = \frac{0.8k_s}{(\bar{w}_B)^{0.2}}(\bar{T}_{ws} - \bar{T}_s)\,\Delta w_B + k_s(\bar{w}_B)^{0.8}(\Delta T_{ws} - \Delta T_s) \qquad (20.32b)$$

If the heat input rate to the superheater walls from hot combustion gases is Q_{gs}, then

$$Q_{gs} - Q_s = M_s C_s \frac{dT_{ws}}{dt} \qquad (20.33a)$$

where M_s is the total mass of the superheater tubes and C_s is its heat capacitance.

$$\Delta Q_{gs} - \Delta Q_s = M_s C_s S\,\Delta T_{ws} \qquad (20.33b)$$

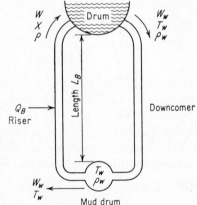

(c) *Downcomer-riser Loop.* Figure 20.8 shows the simplified diagram of the downcomer-riser loop with the variables indicated along the path. The downcomer is assumed to have simple fluid flow character, with no heat input or temperature delays between the top and the bottom. However, entrance and exit heat losses are taken into account, and the downcomer particularly is assumed to terminate at a mud drum to dissipate all available kinetic energy in turbulence.

Fig. 20.8 Simplified downcomer-riser loop.

Flow equations are similar to those for the superheater, with the inclusion of the inertial terms. Density and the enthalpy in the riser are written in terms of the mixtures quality x.

Heat transfer from riser tube walls into boiling liquid is given by the equation

$$Q_B = k_g(T_{wB} - T_B)^3 \qquad (20.34a)$$

where k_g is determined from steady-state conditions and T_{wB} is a function of the heat-flow rates into and out of the tube wall and is formed from an equation similar to (20.33b). Equation (20.34a) may be written in the perturbed form as:

$$\Delta Q_B = 3k_g(\bar{T}_{wB} - \bar{T}_B)^2(\Delta T_{ws} - \Delta T_B) \qquad (20.34b)$$

(d) Drum. Drum dynamic equations are derived by considering the mass and heat balances in the drum for both the vapor and the liquid

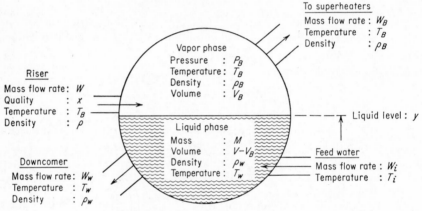

Fig. 20.9 Simplified drum diagram.

phases. Figure 20.9, the drum diagram, shows various input and output variables. In this analysis the effect of mass and heat transport phenomena between the two phases are taken into consideration, but the water-level variation due to bubbles within the liquid is neglected.

Three drum equations are obtained in the following perturbed form after appropriate algebraic manipulations:

$$[\bar{M}S + w_w + k_e(h_B - \bar{T}_w)]\,\Delta T_w = (1 - \bar{x})(\bar{T}_B - \bar{T}_w)\,\Delta w$$
$$+ [(1 - \bar{x})\bar{w} + k_e(h_B - \bar{T}_w)]\,\Delta T_B$$
$$- (\bar{T}_w - \bar{T}_i)\,\Delta w_i + \bar{w}_i\,\Delta T_i - (\bar{T}_B - \bar{T}_w)\bar{w}\,\Delta x \qquad (20.35)$$

$$\left(\frac{\bar{V}_B}{r}\right)S\,\Delta\rho_B + k_e\,\Delta T_B - \frac{1 - r}{r + \bar{x}}\,\Delta w + \frac{1 - r}{r}\,\Delta w_w$$

$$- \bar{w}\,\Delta x - k_e\,\Delta T_w + \Delta w_B = \frac{1 - r}{r}\,\Delta w_i \qquad (20.36)$$

$$\rho_w S\,\Delta y = \Delta w_i + (1 - \bar{x})\,\Delta w - \bar{w}\,\Delta x - \Delta w_w - k_e(\Delta T_w - \Delta T_B) \qquad (20.37)$$

where $r = 1 - \rho_B/\rho_w$.

State equations are obtained from steam tables and approximated as linear functions about a steady-state operation condition. Dynamic equations relating heat and mass transport phenomena between the hot combustion gases and various boiler components can be derived by considering the turbulent heat-transfer equations (empirical equations) and the effect of the heat transfer to riser and superheater tubes on the average combustion gas temperature. Heat transfer and frictional coefficients are determined from the unperturbed forms of the equations, by substituting the proper steady-state values of the variables. Similarly, steady-state values of the quality in the riser tube discharge and the

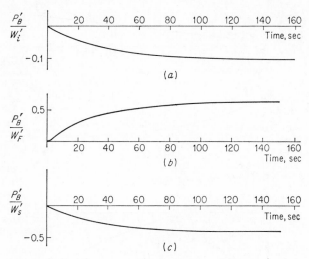

Fig. 20.10 Open-loop transient response of pressure with step changes in feed water rate W_i, fuel rate W_F, and steam rate W_s.

circulation rate may be obtained by simultaneous solution of the unperturbed riser-downcomer loop equations. This simply means solving a third-order algebraic equation in quality x.

Determination of friction and heat-transfer coefficients and the steady-state values of the quality and circulation rate makes it possible to set up the boiler's complete dynamic equations. Some of the relations are simple enough to be eliminated by hand computation, so that the final set obtained for computer solution consists of 18 equations. These equations are not shown because their coefficient values apply specifically to the particular boiler under consideration.

The set of simultaneous dynamic equations (in Laplace-transform form) obtained from analysis and linearization is solved on an analog (or digital) computer.

Figure 20.10 shows the responses of drum pressure P_B to step changes in feed-water rate a, fuel rate b, and steam flow rate c. The variables for these curves are normalized such that $'$ indicates per cent change from the steady-state value of that particular variable. The response curves indicate that transfer functions P'_B/W'_i, P'_B/W'_F, and P'_B/W'_s can be approximated, with reasonable accuracy, by single time constants.

Figure 20.11 shows the transient response of water level y to a step change in feed-water rate a, fuel rate b, and steam c. Note that for a sudden change in the steam-flow rate, the water level first goes up, then decreases at a more or less uniform rate. The swell observed here is the result of the sudden increase in load, although as was mentioned before,

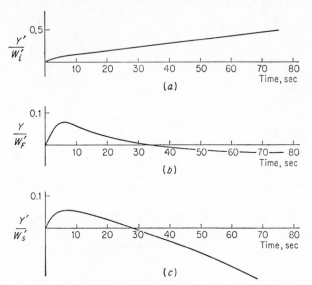

Fig. 20.11 Open-loop transient response of water level with step changes in feed water rate W_i, fuel rate W_F, and steam rate W_s.

the analysis does not include the effect of the bubble formation within the drum liquid. Hence, the set of equations developed will predict swell and shrink, but only qualitatively.

2. THE NONINTERACTING CONTROLLER. The transfer functions of the boiler are defined as the time-dependent functional relations between input and output variables. When one input variable (steam rate) is changed, the output variables under consideration (drum pressure and water level) change as a function of time in a manner determined by the boiler's dynamic equations. These relationships can be expressed in the following form:

$$\Delta P_B = E_{PS}\,\Delta w_S + E_{PF}\,\Delta w_F + E_{Pi}\,\Delta w_i \qquad (20.38a)$$
$$\Delta y = E_{YS}\,\Delta w_S + E_{yF}\,\Delta w_F + E_{yi}\,\Delta w_i \qquad (20.38b)$$

These expressions relate a change in the input variables steam rate

ΔW_x, fuel rate ΔW_F, and feed-water rate ΔW_i caused by a change in drum pressure ΔP_B and water level Δy from certain steady-state operating conditions.

The noninteracting controller will, in principle, adjust both fuel and feed-water rates in a prescribed manner when the steam-flow rate changes so that neither drum pressure nor drum liquid is disturbed. The controller will, then, receive signals from steam-flow rate W_s, drum pressure P_B and y, and adjust the feed-water and fuel rates. Hence, the functional relations for the controller are

$$\Delta w_F = C_{FP}(\Delta P_B)_e + C_{Fy}(\Delta y)_e + C_{FS}\,\Delta w_S \qquad (20.39a)$$
$$\Delta w_i = C_{iP}(\Delta P_B)_e + C_{iy}(\Delta y)_e + C_{iS}\,\Delta w_S \qquad (20.39b)$$

(The time-dependent coefficients E_{Ps}, E_{PF}, E_{Pi}, E_{ys}, E_{yF}, and E_{yi} in

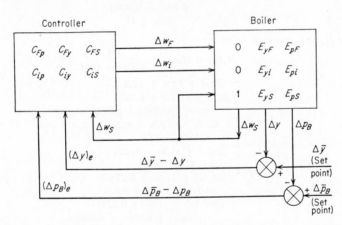

Fig. 20.12 Relations between the boiler and the noninteracting controller transfer functions.

Eqs. (20.38a) and (20.38b) are known from boiler dynamic analysis. But the controller transfer functions C_{FP}, C_{Fy}, C_{Fs}, C_{iP}, C_{iy}, and C_{is} still have to be determined.)

The following equations are obtained by substituting the values of W_F and w_i from Eqs. (20.39a) and (20.39b) into (20.38a) and (20.38b):

$$\Delta P_B = (C_{FP}E_{PF} + C_{iP}E_{Pi})(\Delta P_B)_e + (C_{Fy}E_{PF} + C_{iy}E_P)(\Delta y)_e$$
$$+ (E_{PS} + C_{FS}E_{PF} + C_{iS}E_{Pi})\,\Delta w_S \qquad (20.40a)$$
$$\Delta y = (C_{Fy}E_{yF} + C_{iy}E_{yi})(\Delta y)_e + (C_{FP}E_{yF} + C_{iP}E_{yi})(\Delta P_B)_e$$
$$+ (E_{yS} + C_{FS}E_{yF} + C_{iS}E_{yi})\,\Delta w_S \qquad (20.40b)$$

Figure 20.12 and Table 20.3 show Eqs. (20.40a) and (20.40b) in physicomathematical form. The boxes as drawn are the matrix relations between the inputs and outputs of both the controller and the boiler, while the lines indicate the flow of the signals generated by the two boxes. Set points y and P_B are necessary to change the steady-state drum pressure and water level. In general, however, only steady-state water level is changed for different steam loads.

Table 20.3 Equations for System of Fig. 20.12

$$E_{pF} = k_1 \frac{2.2}{40s + 1}$$

$$E_{pi} = k_2 \frac{-86}{40s + 1}$$

$$E_{pS} = k_3 \frac{-24.3}{40s + 1}$$

$$E_{yF} = k_4 \frac{0.341s - 0.0028}{(3s + 1)(40s + 1)}$$

$$E_{yi} = k_5 \frac{0.124}{s}$$

$$E_{yS} = k_6 \frac{0.101s - 0.0063}{s(3s + 1)}$$

$H_p(s) = H_y(s)$ is assumed to be

$$H_p(s) = H_y(s) = \frac{1}{5.88s(3s + 1)}$$

$$C_{FS} = k_7 \frac{14s^2 + 143s + 3.56}{62.1s^2 + 11.5 + 0.273}$$

$$C_{iS} = k_8 \frac{-16.9s^2 + 0.401s + 0.014}{62.1s^2 + 11.5s + 0.273}$$

$$C_{Fy} = k_9 \frac{585s + 14.6}{62.1s^2 + 11.5s + 0.273}$$

$$C_{iy} = k_{10} \frac{15s + 0.374}{62.1s^2 + 11.5s + 0.273}$$

$$C_{Fp} = k_{11} \frac{33.7s^2 + 1.69s + 0.021}{s(62.1s^2 + 11.5s + 0.273)}$$

$$C_{ip} = k_{12} \frac{-(2.32s^2 + 0.039s - 0.0005)}{(3s + 1)(62.1s^2 + 11.5s + 0.273)}$$

Noninteraction may now be defined from Eqs. (20.40a) and (20.40b). It is required that drum pressure will not change ($P_B = 0$) for any change in the steam flow rate ($W_S \neq 0$) and water level ($y \neq 0$), and that for a change in pressure set point ($P_B \neq 0$), drum pressure will respond in a manner prescribed by a transfer function $H_P(S)$, which determines how (in terms of time) the drum pressure should change from one steady-state condition to the new pressure set point. As an example, $H_P(S)$ may state that drum pressure should change instantaneously when the new set point is selected, but this is, of course, not reasonable on physical grounds, and a more realistic choice of $H_P(S)$ is necessary.

The above requirements for noninteraction of pressure can be obtained from Eq. (20.40a).

$$E_{PS} + C_{FS}E_{PF} + C_{iS}E_{Pi} = 0 \tag{20.41}$$

$$C_{Fy}E_{PF} + C_{iy}E_{Pi} = 0 \tag{20.42}$$

$$C_{FP}E_{PF} + C_{iP}E_{Pi} = H_P \tag{20.43}$$

A similar set of equations for noninteraction for water level y may be obtained, through the same type of reasoning, from Eq. (20.40b):

$$E_{yS} + C_{FS}E_{yF} + C_{iS}E_{yi} = 0 \qquad (20.44)$$
$$C_{FP}E_{yF} + C_{iP}E_{yi} = 0 \qquad (20.45)$$
$$C_{Fy}E_{yF} + C_{iy}E_{yi} = H_y \qquad (20.46)$$

Simultaneous solutions of Eqs. (20.41) through (20.46) (containing six unknown control transfer functions C_{FP}, C_{Fy}, C_{FS}, C_{iP}, C_{iy}, and C_{iS}) determine the controller transfer functions.

From equations

$$C_{FS}E_{PF} + C_{iS}E_{Pi} = -E_{PS}$$
$$C_{FS}E_{yF} + C_{iS}E_{yi} = -E_{yS}$$

Hence
$$C_{FS} = \frac{E_{yS}E_{Pi} - E_{PS}E_{yi}}{D} \qquad (20.47)$$

and
$$C_{iS} = \frac{E_{yF}E_{PS} - E_{PF}E_{yS}}{D} \qquad (20.48)$$

where $D = E_{PF}E_{yi} - E_{Pi}E_{yF}$
From Eqs. (20.42) and (20.46)

$$C_{Fy} = -\frac{H_y E_{Pi}}{D} \qquad (20.49)$$

and
$$C_{iy} = \frac{H_y E_{PF}}{D} \qquad (20.50)$$

From Eqs. (20.43) and (20.45)

$$C_{FP} = \frac{H_P E_{yi}}{D} \qquad (20.51)$$

and
$$C_{iP} = -\frac{H_P E_{yF}}{D} \qquad (20.52)$$

A controller having the transfer functions defined by Eqs. (20.47) through (20.52) will be noninteracting, a change in steam-flow rate or water level set points will not affect drum pressure, and similarly, a change in steam-flow rate and pressure set points will not affect water level.

Dynamic responses of the drum pressure and water level for three boiler inputs (Figs. 20.10 and 20.11) are obtained from analog simulation of the boiler and are, of course, in the time domain. To get controller transfer functions C_{FP}, C_{Fy}, C_{FS}, C_{iP}, C_{iy}, and C_{iS}, boiler transfer functions have to be expressed in the frequency domain as E_{PF}, E_{Pi}, E_{PS}, E_{yF}, E_{yi}, and E_{yS}. For simplicity, transfer functions relating pressure to boiler input variables are approximated as single time constants in the form

$$E_{PF} = \frac{K_1}{1 + s\tau_1} \qquad E_{Pi} = \frac{K_2}{1 + s\tau_1} \qquad E_{PS} = \frac{K_3}{1 + s\tau_1} \qquad (20.53)$$

The transfer functions for water level are assumed as:

$$E_{yF} = \frac{K_4 s + K_5}{(1 + s\tau_1)(1 + s\tau_2)} \qquad E_{yi} = \frac{K_6}{s} \qquad E_{yS} = \frac{K_7 s + K_8}{s(1 + s\tau_2)} \qquad (20.54)$$

Actually, the characteristic determinant of the 18 equations derived by dynamic analysis in ninth order is s. Therefore, each transfer function theoretically contains nine time constants. Fortunately, only two or three time constants dominate, and the rest can be ignored without appreciable loss of accuracy.

The analog-computer results (Figs. 20.10 and 20.11) give the open-loop responses of boiler pressure and water level to three step inputs.

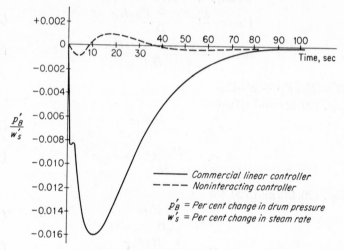

Fig. 20.13 Response of drum pressure for a step change in steam rate for two controllers.

The gains K_1 through K_8 and time constants τ_1 and τ_2 can be determined from them. Then, simulated controller transfer functions are determined in numerical form from Eqs. (20.47) through (20.52), as shown in Table 20.3 for a specific boiler under consideration.

The controller transfer functions are shown in the controller box of Fig. 20.12. Each transfer function is independent, from a hardware point of view. The internal connections between them and the inputs and outputs to the controller follow the matrix relationships specified by Eqs. (20.39a) and (20.39b). Here, the computer carries out the multiplication and addition of signals as stipulated by Eq. (20.39a). A similar arrangement for the feed-water rate controller would follow Eq. (20.39a) and the two sections then would comprise the boiler's noninteracting controller.

Once the noninteracting controller is simulated on the analog computer, it can be used to control the simulated boiler.   Figures 20.13 and 20.14 compare it to control by conventional proportional plus reset controllers. Figure 20.13 shows the variation of drum pressure for a step change in the steam-flow rate.   Theoretically, the drum pressure should not change at all when the boiler is controlled by the noninteracting controller, but due to the errors in potentiometer settings and the basic accuracy limitations of an analog computer, the drum pressure varies slightly.   Nevertheless, the improvement in response over that obtained with the conventional controller is better by a factor of 10.   It should be mentioned

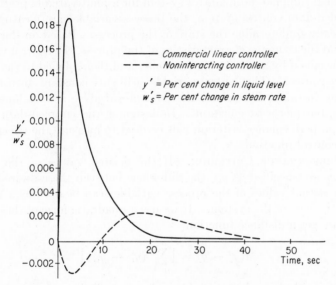

Fig. 20.14   Response of water level for a step change in steam rate for two controllers.

that the gain settings for the conventional controller were adjusted until an optimum response (minimum overshoot and settling time) was obtained in analog simulation.

Figure 20.14 shows the response of water level for a step change in steam-flow rate against the improvement obtained by the noninteracting controller over that of a conventional controller is severalfold.   Shrink or swell is almost completely eliminated, and any variation in drum liquid level is due only to mismatch between the noninteracting control parameters.

3   DISCUSSION.   After an optimum process operational condition has been determined, and if this optimum point does not vary as a function of the disturbances, the objective of the process control system is then merely to prevent the process from moving away from this optimum condition.   In this case, to design a special-purpose analog computer of the noninteracting type may be the best approach.   In other cases where

the steady-state optimization is required as part of the control scheme, as in the first example, a digital-computer control scheme may be more desirable. The noninteracting control system approach can still be applied in this latter case if the dynamic effect of the disturbance is significant, and the constraints may not be violated during the transient condition.

C *Example 3: Optimal Sampled-data Control System for Process Control.*[16] In the previous example of the boiler control problem, the control variables are continuous time functions. We will consider next an optimal sampled-data control system for a multivariable process. In a sampled-data control system, the process variables are measured only periodically to determine the state of the process. Based on the present state and the dynamic characteristics of the process, the control variables are determined by a computing controller and then applied to the process to effect control. The control variables will stay constant until the next sampling instant. Therefore, the control variables are no longer continuous, but piecewise constant. In designing the sampled-data control system, a performance criterion will be used to measure the effectiveness of the control function.

1 PERFORMANCE CRITERION. If the desired values of the process variables are specified as y_i^d, the difference between these desired values and the actual values of the process variables can be used as a measure of effectiveness of the system. If we use a quadratic form of these differences, we get a distance function

$$d(y^d - y) = \Big[\sum_{i=1}^{r} (y_i^d - y_i)^2 \Big]^{1/2} \tag{20.55}$$

where y_i = ith dependent variable to be controlled
y_i^d = the desired state of the ith dependent variable
r = total number of dependent variables to be controlled
Since the control function is to bring the process to the desired condition as rapidly as possible, we can measure the performance with a time integral of the above distance function weighted by an exponential time function. We get the performance index

$$P[y(t_0)] = \int_{t_0}^{\infty} d(y^d - y) \exp [a(t - t_0)] \, dt \tag{20.56}$$

where a is an arbitrary constant.

Now, we can define the optimal performance as the case where $P[y(t_0)]$ is a minimum, denoted by $P^0[y(t_0)]$.

In sampled-data control systems, applying discrete control signals, we have the performance index

$$P[y(t_0)] = \sum_{k=1}^{\infty} d[y^d - y(t_0 + k\tau)]b^k \cdots \tag{20.57}$$

where k = a number indicating sequence of sampling instants
τ = sampling period
$b = \exp a$

For optimal control, the performance index is minimized.

$$P^0[y(t_0)] = \min \sum_{k=1}^{\infty} d[y^d - y(t_0 - k\tau)]b^k \qquad (20.58)$$

2 DYNAMIC MODEL OF THE PROCESS. In general, the dynamics of the process can be expressed by the following functions:

$$\frac{dy_i}{dt} = f_i(y_1, \ldots, y_n, x_1, \ldots, x_m) \qquad i = 1, \ldots, n \quad (20.59)$$

where y_i = dependent variables which determine state of process
x_j = independent variables used to effect control

Higher-order time derivatives of the dependent variables can be eliminated by substitution of secondary variables.

Linearizing the above set of equations and using matrix representation, we get

$$\frac{dy}{dt} = Fy + Dx \qquad (20.60)$$

where x = control vector (n elements)
y = state vector (m elements)
F = constant $n \times n$ matrix whose elements are

$$F_{ij} = \frac{\delta f_i}{\delta y_j}$$

evaluated at $y = y^*$ $x = x^*$ $i,j = 1, \ldots, n$ $\qquad$ (20.61)

$D = n \times m$ matrix whose elements are

$$D_{ij} = \delta f_i / \delta x_j \qquad (20.62)$$

evaluated at

$$x = x^* \qquad y = y^* \qquad \begin{matrix} i = 1, \ldots, n \\ j = 1, \ldots, m \end{matrix}$$

x^* and y^* are the equilibrium values of the control and state variables. The solution of the above set of linear differential equations has the form

$$y(t) = \phi(t - t_0)y(t_0) + \int_{t_0}^{t} (t - \tau)Dx(\tau)\, d\tau \qquad (20.63)$$

The matrix ϕ is called the transition matrix and is given by

$$\phi = \exp F\tau = \sum_{k=0}^{\infty} \frac{F^k \tau^k}{k!} \qquad (20.64)$$

When $x(t)$ is held constant during the intervals between sampling instants, we get

$$y(t) = \phi(\tau)y(t_0) + \Delta(\tau)x(t_0) \qquad (20.65)$$

where

$$\Delta(\tau) = \int_0^t \phi(t - \sigma)D d\sigma \qquad (20.66)$$

and both $\phi(\tau)$ and $\Delta(\tau)$ become constant matrices.

3   OPTIMAL CONTROL. Optimal control, based on the performance criterion P, is the problem of selecting the sequence of control vectors

$$x^0(t_0),\ x^0(t_0 + \tau),\ x^0(t_0 + 2\tau),\ \ldots$$

such that P is minimized. Therefore, it would appear that we must simultaneously minimize the performance criterion with respect to all the terms of the sequence, which is an impossible job.

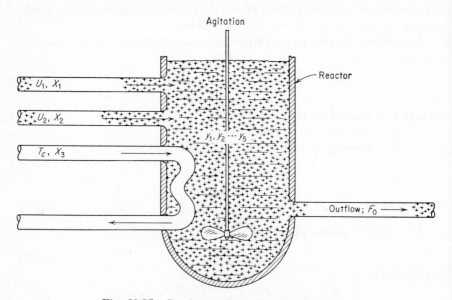

Fig. 20.15   Continuous flow, stirred-tank reactor.

Fortunately, this problem can be transformed into a sequential decision process by applying R. E. Bellman's principle of optimality. The methods derived from this principle are known as dynamic programming. By applying dynamic programming, the optimal sequence of control signals can be determined for a linear dynamic system as described by Eq. (20.63). The detailed solution of this problem is too involved to be included here. However, the general result will be given, and an example will be used to illustrate the nature of the solutions.

For a linear dynamic system, minimization of the performance criterion yields the following expression for the optimal control signal:

$$x^0(t_0) = A y(t_0) + B y^d \qquad (20.67)$$

where A and B are constant matrices.

This shows the important result that for a linear system the optimal control variables are linear functions of the actual and desired states of the process.

4 EXAMPLES. We will consider the optimal control of a continuous-flow, stirred tank of chemical reactor as shown in Fig. 20.15; x_1 and x_2 are the volume-flow rates of the two input streams. V_1 and V_2 are their concentrations in moles per unit volume. T_c and x_3 are the temperature and volume flow rates, respectively, of the cooling water. y_1, y_2, y_3, and y_4 denote the concentrations of the various compounds inside the reactor. y_5 is the temperature of the material inside the reactor which has a volume V. Due to agitation, both concentration and temperature are assumed to be same at every point inside the reactor. It is also assumed that a level controller keeps the output stream F equal to the sum of the input streams x_1 and x_2.

The objective of the control system is to manipulate the control variables x_1 and x_2 in such a manner as to bring rapidly the concentrations y_3 and y_4 in the reactor as close as possible to the desired concentrations y_3^d and y_4^d.

The two reactions taking place in the reactor are the following:

$$A + B \xrightarrow{k_1(T)} C \qquad (20.68)$$
$$2B + C \xrightarrow{k_2(T)} 2D \qquad (20.69)$$

The objective of the process is to convert raw material A and B by means of reaction (20.68) into C obtaining as much C as possible. However, there is a side reaction which produces the undesirable product D, which should be kept to a minimum.

The concentrations A, B, C, D are denoted by y_1, y_2, y_3, y_4 and the flow rates of A and B by x_1 and x_2. Applying the well-known Arrhenius equation and law of conservation of mass, we obtain

$$
\begin{aligned}
\frac{dy_1}{dt} &= -k_1(t)y_1y_2 + \frac{x_1}{V} V_1 - \frac{x_1 + x_2}{V} y_1 \\
\frac{dy_2}{dt} &= -k_1(t)y_1y_2 - 2k_2(t)y_2^2 y_3 + \frac{x_2}{V} V_2 - \frac{x_1 + x_2}{V} y_2 \\
\frac{dy_3}{dt} &= -k_2(t)y_1y_2 - k_2(t)y_2^2 y_3 - \frac{x_1 + x_2}{V} y_3 \\
\frac{dy_4}{dt} &= 2k_1(t)y_2^2 y_3 - \frac{x_1 + x_2}{V} y_4
\end{aligned}
\qquad (20.70)
$$

Let T_1 and T_2 denote the temperatures of the input flows x_1 and x_2, and let h be the heat-transfer coefficient per unit cooling water flow. Furthermore, let H_1 and H_2 be the heat generated per molecule of the first and second reaction; ρ and c the density and heat capacity of the material in the reactor. Conservation of energy yields the following equation:

$$\frac{dy_5}{dt} = k_1(t)y_1y_2H_1 + k_2(t)y_2{}^2y_3H_2 + \frac{x_1}{V\rho c}(T_1 - y_5)$$
$$+ \frac{x_2}{V\rho c}(T_2 - y_5) + \frac{h}{V\rho c}x_3(T_c - y_5) \quad (20.71)$$

At equilibrium, the conditions of the reactor can be represented by the values of the variables as shown in Table 20.4. Using formulas (20.61) and (20.62), we obtain:

$$F = \begin{pmatrix} -0.325 & -0.5625 & 0 & 0 & -0.200 \\ -0.225 & -0.8125 & -0.014286 & 0 & -0.368 \\ 0.225 & 0.4875 & -0.107143 & 0 & 0.116 \\ 0 & 0.1500 & 0.014286 & -0.1 & 0.168 \\ 0.450 & 0.7500 & -0.035714 & 0 & -0.060 \end{pmatrix}$$

Assuming that only the flow rates x_1 and x_3 can be changed to effect control, we get:

$$D = \begin{pmatrix} 55 & 0 & 0 \\ -4 & 0 & 0 \\ -21 & 0 & 0 \\ -3 & 0 & 0 \\ -2 & 0 & 35.5 \end{pmatrix}$$

Table 20.4   Values of Reactor Constants

V_1	V_2	x_1^*	x_2^*	x_3^*	y_1^*	y_2^*	y_3^*	y_4^*	y_5^*
65	59	0.05	0.05	0.1	10	4	21	3	120

$k_1(y_5^*)$		$k_2(y_5^*)$		$\delta k_1(y_5^*)/\delta y_5$		$\delta k_2(y_5^*)/\delta y_5$			
0.05625		0.00044643		0.005		0.00025			

T_1	T_2	T_c	H_1	H_2	V	$h/V\rho c$		ρc	
100	100	49	2	-5	1	0.5		10	

The performance index is defined as

$$P = \sum_{k=1}^{\infty} [y_3{}^d - y_3(t_0 + k)]^2 + [y_4{}^d - y_4(t_0 + k)]^2 \quad (20.72)$$

The optimal control variables for this performance index are given by the following functions of the desired and actual state of the reactor

$$x = \begin{pmatrix} 0 & 0 & -0.0680 & 0.0217 & 0 \\ 0 & 0 & 0 & 0 & 0 \\ 0 & 0 & -0.0788 & 0.3932 & 0 \end{pmatrix} y^d$$

$$+ \begin{pmatrix} -0.0102 & 0.0164 & 0.0605 & -0.0197 & -0.0012 \\ 0 & 0 & 0 & 0 & 0 \\ -0.0064 & 0.0327 & 0.0668 & -0.3537 & -0.0504 \end{pmatrix} y$$

If the desired state of the reactor is defined as $y_3{}^d = 5$, $y_4{}^d = -1$ and assuming that the reactor starts out at the old equilibrium state

$$(y_1 = y_2 = \cdots = x_1 = x_2 = x_3 = 0)$$

the behavior of the state and control variables as a function of time are shown in Fig. 20.16.

5 DISCUSSION. It is of interest to note that in order to obtain optimal control of the reactor in terms of the desired concentrations of y_3 and y_4, the control variables x_1 and x_3 must be manipulated in an oscillatory manner. Furthermore, as a result of the optimal control, the reactor temperature y_5 exhibits a rather violent oscillation. Since the performance criterion, as defined in this problem, is not a function of the reactor temperature y_5, a good regulation of the reactor temperature is of no economical value. Therefore, it is reasonable to expect that the optimal control scheme will call for the best possible sequence of control signals to minimize the performance index in terms of the concentrations, even though it may introduce some instability in the reactor temperature.

On the other hand, the common manual control practice in the process industry is for the operator to attempt to hold every process variable as constant as possible, regardless of its economic significance. Compared to the above example of optimal control, this common practice of holding every variable constant is probably not the best process control procedure. However, in order to be able to consider the dynamic interactions of all the process variables of economical significance so that an optimal control scheme can be determined, a controller with much higher information processing capability than that of the human operator is required.

Of course, in some cases, reactor temperature may also have to be restricted within a small operating range for safety reasons and, therefore, the temperature oscillation in the solution of the example may not be tolerated. For such cases, it simply would be necessary to include an additional term, involving the desired reactor temperature, in the performance index of the control system, provided the reactor temperature is a "soft" constraint. Soft constraints are defined as constraints which can be violated for a brief period although such violation is undesirable. In contrast to these, "hard" constraints are those which must not be violated at any time. The dynamic optimization technique described in the example cannot handle hard constraints directly, but it can be extended to do so.

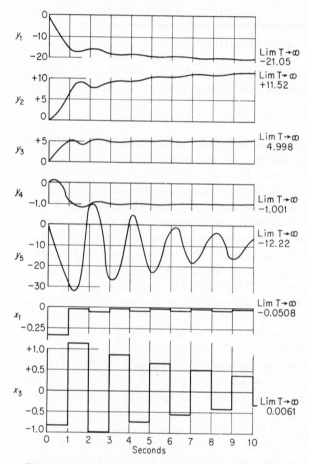

Fig. 20.16 Behavior of state and control variables.

20.5 Conclusion

The computer control applications in process industry have been discussed mainly in terms of the characteristics of the problem and the methods of solution. Due to space limitation, the equipment requirements for the computer control system were not included in the discussion. Three examples have been used to illustrate the various aspects of the computer control problem. The need for optimization in terms of process economics has been emphasized.   The effectiveness of steady-state and dynamic optimization has been discussed as a function of the characteristics of the process responses and disturbances.   For processes with relatively infrequent disturbances, a control scheme applying steady-state optimization, as illustrated in the first example, may suffice.   In this case, any additional sophistication in the control scheme to optimize the dynamic effect may not be economically justifiable.   However, for a process where the disturbance becomes relatively frequent compared to the time constants of the process, dynamic effects must be taken into consideration in the control system design so that the economic benefit determined by the steady-state optimization scheme can be realized. Examples 2 and 3 were used to demonstrate dynamic process control schemes for two different problems.   Example 2 considered the process constraints on a dynamic basis.   A noninteracting control system was applied using an analog computer as the control element.   Example 3 illustrated an approach for applying a digital computer to control a process with optimal dynamic response.

In conclusion, various techniques applicable for a computer control system design have been discussed.   Some of these have been illustrated in the examples.   The actual requirements of a computer control system for a particular process depend not only on the physical characteristics and the economic objective of the process operation but also on the nature of the disturbances which make the control system necessary in the first place.

REFERENCES

1. Charnes, A., W. W. Cooper, and R. Mellon: Blending Aviation Gasolines: A Study in Programming Interdependent Activities in an Integrated Oil Company, *Econometrica*, vol. 20, no. 2, pp. 135–159, April, 1952.
2. Campbell, D. P.: "Process Dynamics," John Wiley & Sons, Inc., New York, 1958.
3. Goodman, T. P., and J. B. Reswick: Determination of System Characteristics from Normal Operating Records, *Trans. ASME*, vol. 78, p. 259, 1956.
4. Davies, O. L.: "Design and Analysis of Industrial Experiments," Hafner Publishing Company, New York, 1954.
5. Bennett, C. A., and N. L. Franklin: "Statistical Analysis in Chemistry and the Chemical Industry," John Wiley & Sons, Inc., New York, 1954.
6. Box, G. E. P.: The Exploration and Exploitation of Response Surface: Some General Considerations and Examples, *Biometrics*, March, 1954.
7. Gass, S. I.: "Linear Programming, Methods and Applications," McGraw-Hill Book Company, Inc., New York, 1958.
8. Tsien, H. S.: "Engineering Cybernetics," pp. 63–69, McGraw-Hill Book Company, Inc., New York, 1954.
9. Draper, C. S., and Y. T. Li: Principles of Optimalizing Control Systems and an Application to Internal Combustion Engines, *ASME Publications*, 1951.
10. Tou, J. T.: "Digital and Sampled-data Control Systems," McGraw-Hill Book Company, Inc., New York, 1959.

11. Savas, E. S.: Steady State Optimization for a Catalytical Cracking Unit, presented at IBM Process Control Seminar, March, 1960.
12. Crawford, P. B., and W. A. Cunningham: *Petroleum Refiner*, p. 169, January, 1956.
13. Voorhies, A., Jr.: *Ind. Eng. Chem.*, vol. 37, no. 318, 1945.
14. Olsen, C. R., and M. J. Sterba: *Chem. Eng. Progr.*, vol. 45, no. 692, 1949.
15. Chien, K. L., E. I. Ergin, C. Ling, and A. Lee: *Control Eng.*, pp. 95–101, October, 1958.
16. Kalman, R. E., and R. W. Koepcke: The Role of Digital Computers in the Dynamic Optimization of Chemical Reactions, *IBM Research Rept.* RC-77, December, 1958.

Index

637